Alien Invaders

*in Canada's Waters,
Wetlands, and Forests*

Edited by

Renata Claudi, Patrick Nantel, and
Elizabeth Muckle-Jeffs

Published by

Natural Resources Canada, Canadian Forest Service,
Science Branch, Ottawa

©Her Majesty the Queen in Right of Canada, 2002
ISBN 0-660-18825-2
Cat. no. Fo42-329/2002E

Published by the Canadian Forest Service, Natural Resources Canada, Ottawa, ON K1A 0E4.

Cet ouvrage est publié en français sous le titre : *Envahisseurs exotiques des eaux, milieux humides et forêts du Canada*

Project Management: Catherine Carmody
Linguistic and Scientific Editing: Catherine Carmody, Paula Irving, Peggy Robinson, and Jocelyn Tomlinson
Graphic Design: Danielle Monette and Sandra Bernier
Layout: Sandra Bernier, Danielle Monette, Roberta Gal and Julie Piché
Cover Design: Sandra Bernier
Glossary: Gregory Crook, Catherine Carmody, and Patrick Nantel
Index: Patricia Buchannan

National Library of Canada Cataloguing in Publication Data

Main entry under title:

Alien invaders in Canada's waters, wetlands, and forests

Issued also in French under title: Envahisseurs exotiques des eaux, milieux humides et forêts du Canada.
ISBN 0-660-18825-2
Cat. no. Fo42-329/2002E

1. Nonindigenous pests—Canada.
2. Pest introduction—Canada.
3. Ecosystem health—Canada.
I. Claudi, Renata.
II. Nantel, Patrick, 1963-   .
III. Muckle-Jeffs, Elizabeth.
IV. Canadian Forest Service. Science Branch.

SB990.5C3A54 2002   363.7'8   C2002-980262-8

Cover photos: Purple loosestrife, by Denis Rochon. Back cover (*top to bottom*): European frog-bit, by Eric Haber; rainbow smelt, ©John G. Shedd Aquarium, Chicago, IL; *Codium fragile* subsp. *tomentosoides,* by R.E. Scheibling; gypsy moth larva, by Klaus Bolte; common (European) buckthorn, by Erich Haber.

Photo on contents page: *Galerucella calmariensis* feeding on purple loosestrife, by Eric Coombs.

Disclaimer: This publication has been reviewed and edited by the Canadian Forest Service (CFS), Natural Resources Canada. The views expressed, however, are those of the authors and do not necessarily reflect the views and policies of the CFS.

 Printed on recycled paper

 PRINTED IN CANADA

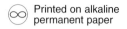 Printed on alkaline permanent paper

Contents

About the Editors

Renata Claudi, MS, is a biologist with over 20 years of diverse business and technical experience. From 1989 to 2000 she was employed by a major Canadian electrical utility where, among other things, she assessed the impact of zebra mussels on operating stations and developed mitigation plans for their control. She was one of the founding organizers of an annual international conference on aquatic invasive species and continues to serve as a consultant to the technical program committee. Ms. Claudi co-authored a ground-breaking volume on zebra mussel control options, *Practical Manual for Zebra Mussel Monitoring and Control* (Lewis Publishers, 1993), and was the lead editor of *Fresh Water Alien Organisms in North America* (Lewis Publishers, 1999), a comprehensive volume with contributions from 43 experts from Canada, the United States, and Mexico. Ms. Claudi is currently the Chief Scientist of RNT Consulting Inc., an environmental consulting firm that focuses on various aspects of alien species invasions, including their economic impact and the selection and implementation of appropriate control mechanisms.

Patrick Nantel has a PhD in Environmental Sciences. His research area focuses on the use of population dynamics models for population viability analyses and estimation of sustainable harvest rates. At present, he is collaborating on similar research with scientists from the University of Hawaii at Manoa, the Université du Québec à Montréal, and Montréal's Biodome. Dr. Nantel has been a contributor to many books, leaflets, and Web sites popularizing and promoting native plant diversity, ecology, and conservation, and an advisor on many publications, including the beautiful *Flore printanière* (Fleurbec Éditeur, 2002). Currently, he is the Science Advisor and Research Coordinator for the Ecosystem Processes Network of the Canadian Forest Service, Natural Resources Canada, Ottawa.

Elizabeth Muckle-Jeffs has provided consultation to science-based organizations for over a decade. She works with both public and private sector clients, primarily on environmental issues related to alien species, ballast water, and rural water quality. Ms. Muckle-Jeffs has an extensive background in compiling, editing and publishing technical literature, including proceedings for national and international scientific conferences, such as the National Conference on Agricultural Nutrients and Their Impact on Rural Water Quality and the International Conference on Aquatic Invasive Species. She owns and operates The Professional Edge, a marketing, sales, and communications business dedicated to achieving results for clients through strategic planning, effective marketing and promotion, and total quality management.

Contributors

Annelise S. Chapman
Department of Biology
Dalhousie University
Halifax, NS B3H 4J1

Anthony R.O. Chapman
Department of Biology
Dalhousie University
Halifax, NS B3H 4J1

Renata Claudi
RNT Consulting, Inc.
823 County Road 35
Picton, ON K0K 2T0

James E. Corrigan
P.O. Box 291
Harriston, ON N0G 1Z0

Georges Costan
St. Lawrence Centre
Environment Canada
105 McGill Street, 7th Floor
Montréal, QC H2Y 2E7

Marcel Dawson
Plant Health and Production Division
Canadian Food Inspection Agency
Room 2013 West
59 Camelot Drive
Ottawa, ON K1A 0Y9

Yves de Lafontaine
St. Lawrence Centre
Environment Canada
105 McGill Street, 7th Floor
Montréal, QC H2Y 2E7

Alan Dextrase
Ontario Parks
Ontario Ministry of Natural Resources
Box 7000
Peterborough, ON K9J 8M5

Sarah Dudas
Science Branch
West Vancouver Laboratory
Pacific Region
Fisheries and Oceans Canada
4160 Marine Drive
West Vancouver, BC V7V 1N6

Pierre Dumont
Société de la faune et des parcs
  du Québec
201 Place Charles-Le Moyne
Longueuil, QC J4K 2I5

Richard H.M. Espie
Fish and Wildlife Branch
Saskatchewan Environment
3211 Albert Street
Regina, SK S4S 5W6

Aymeric Guibert
Cemagref, Groupement de Bordeaux
33612 Cestas Cedex
France

Erich Haber
National Botanical Services
604 Wavell Avenue
Ottawa, ON K2A 3A8

Peter Harris
Lethbridge Research Centre
Agriculture and Agri-Food Canada
P.O. Box 3000
Lethbridge, AB T1J 4B1

Ole Hendrickson
Canadian Wildlife Service
Environment Canada
Place Vincent Massey
351 St. Joseph Blvd., 9th Floor
Hull, QC K1A 0H3

Paul C. James
Fish and Wildlife Branch
Saskatchewan Environment
3211 Albert Street
Regina, SK S4S 5W6

Glen S. Jamieson
Pacific Biological Station
Fisheries and Oceans Canada
Nanaimo, BC V9R 5K6

Dorothee Kieser
Pacific Biological Station
Fisheries and Oceans Canada
Nanaimo, BC V9R 5K6

Jean Leclerc
Société de la faune et des parcs
  du Québec
201 Place Charles-Le Moyne
Longueuil, QC J4K 2T5

Gerry Lee
Consulting Associate
Canadian Biodiversity Informatics
  Consortium
144 Oakridge Blvd.
Ottawa, ON K2G 2T9

Colin Levings
Science Branch
West Vancouver Laboratory
Pacific Region
Fisheries and Oceans Canada
4160 Marine Drive
West Vancouver, BC V7V 1N6

Cory J. Lindgren
Manitoba Purple Loosestrife Project
Box 1160
Stonewall, MB R0C 2Z0

Francine MacDonald
Ontario Federation of Anglers and
  Hunters
P.O. Box 2800
Peterborough, ON K9J 8L5

Gerald L. Mackie
Department of Zoology
University of Guelph
Guelph, ON N1G 2W1

Kevin M. Murphy
Fish and Wildlife Branch
Saskatchewan Environment
3211 Albert Street
Regina, SK S4S 5W6

Patrick Nantel
Science Branch
Science Programs Division
Canadian Forest Service
Natural Resources Canada
580 Booth Street, 12th Floor
Ottawa, ON K1A 0E4

Vince G. Nealis
Pacific Forestry Centre
Canadian Forest Service
Natural Resources Canada
506 West Burnside Road
Victoria, BC V8Z 1M5

Laurie E. Neville
Department of Biological Sciences
Stanford University
385 Serra Mall
Stanford, CA 94305-5020

Wendy Ralley
Manitoba Conservation
123 Main Street, Suite 160
Winnipeg, MB R3C 1A5

Robert E. Scheibling
Department of Biology
Dalhousie University
Halifax, NS B3H 4J1

Geoffrey G.E. Scudder
Department of Zoology and Centre
  for Biodiversity Research
University of British Columbia
Vancouver, BC V6T 1Z4

Simon F. Shamoun
Pacific Forestry Centre
Canadian Forest Service
Natural Resources Canada
506 West Burnside Road
Victoria, BC V8Z 1M5

Daniel Simberloff
Department of Ecology and
  Evolutionary Biology
University of Tennessee
569 Dabney Hall
Knoxville, TN 37996-1610

Nathalie Vachon
Société de la faune et des parcs
  du Québec
201 Place Charles-Le Moyne
Longueuil, QC J4K 2T5

Christopher J. Wiley
Fisheries and Oceans Canada
201 N. Front Street, Suite 703
Sarnia, ON N7T 8B1

Dennis Wright
Environmental Science Directorate
Central and Arctic Region
Fisheries and Oceans Canada
501 University Crescent
Winnipeg, MB R3T 2N6

Preface

Alien species within the context of this publication are species that have crossed natural barriers and entered ecosystems where they have not existed previously in recorded history. Such species are also often referred to as foreign, exotic, introduced, nonindigenous, or nonnative, depending largely on preference. The natural barriers—oceans, mountains, rivers, and deserts—are usually crossed through the deliberate or inadvertent actions of humans, although range expansions assisted by such phenomena as global climate change have also been recorded.

A small percentage of alien species have characteristics that allow them to flourish and dominate the new ecosystem to the detriment of native species. Such species are referred to as "invasive". The term invasive alien species conjures images of organisms from other continents. While this is true, species, whether they come from another continent or from a neighboring watershed, can have an equally devastating impact on the receiving ecosystem.

Invasive alien species are widely considered to be among the greatest threats to global biological diversity. In Canada, this threat is recognized by relatively few. Except for species such as zebra mussel or purple loosestrife, the impacts of various invading species have not been well defined and the magnitude of this threat to the biodiversity of Canada's waters, wetlands, prairies, and forests has not been quantified.

Because increased global trade and climate change are likely to exacerbate the alien species problem, the Biodiversity Science Board of Canada organized a symposium on alien species at the annual meeting of the Ecological Monitoring and Assessment Network in Toronto, Ontario, in 1999. The aim was to highlight the alien species problem in Canada. *Alien Invaders in Canada's Waters, Wetlands, and Forests* has its roots in that meeting. The publication contains some of the presented papers, updated and reworked into chapters, as well as invited papers that cover the topic more fully than a short symposium could.

Alien Invaders in Canada's Waters, Wetlands, and Forests documents the status of invasive alien species in Canada; their known impacts on the biodiversity of various types of ecosystems; conduits for new introductions; secondary distribution mechanisms; containment,

eradication, and control methods; policy and legislation; national and international collaborative efforts; and public education and outreach programs to reduce the risk of unintentional introductions or spread. However, the publication is as much about what we do not know and should do, as about what we know and have done.

Article 8(h) of the Convention on Biological Diversity, ratified by Canada, states that contracting parties shall "prevent the introduction of, control or eradicate those alien species which threaten ecosystems, habitats or species." No comprehensive overview exists of the alien invasive species issue in Canada. We hope that this publication will be a foundation document, serving as a baseline for future scientific and policy development.

We thank Ole Hendrickson, Canadian Wildlife Service, Environment Canada, and Hans Ottens, Canadian Forest Service, Natural Resources Canada, for championing the development of this book in its early stages.

We also gratefully acknowledge the following for their review of manuscripts: **J. Lars Baker**, Fremont County Weed and Pest Control, Lander, WY; **Guy R. Brassard**, Canadian Forest Service, Ottawa, ON; **Alfred F. Cofrancesco, Jr.**, US Army Corps of Engineers, Engineering Research and Development Center, Vicksburg, MS; **Edwin J. Crossman**, Emeritus, Royal Ontario Museum, Toronto, ON; **Yves de Lafontaine**, St. Lawrence Centre, Environment Canada, Montréal, QC; **Erich Haber**, National Botanical Services, Ottawa, ON; **Ole Hendrickson**, Canadian Wildlife Service, Environment Canada, Hull, QC; **Douglas A. Jensen**, University of Minnesota Sea Grant College Program, Duluth, MN; **Craig Johnson**, Tasmanian Aquaculture and Fisheries Institute, University of Tasmania, Hobart, Australia; **Sandra M. Keppner**, Lower Great Lakes Fishery Resources Office, US Fish and Wildlife Service, Amherst, NY; **Michael Klepinger**, Michigan Sea Grant Program, Michigan State University, East Lansing, MI; **Joseph H. Leach**, Emeritus, Ontario Ministry of Natural Resources, Kingsville, ON; **John Madsen**, Department of Biological Sciences, Minnesota State University, Mankato, MN; **Steve Marshall**, Department of Environmental Biology, University of Guelph, Guelph, ON; **Ralph C. Martin**, Department of Agricultural Sciences, Nova Scotia

Agricultural College, Truro, NS; **Collin McGuire**, Habitat Management Unit, Fish and Wildlife Branch, Saskatchewan Environment, Prince Albert, SK; **Robert F. McMahon**, Center for Biological Macrofouling Research, The University of Texas at Arlington, Arlington, TX; **Edward L. Mills**, Cornell University, Bridgeport, NY; **Judith Myers**, Department of Zoology and Faculty of Agricultural Sciences, University of British Columbia, Vancouver, BC; **Vince G. Nealis**, Pacific Forestry Centre, Canadian Forest Service, Natural Resources Canada, Victoria, BC; **Sandra Parker**, Cornell University, Bridgeport, NY; **Eric Reeves**, Cdr., US Coast Guard (retired), Montague, MI; **Rick Sanden**, Habitat Management Unit, Fish and Wildlife Branch, Saskatchewan Environment, Regina, SK; **Edwin A. Theriot**, US Army Corps of Engineers, Engineering Research and Development Center, Vicksburg, MS; **Alan Watson**, Plant Science Department, McGill University, Ste-Anne-de-Bellevue, QC; **S. Kim Webb**, US Fish and Wildlife Service, Stockton, CA; **Christopher J. Wiley**, Fisheries and Oceans Canada, Sarnia, ON.

Introduction

The concept of species being undesirable when transplanted outside their range or habitat is relatively new. From about the end of the 17th to the end of the 19th century, a number of scientific societies, institutions, and even government agencies spent a great deal of effort and money to introduce as many alien species as they considered desirable into as many new environments as possible. This drive had a multitude of motivations, such as aesthetics and the desire for an inexpensive food supply. Many of these "transplants" became established and in some cases they came to dominate the new environment. Over time it became evident that there were problems with this practice. As our knowledge of the environment grew and as evidence of the effects of transplanted alien species mounted, so did our doubts of the wisdom of such activities. By the beginning of the 20th century, the number of deliberate introductions started to taper off, only to be replaced by accidental introductions, many of which were a by-product of global commerce. As global commerce and international trade continue to grow, so do the number of accidental introductions worldwide.

Over the last 200 years, human activities have dramatically accelerated the rate of ecosystem change in Canada. Like elsewhere in the world, some of this change is the result of the introduction of alien species or the spread of native species to new ecosystems because of human intervention. The problems that invasive alien species can pose for Canada's agriculture, forestry, and fisheries are recognized and attempts have been made to overcome them. Some more recently introduced species, such as zebra mussel, purple loosestrife, and brown spruce longhorn beetle, have been the focus of study and activities because of their ecological impacts—these three have even become media stars. However, knowledge about the impacts of most alien species on Canada's ecosystems remains incomplete and largely anecdotal.

The potential impacts of invasive alien species to biodiversity can be placed into three broad categories:

- Ecological impacts: Displacement of native species through competition for food and other resources and through predation, and alteration of habitat and food webs.

- Genetic impacts: Dilution and potential loss of locally adapted gene pools caused by the introduction of nonlocally adapted strains of the same species, or closely related species that are able to hybridize. This also includes indirect genetic effects brought about by ecological impacts, such as reduction in the size of gene pools from competition and predation.

- Pathological impacts: Infection of native species by a variety of parasitic organisms, such as bacteria, viruses, and fungi, infecting alien animals and plants.

Species introduced into new environments are subject to ecological variables that differ from those of the ecosystems in which they evolved. Therefore, the intentional introduction of species for the perceived short-term benefits to humankind can result in unforeseen long-term ecological and economic costs. The negative impacts of established alien species are usually irreversible, and attempts to control or minimize these impacts can be extremely expensive. As well, resources allocated to repairing or mitigating the damages are then lost for other uses.

Preventing the introduction of alien species involves controlling their pathways into the country (or into new ecosystems). Natural barriers, oceans, mountains, rivers, and deserts, that may have isolated ecosystems for thousands of years are being crossed with ever-increasing frequency. Unique assemblages of plants and animals that evolved in such ecosystems are threatened. There are many different pathways by which the barriers may be crossed. Humans deliberately assist some species. Some organisms take advantage of the various means of transport used for global trade. Others are able to expand their range, aided by breaches in natural barriers such as canal building between watersheds, or by phenomena such as global climate change. The table on the following page provides a quick overview of some of the most well-recognized pathways of introduction into Canada and identifies the types of ecosystems into which these conduits can introduce new species.

Even if all potential conduits of introduction into Canada were controlled, it would still be impossible to

Pathway of introduction	Ecosystem				
	Freshwater	Marine	Wetland	Prairie	Forests
Intentional introduction	●	●	●	●	●
Ballast water	●	●			
Hull fouling	●	●			
Floating oil rigs		●			
Aquaculture	●	●	●		
Bait fish	●		●		
Aquarium trade	●	●	●		
Ornamental ponds and water gardens	●		●		
Recreational fishing and boating	●		●		
Range extension by removal of geographical boundaries	●		●		
Horticulture			●	●	●
Packaging materials, dunnage				●	●
Game farms				●	●
Range extension through global warming	●	●	●	●	●

eliminate all new introductions. For instance, Canada shares thousands of kilometres of border with the United States. Species that are introduced south of the border may eventually invade Canada (the reverse also being true). However, knowing how significantly each of the above pathways contributes to the problem of invasive species introductions would be beneficial; resources could then be allocated to those that pose the greatest risk. The data for such an assessment does not exist at this time.

Some efforts to prevent the introduction and control of certain alien species have been successful. For the most part, however, current management practices in Canada have not been effective in preventing introductions of new alien species nor in controlling most of the associated problems. For example, the rate of introduction of new species to the Great Lakes basin has been relatively constant over the last 120 years. In spite of recent activities aimed at dealing with the alien species problem, such as the introduction of ballast water guidelines, education and outreach programs, and representation on international committees, there are three main reasons why introductions of alien species continue to be a problem for Canada:

- Current federal and provincial/territorial government policies, legislation, staffing, and budgets are inadequate to control the transport of alien species within Canada.

- The general public, and to a lesser degree government management agencies, are largely unaware of the potential serious ecological and economic consequences associated with the introduction of alien species, and of the mechanisms by which species are introduced.

- Gaps in the knowledge of biological interactions make confident analyses of alien species impacts difficult or impossible.

A recurring theme in many of the chapters that follow is the need for more comprehensive legislation dealing with alien species and for one umbrella agency as the first point of contact on alien species issues. Such an agency would coordinate all subsequent action on alien species and be the repository of data on risk assessment, first sightings, action to prevent their spread, and implementation of eradication efforts. Such an agency could also work in cooperation with equivalent agencies and organizations involved in alien species issues in Canada and around the world to implement best management practices.

Part 1 Global Impacts of Alien Species

Alien species are a major cause of species extinction in many countries and a factor in the rearrangement of global biogeography. As well, although no comprehensive study exists, the costs to agriculture, forestry, fisheries, and public health of alien invaders are thought to be enormous. In the United States alone, the cost of alien species to the economy is estimated at US$137 billion annually. The following chapters give an overview of the global impacts of alien invaders, provide profiles of some of the better-known culprits, and describe many of the initiatives to control them or mitigate their ecological and socioeconomic effects.

The ecological impacts of most alien invasions fall into the following categories: habitat change, competition, predation, herbivory, disease, and hybridization. In addition, these invaders also affect economies, resource availability, and human health. Only a minority of alien species become invasive. Predicting which ones and what their impacts will be remains difficult. All the earthworms of much of Canada and the northern United States are Eurasian immigrants. This taxon has become so crucial to ecosystem function that it would have been expected to have had major impacts on an entire ecosystem. However, none has been apparent.

Scientists worldwide are striving to provide more knowledge on alien species. At the same time, it is recognized that the issue is global and calls for the collaboration of all nations. Knowledge and resources must be shared. Nations need to strive for consistency in policies, legislation, and practices to prevent the introduction of invasive alien species and to control and manage them. Over 40 international instruments or programs dealing with various aspects of the alien species problem currently exist, and institutional linkages between relevant organizations have been expanding. The first global agreement on the conservation of biological diversity was the 1992 Convention on Biological Diversity. Its Article 8(h) specifically mentions alien species and their effects on biodiversity. One ambitious and comprehensive initiative is the Global Invasive Species Programme or GISP. This program encourages governments and other organizations to access the best practices available to prevent and to manage invasive alien species and to promote the development of additional tools and strategies.

Alien Invaders: An Introduction

Geoffrey G.E. Scudder

Biological invaders worldwide threaten biodiversity, ecosystem function, economic impacts, resource availability, and human health (Ruesink et al. 1995; Simberloff 1996; Vitousek et al. 1997; Ricciardi et al. 2000). Alien species are second only to habitat loss as a cause of native species decline (Enserink 1999; Wilcove et al. 1998).

There is no agreed upon framework for quantifying or comparing the total impact of invaders (Parker et al. 1999), but the consequences of these invasions can be surprising, and often will demand ingenious countermeasures and creative accommodations (Soulé 1990). Alien organisms have even caused the downfall of prime ministers (Horsfall 1983).

Biodiversity Loss

Alien invaders threaten rare and endangered species and biodiversity conservation (Walker and Steffen 1997). Some of the most dramatic effects of alien species have been on islands (Coblentz 1990; Vitousek 1988). The brown tree snake (*Boiga irregularis* (Merrem)) (Figure 1), in a little over 40 years after its accidental introduction probably via surface cargo movements of surplus US military equipment, has caused the extinction of at least 10 endemic bird species in Guam, an island in the North Pacific Ocean (Savidge 1987; McCoid 1991).

The Indian mongoose (*Herpestes javanicus* (E. Geoffroy Saint-Hilaire)) has caused at least seven amphibia and reptile extinctions in Puerto Rico and other islands in the West Indies (Henderson 1992). The introduced European red fox (*Vulpes vulpes* (L.)) has been implicated in the extinction of 20 species of Australian marsupials (Morrell 1993). Likewise, in New Zealand, cats (*Felis catus* L.) have been implicated in the extinction of at least six species of endemic birds, as well as 70 populations of island birds (King 1985).

Feral goats (*Capra hircus* L.) introduced onto San Clemente Island in California have caused the extinction of eight endemic plant species, and the endangerment of eight others (Kurdila 1995). Goats introduced onto St. Helena, an island in the South Atlantic Ocean, in 1513 almost certainly extinguished more than 50 endemic plant species (Groombridge 1992).

On the Galapagos Islands, the introduced little fire ant (*Wasmannia auropunctata* (Roger)) has eliminated most Galapagos ant species where it has become established (Meier 1983). In Hawaii, the introduced bigheaded ant (*Pheidole megacephala* (Fabricius)) may have been responsible for the extinction of about 200 endemic endodontid snails (Gagné and Christensen 1985). In parts of the southern United States, the red imported fire ant (*Solenopsis wagneri* Santschi) has decimated the indigenous ant fauna, and now poses a substantial threat to the biodiversity of native arthropod communities (Porter and Savignang 1990).

The Nile perch (*Lates niloticus* (L.)), introduced into Lake Victoria in 1957 to increase the availability of food for the human population, has virtually wiped out the entire ichthyofauna of several hundred endemic haplochromine cichlid fish species (Barel et al. 1985; Hughes 1986). It is claimed that the potential loss of vertebrate genetic diversity as a result of this single ill-advised step is probably unparalleled in the history of human manipulation of ecosystems (Barel et al. 1985).

Rapid and widespread die-off and impending extinction of native freshwater mussels are occurring because of the alien zebra mussel (*Dreissena polymorpha* (Pallas)) introduction into the Great Lakes region of North America (Ricciardi et al. 1998).

Alien environmental weeds, namely weeds that have invaded natural ecosystems, are considered to be a serious threat to nature conservation (Williams and West 2000). Such plants have invaded diversity hot spots (Stohlgren et al. 1999), nature reserves, and protected areas (Macdonald et al. 1989), and can pose difficult management problems (Westman 1990). They are considered to be one of the greatest threats to nature conservation in both Australia and New Zealand (Williams and West 2000), having been implicated in the extinction of four plant species in Australia (Groves and Willis 1999).

Overall, the establishment of alien species and the loss of native species are leading to biotic homogenization (Rahel 2000). There is little likelihood that this can be stopped or reversed.

Ecosystem Function

Alien species are increasingly altering the composition and sustainable functioning of Earth's natural ecosystems in innumerable ways (D'Antonio and

Figure 1. Brown tree snake. Photo by Gordon H. Rodda, US Geological Survey, Fort Collins, CO.

Vitousek 1992; Vitousek et al. 1996; Dukes and Mooney 1999). Biotic invasions are becoming more and more extreme and exerting greater effects on extant communities (Gili 2000). The net result of such events is a new biological order (Mooney and Drake 1989).

For example, feral goats not only have impacted the biota, but have had devastating and far-reaching effects on ecosystems (Coblentz 1978). They often end up destroying the physical habitat (Coblentz 1990).

Scotch broom (*Cytisus scoparius* (L.) Link) in many parts of the world is creating disturbance-prone environments, owing to its impact on other biota, and alteration to fire regimes (Downey and Smith 2000). The European cheatgrass or downy brome (*Bromus tectorum* L.), which has invaded grassland and shrub-steppe ecosystems in western North America, has dramatically altered fire cycles which has led to changes in community structure and function (Kurdila 1995; Vitousek et al. 1996, 1997). Fire cycles that occurred every 60–100 years have been shortened to 3–5 years. Biological soil crusts have been removed, as the fire intervals are now shorter than the period required for the crusts to recover (Greene et al. 1990; Whisenant 1990). Some invasive plants may have succeeded because they bring novel mechanisms of interaction to natural plant communities (Callaway and Aschehoug 2000). However, few changes are positive.

Economic Impacts and Resource Availability

Comb jelly stowaways, lurking in the ballast water of a ship traveling from the coast of the Americas to the Black Sea, have taken over both the Azov and Black Seas, and devastated local fisheries (Travis 1993).

Similarly, zebra mussels introduced into the Great Lakes in the late 1980s have cost the economy billions of dollars by fouling and clogging water pipes (US Congress 1993).

It is estimated that approximately 50 000 alien species have become established in the United States, the ones that have become pests resulting in costs approaching US$137 billion per year (Pimentel et al. 2000). Alien insects and mites are responsible for a disproportionate share of crop losses in the United States (Sailer 1983), and have had major impacts on North American forests (Niemelä and Mattson 1996; Krcmar-Nozic et al. 2000). Yet the arthropod fauna of North America is many eons away from a "saturation point" (Lattin and Oman 1983).

Human Health

The early invaders of the New World brought smallpox and measles that devastated the American Indians (Horsfall 1983). More recently, the Yanomami of South America have likewise been affected by similar alien diseases (Tierney 2000).

The West Nile virus, which caused encephalitis in New York in 1999, probably rode to the New World in an infected bird, mosquito, or human traveler (Enserink 1999). Malaria infections acquired during flight and on the ground at European airports attest to the potential for movement of pathogens with vectors in international air traffic (Curtis and White 1984; Isaacson 1989; Russell 1991).

Conclusion

The previous examples of the worldwide impact of alien invaders on biodiversity, ecosystem function, economics, resources, and human health can be multiplied many times. They indicate that much more attention should be given to alien species.

To date, alien invaders have not been a major focus of concern in Canada. Yet there is no reason to believe that this country is immune to their onslaught. Indeed, there are now enough examples to indicate otherwise.

References

Barel, C.D.N.; Dorit, R.; Greenwood, P.H.; Fryer, G.; Hughes, N.; Jackson, P.B.N.; Kawanabe, H.; Lowe-McConnell, R.H.; Nagoshi, M.; Ribbink, A.J.; Trewavas, E.; Witte, F.;

Yamaoka, K. 1985. Destruction of fisheries in Africa's lakes. Nature 315:19–20.

Callaway, R.M.; Aschehoug, E.T. 2000. Invasive plants versus their new and old neighbors: a mechanism for exotic invasion. Science 290:521–523.

Coblentz, B.E. 1978. The effects of feral goats (*Capra hircus*) on island ecosystems. Biol. Conserv. 13:279–286.

Coblentz, B.E. 1990. Exotic organisms: a dilemma for conservation biology. Conserv. Biol. 4:261–265.

Curtis, C.F.; White, G.B. 1984. *Plasmodium falciparum* transmission in England: entomological and epidemiological data relative to cases in 1983. J. Trop. Med. Hyg. 87:101 114.

D'Antonio, C.M.; Vitousek, P.M. 1992. Biological invasions by exotic grasses, the grass/fire cycle and global change. Annu. Rev. Ecol. Syst. 23:63–67.

Downey, P.O.; Smith, J.M.B. 2000. Demography of the invasive shrub Scotch broom (*Cytisus scoparius*) at Barrington Tops, New South Wales: insights for management. Austral Ecol. 25:477–485.

Dukes, J.S.; Mooney, H.A. 1999. Does global change increase the success of biological invaders? Trends Ecol. Evol. 14:135–139.

Enserink, M. 1999. Biological invaders sweep in. Science 285:1834–1836.

Gagné, W.C.; Christensen, C.C. 1985. Conservation status of native terrestrial invertebrates in Hawaii. Pages 105–106 *in* C.P. Stone and J.M. Scott, eds. Hawaii's Cooperative National Park Resources Studies Unit, University of Hawaii, Manoa, HI.

Gili, J.M. 2000. Frontline view of an invasion. Science 287:1762.

Greene, R.S.B.; Chartes, C.J.; Hodgkinson, K.C. 1990. The effects of fire on the soil in a degraded semi-arid woodland. 1. Cryptogam cover and physical and micromorphological properties. Aust. J. Soil Res. 28:755–777.

Groombridge, B., ed. 1992. Global biodiversity: Status of the Earth's living resources. Chapman and Hall, London.

Groves, R.H.; Willis, A.J. 1999. Environmental weeds and loss of native plant biodiversity: some Australian examples. Aust. J. Environ. Manag. 6:164–171.

Henderson, R.W. 1992. Consequences of predator introductions and habitat destruction on amphibians and reptiles in the post-Columbus West Indies. Caribb. J. Sci. 28:1–10.

Horsfall, J.G. 1983. Impact of introduced pests on man. Pages 1–13 *in* C.L. Wilson and C.L. Graham, eds. Exotic plant pests and North American agriculture. Academic Press, New York, NY.

Hughes, N.F. 1986. Changes in the feeding biology of the Nile perch (*Lates nilotica* L.) (Pisces: Centropomidae) in Lake Victoria, East Africa, since its introduction in 1960, and its impact on the native fish community of the Nyanza Gulf. J. Fish Biol. 29:541–548.

Isaacson, M. 1989. Airport malaria: a review. Bull. WHO 67:737–743.

King, W.B. 1985. Island birds: will the future repeat the past? Pages 3–15 *in* P.J. Moors, ed. Conservation of island birds. Int. Counc. Bird Preserv. Tech. Publ. 3.

Krcmar-Nozic, E.; van Kooten, G.C.; Wilson, B. 2000. Threat to biodiversity: the invasion of exotic species. Pages 68–87 *in* G.C. van Kooten, E.H. Bulte, and A.E.R. Sinclair, eds. Conserving nature's diversity: Insights from biology, ethics and economics. Ashgate Publishing Ltd., Aldershot, England.

Kurdila, J. 1995. The introduction of exotic species into the United States: There goes the neighborhood. Environ. Aff. 16:95–118.

Lattin, J.D.; Oman, P. 1983. Where are the exotic insect threats? Pages 93–137 *in* C.L. Wilson and C.L. Graham, eds. Exotic plant pests and North American agriculture. Academic Press, New York, NY.

Macdonald, I.A.W.; Loope, L.L.; Usher, M.B.; Hamann, O. 1989. Wildlife conservation and the invasion of nature reserves by introduced species: a global perspective. Pages 215–255 *in* J.A. Drake, H.A Mooney, F. di Castri, R.H. Groves, F.J. Kruger, M. Rejmánek, and M. Williamson, eds. Biological invasions: a global perspective. Scope 37. John Wiley and Sons, New York, NY.

McCoid, M.J. 1991. Brown tree snake (*Boiga irregularis*) on Guam: a worst case scenario of an introduced predator. Micronesica Suppl. 3:63–69.

Meier, R.E. 1983. Coexisting patterns and foraging behaviour of ants within the arid zone of three Galapagos islands. Charles Darwin Res. Stn Annu. Rep.1983:25–27.

Mooney, H.A.; Drake, J.A. 1989. Biological invasions: A SCOPE program overview. Pages 491–507 *in* J.A. Drake, H.A Mooney, F. di Castri, R.H. Groves, F.J. Kruger, M. Rejmánek, and M. Williamson, eds. Biological invasions: a global perspective. John Wiley and Sons, New York, NY.

Morrell, V. 1993. Australian pest control by virus causes concern. Science 261:683–684.

Niemelä, P.; Mattson, W.J. 1996. Invasion of North American forests by European phytophagous insects. BioScience 46:741–753.

Parker, I.M.; Simberloff, D.; Lonsdale, W.M.; Goodell, K.; Wonham, M.; Kareiva, P.M.; Williamson, M.H.; Von Holle, B.; Moyle, P.B.; Byers, J.E.; Goldwasser, L. 1999. Impact: toward a framework for understanding the ecological effects of invaders. Biol. Invasions 1:3–19.

Pimentel, D.; Lach, L.; Zuniga, R.; Morrison, D. 2000. Environmental and economic costs of nonindigenous species in the United States. BioScience 50:53–65.

Porter, S.D.; Savignang, D.A. 1990. Invasion of polygyne fire ants decimates native ants and disrupts arthropod community. Ecology 71:2095–2106.

Rahel, F.J. 2000. Homogenization of fish faunas across the United States. Science 288:854–856.

Ricciardi, A.; Neves, R.J.; Rasmussen, J.B. 1998. Impending extinctions of North American freshwater mussels (Unionida) following the zebra mussel (Dreissena polymorpha) invasion. J. Anim. Ecol. 67:613–619.

Ricciardi, A.; Steiner, W.W.M.; Mack, R.N.; Simberloff, D. 2000. Toward a global information system for invasive species. BioScience 50:239–244.

Ruesink, J.L.; Parker, I.M.; Groom, M.J.; Kareiva, P.M. 1995. Reducing the risks of nonindigenous species introductions. BioScience 45:465–471.

Russell, R.C. 1991. Introduced vector-borne diseases in the Pacific. Micronesica Suppl. 3:33–39.

Sailer, R.I. 1983. History of insect introductions. Pages 15–38 in C.L. Wilson and C.L. Graham, eds. Exotic plant pests and North American agriculture. Academic Press, New York, NY.

Savidge, J.A. 1987. Extinction of an island forest avifauna by an introduced snake. Ecol. 68:660–668.

Simberloff, D. 1996. Impacts of introduced species in the United States. Consequences 2(2):13–22.

Soulé, M.E. 1990. The onslaught of alien species, and other challenges in the coming decades. Conserv. Biol. 4:233–239.

Stohlgren, T.J.; Buikley, D.; Chong, C.W.; Kalkhan, M.A.; Schell, L.D.; Bull, K.A.; Otsuki, Y.; Newman, G.; Bashkin, M.; Son, Y. 1999. Exotic plant species invade hot spots of native plant diversity. Ecol. Monogr. 69:25–46.

Tierney, P. 2000. Darkness in El Dorado: How scientists and journalists devastated the Amazon. W.W. Norton, New York, NY. 417 p.

Travis, J. 1993. Invader threatens Black, Azov Seas. Science 262:1366–1367.

US Congress, Office of Technology Assessment. 1993. Harmful non-indigenous species in the United States. OTA-F-565 US Government Printing Office, Washington, DC.

Vitousek, P.M. 1988. Diversity and biological invasions of oceanic islands. Pages 181–189 in E.O. Wilson, ed. Biodiversity. National Academy Press, Washington, DC.

Vitousek, P.M.; D'Antonio, C.M.; Loope, L.L.; Rejmánek, M.; Westbrooks, R. 1997. Introduced species: A significant component of human-caused global change. N. Z. J. Ecol. 21:1–16.

Vitousek, P.M.; D'Antonio, C.M.; Loope, L.L.; Westbrooks, R. 1996. Biological invasions as global environmental change. Am. Sci. 84:468–478.

Walker, B.; Steffen, W. 1997. An overview of the implications of global change for natural and managed terrestrial ecosystems. Conserv. Ecol. 1(2):2 [Print and online] http://www.consecol.org/vol1/iss2/art2

Westman, W.E. 1990. Park management of exotic plant species: problems and issues. Conserv. Biol. 4:251–260.

Whisenant, S.G. 1990. Changing fire frequencies on Idaho's Snake River Plains: ecological and management implications. Pages 4–10 in E.D.McArthur, E.M.Romney, S.D. Smith, and P.T. Tueller, eds. Proceedings of Symposium on Cheatgrass Invasion, shrub die off, and other aspects of shrub biology and management. General Technical Report IWT-276. USDA For. Serv., Intermountain Res. Stn, Ogden, UT.

Wilcove, D.S.; Rothstein, D.; Dubow, J.; Phillips, A.; Losos, E. 1998. Quantifying threats to imperiled species in the United States. BioScience 48:607–615.

Williams, J.A.; West, C.J. 2000. Environmental weeds in Australia and New Zealand: issues and approaches to management. Austral Ecol. 25:425–444.

Invasive Alien Species: An International Perspective on a Borderless Issue

Laurie E. Neville

Biological invasions have become a growing concern in recent years and are now recognized as one of the greatest threats to the ecological and economic well-being of the planet. Continuing globalization has brought tremendous benefits to many nations. It has, however, facilitated the spread of invasive alien species with increasingly negative impacts. This issue does not respect borders and addressing the problem requires international cooperation to supplement the actions of governments, economic sectors, and individuals at national and local levels.

Between 1982 and 1988, the Scientific Committee on Problems of the Environment (International Council for Science) engaged a substantial group of scientists in an effort to document the nature of the invasive species problem. The results appeared in a number of publi-

cations and as a synthesis in 1989 entitled *Ecology of Biological Invasions: A Global Perspective* (Drake et al.). This synthesis clearly established that invasive species could have major impacts on ecosystem functioning and that they affected virtually all ecosystems, including those under preservation management. It was also clear a whole new biotic order on the Earth was on its way to being established due to the massive breakdown of biogeographic barriers to migration (Mooney 1999).

Numerous international and regional agreements, regulations, decisions, and recommendations are addressing the problem of invasive alien species. Coordination of implementation and practical cooperation among those responsible for these instruments has not been sufficient to cope with the problem and the rate at which it is increasing. To resolve the gaps and inconsistencies, there is a greater movement towards a consolidated action plan. This chapter gives an overview of the main international instruments, agreements, conventions, organizations, and programs. It then describes a global program that uses a holistic approach to address the multifaceted issues surrounding the prevention and management of invasive alien species. The chapter concludes with a discussion of the social aspects that should be considered in decisions on invasive alien species.

Regional Collaborations

Many regional agreements contain requirements to regulate the introduction of alien species. They vary widely in scope and content. For example, some apply only to intentional introductions; others just to releases within protected areas. The list includes:

- African Convention on the Conservation of Nature and Natural Resources (1968);
- ASEAN Agreement on the Conservation of Nature and Natural Resources (1985);
- Convention on the Conservation of European Wildlife and Natural Resources (1982) (known as the Bern Convention);
- Convention for the Conservation of the Biodiversity and the Protection of Wilderness Areas in Central America (1992);

A slithery stowaway

The brown tree snake (*Boiga irregularis* (Merrem)) probably arrived on Guam, a previously snake-free island in the western North Pacific, as a stowaway in military equipment after World War II. In the absence of natural population controls, and with vulnerable prey on Guam, the snakes have become a common pest, causing major ecological damage. Up to 5000 snakes/km^2 may occur in some forested areas of Guam. The snakes feed on a wide variety of animals including lizards, birds, and small mammals, as well as bird and reptile eggs. Since the arrival of the brown tree snake, 12 species of birds, some found nowhere else, have disappeared from the island; several other species of birds are close to extinction. Of the 12 native species of lizard, 9 are expected to become extinct.

To date, the brown tree snake is not known to be established on any other island in the South Pacific. However, snakes are frequent stowaways in cargo leaving Guam. With increased awareness through public campaigns and careful inspection of cargo arriving from Guam, it may be possible to prevent the spread of the brown tree snake to other islands. Source: Fritts 2000.

- Convention on the Conservation of Nature in the South Pacific (1990); and
- Protocol for the Implementation of the Alpine Convention in the Field of Nature Protection and Landscape Conservation (1994).

The Standing Committee to the Bern Convention has played a particularly active role in analyzing legal frameworks related to invasive alien species and adopting detailed recommendations on introductions, reintroductions, and eradication measures. This committee also oversees the implementation, monitoring, and compliance of Bern Convention recommendations.

Strict legal provisions have been developed under the Antarctic Treaty Regime, in view of the region's isolation and vulnerability to invasion. The 1991 Madrid Protocol on Environmental Protection provides that no species of animal or plant not native to the Antarctic Treaty Area may be introduced onto land or ice shelves nor into water in the Antarctic Treaty Area, except in accordance with a permit.

Some regional economic integration organizations, including the European Community, address potential impacts of alien species on biodiversity.[1] The Southern African Development Community has included measures related to alien species in its draft Protocol on the Conservation, Sustainable Management and Sustainable Development of Forests and Forest Lands in the South African Development Community Region.

At regional levels many agreements and action plans developed within the United Nations Environment Programme (UNEP) Regional Seas Programme include provisions on alien species. Binding requirements are laid down by the four protected area protocols concluded to date for certain regional seas (the Mediterranean, Wider Caribbean Area, South East Pacific, and Eastern African Region).

The South Pacific Regional Environment Program (SPREP) has worked to define the priorities for the South Pacific region and, through a series of activities and the drafting of a regional strategy, is working to address the impacts and management of a myriad of species, such as the brown tree snake, that threaten the biodiversity and economies of the South Pacific region (Fritts 2000). The SPREP Regional Invasive Species Strategy supports a regional system of information collection and exchange as well as collaboration on preparation of invasive alien species lists. The strategy provides a basis for future harmonization of legal frameworks for border controls and mitigation planning (Shine et al. 2000).

Similar efforts throughout many regions are being planned or are underway. A consolidated network and approach to addressing the issue of alien invasive species affecting regions of the world will facilitate the extent to which countries will successfully address the best prevention and management practices available to them.

Broader International Efforts

Most international efforts focus on a specific dimension of the issue of alien species, such as a particular protection objective (for example, migratory species), kind of activity (for example, introductions for aquaculture), or potentially damaging organisms (the "pest"). Many of these instruments have their own institutional mechanisms and decision-making procedures. Institutional linkages between relevant organizations have expanded significantly over the last five years. Tools to facilitate and make cooperation operational, including memoranda of cooperation or agreement, are now routinely used between conservation treaty

Machu Picchu Program

In 1996, Finland signed an agreement with Peru forgiving most of a debt the latter owed to Finland and stipulating that the rest of the debt be used for nature conservation, a concept know as "debt-for-nature swap". Subsequently 25% of the total debt was channelled to the Machu Picchu Program; in addition, the Finnish Forest Service has provided technical assistance to the program (Metsähallitus Consulting 1999). In preparation for a master plan for the sanctuary, a survey was done of the alien plant species in this protected area. Management priorities were defined and the definition of a monitoring protocol to prevent biodiversity losses due to the spread of invasive alien species into the protected area was established (Ochoa and Andrade 2000). This effort put forth by Finland and Peru mirrors other collaborative attempts that have been made to assist developing countries with measures to address issues of invasive alien species impacts on biodiversity resources.

---

[1] Directive 79/409/EEC on the Conservation of Wild Birds; Directive 92/43/EEC on the Conservation of Natural Habitats and of Wild Fauna and Flora.

secretariats and can provide a flexible basis for joint work programs. Over 40 international instruments or programs are already in force, and several more are awaiting finalization and ratification.

Biological Diversity

In 1992, a landmark meeting of world leaders took place at the United Nations Conference on Environment and Development in Rio de Janeiro, Brazil. A historic set of agreements was signed at the "Earth Summit," including the first global agreement on the conservation and sustainable use of biological diversity. The Convention on Biological Diversity (CBD) gained rapid and widespread acceptance. Over 150 governments signed the document at the Rio conference, and since then 168 countries have signed the agreement.

The CBD has three main goals: the conservation of biodiversity; the sustainable use of the components of biodiversity; and the fair and equitable sharing of the benefits arising from commercial and other utilization of genetic resources. The agreement covers all ecosystems, species, and genetic resources. It links traditional conservation efforts to the economic goal of using biological resources sustainably. The CBD, as an international treaty, identifies a common problem, sets overall goals, policies, and general obligations, and organizes technical and financial cooperation. However, the responsibility for achieving its goals rests largely with the countries themselves.

The CBD calls on its contracting parties (183 as of the year 2002) to"prevent the introduction of, control or eradicate those alien species which threaten ecosystems, habitats, or species." (Article 8(h)). In 1998, the CBD Conference of the Parties (COP) declared that the alien species issue must be taken into account in each of its thematic work programs and requested that the CBD's Subsidiary Body on Scientific, Technical and Technological Advice (SBSTTA) develop guiding principles for implementation of Article 8(h).[2] The Guiding Principles for the prevention, introduction, and mitigation of impacts of alien species were annexed to Decision V/8 adopted by the COP in 2000. This decision urges parties, governments, and relevant organizations to apply the Guiding Principles (previously noted as "Interim Guiding Principles") as appropriate in activities to implement Article 8(h) and in the various sectors. The Guiding Principles support a hierarchical approach to alien species control, based on the following steps (SCBD 2001):

- priority should be given to preventing entry of alien invasive species, both between and within states;

- if entry has already taken place, actions should be undertaken to prevent the establishment and spread of alien species;

- the preferred response would be eradication at the earliest possible stage; and

- if eradication is not feasible or cost-effective, containment and long-term control measures should be considered.

The CBD Clearing-house Mechanism, which brings together seekers and providers of science and technology knowledge, is critical in facilitating cooperation among the Parties in the development of a shared database on invasive alien species. It will work through the Global Taxonomy Initiative, established by COP to address the lack of taxonomic information and expertise, and other taxonomic networks. The key to the success of this initiative is collaboration.

The SBSTTA and COP discussions on alien species, and on the Guiding Principles in particular, reflect the complexity of the scientific and legal issues involved, the need for more information and institutional coordination, and the range of views currently held by different countries and regions. Decision V/8 mandates further consideration of options for the full and effective implementation of Article 8(h) at COP6 (2002), including further development of the Guiding Principles and/or development of an international instrument. It also calls for closer cooperation and collaboration between the CBD Secretariat and key international institutions[3] (SCBD 2001).

The CBD COP has specifically addressed introductions to marine and coastal ecosystems through the Jakarta Mandate on Marine and Coastal Biological Diversity, and the program of work arising from the mandate.[4] Because complete containment is so difficult, the Jakarta Mandate recommends that introductions of alien species,

---

[2] Decision IV/1/C.

[3] UN Food and Agriculture Organization-International Plant Protection Convention, World Health Organization, International Maritime Organization, Office International des Epizooties, Codex Alimentarius Commission, UNESCO, Secretariats of Convention on International Trade in Endangered Species of Wild Flora and Fauna (CITES), the Ramsar Convention on Wetlands in cooperation with the Convention on the Conservation of Migratory Species of Wild Animals (the Bonn Convention), and other instruments.

[4] See Jakarta Mandate on Marine and Coastal Biological Diversity, Decision II/10, 1995, and the thematic work program annexed to Decision IV/5, 1998, at http://www.biodiv.org/programmes/areas/marine/background.asp.

products of selective breeding, and genetically modified organisms resulting from modern biotechnology that may have adverse effects on the conservation and sustainable use of marine and coastal biodiversity should be responsibly conducted, using necessary precautions. One of the operational objectives of the work program calls for the identification of gaps in existing or proposed legal instruments, guidelines, and procedures to counteract the introduction of, and adverse effects exerted by, alien species and genotypes that threaten marine ecosystems, habitats, or species, paying particular attention to transboundary effects (Shine et al. 2000).

Wetlands and Inland Waters

At the global level, inland waters are the subject of the UN Convention on the Law of Non-Navigational Uses of International Watercourses (New York, 1997: not in force). Article 22 requires watercourse states to take all necessary measures to prevent the introduction of species, alien or new, into an international watercourse, which may have effects detrimental to the ecosystem of the watercourse resulting in significant harm to other watercourse states (Shine et al. 2000).

Wetlands are particularly vulnerable to biological invasions because the presence of water attracts invaders that can quickly compete with local species. Although the Convention on Wetlands (signed in Ramsar, Iran, in 1971 and also known as the Ramsar Convention) does not reference invasive alien species, its COP adopted a resolution in 1999[5] that urges parties to address the environmental, economic, and social impacts of invasive species on wetlands, prepare inventories and assessments of alien species, establish control or eradication programs, and adopt legislation to prevent the introduction of new and environmentally dangerous alien species into their jurisdictions and to regulate their movement or trade within their jurisdictions (Shine et al. 2000; Davidson, Ramsar Wetlands Convention Secretariat, personal communication, 2000).

Ballast Water

Since the mid-1970s, the International Maritime Organization (IMO) has been working on ways to prevent the spread of alien marine organisms in ballast water and sediments. In 1997, the IMO Assembly adopted Guidelines for the Control and Management of Ships' Ballast Water to Minimize the Transfer of Harmful Aquatic Organisms and Pathogens (Annex

to Resolution A.868(29), Twentieth Assembly).[6] These are intended to assist governments and appropriate authorities, ships' masters, operators, and owners, and port authorities, as well as other interested parties, to establish common procedures to minimize the risk of introducing harmful aquatic organisms and pathogens from ships' ballast water and associated sediments while protecting ships' safety (Shine et al. 2000).

The IMO has also joined forces with the United Nations Development Programme (UNDP) and the Global Environment Facility (GEF) to implement the Global Ballast Water Management Programme (GloBallast program). This effort is a global technical cooperation program designed to provide assistance to developing countries to implement the IMO 1997 guidelines and to prepare countries for implementation of a future IMO legal instrument on ballast water. The program uses a demonstration site approach and has been established in six countries (IMO-GloBallast website http://globallast.imo.org).

Trade: Health Protection and the Environment

International trade in goods, services, and intellectual property between the 138 current members of the World Trade Organization (WTO) is disciplined by the 1994 Uruguay Round Agreements. This regime provides for binding rules, enforced by a compulsory dispute settlement mechanism, designed to ensure that governments extend free market access to each other's products and services. These rules are based on the key principles of nondiscrmination, transparency, and predictability.

The 1994 WTO Agreement on the Application of Sanitary and Phytosanitary Measures (SPS Agreement) allows members to adopt national measures or standards (1) to protect human, animal, and plant life or health from the risks arising from the entry, establishment, or spread of pests, diseases, or disease-carrying organisms; and (2) to prevent or limit other damage within the territory of the member from the entry, establishment, or spread of pests.[7] The SPS Agreement is designed primarily to ensure that import restrictions

---

[6] These guidelines update the 1993 IMO Guidelines for Preventing the Introduction of Unwanted Aquatic Organisms and Pathogens from Ships' Ballast Waters and Sediment Discharges (Assembly Resolution, 1993: Resolution A.774(18)).

[7] Text of the SPS Agreement can be obtained at the WTO Web site: http://www.wto.org.

---

[5] Resolution VII/14.

are not used as a disguised form of commercial protectionism. It is not a mechanism to ensure that governments have adequate standards in place. However, the import restrictions must be based on scientific evidence and applied only to the extent necessary to protect human, animal, or plant life or health. The burden of proof remains with the recipient country. The SPS Agreement seeks to protect countries from various pest species while fostering the principles of free and fair trade and makes provision for safe trade by promoting or requiring the use of:

- international standards as a basis for SPS measures;
- risk assessment based on scientific principles and evidence;
- consistency in the application of appropriate levels of protection;
- least trade-restrictive alternatives;
- acceptance of equivalent measures; and
- transparency through notification of trade measures.

Three international instruments are currently recognized under the SPS Agreement as standard-setting in the area of food safety and human, animal, and plant health. These are the Codex Alimentarius Commission (which sets standards on food safety and human health), the Office International des Epizooties (OIE) (which sets standards on pests and diseases of animals but not

on animals themselves as pests), and the International Plant Protection Convention (IPPC) (which sets standards for phytosanitary measures).

The Codex Alimentarius Commission was established in 1963 by the Food and Agriculture Organization (FAO) and the World Health Organization (WHO) of the United Nations. The Commission is responsible for preparing food standards and publishing them in the *Codex Alimentarius*. The procedures for preparing standards are open and transparent and involve a well-defined series of steps. The Codex includes general standards, which apply to all foods, in relation to processes such as food import and export inspection and certification systems. To adopt Codex standards, countries require adequate food legislation as well as a technical and administrative infrastructure with the capacity to implement the law and ensure compliance to it.

The OIE was established in 1924. Its standards are set out in the International Animal Health Code for Mammals, Birds and Bees (which includes an import risk analysis and import and export procedures) and in the International Aquatic Animal Health Code (which aims to facilitate trade in aquatic animal products). The latter specifies minimum health guarantees required of trading partners to avoid the risk of spreading aquatic animal diseases. It contains model international certificates for trade in live and dead aquatic animals.

The IPPC (Rome, 1951: revised 1997, revised version not yet in force) provides a framework for international cooperation to "secure common and effective action to prevent the spread and introduction of pests of plants and plant products, and to promote appropriate measures for their control" (Article1.1). Its objectives include the development and application of international standards in international trade to prevent the introduction and dissemination of plant pests, taking into account internationally approved principles governing the protection of plant, animal, and human health and the environment (Durand and Chiaradia-Bousquet 1997).

Global Invasive Species Programme

The ever-increasing impacts of invasive alien species on global economies and the environment suggest that further efforts are necessary to strengthen the current framework to effectively manage for their prevention and control. Only a handful of countries had an awareness of the invasive alien species problem in 1992 that would have allowed them to adequately address their

An aggressive biter

Asian tiger mosquito (*Aedes albopictus* (Skuse)) was accidentally introduced to the United States from Japan in the mid-1980s. It was transported in water collected in used tires, in which they often breed. Asian tiger mosquito, so named because of its black body with white stripes, is an aggressive biter. It feeds on many other species and thus has the potential to transfer diseases between wildlife and humans. Although a disease-causing organism may be present in a population, an outbreak of disease only occurs when a suitable means of transfer, such as this mosquito, is present. Unlike other mosquitoes, which feed in morning and late evening, Asian tiger mosquito is active during daylight hours. It is a known vector of dengue fever in Southeast Asia. Asian tiger mosquito has now been reported in 25 states. Source: Moor, personal communication; Lyon and Berry 1998.

responsibilities under Article 8(h) of the Convention on Biological Diversity, namely to "prevent the introduction of, control or eradicate those alien species which threaten ecosystems, habitats and species."

The need for a global invasive species program emerged in 1996 at the Norway/UN Conference on Alien Species, in Trondheim, Norway. This conference brought together experts from over 80 countries to examine the understanding and extent of the alien species problem and the capability of addressing it. The conference concluded that invasive alien species were a major threat to biodiversity conservation; indeed they were probably the greatest threat next to habitat destruction, and almost certainly the single greatest threat in ecosystems of unique biodiversity such as oceanic islands. (Sandlund et al. 1996).

It also emerged from the conference that most countries had insufficient awareness, information, or ability to address their invasive alien species problems; where such information and even solutions existed, many governments, and environmental agencies in particular, had limited access to such resources.

The brilliant green killer

An aggressive clone of the algal species *Caulerpa taxifolia* (M. Vahl) C. Agardh has destroyed more than 4000 ha of Mediterranean seabed habitat in coastal areas of France, Spain, Monaco, and Italy. When patches of this brilliant green alga were discovered there in the 1980s, they were not immediately destroyed, allowing it to spread. *Caulerpa taxifolia* has also found a foothold in the waters off Sydney, Australia. In 2000, the alga was discovered in waters north of San Diego, California, by divers who were monitoring beds of eelgrass (*Zostera marina* L.) planted to restore habitat. The National Marine Fisheries Service noted that this alga eliminates kelp beds and poses an extreme threat to flora and fauna in the area. This was the first time the alga had been discovered anywhere along the western coasts of the Americas. It is genetically identical to the Mediterranean clone. It was detected in the Agua Hedionda Lagoon, San Diego County, where the largest of 10 patches measures 200 m^2 and has now also been recorded in Huntington Harbor. Scientists have been moving quickly to destroy the alga. Source: Southern California Wetlands Recovery Project, 2000; Guiry and Dhonncha 2002.

The Global Invasive Species Programme (GISP) was initiated in response to recommendations stemming from the Norway/UN Conference. GISP focuses on alien species that disrupt ecosystem processes, thereby threatening biological diversity, health, and economies. GISP is a cooperative effort involving invasive alien species specialists, scientists, lawyers, environmentalists, policymakers, economists, resource managers, and others. The key aim of GISP is to inform and enable governments and other organizations to access the best management and prevention practices available to address invasive alien species. GISP provides support to the implementation of Article 8(h) of the Convention on Biological Diversity and strives to promote collaboration and partnerships within a holistic framework. This holistic approach considers impacts and resources with respect to agriculture, the environment, trade, health, and other key sectors on a global scale.

The GISP framework is open to all individuals and institutions that wish to cooperatively develop practical approaches to the problem of invasive alien species. GISP partners have the opportunity to provide direction for and fully participate in the GISP program of work—to inform policy and to help translate policy into effective practice. Initial support for GISP came from the Scientific Committee on Problems in the Environment (SCOPE), the World Conservation Union (IUCN), and the Centre for Agriculture and Biosciences International (CABI), international organizations with long and complementary experience in invasive alien species problems. Additional support has been given by UNEP, GEF, and several other groups.

GISP has identified an urgent need to focus more attention on invasive alien species in developing countries. In these countries, invasive species are not just a conservation or an agricultural issue, but a profound sustainable development issue, affecting poverty, rural livelihoods, health, and gender equity. Invasive alien species affect crucial and limiting ecosystem services and processes such as soil recovery, reforestation, and water conservation. Invasive alien species interfere with many development objectives in parts of the world currently least able to assess, prevent, and mitigate these species. They are, like climate change, pollution, and other global processes, a global challenge to sustainable development for all to consider.

GISP began with a three-year work plan centered on 11 components and the delivery of a specific set of outputs. Each component had a coordinator. Some of these projects were aimed at establishing the background and the scientific and social basis of invasive alien species problems. This included the current status of invasive species, their ecology, human dimensions of the invasive species problem, and the relationship between invasive alien species and global change. Another set of projects addressed more practical considerations: the identification of pathways of invasion, information and early-warning systems, methods for prevention, early detection and management, risk assessment, legal and institutional frameworks, the economics of invasive alien species, and educational programs. Specific outputs are a series of publications and products directed at different stakeholder groups. They include a global strategy for invasive alien species, a database for identification and early warning, a toolkit of best prevention and management practices, various scientific volumes addressing specific issues, and a popular book for a general audience.

Based on these principles and expertise provided during the Phase I Synthesis Conference in Cape Town, South Africa, in September 2000, a large contingency from over 40 countries, including representatives from governments and nongovernmental and intergovernmental organizations, identified priorities that resulted in the development of a global strategy and 10 strategic responses intended to guide policy-makers and managers:

1. Build national capacity to manage invasive alien species problems.

2. Build capacity to undertake critical scientific, social, and economic research.

3. Promote the sharing of information on invasive alien species and their management.

4. Develop economic policies and practical and effective economic tools.

5. Strengthen national, regional, and international legal and institutional frameworks.

6. Institute a system of environmental risk analysis.

7. Build public awareness and engagement.

8. Prepare national strategies and plans.

9. Build invasive species issues into global change initiatives.

10. Promote international cooperation to mitigate the problems of invasive alien species.

This international contingency also finalized an approach for best prevention practices and established initial priorities for Phase II of GISP.

GISP Phase II

Phase I of GISP (1997–2000) contributed to a knowledge base on invasive alien species. Phase II (initiated in 2001) promotes new partnerships with stakeholders and regional activities to encourage regional and national capacity building efforts and emphasizes capacity building and international cooperation to increase awareness and share resources on prevention and management. The aim is to support managers and policy-makers in addressing the many aspects of the alien species issue. The Phase II initiative and work plan will enable governments and development agencies to identify and initiate national and regional projects to mitigate threats resulting from invasive species impacts. It supports existing programs and initiatives and promotes international capacity building and networking. Major components of regional and national initiatives encourage (1) consideration of invasive species in the development of national strategies and action plans, (2) evaluation of these species through research and taxonomic support, and (3) development of pilot projects on prevention and management, including aspects of pathway assessment, habitat restoration, and education and outreach activities.

The working groups that have been established to carry out the mission of GISP's Phase II work plan are listed below along with their goals.

National and Regional Facilitation and Cooperation: Improve national and regional capacity (scientific, technical, and technological) to prevent and manage invasive alien species problems worldwide.

Education, Communication, and Outreach: Carry out and support communication, education, and outreach initiatives in order to motivate and empower key stakeholder groups, including natural resource managers, policy-makers, and the general public, to minimize the spread and impact of invasive alien species.

Global Information Management: Provide accessible information on scientific, technical, and other aspects of invasive alien species and facilitate access to relevant expertise on topics such as invasive alien species identification, prevention, eradication, and control.

Pathway Management: Prevent and minimize the impact of invasive alien species, focusing on key sectoral pathways of introduction or redistribution.

Evaluation and Assessment: Support the development and applications of research and research capacity on invasive alien species.

Law and Policy: Inform development and strengthening of policy and legal instruments at all levels.

Further information on the Phase II working groups and details on their specific objectives can be found at the GISP Web site (http://jasper.Stanford.EDU/gisp/).

Social Dimensions and Considerations

The cultural differences, priorities, and beliefs of people must be considered in the issue of invasive alien species and be a key element of decision-making. The dependency of the economy, health, and well-being of a society on particular species is important in considering which approach to take when making decisions. Many introduced species have tremendous benefits to local economies; the majority of agricultural crops and live-stock that have been introduced over decades have proven this. However, when particular aspects of the introductions are overlooked, problems may arise, and the costs to mitigate a resultant problem may be astounding. Costs to society should reflect the impacts on natural resources, health, agriculture, and industry. These costs are too often difficult to determine with the current assessment processes, given the uncertainty about how invasive species affect ecosystem services. Collaboration and sharing of information will assist in providing adequate assessments and the best prevention and management measures.

Human values and perspectives are determining factors and a driving force behind the accelerated movement of species and products through trade, and consideration of this aspect is necessary to minimize threats posed by invasive alien species. The diversity of these values will be important considerations when applying management programs for prevention and mitigation at national and local levels and for successful collaboration in capacity-building programs. Facilitation of resource and information sharing between countries will help minimize the impacts of invasive alien species and promote cooperation overall.

Many of the serious invasive alien species in the developing world are, sadly, associated with development assistance projects. In some cases, alien species are unintentionally introduced with planting and packaging material. In other cases, invasives are introduced deliberately, but unintentionally, as new crops or other organisms and subsequently become invasive. Development assistance in Africa and Asia has been a major source of serious insect and weed invaders, which now threaten food security in some countries. This sensitive issue must be addressed to assess the full cost

Working for Water Programme

Over the last few centuries, 750 tree species and 8000 herbaceous plants have been introduced to South Africa. Although many have become naturalized, about 200 are invasive, affecting over 10 million ha of land and wasting 7% of the country's water resources (Government of South Africa 2000a). These invasive plants can convert species-rich vegetation to single-species stands, increasing biomass, providing fuel for wildfires, and dramatically decreasing stream flow (van Wilgen et al. 1998). The Working for Water (WfW) Programme was established in 1995 to control invasive alien plants and thereby enhance water security; improve the ecological integrity of natural systems; create employment; restore the productive potential of the land; and develop economic benefits from wood, land, water, and trained people (Government of South Africa 2000b) .

In 1995, R25 million (US$5.5 million) was allocated to the WfW national program, with R13.5 million of this going to the 1.14 million ha of fynbos catchments of the Western Cape Province. South

Africa is home to the smallest and richest of the six floral kingdoms of the world, the Cape Floral Kingdom, and fynbos is the major vegetation type. Invasive alien plants occur in almost half of this area. Of the total invaded area, more than 60 000 ha are covered with alien plant stands, having canopy cover of 25–100%. Between the start of the WfW program and the end of August 1996, 39 000 ha had been cleared, including nearly 7000 ha of dense stands (having greater than 25% canopy cover). The WfW fynbos program employed more than 3000 people at its initial peak in March 1996. More people are now being employed following the injection of a further R40+ million into the project. In this program, short-term social benefits contribute towards the realization of long-term development and environmental goals (Marais and Richardson 1997).

and benefits involved and to identify precautionary measures. Countries that have the resources and abilities to assist others should be aware of the ramifications and risks associated with this undeniably necessary service.

The role of the military must also be considered. The transport of people, equipment, and supplies during times of war and unrest and during routine training regimes should not be overlooked as they are proven and potential vectors in the spread of potentially harmful organisms among ecosystems. For example, as early as 1768, the French intentionally introduced common prickly-pear cactus (*Opuntia monacantha* (Willd.) Haw.) to Fort Dauphin (Taolañaro) in southeast Madagascar to provide an impregnable barrier around the fort (McNeely 2001). More recently, Australian military activities in East Timor revealed that machines, troops, and equipment were carefully monitored and cleaned upon returning to Australia from missions in the islands, and this particular effort provides an important model for other countries (Wittenberg and Cock 2001). However, such careful monitoring of the machines, troops, and equipment heading out from Australia and landing in East Timor was not considered at the time of the operation. Such inequities must be addressed, and international standards and codes of conduct established to avoid the potential impacts that follow such activities.

The globalization of trade has accelerated the transport of goods via various pathways and vectors. Consequently, the transfer of biotic material now occurs at much greater rates and volumes. The effect of alien species, whether introduced by accident or intentionally, on trade, transport, and tourism is a complex issue that must be addressed by the many stakeholders.

Conclusion

Invasive alien species are found in nearly all of the major taxonomic groups of organisms. Even though only a small percentage of species that are moved across biogeographic borders become invasive, they have extensive impacts. The dramatic increase in global trade over the past 200 years has accelerated the rate of spread of various organisms over natural barriers. The relocation of organisms, whether intentional or accidental, can often have devastating effects on those resources that are of value to society, whether it be costs to the native biodiversity of natural ecosystems, or to agricultural systems, industry, and human health (Perrings et al. 1999; McNeely et al. 2001).

Raising awareness of the issue is paramount to achieving new, innovative approaches to managing the problem. The engagement of research institutions, governments, agencies, industries, communities, and other stakeholders is imperative if the impacts of invasive species are to be minimized and, ideally, prevented. This complex and expansive issue is increasingly demanding the attention of scientists, economists, industry, and decision-makers as the costs to society and to biodiversity cannot be ignored. At the regional and national levels, mutual cooperation is essential for effective action and results. Efficacy in dealing with the issues can be increased by sharing information and resources; establishing consistency in policies, legislation, and practice; and cooperating on risk-assessment and mitigation programs. Above all, nations must collaborate—this is key to effectively addressing the issue, realizing new and innovative approaches and solutions, and ultimately minimizing the impacts of a complex problem.

References

Drake, J.A.; Mooney, H.A.; di Castro, F.; Grooves, R.H.; Kruger, F.J.; Rejmanek, M.; Williamson, M., eds. 1989. Ecology of biological invasions: a global perspective. John Wiley and Sons, New York, NY. 450 p.

Durand, S.; Chiaradia-Bousquet, J.-P. 1997. New principles of phytosanitary legislation. FAO Legislative Study 62. Food and Agriculture Organization, Rome.

Fritts, T.H. 2000. The brown tree snake: a fact sheet for Pacific Island residents and travelers [online]. US Geological Survey, Midcontinent Ecological Science Centre, Fort Collins, CO. Accessed 29 Jan. 2002. http://www.pwrc.usgs.gov/btreesnk.htm

Government of South Africa. 2000a. The Working for Water Programme. The Problem [Web page]. Department of Water Affairs and Forestry, Pretoria, South Africa. http://www.dwaf.gov.za/wfw

Government of South Africa. 2000b. The Working for Water Programme. Annual Report 1999/2000 [online]. Department of Water Affairs and Forestry, Pretoria, South Africa. http://www.dwaf.gov.za/wfw

Guiry, M.D.; Dhonncha, E.N. 2002. AlgaeBase [online]. Accessed 29 Jan. 2002. http://www.algaebase.com

Lyon, W.F.; Berry, R.L. 1998. Asian tiger mosquito [online]. Ohio State University Extension Fact Sheet HYG-2148-98. Accessed 29 Jan. 2002. http://ohioline.osu.edu/hyg-fact/2000/2148.html

Marais, C.; Richardson, D.M. 1997. The fynbos "Working for Water" program: an environmental project that combines social and environmental benefits [print and online]. Aliens (Invasive Species Specialist Group of IUCN Species Survival Commission Newslett.) 5:9–10. http://www.issg.org/newsletter.html#Aliens

McNeely, J.A., ed. 2001. The great reshuffling: human dimensions of invasive alien species. IUCN, Gland, Switzerland, and Cambridge, UK. vi+242 p.

McNeely, J.A.; Mooney, H.A.; Neville, L.E.; Schei, P.; Waage, J.K., eds. 2001. A global strategy on invasive alien species. IUCN, Gland, Switzerland, and Cambridge, UK.

Metsähallitus Consulting. 1999 Finnish aid and the Machu Picchu Program. Web site. http://www.metsa.fi/eng/tat/machu%20picchu/web%20pages/pohja5.htm

Mooney, H.A. 1999. The Global Invasive Species Programme (GISP). Biol. Invasions 1:97-98.

Mooney, H.A.; Drake, J.A. 1989. Biological invasions: a SCOPE program overview. Pages 491–506 in J.A. Drake, H.A. Mooney, F. di Castri, R.H. Groves, F.J. Kruger, M. Rejmanek, and M. Williamson, eds. Ecology of biological invasions: a global perspective. John Wiley and Sons, New York, NY. 528 p.

Ochoa J.G.; Andrade, G.I. 2000. The introduced flora to Machu Picchu Sanctuary: inventory and management priorities for biodiversity conservation. Aliens (Invasive Species Specialist Group of the IUCN Species Survival Commission Newslett.) 12:63–4.

Perrings, C.; Williamson, M.; Dalmazzone, S. 2000. The economics of biological invasions. Edward Elger, Cheltenham, UK.

Sandlund, O.T.; Schei, P.J.; Viken, Å., eds. 1996. Proceedings: Norway/UN Conference on Alien Species: the Trondheim Conferences on Biodiversity, 1–5 July 1996, Trondheim, Norway. Directorate for Nature Management/Norwegian Institute for Nature Research, Trondheim, Norway. 233 p

[SCBD] Secretariat of the Convention on Biological Diversity. 2001. Assessment and management of alien species that threaten ecosystems, habitats and species. Abstracts of keynote addresses and posters presented at the 6th meeting of the Subsidiary Body on Scientific, Technical and Technological Advice, 12–16 March 2001, Montreal, QC. CBD Tech. Publ. 1. 146 p.

Shine, C.; Williams, N.; Gundling, L. 2000. A guide to designing legal and institutional frameworks on alien invasive species. IUCN, Gland, Switzerland, Cambridge and Bonn. xvi+138 p.

Southern California Wetlands Recovery Project, Coast Conservancy. 2000. Invasion of Caulerpa taxifolia to southern California [online]. Wetland Managers Group Report. Accessed 29 Jan. 2002. http://www.coastalconservancy.ca.gov/scwrp/BOGMtgs/BOG102000/Caulerpa.htm

van Wilgen, B.W.; Cowling, R.M.; Le Maitre, D.C. 1998. Ecosystem services, efficiency, sustainability and equity: South Africa's Working for Water Programme. Trends Ecol. Evol. 13:378.

Wittenberg, R.; Cock, M.J.W. 2001. AQIS media release "The Australian Defence Force is involved in keeping alien species out." Page 88 in Invasive alien species: a toolkit of best prevention and management practices. CAB International on behalf of the Global Invasive Species Programme, Wallingford, Oxon, UK.

Photo with chapter title: Fifty years after a few pairs were imported for commercial fur farming, the North American beaver (*Castor canadensis* Kuhl), in numbers reaching 100 000, is overrunning Tierra del Fuego, an island at the tip of South America. Photo by Roberta Gal.

Ecological and Economic Impacts of Alien Species: A Phenomenal Global Change

Daniel Simberloff

Invasive alien species have a plethora of impacts on the environment and the economy. Some effects are apparent to the most casual observer; others are more subtle, and some effects are so idiosyncratic that they would never have been predicted. Worldwide, alien species now rank second to habitat conversion as a cause of species endangerment and extinction (Wilcove et al. 1998). There is no comprehensive estimate of their economic cost to such human enterprises as agriculture, forestry, and fisheries, nor of their public health cost, and remarkably little study of the economics of invasions (Perrings 2000). A recent estimate of their cost to the United States economy alone is US$137 billion annually (Pimentel et al. 2000). The impacts of some alien species, such as the sea lamprey (*Petromyzon marinus* L.) in the Great Lakes and the gypsy moth (European race, *Lymantria dispar* (L.)) in eastern North America, have long been known. Other more recent invaders, such as the zebra mussel (*Dreissena polymorpha* (Pallas)) and the Asian long-horned beetle (*Anoplophora glabripennis* (Mots.)), have burst onto the scene with much publicity and (in the case of the mussel) rapid substantial ecological and economic damage. However, because the impacts of alien species are so multifarious and often quite subtle, we have just begun to detect the full scope and depth of this problem. Further, alien species sometimes remain innocuous and restricted in range and/or habitat for decades or longer, then suddenly expand to become serious pests (Kowarik 1995; Crooks and Soulé 1996). Thus, some fraction of species already introduced to a location but not currently seen as problematic are destined to become so in the future. In sum, the rearrangement of global biogeography is an enormous global change, and its ecological and economic impacts over the last century surely exceed those caused by global warming. However, it has received far less public attention than the latter phenomenon.

No two invasions are identical, but the impacts of the majority fall into several well-defined categories: habitat change, competition, predation, herbivory, disease, and hybridization. Some impacts are more complex as they combine various effects. Also, some impacts are difficult to predict because of phenomena such as invasional meltdown, lag times, and spontaneous population explosions and collapses. This chapter will review impacts of invasions in each category, with examples from various habitats and taxa. It shows how difficult it is to predict which invasions will produce which impacts of what magnitude. This fact suggests a much more cautious and comprehensive approach to alien species than we have seen in the past.

Habitat Change

Because so many species are closely tied to particular habitats, impacts of an alien species that greatly changes the habitat can ripple through an entire community. For example, in the 18th and 19th centuries, the northeastern North American coast comprised extensive mud flats and salt marshes. Today it is usually characterized by rocky beaches. This dramatic change is due to the common periwinkle (*Littorina littorea* L.). Introduced (probably for food) to Nova Scotia around 1840, it slowly spread southward, eating algae on rocks and also rhizomes of marsh grasses. Experimental exclusion studies (Bertness 1984) show that exclusion of the periwinkle leads to rapid coverage of rocks by algae and mud, followed by grass invasion. Thus the periwinkle has modified the entire physical structure of the intertidal zone. In so doing, it has many impacts on other species. For example, in parts of New England, almost all long-armed hermit crabs (*Pagurus longicarpus* Say) occupy periwinkle shells, implying that these crabs are probably more numerous than they had been. The periwinkle displaces its native congener, the rough periwinkle (*L. saxatilis*) (Yamada and Mansour 1987), and prevents *Fucus* germlings and barnacle cyprids from establishing (Lubchenko and Menge 1978; Lubchenko 1983; Petraitis 1983). It has competitively excluded the native eastern mud snail (*Ilyanassa obsoleta* (Say)) from habitats, such as salt marshes and eel grass beds, where it had been common (Brenchley and Carlton 1983). Indirect effects—that is, changes in interactions between these directly affected species and other species not directly interacting with the periwinkle—must abound. In sum, the entire ecosystem is transformed.

Similarly, the zebra mussel (a native of southern Russia) has greatly modified large parts of many ecosystems (Williamson 1996; Ricciardi et al. 1997, 1998). It was first noticed in Lake St. Clair in 1988, probably transported in ballast water or attached to a ship's hull, and by 2000 it ranged over much of the eastern United States and Canada (Johnson and Carlton 1996). Most public attention has been focused on its economic impacts through fouling and clogging water pipes, with costs to date estimated as billions of dollars (US Congress 1993). However, its ecological impacts are equally drastic (Ricciardi et al. 1997, 1998). It settles in dense aggregations that smother native unionid clams, and it has converted the substrate in some areas into a jagged mass of mussel shells. In addition, it filters water at a prodigious rate, thereby increasing water clarity, decreasing phytoplankton densities, and almost certainly affecting populations of fish, zooplankton, and other invertebrates. The very existence of many native mollusks is threatened (Ricciardi et al. 1998), and there are numerous impacts on many other species (Ricciardi et al. 1997; Strayer et al. 1999). Worse, the zebra mussel interacts with other invaders to increase the impact of both the mussel and those species, as will be discussed.

Although the periwinkle and the zebra mussel are animals, introduced plants are probably more frequent causes of ecosystem-wide impacts via habitat change, simply because plants often constitute the habitat for an entire community, and because terrestrial, aquatic, and marine plants can all overgrow large areas (Simberloff 2000). A cold-resistant strain of the tropical alga *Caulerpa taxifolia* (Vahl) C. Agardh has overrun about 5000 ha of the near-shore marine benthos of the northwestern Mediterranean in less than 20 years after being dumped into the sea from a commercial aquarium at Monaco (Meinesz 1999). Infestations of the same species have recently been discovered in coastal California and Australia. In the Mediterranean, it has already overgrown beds of the sea grass *Posidonia oceanica* (L.), a drastic habitat change that has led to the decline of fish and invertebrate populations. Its toxic terpenes may further affect them, either directly through poisoning or avoidance, or indirectly through the food chain. The Japanese green alga *Codium fragile* (Suringar) Hariot subsp. *tomentosoides* (van Goor) Silva (dead man's fingers or oyster thief) may have equally profound effects in North America. It arrived in the western North Atlantic at Long Island Sound by 1957 through unknown means and has since spread south to North Carolina and north to Canada. It affects mollusks by attaching to them, and it may displace native algae. In the Gulf of Maine, it is the main species in a group of invaders that has completely transformed native communities (L.G. Harris and M. Tyrrell, University of New Hampshire, Durham, NH, personal communication).

Plants can change entire ecosystems even without overgrowing the native dominants, through modification of various ecosystem traits and processes. For example, in Florida, Australian melaleuca (*Melaleuca quinquenervia* (Cav.) Blake) has a combination of traits (spongy outer bark, highly flammable leaves and litter) that has led to increased fire intensity and frequency. These changes, in turn, have helped melaleuca to replace native plants not adapted to this fire regime on about 200 000 ha. Subsequently there have been many other changes to the regional community (Schmitz et al. 1997). This is one among many cases in which introduced plants, by modifying various natural disturbance regimes, affect entire ecosystems (Mack and D'Antonio 1998). In the US southwest, Mediterranean salt cedars (*Tamarix* spp.) cause severe water loss in arid areas because of their deep roots and rapid transpiration. In California, salt cedar drained the surface water of a large marsh, thus eliminating much of the associated biota (Vitousek 1986). Introduced plants can also modify nutrients. On the volcanic island of Hawaii, the Atlantic nitrogen-fixing shrub, firetree (*Myrica faya* Ait.), has invaded young, nitrogen-poor areas. As there are no native nitrogen-fixers, the native species have adapted to the nitrogen-poor soil, while alien species are generally poorly adapted to it. Now there is the prospect that a wave of plant invaders will establish over large areas because they are facilitated by *M. faya* (Vitousek 1986).

As is evident from the example of the common periwinkle, an alien species that removes a dominant plant or plants can affect an entire community. Pathogens as well as herbivores can generate such an effect. For example, the Asian chestnut blight fungus (*Cryphonectria parasitica* (Murr.) Barr) reached New York on nursery stock in the late 19th century, spread over 100 million ha of eastern North America from southern Ontario to north Georgia and Alabama in less than 50 years, and killed almost all mature American chestnuts (*Castanea dentata* (Marsh.) Borkh.) (Anderson 1974; von Broembsen 1989). Because chestnut had been a dominant tree in many areas, impacts on the native community must have been major. Occasional statements that the chestnut blight invasion shows that a dominant species can be replaced with minimal impact on the ecosystem (for example, Williamson 1996) reflect lack of knowledge, rather than lack of impact. There are few data from before this invasion, but they suggest major impacts. For example, several moths that were host-specific to chestnut became extinct (Opler 1979), and nutrient cycling was probably affected (K. Cromack, Oregon State University, Corvallis, OR, personal communication).

There is, of course, a gradient between ecosystem- and community-wide impact, as is often caused by drastic habitat change of the sort just described, and impact on one or a few species. There is no clear demarcation of how many species must be affected, and to what extent, before an impact should be termed system-wide rather than affecting particular populations. The various forces discussed below will be treated primarily in terms of how one species affects another. There may be little further impact on the recipient community, or the impact may be propagated to many species (especially if the affected species is ecologically important). Often, as in the chestnut blight case, it appears that an invasion must have had drastic impacts on a wide swath of the community, though data do not exist to test this hypothesis. Similarly, all the earthworms of much of Canada and the northern United States are Eurasian immigrants (Samuels 2000). It is difficult to believe that the immigrant nature of a taxon so crucial to ecosystem function as earthworms cannot have had major impacts on an entire ecosystem, but there has been no published research on the problem.

Competition

Competition can entail interference; that is, individuals of one species can prevent individuals of another from garnering resources, by fighting, for example, or intimidation. Or two species can affect each other's populations when both try to use a resource in short supply. In the latter phenomenon, often called resource competition, two species can affect each other even if individuals are never in contact (as when diurnal and nocturnal species compete for the same food). Resource competition is notoriously difficult to document. However, some of the best-known cases concern impacts of alien species on native ones. For example, in Great Britain, resource competition with the introduced gray squirrel (*Sciurus carolinensis* Gmelin) of North America has caused a decline in populations of the native red squirrel (*S. vulgaris* L.). Extensive research (summarized by Williamson 1996) shows that the invader forages more efficiently for food. The alewife (*Alosa pseudoharengus* (Wilson)), an Atlantic coastal fish, may have

been native to Lake Ontario (Burgess 1980) or may have been introduced (Smith 1970). In any event, it then spread through the other Great Lakes by the Welland Canal (Burgess 1980). The alewife reduced zooplankton populations of the Great Lakes (Wells 1970), and competition for this resource contributed to the disappearance of native planktivorous salmonids (Fuller et al. 1999). Crowder (1984) attributed both morphological change and a habitat shift in the native Lake Michigan bloater (*Coregonus hoyi* (Gill)) to competition with alewives, which are now the dominant fish in Lake Michigan and account for 70–90% of fish weight (Becker 1983). Plants, of course, can compete with one another for light and nutrients.

Interference competition is easier to observe, though documentation of population impact is not trivial. Brown trout (*Salmo trutta* (L.)) interfere with feeding by brook trout (*Salvelinus fontinalis* (Mitchill)) not only by displacing brook trout from their favored feeding habitats (Fausch and White 1981) but also by increasing their periods of inactivity and reducing feeding activity (DeWald and Wilzbach 1992; Kerr and Grant 2000). Introduced plants can engage in a form of aggressive interference competition. For example, the African ice plant (*Mesembryanthemum crystallinum* L.) accumulates salt, which remains in the soil when the plant decomposes. In California, this plant excludes native plants that cannot tolerate salt (Vivrette and Muller 1977). In both of these examples, the invader does not render a resource in short supply for native species; rather, it inhibits the native.

Predation

Many alien species prey on native species, sometimes driving them to local or global extinction. The sea lamprey (*Petromyzon marinus* L.) first arrived in Lake Ontario in the 1830s either by migrating through the Erie Canal or by hitchhiking on ships moving through the Erie and St. Lawrence canal systems; it then moved to Lake Erie through the Welland Canal (Fuller et al. 1999). In combination with other factors, as discussed below, predation by the lamprey led directly to the extinction of three endemic Great Lakes fishes, the longjaw cisco (*Coregonus alpenae* (Koelz)), the deepwater cisco (*C. johannae* (Wagner)), and the blackfin cisco (*C. nigripinnis* (Gill)) (Miller et al. 1989). Along with overfishing, watershed deforestation, and pollution, lampreys devastated populations of all large native fish, even though they did not cause extinction (Christie 1974;

Cox 1999). Economic impacts were dramatic, as catches of many species declined 90% or more. Declines of these large fish rippled through the food web, and populations of several smaller fish species increased. Ultimately, as lampreys switched to these species in the absence of larger prey, many of them declined.

There are even more dramatic impacts of introduced predators. For example, the rosy wolfsnail (*Euglandina rosea* (Férussac)) (Figure 1) of Florida and Central America was introduced to many Pacific islands and several others around the world in a failed attempt at biological control of the previously introduced giant African snail (*Achatina fulica* (Férussac)). The rosy wolfsnail attacks many native terrestrial, arboreal, and even aquatic snails on these islands and has already caused the extinction of at least 30 species (Civeyrel and Simberloff 1996). The brown tree snake (*Boiga irregularis* (Merrem)), introduced in cargo from the Admiralty Islands, has eliminated 9 of the 11 native forest bird species on Guam (Williamson 1996).

Herbivory

Although ecological impacts such as that wrought by the periwinkle can be enormous, probably the best known impact of herbivores is economic damage caused by various insect pests of agricultural crops and forests. In 1869, the European gypsy moth was brought to North America from Europe in a futile effort to generate a silk industry. It quickly escaped to the wild in Massachusetts, and by 1991 it occupied 500 000 km² of the northeastern United States and eastern Canada (Cox 1999). The moth feeds on many woody plants, preferring oaks (*Quercus* spp.) and trembling aspen (*Populus tremuloides* Michx.) in Canada (Liebhold et

Figure 1. Rosy wolfsnail. Photo by Ron Heu, State of Hawaii Department of Agriculture, Honolulu, HI.

al. 1997). An Asian strain of the same species has appeared near Portland, Oregon, and Vancouver, British Columbia, but these infestations have so far been eradicated (Cox 1999). Defoliation by the gypsy moth weakens trees and thereby increases their susceptibility to other insects and diseases (Liebhold et al. 1996). In some areas, repeated defoliation has caused up to 90% mortality of preferred host trees, thus greatly changing forest composition (Cox 1999). For details of the gypsy moth story, see Nealis in this publication (p.151).

There are many subsequent impacts on other community members after a major infestation of woody plants. Litter amounts and decomposition increase, thus increasing nitrogen loss in stream flow, while both defoliation and reduction of oak mast production can have varied impacts on bird populations (Cox 1999).

The Russian wheat aphid (*Diuraphis noxia* (Mordvilko)), a native of southeastern Europe and southwestern Asia, spread to Mexico in the 1980s, arrived in the United States from Mexico in 1986, and quickly spread through the western part of the United States and Alberta and Saskatchewan (US Congress 1993). It attacks not only wheat but also barley and, less intensively, some other members of the Poaceae, including rye and triticale (Kindler and Springer 1989). It has cost about US$1 billion so far in yield losses and control costs, and it has led to the near elimination of wheat and barley crops in some regions (US Congress 1993). In addition to crop impacts, it has ecological impacts. For example, it infests crested wheatgrass (*Agropyron cristatum* (L.) Gaertn.), widely planted for soil conservation (US Congress 1993), and the Eurasian sevenspotted lady beetle (*Coccinella septempunctata* L.), widely distributed to combat the aphid, has displaced native lady beetles in widely separated areas (Obrycki et al. 2000).

Disease

In addition to major ecosystem-wide impacts such as that described for chestnut blight, an introduced pathogen can have impacts more narrowly focused on one or a few species. Whirling disease, caused by *Myxobolus cerebralis* (Hofer), is a European metazoan parasite that penetrates the head and spine of juvenile trout, where it multiplies and exerts pressure on the organ of equilibrium. The fish then swim erratically, impeding their ability to feed and to avoid predators. Severe infections kill many young-of-the-year fish. Spores of *M. cerebralis* reach the substrate when an infected fish dies or when it is eaten by a predator (in which case the spores are expelled in feces). There they can withstand freezing and drying, remaining viable for up to 30 years. They must then be ingested by the alternate host, an aquatic worm (*Tubifex tubifex* Muller); in the gut of this worm, the spore is converted to a mature form that can infect trout. This mature form enters the water, where it contacts young trout; trout may also eat infected worms (Markiw 1992).

Rainbow trout (*Oncorhynchus mykiss* (Walbaum)) are particularly susceptible to whirling disease, which reached North America in 1955 and has since spread widely in the United States (though not yet to Canada; six border states are infested). It arrived in North America by a tortuous route. North American rainbow trout were transplanted to Europe, and whirling disease was discovered in them in Germany in 1893 and has since been found in all European populations. It was probably acquired from the brown trout, a European native that harbors the parasite but is resistant to the disease. Rainbow trout from the American West were exported to Europe for hatchery culture; frozen rainbow trout from Scandinavia were then exported to grocery stores in Pennsylvania. A stream flowing through a residential area then probably carried the parasite to a nearby fish hatchery. Fish transfers from this hatchery probably spread the parasite to many other states (Bergersen and Anderson 1997). It has been an economic disaster in several areas; in many streams in Montana and Colorado, whirling disease afflicts over 95% of the rainbow trout, devastating the sport fishery (Robbins 1996).

Hybridization

Alien species can gradually change a native species, even to the point of extinguishing it as a recognizable, distinct form, by mating with it. Introduced rainbow trout, for example, hybridize with at least some populations of five native trout species listed under the United States *Endangered Species Act* (Kerr and Grant 2000). The gene pools of these species are gradually coming to resemble that of rainbow trout. Brown trout hybridize with brook trout (Sorensen et al. 1995; Kerr and Grant 2000). In addition to game fish, fish species introduced for biological control and released for bait have caused introgressive hybridization and even extinction, and there are numerous similar examples among mammals, birds, and plants (Rhymer and Simberloff 1996).

In both previous cases, hybridization is followed by introgression as the hybrids are viable and produce fertile backcrosses with the parental populations. However, no gene flow need occur in order for hybridization with an alien species to threaten a native population. The bull trout (*Salvelinus confluentus* (Suckley)), a candidate for threatened status under the US *Endangered Species Act*, hybridizes with introduced brook trout in parts of northwestern North America. Because of sterility, poor mating success, or low progeny survival, there is almost no backcrossing into the parental populations (Leary et al. 1993). Nevertheless, in some populations the less numerous bull trout are at a disadvantage because a greater fraction of their reproductive effort is wasted in these hybrid matings.

Hybridization between a native and an alien species can even produce a new invasive pest. For example, smooth cordgrass (*Spartina alterniflora* Loisel.) of coastal eastern North America was introduced to the United Kingdom in the mid-19th century, but it was a harmless, uncommon alien species there. Occasionally it hybridized with the native *S. maritima*, but these hybrids were sterile. Then, in about 1890, one such hybrid individual underwent a spontaneous chromosomal mutation (doubling its number of chromosomes) to become a fertile invasive weed, *S. anglica* C.E. Hubbard, which has damaged large patches of the softbottom intertidal zone of the United Kingdom (Thompson 1991). It has more recently invaded northern Puget Sound, where it is the target of an active control effort, but it has not yet reached Canada (S.D. Hacker, Washington State University, Pullman, WA, personal communication).

The ability to hybridize requires close genetic relationship (animals must usually be congeners); subsequent genetic introgression requires even closer relationship. Thus, in some areas (for example, Australia and New Zealand) in which invaders are primarily from distant regions whose denizens have long been evolutionarily separated from the natives, threats posed by hybridization are minimal (Simberloff 2000). However, by far the greatest number of invaders of North America are Eurasian (for example, Niemelä and Mattson 1996). By virtue of their geological histories, these continents have many closely related species, and hybridization is thus a common threat.

Complex Impacts and Combinations of Effects

In several of the previous examples, an alien species interacts with natives in a variety of ways. For example, we have seen that the brown trout competes with brook trout for food and also hybridizes with it. In fact, brown trout can also compete with brook trout for spawning and nursery areas and prey heavily on brook trout (Kerr and Grant 2000). In addition, brown trout can interact in important ways with Arctic char (*Salvelinus alpinus* (L.)), lake trout (*S. namaycush* (Walbaum)), and Atlantic salmon (*Salmo salar* L.) (Kerr and Grant 2000). Brown trout may also affect stream invertebrate populations, though this impact has barely been studied. All of these species may interact with brook trout. Clearly, the population impact of brown trout on brook trout is complicated and not yet fully understood.

Alien species often interact with other factors to generate an impact, and these interactions can be complex. Wilcove et al. (1998, 2000) examined the causes of imperilment for the 1880 species whose existence in the United States they recognized as threatened. They found habitat loss to be the most common problem (85% of all imperiled species), followed by alien species (49%), which exceeded the sum of the next three most common factors, pollution (24%), overexploitation (17%), and disease (3%). However, a striking finding is that most species are threatened by more than one factor, as evidenced by the fact that the sum of these percentages far exceeds 100%. Previously, for example, we saw that the impact of sea lampreys combined with those of overexploitation, habitat destruction, and pollution in the Great Lakes reduced many populations of large fishes dramatically. Similarly, although predation by the lamprey was probably the single biggest cause of the extinction of the three species of cisco, overexploitation and hybridization with more common cisco species were contributing factors (Miller et al. 1989). Recall also that one important impact of defoliation by gypsy moths is to weaken trees generally, thereby rendering them more liable to damage and death by a host of other causes, including impacts of other insects and diseases, both native and alien (Liebhold et al. 1996).

Although the ways in which alien species interact with other factors to produce enormous ecological and/or economic impacts are as numerous as the idiosyncrasies of the biology of the invaders, certain types of interactions are particularly common. For example, in many genera of plants and animals, interfertile congeners (including alien and native species) are reproductively isolated by major habitat differences, and habitat destruction can obliterate these (Rhymer and Simberloff 1996). Overharvest and/or habitat destruction

frequently reduce a native species' population relative to that of an alien congener, thus increasing the likelihood of hybridization (Rhymer and Simberloff 1996). Roads and habitat fragmentation are often claimed to aid the invasion of natural areas by alien species (for example, Greenberg et al. 1997), and though there is not much evidence on this proposition, some well-studied cases suggest that the phenomenon could be widespread. For instance, in northern California and southern Oregon, the introduced root fungus (*Phytophthora lateralis* Tucker & Milbrath) of Port-Orford-cedar (*Chamaecyparis lawsoniana* (A. Murr.) Parl.) is distributed by vehicles and drainage water along logging and mining roads (Zobel et al. 1985).

Invasional Meltdown

Certainly one of the most common ways in which the impact of an alien species interacts with another factor to the detriment of native species, communities, and ecosystems is by synergism with other alien species (Simberloff and Von Holle 1999). Often an alien species remains quite innocuous in its new home until another alien species invades, when the prior species becomes dramatically more problematic. Highly evolved pollination syndromes are an example. In south Florida, ornamental fig (*Ficus*) trees were common for at least a century, restricted to anthropogenic settings because they could not reproduce without their host-specific fig wasps (*Parapristina verticillata* (Waterson)). Recently, the fig wasp of *Ficus microcarpa* L. f. (=*F. thonningii* Blume) invaded, and the latter is now spreading rapidly, including into natural areas (Kauffman et al. 1991; McKey and Kauffman 1991). The impact of an introduced plant species is often exacerbated, or at least accelerated, by introduced animals that disperse its seeds. For example, seeds of the nitrogen-fixing *Myrica faya* in Hawaii are primarily dispersed by the introduced Japanese white-eye (*Zosterops japonicus* Temminck & Schlegel) (Woodward et al. 1990), while introduced feral pigs and rats also disperse these seeds (Stone and Taylor 1984).

One alien species can also modify the habitat to be more favorable to a second invader. Thus, through its filtering activities and modification of the substrate, the presence of the zebra mussel increases populations of the invasive common bithynia (*Bithynia tentaculata* (L.)) (Ricciardi et al. 1997). Such interactions can even be mutualistic. Mussel filtration increases water clarity, which in turn promotes growth of Eurasian water-milfoil

(*Myriophyllum spicatum* L.) (MacIsaac 1996). This invasive aquatic weed was probably intentionally introduced to a pond in Washington, DC, in 1942 (Couch and Nelson 1985); from there it spread to most of the United States plus British Columbia, Ontario, and Quebec in water currents and by aquarists and motorboats (Westbrooks 1998). The direct impacts of Eurasian watermilfoil make it one of the most troublesome aquatic invaders of North America, but it also facilitates the growth of zebra mussel populations by providing additional settling substrates (Lewandowski 1982) and can help disperse zebra mussels between water bodies (Johnson and Carlton 1996). Thus a mutualism between two damaging invaders worsens the impact of both.

There are numerous varieties of indirect effects between species (Menge 1995), and many of them entail facilitation of population growth of one or several interacting species. Although the study of facilitation among alien species is in its infancy, several examples have already been detected in addition to those documented previously (Simberloff and Von Holle 1999), and the limitless variety of ways in which species interact suggests that such facilitating impact will be common and diverse.

Lag Times, Explosions, and Collapses

Often an alien species remains innocuous and restricted in the environment for decades or longer, then undergoes a rapid population explosion to become a raging pest (Mack et al. 2000). The fig tree *Ficus microcarpa* in Florida waiting for its pollinating wasp to arrive is an excellent example. The mutated *Spartina alterniflora* Loisel. in England is another. Perhaps the most dramatic case is that of a Japanese fungus, *Entomophaga maimaiga* Humber, Shimazu & Soper, released in the United States in 1910–1911 to control the gypsy moth. After being unrecorded for 79 years, it surfaced again in 1989 and is now having a major impact on gypsy moth populations in the northeastern United States (Hajek et al. 1995; Hajek 1997).

Why a lag has occurred is sometimes obvious (for example, the case of the fig and fig wasp in Florida) but is often mysterious (Williamson 1996; Mack et al. 2000). Although new mutations are often invoked, they have rarely been documented. Strong evidence that mutations can produce an invasive genotype comes from the demonstration that the aquarium strain of the alga *Caulerpa taxifolia* is cold-tolerant, thus able to survive

the winters of the northwest Mediterranean, while populations from nature are not (Meinesz 1999). However, the initial invasion after the aquarium strain was released to the wild from the Oceanographic Museum of Monaco displayed but a short lag (Meinesz 1999). Another explanation for the sudden population explosion of a hitherto harmless alien species is a subtle change in the biotic or abiotic environment. Or there could be an inherent aspect of population growth, possibly combined with the vagaries of the location of the initial infestation, that dictates that a population will increase slowly, if at all, for an extended period, then increasingly rapidly (van den Bosch et al. 1992; Kowarik 1995; Mack et al. 2000). How many invasions entail lags is unknown, but the documentation of some well-studied cases suggests that any assessment of impact of an invasive species is subject to rapid change, and that a decision against controlling an invasion, especially in its early stages, should consider this possibility.

An analogous phenomenon has been far less remarked upon, perhaps because it is less common — some explosive, damaging invasions rather quickly collapse for unknown reasons, and the alien persists as a less prominent, perhaps even innocuous, new member of the biota. Probably the best-known example is elodea, or the Canadian waterweed (*Elodea canadensis* Michx.), introduced to England (Arber 1920; Elton 1958; Simpson 1984). First seen in a pond near the Scottish border, it spread rapidly to rivers, canals, ditches, and ponds throughout much of Great Britain, achieving its greatest profusion in the 1860s. At that point, it clogged the River Cam to the extent that it interfered with rowing, and extra horses were required to tow barges. At least one bather drowned after being caught in it. It prevented fishermen from using their nets on the River Trent; parts of the Thames were impassable. Then it suddenly declined to a moderate or even lesser status throughout its British range without human intervention. The plant was clonal at that time in Great Britain, and it has been suggested that the decline was simply a sort of senescence (Arber 1920), an unlikely explanation in light of the fact that its subsequent sexual status there (Simpson 1986) did not lead to a recrudescence of the invasion. Another explanation is the exhaustion of some subtle nutritional requirement (Elton 1958), but this possibility has not been substantiated.

Several other prominent invasions that rather rapidly collapsed, or in which the interloper at least became much less numerous, include that of the giant African snail on several Pacific islands (Mead 1979) and the cane toad (*Bufo marinus* (L.)) in Australia (Freeland 1986; Freeland et al. 1986). Various explanations, including unidentified pathogens and resource limitations, have been suggested, but these declines remain as mysterious as that of the waterweed. In fact, the entire phenomenon of spontaneous rapid decline seems mysterious. Certainly it is even less well-studied than that of sudden increase. At least in the current state of relative ignorance of both processes, sudden decline seems less frequent than sudden increase.

Conclusion

Some alien species produce major ecological and economic impacts. Habitat change, competition, predation, disease, and hybridization are the main ways in which these impacts are wrought. Further, invaders may have multiple impacts and may interact to worsen one another's impacts. Finally, impacts may worsen through time, sometimes rapidly. This litany of high points of invasion biology, plus the variety and plethora of examples, may induce a reader to believe that all alien species are plagues. In fact, a minority has substantial impacts. For ecological impacts, Williamson (1996) argues that his "tens rule" is a good rule of thumb (Williamson and Brown 1986)—about 10% of alien species given the chance (that is, released to the wild) will establish populations in nature, and about 10% of these will become pests. Recent tabulation of invasive plants in natural areas of the United States supports this contention (Lockwood et al. 2001). For economic impacts, there are no such tabulations. Even if the tens rule should prove to have wide application, the larger problem has been that it has proven devilishly difficult to predict which invasions will have substantial impacts and which will be quite innocuous (Goodell et al. 2000; Williamson 2000). A variety of prediction methods have been proposed, but very few have proven to be accurate. Even these are generally applicable to but a small group of species, and there are always exceptions (Mack et al. 2000). The rate of false positives for any method aimed at predicting which alien species will have major impacts may be very high (Smith et al. 1999). Thus, society may be unwilling to accept the economic costs of imposing such a method as a decision tool for permitting deliberate introductions. This is not to say that ecologists cannot do substantially better than random guessing when they attempt to identify which invaders will have impacts, only that their predictions will be far from perfect.

The policy implications of this outline of invasion impacts, and of the fact that there probably never will be an accurate way to predict which invasions will produce which impacts of what magnitude, are not fundamentally scientific matters. As scientists, the best we can do is to provide accurate knowledge that society as a whole can use as it determines what to do about a problem. To me, it seems obvious that the scope and costs of impacts already recognized, plus the fact that we have surely not even recognized all the problems caused by invaders already present, and the fact that we are not very accurate about predicting the trajectories of future invaders, warrant a much more cautious and comprehensive approach to alien species than we have seen in the past. The precautionary principle seems highly appropriate with respect to planned invasions and regulation of pathways (for example, ballast water, untreated wooden crates) that are conducive to unplanned invasions. The 1992 UN Convention on Biological Diversity stated as much, calling for its parties "to prevent the introduction of, control, or eradicate those alien species which threaten ecosystems, habitats or species" (article 8[h]) and stating that absence of full knowledge is not an excuse for inaction (Glowka and de Klemm 1996). Whether society as a whole decides to regulate more thoroughly the movement of living organisms, in an era when free trade is a virtual religion, may be an entirely different matter.

Acknowledgments

Sally D. Hacker provided unpublished distributional data, and Mary Tebo commented on an earlier draft of this manuscript.

References

Anderson, T.W. 1974. The chestnut pollen decline as a time horizon in lake sediments in eastern North America. Can. J. Earth Sci. 11:678–685.

Arber, A. 1920. Water plants. A study of aquatic angiosperms. Cambridge University Press, Cambridge, England. Reprint 1963, J. Cramer, Lehre. Reprint 1972, Codicote, Herts, Wheldon & Wesley.

Becker, G.C. 1983. Fishes of Wisconsin. University of Wisconsin Press, Madison, WI.

Bergersen, E.P.; Anderson, D.E. 1997. The distribution and spread of *Myxobolus cerebralis* in the United States. Fisheries (Bethesda) 22(8):6–7.

Bertness, M.D. 1984. Habitat and community modifications by an introduced herbivorous snail. Ecology 65:370–381.

Brenchley, G.A.; Carlton, J.T. 1983. Competitive displacement of native mud snails by introduced periwinkles in the New England intertidal zone. Biol. Bull. (Woods Hole) 165:543–558.

Burgess, G.H. 1980. *Alosa pseudoharengus*, alewife. Page 65 *in* D.S. Lee, C.R. Gilbert, C.H. Hocutt, R.E. Jenkins, D.E. McAllister and J.R. Stauffer, Jr, eds. Atlas of North American freshwater fishes. North Carolina State Museum of Natural History, Raleigh, NC.

Christie, W.J. 1974. Changes in the fish species composition of the Great Lakes. J. Fish. Res. Board Can. 31:827–854.

Civeyrel, L.; Simberloff, D. 1996. A tale of two snails: is the cure worse than the disease? Biodivers. Conserv. 5:1231–1252.

Couch, R.; Nelson, E. 1985. *Myriophyllum spicatum*. Pages 8–18 *in* L. Anderson, ed. Proceedings of the First International Conference on Water Milfoil (*Myriophyllum spicatum*) and Related Haloragaceae Species. Aquatic Plant Management Society, Vicksburg, MS.

Cox, G.W. 1999. Alien species in North America and Hawaii. Impacts on natural ecosystems. Island Press, Washington, DC.

Crooks, J.; Soulé, M.E. 1996. Lag times in population explosions of invasive species: causes and implications. Pages 39–46 *in* O.T. Sandlund, P.J. Schei, and A. Viken, eds. Proceedings Norway/UN Conference on Alien Species. Directorate for Nature Management and Norwegian Institute for Nature Research, Trondheim, Norway.

Crowder, L.B. 1984. Character displacement and habitat shift in a native cisco in southeastern Lake Michigan: evidence for competition? Copeia 1984(4):878–883.

DeWald, L.; Wilzbach, M.A. 1992. Interactions between native brook trout and hatchery brown trout: effects of habitat use, feeding, and growth. Trans. Am. Fish. Soc. 121:287–296.

Elton, C.S. 1958. The ecology of invasions by animals and plants. Methuen, London. Reprint 2000, University of Chicago Press, Chicago, IL.

Fausch, K.D.; White, R.J. 1981. Competition between brook trout (*Salvelinus fontinalis*) and brown trout (*Salmo trutta*) for positions in a Michigan stream. Can. J. Fish. Aquat. Sci. 38:1220–1227.

Freeland, W.J. 1986. Populations of cane toad, *Bufo marinus*, in relation to time since colonization. Aust. Wildl. Res. 13:321–329.

Freeland, W.J.; Belvinqueir, B.L.J.; Bonnin, B. 1986. Food and parasitism of the cane toad, *Bufo marinus*, in relation to time since colonization. Aust. Wildl. Res. 13:489–499.

Fuller, P.L.; Nico, L.G.; Williams, J.D. 1999. Nonindigenous fishes introduced into inland waters of the United States. Am. Fish. Soc., Bethesda, MD.

Glowka, L.; de Klemm, C. 1996. International instruments, processes, organizations and non-indigenous species introductions: is a protocol to the Convention on Biological Diversity necessary? Pages 211–219 *in* O.T. Sandlund, P.J. Schei, and A. Viken, eds. Proceedings, Norway/UN Conference on Alien Species. Directorate for Nature Management and Norwegian Institute for Nature Research, Trondheim, Norway.

Goodell, K.; Parker, I.M.; Gilbert, G.S. 2000. Biological impacts of species invasions: implications for policymakers. Pages 87–117 *in* National Research Council (US), Incorporating Science, Economics, and Sociology in Developing Sanitary and Phytosanitary Standards in International Trade. National Academy Press, Washington, DC.

Greenberg, C.H.; Crownover, S.H.; Gordon, D.R. 1997. Roadside soils: a corridor for invasion of xeric scrub by nonindigenous plants. Nat. Areas J. 17:99–109.

Hajek, A.E. 1997. Fungal and viral epizootics in gypsy moth (Lepidoptera: Lymantriidae) populations in central New York. Biol. Control 10:58–68.

Hajek, A.E.; Humber, R.A.; Elkinton, J.S. 1995. The mysterious origins of *Entomophaga maimaiga* in North America. Am. Entomol. 41:31–42.

Johnson, L.E.; Carlton, J.T. 1996. Post-establishment spread in large-scale invasions: dispersal mechanisms of the zebra mussel *Dreissena polymorpha*. Ecology 77:1686–1690.

Kauffman, S.; McKey, D.B.; Hossaert-McKey, M.; Horvitz, C.C. 1991. Adaptations for a two-phase seed dispersal system involving vertebrates and ants in a hemiepiphytic fig (*Ficus microcarpa*: Moraceae). Am. J. Bot. 78:971–977.

Kerr, S.J.; Grant, R.E. 2000. Ecological impacts of fish introductions: evaluating the risk. Fish and Wildlife Branch, Ontario Ministry of Natural Resources, Peterborough, ON.

Kindler, S.D.; Springer, T.L. 1989. Alternate hosts of Russian wheat aphid (Homoptera: Aphididae). J. Econ. Entomol. 82:1358–1362.

Kowarik, I. 1995. Time lags in biological invasions with regard to the success and failure of alien species. Pages 15–38 *in* P. Pysek, K. Prach, M. Rejmánek, and M. Wade, eds. Plant invasions: general aspects and special problems. SPB Academic Publishing, Amsterdam.

Leary, R.F.; Allendorf, F.W.; Forbes, S.H. 1993. Conservation genetics of bull trout in the Columbia and Klamath River drainages. Conserv. Biol. 7:856–865.

Lewandowski, K. 1982. The role of early developmental stages in the dynamics of *Dreissena polymorpha* (Pall.) (Bivalvia) populations in lakes. II. Settling of larvae and the dynamics of numbers of settled individuals. Ekol. Pol. 30:223–286.

Liebhold, A.M.; Gottschalk, K.W.; Mason, A.; Bush, R.R. 1997. Forest susceptibility to the gypsy moth. J. For. 95(5):20–24.

Liebhold, A.M.; MacDonald, W.L.; Bergdahl, D.; Mastro, V.C. 1996. Invasion by exotic forest pests: a threat to forest ecosystems. For. Sci. Monogr. 30:1–49.

Lockwood, J.L.; Simberloff, D.; McKinney, M.L.; Von Holle, B. 2001. How many, and which, plants will invade natural areas? Biol. Invasions 3:1–8.

Lubchenco, J. 1983. *Littorina* and *Fucus*: effects of herbivores, substratum heterogeneity and plant escape during succession. Ecology 64:1116–1123.

Lubchenco, J.; Menge, B.A. 1978. Community development and persistence in a low rocky intertidal zone. Ecol. Monogr. 48:67–94.

MacIsaac, H.J. 1996. Potential abiotic and biotic impacts of zebra mussels on inland waters of North America. Am. Zool. 36:287–299.

Mack, M.C.; D'Antonio, C.M. 1998. Impacts of biological invasions on disturbance regimes. Trends Ecol. Evol. 13:195–198.

Mack, R.N.; Simberloff, D.; Lonsdale, W.M.; Evans, H.; Clout, M.; Bazzaz, F.A. 2000. Biotic invasions: causes, epidemiology, global consequences, and control. Ecol. Appl.10:689–710.

Markiw, M.E. 1992. Salmonid whirling disease. US Fish and Wildlife Service, Fish and Wildlife Leaflet 17, Washington, DC.

McKey, D.B.; Kauffman, S.C. 1991. Naturalization of exotic *Ficus* species (Moraceae) in south Florida. Pages 221–236 *in* T.D. Center, R.F. Doren, R.L. Hofstetter, R.L. Myers, and L.D. Whiteaker, eds. Proceedings of the Symposium on Exotic Pest Plants. US Department of the Interior/National Park Service, Washington, DC.

Mead, A.R. 1979. Economic malacology: with particular reference to *Achatina fulica*. *In* V. Fretter, J. Fretter, and J. Peake, eds. Pulmonates. Vol. 2B. Academic Press, London.

Meinesz, A. 1999. Killer algae. University of Chicago Press, Chicago, IL.

Menge, B.A. 1995. Indirect effects in marine rocky intertidal interaction webs: patterns and importance. Ecol. Monogr. 65:21–74.

Miller, R.R.; Williams, J.D.; Williams, J.E. 1989. Extinctions of North American fishes during the past century. Fisheries (Bethesda) 14(6):22–38.

Niemelä, P.; Mattson, W.J. 1996. Invasion of North American forests by European phytophagous insects. BioScience 46:741–753.

Obrycki, J.J.; Elliott, N.C.; Giles, K.L. 2000. Coccinellid introductions: Potential for an evaluation of non-target effects. Pages 127–145 *in* P.A. Follett and J.J. Duan, eds. Non-target effects of biological control. Kluwer Academic Publishers, Boston, MA.

Opler, P.A. 1979. Insects of American chestnut: Possible importance and conservation concern. Pages 83–85 *in* W. McDonald, ed. The American Chestnut Symposium. University of West Virginia Press, Morgantown, WV.

Perrings, C. 2000. The economics of biological invasions. Pages 34–45 *in* G. Preston, G. Brown, and E. van Wyk, eds. Symposium Proceedings. Best management practices for preventing and controlling invasive alien species. The Working for Water Programme, Cape Town.

Petraitis, P.S. 1983. Grazing patterns of the periwinkle and their effect on sessile intertidal organisms. Ecology 64:522–533.

Pimentel, D.; Lach, L.; Zuniga, R.; Morrison, D. 2000. Environmental and economic costs of non-indigenous species in the United States. BioScience 50:53–65.

Rhymer, J.; Simberloff, D. 1996. Extinction by hybridization and introgression. Annu. Rev. Ecol. Syst. 27:83–109.

Ricciardi, A.; Neves, R.J.; Rasmussen, J.B. 1998. Impending extinctions of North American freshwater mussels (Unionida) following the zebra mussel (*Dreissena polymorpha*) invasion. J. Anim. Ecol. 67:613–619.

Ricciardi, A.; Whoriskey, F.G.; Rasmussen, J.B. 1997. The role of the zebra mussel (*Dreissena polymorpha*) in structuring macroinvertebrate communities on hard substrate. Can. J. Fish. Aquat. Sci. 54:2596–2608.

Robbins, J. 1996. Trouble in fly fishermen's paradise. The New York Times, 23 August 1996, p. A7.

Samuels, S.H. 2000. Alien earthworms' offspring thrive, and alter soil. The New York Times, 29 August 2000, p. D1–D2.

Schmitz, D.C.; Simberloff, D.; Hofstetter, R.H.; Haller, W.; Sutton, D. 1997. The ecological impact of nonindigenous plants. Pages 39–61 *in* D. Simberloff, D.C. Schmitz, and

T.C. Brown, eds. Strangers in paradise. Impact and management of nonindigenous species in Florida. Island Press, Washington, DC.

Simberloff, D. 2000. Nonindigenous species—a global threat to biodiversity and stability. Pages 325–334 in P.H. Raven, ed. Nature and Human Society. National Academy Press, Washington, DC.

Simberloff, D.; Von Holle, B. 1999. Positive interactions of nonindigenous species: invasional meltdown? Biol. Invasions 1:21–32.

Simpson, D.A. 1984. A short history of the introduction and spread of *Elodea* Michx. in the British Isles. Watsonia 15:1–9.

Simpson, D.A. 1986. Taxonomy of *Elodea* Michx. in the British Isles. Watsonia 16:1–14.

Smith, C.S.; Lonsdale, W.M.; Fortune, J. 1999. When to ignore advice: invasion predictions and decision theory. Biol. Invasions 1:89–96.

Smith, S.H. 1970. Species interactions of the alewife in the Great Lakes. Trans. Am. Fish. Soc. 99:754–765.

Sorensen, P.W.; Cardwell, J.R.; Essington, T.; Weigel, D.E. 1995. Reproductive interactions between sympatric brook and brown trout in a small Minnesota stream. Can. J. Fish. Aquat. Sci. 52:1958–1965.

Stone, C.P.; Taylor, D.D. 1984. Status of feral pig management and research in Hawaii Volcanoes National Park. Proceedings of the Hawaii Volcanoes National Park Natural Science Conference 5:106–117. Hilo, Hawaii.

Strayer, D.L.; Caraco, N.F.; Cole, J.J.; Findlay, S.; Pace, M.L. 1999. Transformation of freshwater ecosystems by bivalves. BioScience 49:19–27.

Thompson, J.D. 1991. The biology of an invasive plant. BioScience 41:393–401.

US Congress, Office of Technology Assessment. 1993. Harmful non-native species in the United States. OTA-F-565, US Government Printing Office, Washington, DC.

van den Bosch, F.; Hengeveld, R.; Metz, J.A.J. 1992. Analyzing the velocity of animal range expansion. J. Biogeogr. 19:135–150.

Vitousek, P. 1986. Biological invasions and ecosystem properties: Can species make a difference? Pages 163–176 in H.A. Mooney and J.A. Drake, eds. Ecology of biological invasions of North America and Hawaii. Springer-Verlag, New York, NY.

Vivrette, N.J.; Muller, C.H. 1977. Mechanism of invasion and dominance of coastal grassland by *Mesembryanthemum crystallinum*. Ecol. Monogr. 47:301–318.

von Broembsen, S.L. 1989. Invasions of natural ecosystems by plant pathogens. Pages 77–83 in J.A. Drake, H.A. Mooney, F. di Castri, R.H. Groves, F.J. Kruger, M. Rejmánek, and M. Williamson, eds. Biological invasions: A global perspective. Scope 37. John Wiley and Sons, New York, NY.

Wells, L. 1970. Effects of alewife predation on zooplankton populations in Lake Michigan. Limnol. Oceanogr. 15:556–565.

Westbrooks, R.G. 1998. Invasive plants, changing the landscape of America: Fact book. Federal Interagency Committee for the Management of Noxious and Exotic Weeds, Washington, DC.

Wilcove, D.S.; Rothstein, D.; Dubow, J.; Phillips, A.; Losos, E. 1998. Quantifying threats to imperiled species in the United States. BioScience 48:607–615.

Wilcove, D.S.; Rothstein, D.; Dubow, J.; Phillips, A; Losos, E. 2000. Leading threats to biodiversity. Pages 239–254 in B.A. Stein, L.S. Kutner, and J.S. Adams, eds. Precious heritage. The status of biodiversity in the United States. Oxford University Press, Oxford.

Williamson, M. 1996. Biological Invasions. Chapman & Hall, London.

Williamson, M. 2000. The ecology of invasions. Pages 56–65 in G. Preston, G. Brown, and E. van Wyk, eds. Best management practices for preventing and controlling invasive alien species. Symposium Proceedings. The Working for Water Programme, Cape Town.

Williamson, M.; Brown, K.C. 1986. The analysis and modelling of British invasions. Philos. Trans. R. Soc. Lond. B Biol. Sci. 314:505–522.

Woodward, S.A.; Vitousek, P.M.; Matson, K.; Hughes, F.; Benvenuto, K.; Matson, P.A. 1990. Use of the exotic tree *Myrica faya* by native and exotic birds in Hawaii Volcanoes National Park. Pac. Sci. 44:88–93.

Yamada, S.B.; Mansour, R.A. 1987. Growth inhibition of native *Littorina saxatilis* (Olivi) by introduced *L. Littorea* (L.). J. Exp. Mar. Biol. Ecol. 105:187–196.

Zobel, D.B.; Roth, L.F.; Hawk, G.M. 1985. Ecology, pathology, and management of Port Orford cedar (*Chamaecyparis lawsoniana*). General Technical Report PNW–184. US Forest Service, Portland, OR.

Photo with chapter title: Rosy wolfsnail. Photo by Ron Heu, State of Hawaii Department of Agriculture, Honolulu, HI.

Part 2 Alien Species in Canada: State of the Nation

A lack of funding for alien species research and monitoring and the arbitrary division of responsibilities for these species by government have contributed to the serious lack of accurate data on the total number of alien invaders in the various bioregions of Canada and on their ecological and socioeconomic impacts. Chapters in this part aim to answer these basic questions:

- How many alien species have established viable populations in a given portion of Canada or in a given type of ecosystem and how did they get here?

- What have some of these species changed in their recipient environment and how significant have these changes been?

The "invasibility" of a place and its accessibility to species from elsewhere are factors that govern the numbers of invaders. About 25% of the 5800 or so species composing Canada's flora are aliens, the majority from Europe or Eurasia. Most thrive mainly in disturbed habitats, such as roadsides and agricultural fields. Fewer than 10% of these (about 120–160 species) may invade natural habitats. Some have established dense populations in urban areas and subsequently spread into adjacent native ecosystems. Well-documented examples include purple loosestrife, garlic mustard, European frog-bit, and common and glossy buckthorns.

Canada's forests have about 180 species of alien insects feeding on woody plants, about 30 species of alien invasive vascular plants, a few alien earthworms, and at least 5 alien fungi causing widespread diseases to trees.

The largest and most economically important watershed in Canada, the Great Lakes–St. Lawrence River drainage basin, supports 163 alien species introduced during the last two centuries, including the infamous zebra mussel and round goby. Analyses show that new alien species continue to spread in the St. Lawrence River as a result of downstream transfer of organisms already established elsewhere.

Relatively few aquatic alien species—about 15 freshwater fishes and invertebrates—have colonized the waters and wetlands of Manitoba and Saskatchewan. However, many potential pathways exist, such as agriculture, forestry, and aquarium and horticultural trade. Of particular concern is the risk of accidental introductions from transport on recreational watercraft and from live bait releases by anglers.

The Strait of Georgia on the Pacific coast is home to 118 established alien species, mostly invertebrates, algae, and vascular plants, but also a few fishes, birds, and one mammal. Many arrived as hitchhikers with oysters that were intentionally introduced; others came via such conduits as ballast water, ship fouling, and the aquarium trade. Some of these species may have simply extended their range, and a few are not demonstrably native or introduced.

Five species of anchored seaweeds and a dozen bottom-dwelling invertebrates have invaded the coastal waters of Atlantic Canada since the early 19th century. Their most likely vectors were ship hulls and ballast. In contrast to the situation in other parts of the world, the number on the Atlantic coast is relatively low.

What changes have these species wrought in our nation? Because of their ability to grow in dense monospecific stands, some alien invasive plants have contributed to the decline of rare plant species and to changes in rare habitats. In Canada, this type of impact has been most evident within the Carolinian Floristic Zone of southwestern Ontario, the Prairies Ecozone, and the Pacific Maritime and Montane Cordillera Ecozones.

In Canada's forests, alien fungal pathogens have perhaps had the most impact; these disease-causing organisms have caused shifts in forest composition by the virtual elimination of once-dominant trees, such as white elm and American chestnut. Some of the alien insects feeding on woody plants in Canada have also caused rapid and extensive changes in native forests.

Common carp and purple loosestrife have damaged water and wetland ecosystems in Manitoba, but the effects of other aquatic alien species such as rainbow smelt and white bass are less documented in the province. Along Canada's Atlantic coast, some of the alien invaders have had major, sometimes devastating, effects on native communities and the harvest of commercial species. Two alien invaders have disrupted sea urchin–kelp dynamics and modified the sublittoral ecosystem.

The nation's state with respect to actions to prevent or mitigate the impacts of alien species is unclear. What has mostly been addressed by the authors of these chapters are needs and shortcomings. At present, federal and provincial authorities in Canada use a blacklist approach for intentional introductions; that is, species that have been shown to have negative effects here or elsewhere are banned from import. Some suggest that a better alternative would be to permit entry of only those species that have been shown to have negligible impacts. The "white-list" approach would require that applications to intentionally introduce or transfer organisms be assessed based on independent scientific research.

Other perceived needs include an adequately funded national program that safeguards certain natural areas and rare habitats and species from the impacts of alien invaders; the ability to monitor insects, diseases, and weeds, along with the taxonomic capacity to identify alien species; and stringent measures with adequate monitoring to control and eliminate future introductions of alien species in main watersheds and to reduce species transfer within or between basins.

Because of the multiple pathways available for alien species to spread into coastal waters, comprehensive and effective controls to minimize or prevent new introductions have proven difficult to implement. However, Canada now has national guidelines for the management of ballast water, which may lead to a mandatory regulatory regime for all Canadian waters.

Spread and Impact of Alien Plants across Canadian Landscapes

Erich Haber

The rampant spread of introduced species is recognized as a major threat to global biodiversity and natural ecosystems (Usher 1988; Clout 1995; Pimm et al. 1995). In North America, billions of dollars are spent annually for pesticide application, biological control programs, and other remedial actions to mitigate the impacts of harmful alien species of economic importance. In comparison, little is spent on the control of invasives impacting natural ecosystems and species at risk. Yet, alien species pose a serious threat to natural ecosystems. Plant invasions can result in extensive areas covered by near monospecific populations of alien species that impede natural successional events and prevent the establishment of native species. Specific examples of impacts on native plants have been shown by authors such as Musil (1993) and Meyer and Florence (1996). Habitat characteristics, including flammability (Anable et al. 1992), carbon assimilation rates (LeMaitre et al. 1996), soil nutrient levels (Vitousek and Walker 1989), and suitability for native animals (Steenkamp and Chown 1996) can be altered by the proliferation of invasive plants.

Virtually all dispersals of alien plants from their native homeland to foreign soils are caused by human actions, either deliberate or inadvertent. Some common European weeds of agricultural fields and disturbed soils, such as the broad-leaved plantain (*Plantago major* L.), are so adaptable and easily dispersed that they are now virtually cosmopolitan and are found in at least 50 countries (Holm et al. 1977). The recognition that European settlers were the agents of the dispersal of some common weeds dates to reports such as that made as early as 1687 in Virginia. It noted that the aboriginal people of the region called the broad-leaved plantain "Englishman's foot" (Figure 1), a reference to the fact that wherever Europeans established a new settlement, plantains always followed in their footsteps (Reader's Digest 1986).

In Canada, the documentation of economically important weeds dates back at least to a 1911 Department of Agriculture bulletin produced in conjunction with the *Seeds Act* (see Department of Agriculture 1935). Subsequent efforts to draw attention to weeds of national and provincial concern were publications such as those by Frankton and Wright (1955), Mont-gomery (1956), and Rousseau (1968). The series *The Biology of Canadian Weeds*, initiated in the *Canadian Journal of Plant Science* in 1973, deals exclusively with weeds of agricultural importance. It, nevertheless, has provided much in-depth knowledge on alien plants that are now also considered to be invasives of natural habitats.

In spite of a long history of alien plant introductions to North America, the identification of problem species within native ecosystems is a relatively recent occurrence in Canada, as well as in North America in general. *Invasive Plants of Natural Habitats in Canada* (White et al. 1993) was a landmark publication initiated by the Canadian Wildlife Service, Environment Canada. Following this seminal publication a series of actions were supported by Environment Canada and nongovernmental agencies for the compilation of information on invasive plants of national concern. Among the federal initiatives was support for the Invasive Plants of Canada Project (IPCAN) and its Web site, which has provided fact sheets on major invasive plants, the results of national surveys, reports on local activities, and new discoveries of aliens as part of an alert initiative (http://infoweb.magi.com/~ehaber/ipcan.html).

Figure 1. Broad-leaved plantain. Illustration courtesy of Agriculture and Agri-Food Canada.

Relative Importance of Alien Plants in the Floras of Canada

Canada's flora consists of about 5800 species of vascular plants, including hybrids, infraspecific variants, and aliens established in the wild (Nature Conservancy of Canada database and database developed by Dr. Luc Brouillet [personal communication]). Depending on what aliens are recognized as established and what native hybrids and infraspecific taxa are included in the total count of native plants, alien plants make up approximately 20–27% of the total flora of Canada. The numbers of alien plants in different regions and provinces in Canada are determined by various factors that influence the introduction and spread of alien plants, including climate, diversity in floristic zones and habitats, extent of agricultural land use and diversity in agricultural practices, frequency of transportation, communication and power corridors, abundance of lakes and rivers, density of populated places, and population size.

A large province such as Ontario, with a land mass of 1 068 582 km^2, several floristic regions, and a diverse agricultural base in the southern portion of the province, has a flora of about 3340 taxa, when all subspecies and varieties are included (Newmaster et al. 1998). Within this flora there are nearly 1100 alien plants, or about 32% of the flora of Ontario. This is significantly greater than the overall proportion of aliens in Canada. Locally, when abandoned fields, disturbed lots, and roadside habitats are surveyed, the proportion of aliens increases significantly. Southern, and especially southwestern Ontario, contains only a fragment of the deciduous and mixed forests that once covered its soils. This region of the province, and in fact the whole Mixedwood Plains Ecozone (Ecological Stratification Working Group 1996), is now a haven for alien plants. Extensive agricultural lands were developed here on rich woodland soils and patches of disjunct tallgrass prairie and wetland habitats. This area now supports about 50% of Canada's population in a zone stretching from Windsor to Québec City.

In contrast, the province of Alberta, with a landmass of only 661 185 km^2 (62% that of Ontario), has a much lower floral diversity of about 1775 species (Moss 1983) and has fewer aliens. Proportionately, alien plants represent only about 19% of the flora. The lower percentage of aliens present in this province, as compared with that in Ontario, could be due to the presence of large areas of relatively undisturbed mountain and boreal coniferous forests, a more northern and continental climate, a less diverse agricultural base as compared with Ontario, and fewer cities and towns in which to develop local centers for the establishment of alien plants. Although Alberta has fewer alien plants than Ontario, a number of these have impacted considerably the remaining native grasslands and pastures. Biocontrol insects have been released (Haber 2000) to combat such flowering herbs as leafy spurge (*Euphorbia esula* L.), hound's-tongue (*Cynoglossum officinale* L.), Dalmatian toadflax (*Linaria genistifolia* (L.) Miller ssp. *dalmatica* (L.) Maire and Petitmengin), yellow toadflax (*L. vulgaris* Miller), and spotted knapweed (*Centaurea maculosa* Lam.). Alien grasses such as crested wheatgrass (*Agropyron cristatum* (L.) Gaertn.), smooth brome (*Bromus inermis* Leyss.), and Kentucky bluegrass (*Poa pratensis* L.) have also become serious invaders of native fescue (*Festuca* spp.) grasslands (Haber 1996; Haber 2000).

In Atlantic Canada, a small coastal province such as Nova Scotia, with a landmass of only 55 491 km^2, has a flora of about 2000 vascular plants, about 20% of which are alien species (Roland and Smith 1969). Nova Scotia represents one of the oldest areas of settlement in Canada and combines species typical of several floristic regions. These include arctic–alpine and boreal species; wide-ranging plants of northeastern North America; species of rich deciduous woodland habitats more characteristic of rich woodlands in southern Ontario, southwestern Quebec, and the US Alleghenies; disjuncts in the southwestern region of the province that are common much farther south along the US eastern seaboard; and globally widespread maritime shoreline plants. Common weeds are found throughout the province. Some are present mainly along railway tracks and many are introduced from western Canada in grains and feed (Roland and Smith 1969). Alien plants, such as angelica (*Angelica sylvestris* L.), became established at major ports (Sydney and Louisbourg) and spread from these points of introduction along moist roadside ditches.

Characteristics of Alien Plants

The majority of alien plant species in Canada come from Europe or western Asia and grow mainly in disturbed sites, such as roadsides and agricultural fields. A species becomes a weed when it competes with cultivated plants or causes allergic reactions or poisoning. A number of these cause considerable economic losses. The term "alien species", although most commonly applied to a species introduced from another country, is also used for native species, such as Manitoba maple (*Acer negundo* L.), that have spread well beyond their natural ranges primarily as a consequence of human actions.

Many alien plants, like most of the invasive grasses, are perennial. They propagate vegetatively, forming large clones of genetically identical plants (ramets) adapted to local conditions. An example of a perennial alien flowering herb is coltsfoot (*Tussilago farfara* L.). This is a European plant traditionally used for cough remedies. It forms long rhizomes and can readily colonize disturbed areas and even inhospitable substrates such as coke piles, as at an industrial site at Sydney, Nova Scotia (Figure 2). Some, like leafy spurge, have a milky latex with a disagreeable taste; others, like bull thistle (*Cirsium vulgare* (Savi) Ten.), have spines that reduce the degree of herbivory. Many also lack insect pests or pathogens in their adopted countries. Some harbor insects that attack crops or are alternate hosts for some crop pathogens. Invasive plants represent a spectrum of growth and life forms including aquatics and terrestrial herbs, vines, shrubs and trees, as well as annual, biennial, and perennial species.

Invasive plants are alien taxa that are able to establish populations in natural habitats and successfully compete with native species, often to their detriment and exclusion from a site. Less than 10% of alien plants have been identified as being invasive in natural habitats. They exhibit the same combinations of characteristics as common weeds. They grow rapidly under a wide range of climate and soil conditions. Some, such as the garlic mustard (*Alliaria petiolata* (Bieb.) Cavara and Grande) overwinter as rosettes and begin to flower and set seed early in the spring before many of the native plants begin to grow. Most produce abundant seeds and may have dissemination aids that promote easy dispersal, such as long hairy plumes, as on the seeds of dog-strangling vine (*Cynanchum rossicum* (Kleopov) Borhidi) (Figure 3). Commonly, the seeds of weedy species stay viable for many years when buried in the soil. Those of Scotch broom (*Cytisus scoparius* (L.) Link.) remain viable for more than 80 years when properly stored (Hoshovsky 1986).

A weed in one part of the country may become invasive in another region. For instance, some alien grasses and other forage plants such as sweet-clovers are generally considered to be weeds in eastern Canada, where they are found mainly along roadsides and in pastures and other disturbed habitats. These habitats were created through the destruction of the forest ecosystems present at the time of settlement. In western Canada, these forage plants are clearly invasive, forming dominant monocultures over extensive areas of native prairies and grasslands. Such examples illustrate the need to closely control and monitor the arrival and spread of alien species to minimize their impacts on natural areas.

Interestingly, some alien species have become naturalized over large parts of a country but do not seem to have had a negative impact on the native flora. Such a species is the common helleborine orchid (*Epipactis helleborine* (L.) Crantz) introduced from Europe to North America before 1879 (Correll 1978). Although now widespread throughout eastern North America in relatively natural deciduous and mixed woodlands, it does not form extensive growths in its preferred woodland sites. It tends to occur as scattered individuals or small groups of plants. Its range expansion in Ontario was mapped by Soper and Murray (1985). Like common

Figure 2. Coltsfoot colonizing a heap of fine coke particles in Sydney, NS.

Figure 3. Tangle of vines and opened seed pods of dog-strangling vine. The seeds are carried aloft by parachutes of downy hairs. Photo courtesy of Stephen Smith.

weeds, however, this orchid also has the ability to thrive in unusual habitats such as orchards and lawns of urban properties from which it is occasionally reported.

Early Sources and Dispersal of Alien Plants

The introduction of alien plants to North America dates to the earliest arrivals of Europeans. The same ships bringing settlers were laden with a wide variety of alien seeds that would eventually escape the confines of gardens and agricultural fields. Weed seeds were hidden in natural packing materials, in bales of hay used to feed livestock, and were present as contaminants in sacks of seed and grain brought as fodder and for planting. They were also in the soil of rooted transplants and horticultural specimens. The ballast of merchant ships dumped at the harbors of the colonies also contained an abundance of weed seeds.

In time, some of the herbs brought for cooking and medicines, and even some favorite garden ornamentals, spread from their cultivated plots to natural habitats. Goutweed (*Aegopodium podagraria* L.), a popular perennial bedding plant, is known to invade woodlands from its point of origin around old farm homesteads and urban homes and form dense clones in the understory. Along the Atlantic coastline, dusty-miller (*Artemisia stelleriana* Besser), a commonly planted decorative perennial, escaped from cultivation many decades ago and has become widely naturalized along the upper beaches (Figure 4). The local Mi'kmaq gather this alien to use in place of a western species of sage for traditional spiritual ceremonies.

Once locally established, the ever-enlarging woodland clearings and fields, opened through logging, agri-

Figure 4. Dusty-miller on the upper beaches along the Atlantic seaboard.

cultural expansion, and the spread of urban centers, aided the dispersal of alien species. The developing system of roadways, railways, and then canals facilitated the spread of aliens to remote interior destinations. The desire to beautify city streets and parks with graceful and hardy European and western Asian trees and shrubs also contributed to the spread of some alien species whose aggressive nature and ability to disperse widely were not anticipated. The common practice of seeding European forage grasses in North American pastures and prairies, such as various species of brome (*Bromus* spp.), crested wheatgrass, and quack grass (*Elymus repens* (L.) Gould), has led to their widespread dominance in some areas.

The former practice of using farm manure, loaded with viable weed seeds, as fertilizer for city gardens contributed to the establishment and spread of agricultural weeds in cities. In more recent years, the large numbers of people involved in recreational activities, such as hiking, boating, and the development and beautifying of cottage residences, have contributed to the spread of alien plants within recreational lands and natural areas across the landscape. In addition, changing land use has resulted in numerous, formerly marginal agricultural lands being left idle and susceptible to the establishment and build-up of large populations of weedy species and invasives. Purple loosestrife (*Lythrum salicaria* L.) readily spreads into old unused pastures from adjoining low areas. In Renfrew County, Ontario, where only shallow, relatively nonproductive soils have developed over limestone bedrock, purple loosestrife covers extensive areas of abandoned lowland pastures.

Some species have formed dense populations in urban areas and subsequently spread into native ecosystems. Well-documented examples include garlic mustard, European frog-bit (*Hydrocharis morsus-ranae* L.), and common and glossy buckthorns (*Rhamnus cathartica* L. and *R. frangula* L.) [The name *Frangula alnus* Mill. has been adopted by some specialists for glossy buckthorn because of differences from other *Rhamnus* species in important features such as floral structures.]

Garlic mustard (hedge garlic, sauce-alone), a member of the mustard family (Brassicaceae), is a biennial that forms dense mats of overwintering rosettes. Plants develop leafy shoots early the following spring that have characteristic triangular toothed leaves (Figure 5). The generic name, *Alliaria,* is derived from the Latin word for onion or garlic, *allium*, on account of the strong garlic smell of the leaves. The white taproot also has a sharp horseradish-like taste. The plant

Figure 5. Garlic mustard.

has had a variety of uses (Fernald and Kinsey 1958; Syme 1873). Plants were eaten by poor country people in Europe as a salad, used in sauces, boiled as a pot-herb, or mixed with other herbs and used as a stuffing. Plants are known to be eaten by goats and cows; however, cow's milk takes on a strong disagreeable flavor and, when eaten by poultry, the flesh has an unpleasant taste. The small white flowers formed during the second year have the typical four-petal structure of the mustard family and, like other members of the family, is thought to have medicinal values.

Garlic mustard is primarily a native of Europe where it is widespread and common. It ranges from central Scandinavia southward and extends eastward to the Himalayas. In North America it is most abundant and common in the northeastern and central states and the provinces of Ontario and Quebec, with isolated populations in Oregon, British Columbia, and New Brunswick. Its range in Canada is primarily in the Mixedwood Plains Ecozone, lying south of the Precambrian Shield.

In urban centers it is found along wooded edges and thickets, open wooded parklands, in hedgerows and gardens. It grows in full sunlight but also does well in shade under a forest canopy. It grows especially well in floodplain forests and prefers soils high in lime. Garlic

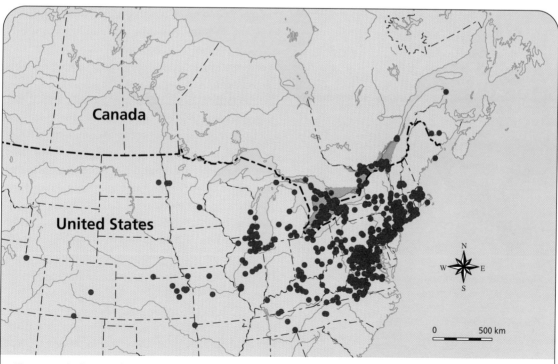

Figure 6. Distribution of garlic mustard within its main region of occurrence in eastern North America, based on specimen, sight, and literature records as of 1996. The orange area in Ontario and Quebec is the Mixedwood Plains Ecozone.

mustard is of particular concern because it is one of the few aliens that do well in woodland sites.

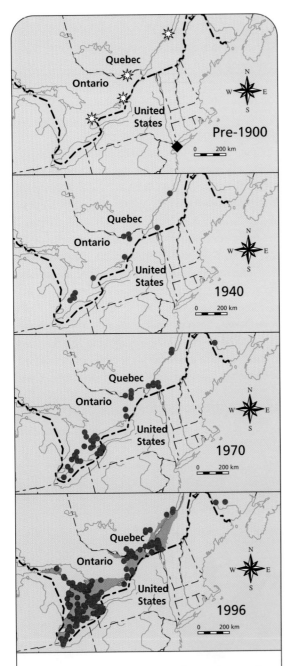

Figure 7. Range expansion of garlic mustard in Canada based on accumulated records at four time intervals. The pre-1900 map shows the earliest collection in North America, on Long Island, in 1868 (◆) and early collections in Canada—(✳ from west to east), at Toronto, 1879; Kingston, 1898; Ottawa, 1891; and Québec City, 1895. Most of the collection, sight, and literature records originate from the Mixedwood Plains Ecozone (the orange area in the 1996 map).

Because of its traditional use as a culinary herb in Europe and of its perceived medicinal value, garlic mustard was likely deliberately introduced to North America. The earliest record of its presence in North America dates to a collection made on Long Island, New York, in 1868. In Canada, it was first recorded at Toronto in 1879. Not long after it was collected at other widely separated cities in eastern Canada (Ottawa, Ontario, 1891; Québec City, Quebec, 1895; Kingston, Ontario, 1898). It was not observed in western Canada until 1948 when it was collected in a garden in Victoria, British Columbia. In Atlantic Canada, it was not recorded until 1968 when a collection was made at Marven Brook, New Brunswick. This dispersed pattern of the earliest records of its occurrence reflects the plant's repeated introduction in different urban centers. It has spread throughout eastern North America from these many disjunct points of introduction (Figure 6). The distribution and spread of garlic mustard in Canada, as documented by specimen, literature, and sight records, is shown for several time periods since its introduction, in Figure 7.

The earliest sighting of this species by the author was along roadside hedges bordering Highway 401 in southwestern Ontario in the 1960s. Garlic mustard was not common within the Toronto metropolitan area at that time, when the author botanized as a graduate student. The species is now extremely common and present in most parks and ravines. The plant has since become abundant in many other urban centers in southern Ontario.

In Ottawa, populations have increased dramatically along shrubby borders and weedy woodland patches of Manitoba maple and red ash (*Fraxinus pennsylvanica* Marsh.), in greenbelt areas along the Ottawa River, and throughout many disturbed wooded areas within the city. It is still present in the woodlands around the Beechwood Cemetery, in the east of Ottawa, where the first collections were made in 1891. Garlic mustard is now found in at least 37 national and provincial parks and Areas of Natural and Scientific Interest in southern Ontario.

European Frog-bit (frog's-bit, frogbit), a member of the frog-bit family (Hydrocharitaceae), is a small, free-floating aquatic herb, reminiscent of a tiny water lily (Figure 8). The plants overwinter as bud-like growths that float to the surface in the spring and develop dense mats of unisexual plants through rapid vegetative growth. Shallow bays, wetland pools, and quiet riverside shorelines become covered with dense mats

Figure 8. Dense mat of European frog-bit covering the open water of a shallow marsh in southeastern Ontario.

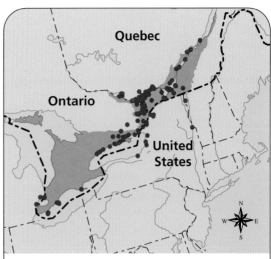

Figure 9. Distribution of European frog-bit in North America. The orange area in Ontario and Quebec is the Mixedwood Plains Ecozone.

Figure 10. Common buckthorn (*left*), photographed late in the season, has numerous small teeth along the leaf margins, small spines in the forks of some branches, and a four-parted flower. Glossy buckthorn (*right*) has smooth leaf margins, no spines in the forks, and a five- parted flower. The young branch tips of glossy buckthorn are slightly hairy in contrast to the hairless branchlets of common buckthorn.

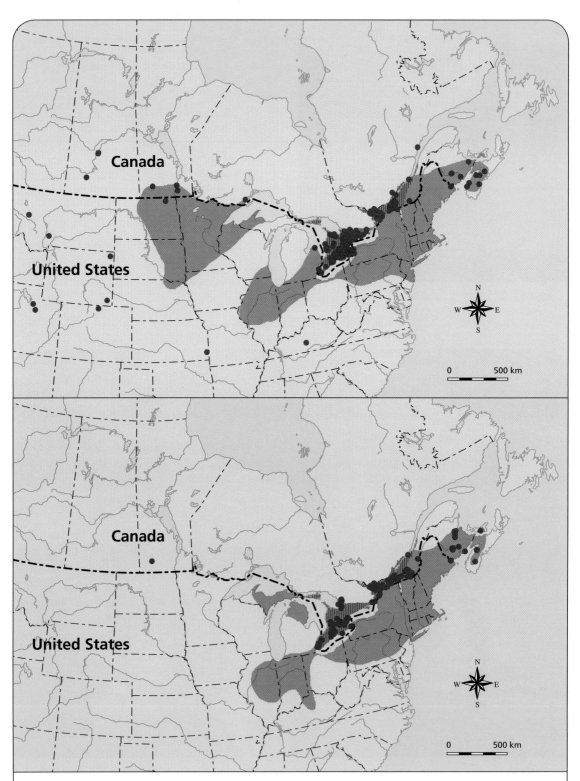

Figure 11. Distribution of common buckthorn (*upper*) and glossy buckthorn (*lower*) in North America. The generalized ranges (purple) are based on floras and other literature sources. Red circles are used to show species locations beyond the main area of distribution, as in the United States and western Canada, or are included to illustrate the abundance of these species in eastern Canada (in Ontario and Quebec the circles obscure the Mixedwood Plains Ecozone, indicated by the striping). Information for Canadian locations is drawn from recent and historical collection and sight records and for the US sites from literature records.

representing monocultures that can fill the entire water column in shallow areas. From its original introduction in 1932 at the Central Experimental Farm, Ottawa, this aquatic spread into the Rideau Canal and subsequently into the rivers and wetlands of southeastern Ontario and adjacent New York State. In the last 10 years it has been gradually extending its range along the north shores of Lake Ontario and Lake Erie as scattered populations (Figure 9). This is a graphic example of how a species, imported for its potential use in water gardens, has spread from its urban center of introduction into native wetlands.

There are, of course, many other species of local or regional concern. Extensive growths of dog-strangling vine (see Figure 3), also known as pale swallowwort (mainly *Cynanchum rossicum*, but black swallowwort, *C. nigrum* (L.) Pers., has also been historically noted), have been reported from a variety of habitats. Dog-strangling vine occurs in meadows, along railway rights-of-way, and in urban ravines and woodlots in major centers such as in Toronto and Ottawa. Studies on best methods for control of these species have been undertaken in Toronto in recent years.

Common buckthorn (European buckthorn) and **glossy buckthorn** (alder buckthorn), members of the buckthorn family (Rhamnaceae), are shrubs native to Europe, western Asia, and North Africa. They were imported in the late 1800s as horticultural hedge stock due to their hardiness, lack of insect pests, and adaptability to various soils. In spite of the name, neither species has thorns, but common buckthorn has short spines at the ends of some of the branches (Figure 10).

Figure 12. A cost-saving measure within the National Capital Region that eliminated mowing of open spaces has resulted in the proliferation of monocultures of common buckthorn (as shown here) in green spaces. Fruit-eating birds subsequently spread viable seeds to nearby natural areas.

Both species now occur throughout much of the northeastern United States and southeastern Canada with disjunct sites in urban centers in the US Midwest and Prairie provinces (Figure 11). Common buckthorn tends to become established on drier sites along fence-rows and edges of forests and urban woodlands. Glossy buckthorn is more common in wetland sites and moist forests, although both can be found side by side along woodland edges.

The two buckthorns have been spreading at an alarming rate within urban areas and woodlands in southern Ontario, especially in the Ottawa–Hull National Capital Region. Their spread is akin to the proliferation of Scotch broom and gorse (*Ulex europaeus* L.), which established themselves as major nuisance species on southeastern Vancouver Island, British Columbia, many years ago.

The presence of buckthorns in great abundance in some urban areas, as evident in fields around Ottawa (Figure 12), attests to the importance of such sites as seed sources for expansion into neighboring natural areas. The extensive monocultures within Ottawa, each generally comprising several hectares of shrubs, serve as a constant reminder of the impact such a buildup of alien species must have in promoting the spread of such species beyond the borders of urban centers. Fruits are spread by various native birds as well as by the ubiquitous European starling (*Sturnus vulgaris* L.), another alien species.

Norway maple (*Acer platanoides* L.), a commonly planted boulevard tree with a number of cultivated varieties (Figure 13), is replacing native trees in forested urban ravines and in suburban woodlands throughout many communities in southern Ontario. It is pollution resistant and readily propagates itself in a wide variety of habitats. The dense shade cast by the foliage reduces ground-cover formation and hinders regeneration of native understory woodland species.

Manitoba maple, also known as box-elder, is a native species of North America originally found primarily in riparian sites in the Prairies, and possibly also in extreme southwestern Ontario. It has spread beyond its natural range throughout the northeastern states and southeastern Canada in urban centers and adjoining wooded areas because it is a commonly planted, fast-growing boulevard and windbreak tree. It grows readily from seed and spreads like a weed from its sites of introduction into urban woodlots and greenspaces. Its widespread and abundant occurrence in habitats beyond its traditional native range must surely impact

Figure 13. Twig of Norway maple with cluster of showy flowers.

Figure 14. English ivy in late winter, 1995, blanketing the trunks and branches of Garry oak in Uplands Park, Victoria, BC. Photo courtesy of Krystal Larocque.

natural successional changes through the reduction of substrate availability to species native to the region.

In the Pacific Northwest states and in some southern British Columbia urban parklands, as in Victoria, English ivy (*Hedera helix* L.) has become a troublesome vine blanketing native vegetation (Figure 14).

Impact of Invasive Alien Species on Plants at Risk

Predicting whether an alien species has the potential of becoming a troublesome invasive is somewhat difficult. Recent attempts have been made to predict the potential of alien plants to spread across the landscape and threaten native plant biodiversity (Higgins et al. 1999) and also to predict the invasiveness of plants based on biological characteristics (Goodwin et al. 1999).

Actual knowledge about the impact of alien plants on natural areas, and on plants at risk, has become increasingly available since the late 1980s in plant status reports prepared by the Committee on the Status of Endangered Wildlife in Canada (COSEWIC). At present, alien plants are implicated in contributing to the threats to about 20% of the 75 endangered and threatened plants listed (COSEWIC 2000). In the United States, about 16% of the 250 plants considered to be endangered or threatened by the US Fish and Wildlife Service in 1993 were listed based on alien species being identified as factors of risk (US Congress, Office of Technology Assessment 1993).

Areas of high human population and intense agricultural and industrial activities, generally near the Canada–US border, coincide not only with extensive natural habitat destruction, degradation, and fragmentation, but also with high risk areas of nationally and provincially rare species. These southern areas of Canada also correlate with high numbers of alien plants.

The three provinces with the highest numbers of rare and endangered vascular plants in Canada (Figure 15), as summarized by Crins (1997), are British Columbia (816), Ontario (542), and Quebec (408). It is in the southern regions of these provinces, close to the Canada–US border, that most of the rare and endangered plants occur. These areas support diverse floras that reach their northern limits near Canada's southern boundaries. For the most part, this diversity of species occurs in regions that are also highly desirable for human habitation and agricultural and industrial activities. It is these activities that have disrupted and fragmented the landscape, destroyed habitats and

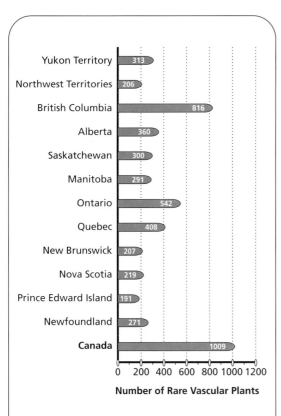

Figure 15. Numbers of nationally rare vascular plants in Canadian provinces and territories based on Crins (1997). Rare plants for the new territory of Nunavut are included in the figure for the Northwest Territories (NT). Provincial/territorial values are compared with the total number for Canada as determined by Argus and Pryer (1990).

populations of some rare native species, and enabled alien plants to prosper and increase their impact on rare species and remnant natural areas.

Impacts of invasive plants on plant species and habitats at risk in Canada tend to be most evident within the Mixedwood Plains Ecozone, especially the Carolinian floristic area of southwestern Ontario; the Prairies Ecozone, most notably some of the southern ecoregions; and the Pacific Maritime and Montane Cordillera Ecozones, particularly on southeastern Vancouver Island and the Thompson–Okanagan Plateau of interior British Columbia.

Carolinian Floristic Area of Southwestern Ontario

In Ontario, active removal of garlic mustard has been required as part of a recovery plan at one of the two sites for the endangered wood-poppy (*Stylophorum diphyllum* (Michx.) Nutt.) in the London area. Garlic

mustard likely played a role in the disappearance of an American ginseng (*Panax quinquefolius* L.) population near Tillsonburg, although the primary cause was probably the opening of the canopy through selective logging. Red mulberry (*Morus rubra* L.), another endangered species, has also been greatly impacted through hybridization with the alien white mulberry (*M. alba* L.).

Prairies Ecozone

In the prairie preserve area within southeastern Manitoba, there is much patrolling and hand weeding being undertaken to prevent the spread of leafy spurge

Figure 16. Two endangered orchids in Canada at risk in some Manitoba sites from expansion by leafy spurge: small white lady's-slipper (*top*), photo by Dr. Donald R. Gunn; single flower of western prairie fringed orchid (*bottom*), photo by Dr. Richard Westwood.

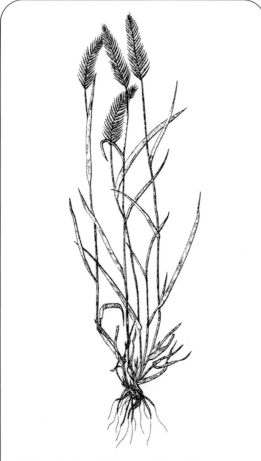

Figure 17. Crested wheatgrass. Illustration courtesy of Agriculture and Agri-Food Canada.

grass, the species has spread to cover about 10 million ha of prairies in North America.

Although primarily a roadside and pasture grass in eastern Canada, smooth brome spreads aggressively by seed and rhizomes and is a major threat to remaining fescue prairies (Grilz and Romo 1994). This invasive grass has also been identified as being a significant problem in the fescue prairies of Riding Mountain National Park, Manitoba, which represents the most easterly of the true fescue prairies.

Pacific Maritime and Montane Cordillera Ecozones

In British Columbia, the loss of the rare Garry oak (*Quercus garryana* Dougl.) ecosystem has been of much concern on southeastern Vancouver Island, especially around Victoria and on the southern Gulf Islands. The high population in this area and the demand for residential and development properties have greatly reduced the formerly continuous ecosystem of Garry oak, which was most abundant in the Victoria area. This ecosystem represents the northernmost end of a narrow band of unique vegetation that extends inland northward from California. The designation by COSEWIC of seven plants from a relatively small geographical area around Victoria is a reflection of both the loss of habitat and the impact of alien shrubs and grasses. These compete with the remnant populations of species designated nationally as at risk in this urban area. The plants at risk include the following species depicted in Figure 18:

- deltoid balsamroot (*Balsamorhiza deltoidea* Nutt.);
- white-top aster (*Aster curtus* Cronq.=*Seriocarpus rigidus* Lindl. in Hook.);
- water-plantain buttercup (*Ranunculus alismaefolius* Geyer ex Benth. var. *alismaefolius*);
- prairie lupine (*Lupinus lepidus* Dougl. ex Lindl. var. *lepidus*);
- seaside bird's-foot lotus (*Lotus formosissimus* Greene);
- golden paintbrush (*Castilleja levisecta* Greenm.); and
- yellow montane violet (*Viola praemorsa* Dougl. ex Lindl. ssp. *praemorsa*).

At present, most of the open woodland sites are dominated by introduced grasses and shrubs such as Scotch broom. The dense growths of these grasses and shrubs, promoted by fire suppression, provides little opportunity for the native flora to persist.

in order to minimize the threat to populations of two endangered orchids (Figure 16), the small white lady's-slipper (*Cypripedium candidum* Muhlenb. ex Willd.) and the western prairie fringed orchid (*Platanthera praeclara* Sheviak and Bowles). Leafy spurge is also a concern at the Lauder Sand Hills in Manitoba and at the dunes in the Mortlach–Caron area of Saskatchewan, where populations of hairy prairie-clover (*Dalea villosa* (Nutt.) Spreng. var. *villosa*), a threatened species in Canada, are located.

Of particular concern in the Prairies are various alien grasses. Crested wheatgrass was implicated as one of the major alien grasses of concern (Figure 17) in the Milk River area of Alberta, where little barley (*Hordeum pusillum* Nutt.), a species at risk nationally, had been collected originally but could not be located in 1992. Crested wheatgrass has been found to reduce the levels of nutrients and organic matter in prairie soils (Christian and Wilson 1999). Since its wide introduction during the drought of the 1930s as a hardy forage

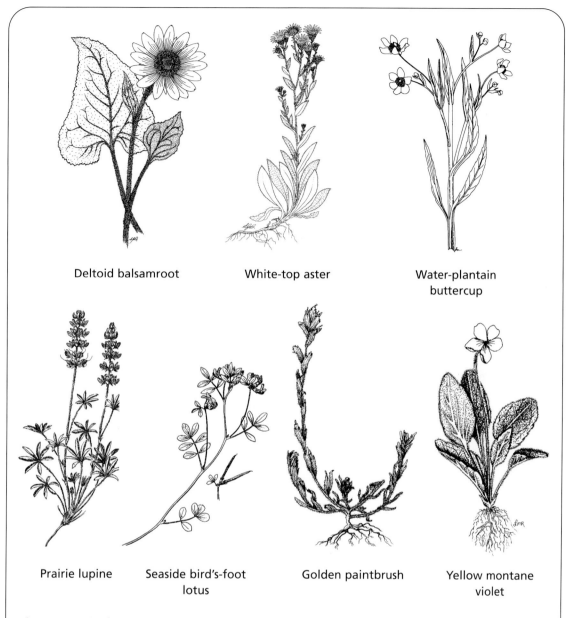

Deltoid balsamroot

White-top aster

Water-plantain buttercup

Prairie lupine

Seaside bird's-foot lotus

Golden paintbrush

Yellow montane violet

Figure 18. Species designated nationally at risk in Canada and threatened by invasive aliens such as the shrub Scotch broom and various introduced grasses on southeastern Vancouver Island. Illustrations courtesy of BC Conservation Data Centre.

Control of Alien Plants in Natural Areas

How do we address some of the problems associated with invasive plants locally or regionally, where practical actions to curb their spread must be initiated? Some ideas for action were proposed as part of a management strategy for invasive plants in southern Ontario at a workshop held in October and December of 1999. This workshop was organized by the City of Toronto Parks and Recreation Division and was hosted by the Metro Toronto Zoo. The following actions were proposed as part of a preliminary strategy:

- Prepare user-friendly guidelines for managing a select group of the top species of concern.

- Develop criteria for identifying priority areas for management.

- Conduct research and disseminate results—for example, species present, their locations and densities; species data (phenology, autecology); rates of displacement of native species; most effective controls; and documentation on troublesome species sold through nurseries and how to mitigate industry losses.

- Prepare educational materials to communicate with the public.
- Recommend changes to public policies and laws.
- Promote local and regional action programs.
- Encourage partnerships.

An example of a regionally coordinated program is the one based on the Northwest Weed Committee's weed management plan for northwestern British Columbia in 2000. The program is facilitated through a staff member of the BC Ministry of Forests. The plan lays the groundwork for actions that include public education, a systematic recording of weed distributions, prevention of the establishment of newly arrived weeds, an integrated weed control program, and coordination of the activities of various agencies. Under the term "weeds" are included a wide range of species, many of which are invasive, within the province (Bob Drinkwater, BC Ministry of Forests, personal communication).

Another exciting program is that of the Bow River Project in Alberta. This initiative is a community-based, multi-agency program that promotes the conservation, enhancement, and wise management of riparian areas through the control of invasive plants, and educational activities. The project has numerous partners including provincial government agencies, private conservation groups, Bow River Basin municipalities, and garden centers. Of special interest are the manual weed control work crews coordinated by the project staff in collaboration with Alberta Justice and Attorney General. These work crews consist of low-risk inmates of correctional institutions and others doing community service who pull weeds (and invasives) listed as restricted (must be eradicated) and noxious (must be controlled) under Alberta's *Weed Control Act*. The program also coordinates a basin-wide Purple Loosestrife Garden Center Exchange Program. The program is run through a coordinator and assistant out of the Agriculture Centre in Airdrie, Alberta.

In Manitoba, the Manitoba Purple Loosestrife Project has been very successful in promoting grassroot partnerships in control of purple loosestrife (Lindgren, this publication, p. 259).

As outlined by Harris and Shamoun in this publication (p. 291), biological controls currently used in agriculture and forestry could also be applied to natural ecosystems to protect species at risk.

Local and regional programs could be widely expanded within major problem areas of every province, if facilitated by a national approach to coordinate actions to redress the spread of all alien species in Canada. An adequately funded national program on invasive species needs to be established in Canada to ensure the preservation, at least, of the most important natural areas and to mitigate the impact on species at risk.

References

Anable, M.E.; McClaran, M.P.; Ruyle, G.B. 1992. Spread of introduced Lehmann lovegrass *Eragrostis lebmanniana* Nees. in southern Arizona, USA. Biol. Conserv. 61:181–188.

Argus, G.W.; Pryer, K.M. 1990. Rare vascular plants in Canada: our natural heritage. Canadian Museum of Nature, Ottawa, ON.

Christian, J.M.; Wilson, S.D. 1999. Long-term ecosystem impacts of an introduced grass in the northern Great Plains. Ecology 80:2397–2407.

Clout, M. 1995. Introduced species: the greatest threat to global biodiversity? Species 24:34–36.

Correll, D.S. 1978. Native orchids of North America, north of Mexico. Stanford University Press, Stanford, CA.

COSEWIC 2000. Canadian species at risk. Unpublished list of officially designated wildlife species in Canada. May 2000. Available from COSEWIC Secretariat, c/o Canadian Wildlife Service, Environment Canada, Ottawa, ON K1A 0H3.

Crins, W.J. 1997. Rare and endangered plants and their habitats in Canada. Can. Field-Nat. 11:506–519.

Department of Agriculture. 1935. Weed and weed seeds. Bull. 137. New series, rev. Department of Agriculture, Ottawa, ON.

Ecological Stratification Working Group. 1996. A national ecological framework for Canada [print and online]. Agriculture and Agri-Food Canada, Research Branch, Ottawa, ON/Environment Canada, Ecozone Analysis Branch, Hull, QC. Report and national map at 1:7 500 000 scale. http://sis.agr.gc.ca/cansis/publications/ecostrat/intro.html

Fernald, M.L.; Kinsey, A.C. 1958. Edible wild plants of eastern North America. Revised by R.C. Rollins. Harper and Row, New York, NY.

Frankton, C.; Wright, W.H. 1955. Weeds of Canada. Publication No. 948. Department of Agriculture, Ottawa, ON.

Goodwin, B.J.; McAllister, A.J.; Fahrig, L. 1999. Predicting invasiveness of plant species based on biological information. Conserv. Biol. 13:422–426.

Grilz, P.L.; Romo, J.T. 1994. Water relations and growth of *Bromus inermis* Leyss. (smooth brome) following spring or autumn burning in a fescue prairie. Am. Midl. Nat. 132:340–348.

Haber, E. 1996. Invasive plants of Canada: 1996 national survey results. Unpublished report. Available from the Biodiversity Convention Office, Environment Canada, Ottawa, ON K1A 0H3.

Haber, E. 2000. Invasive plants of Canada: survey 2000, an overview of people and projects. Unpublished report. Available from Canadian Wildlife Service, Environment Canada, Ottawa, ON K1A 0H3.

Higgins, S.I.; Richardson, D.M.; Cowling, R.M.; Trinder-Smith, T.H. 1999. Predicting the landscape-scale distribution of alien plants and their threat to plant diversity. Conserv. Biol. 13:303–313.

Holm, L.G.; Plucknett, D.L.; Pancho, J.V.; Herberger, J.P. 1977. The world's worst weeds: distribution and biology. The East–West Center. University Press of Hawaii, HI.

Hoshovsky, M. 1986. Element stewardship abstract for *Cytisus scoparius* and *Genista monspessulanus*. The Nature Conservancy, Arlington, VA.

LeMaitre, D.C.; van Wilgen, B.W.; Chapman, R.A.; McKelly, D.H. 1996. Invasive plants and water resources in the Western Cape Province, South Africa: modelling the consequences of a lack of management. J. Appl. Ecol. 33:161–172.

Meyer, J.Y.; Florence, J. 1996. Tahiti's native flora endangered by the invasion of *Micontia calvescens* DC. (Melastomataceae). J. Biogeogr. 23:775–782.

Montgomery, F.H. 1956. The introduced plants of Ontario growing outside of cultivation (part I). Trans. R. Can. Inst. 31:91–102.

Moss, E.H. 1983. Flora of Alberta. 2nd rev. ed. by John G. Parker. University of Toronto Press, Toronto, ON.

Musil, C.F. 1993. Effect of invasive Australian acacias on the regeneration, growth and nutrient chemistry of South African lowland fynbos. J. Appl. Ecol. 30:361–372.

Newmaster, S.G.; Lehela, A.; Uhlig, P.W.C.; McMurray, S.; Oldham, M.J. 1998. Ontario plant list. Ontario Forest Research Institute, Ontario Ministry of Natural Resources, Sault Ste. Marie, ON. For. Res. Inf. Pap. 123.

Pimm, S.L.; Russell, G.J.; Gittleman, J.L.; Brooks, T.M. 1995. The future of biodiversity. Science 269:347–350.

Reader's Digest 1986. Magic and medicine of plants. The Reader's Digest Association, Inc., Montréal, QC.

Roland, A.E.; Smith, E.C. 1969. The flora of Nova Scotia. Nova Scotia Museum, Halifax, NS.

Rousseau, C. 1968. Histoire, habitat et distribution de 220 plantes introduites au Québec. Nat. can. (Que.) 95:49–169.

Soper, J.H.; Murray, L. 1985. Helleborine—A 30-year update and analysis of its distribution in Ontario. Mich. Bot. 24:83–96.

Steenkamp, H.E.; Chown, S.L. 1996. Influence of dense stands of an exotic tree, *Prosopis glandulosa* Benson, on a savannah dung beetle (Coleoptera: Scarabaeinae) assemblage in southern Africa. Biol. Conserv. 78:305–311.

Syme, J.T.B., editor. 1873. English botany; or, coloured figures of British plants. Vol. 1, ed. 3. George Bell and Sons, London, UK.

US Congress, Office of Technology Assessment. 1993. Harmful non-native species in the United States. OTA-F-565, US Government Printing Office, Washington, DC.

Usher, M.B. 1988. Biological invasions of nature reserves: a search for generalizations. Biol. Conserv. 44:119–135.

Vitousek, P.M.; Walker, L.R. 1989. Biological invasion by *Myrica faya* in Hawaii: plant demography, nitrogen fixation, ecosystem effects. Ecol. Monogr. 59:247–265.

White, D.J.; Haber, E.; Keddy, C. 1993. Invasive plants of natural habitats in Canada. Canadian Wildlife Service, Environment Canada/Canadian Museum of Nature, Ottawa, ON.

Invasive Alien Species in Canadian Forests

Ole Hendrickson

Alien species—including insects, fungi, plants, and animals—generally arrive without a full complement of their natural associates. An alien plant species may become an invasive weed in the absence of the pests it has left behind. An alien insect or fungus will have no recent evolutionary history in association with its new-found plant hosts. It may cause them vastly more damage than it causes their Old World relatives (Gibbs and Wainhouse 1986). Examples include balsam woolly adelgid (*Adelges piceae* (Ratz.)) on New World firs (*Abies* spp.), and white pine blister rust (*Cronartium ribicola* J.C. Fisch.) on New World pines (*Pinus* spp.).

Although most of its associates may have been left behind, the introduction of an alien species does create a risk of introducing other harmful aliens. For example, the importation of alien chestnuts (*Castanea* spp.) for ornamental plantings led to introduction of chestnut blight (*Cryphonectria parasitica* (Murr.) Barr) and the virtual eradication of American chestnuts (*Castanea dentata* (Marsh.) Borkh.). Alien fungi that are causing serious losses of North American elms (*Ulmus* spp.) and American beech (*Fagus grandifolia* Ehrh.) were introduced and spread by alien bark beetles.

Alien species do not respect national borders. An annotated checklist of alien insects feeding on woody plants (Mattson et al. 1994) includes 146 species shared by the United States and Canada, compared with only 35 that are found in Canada alone. Of the 83 shared species for which the point of origin is known, 55 first became established in the United States and 28 in Canada. Some of the latter became serious pests, such as the European spruce sawfly (*Gilpinia hercyniae* Hartig) introduced to Ottawa in 1922.

North American forests appear to be at greater risk of invasion by alien insects and fungi than those in other parts of the world. Although there has been some discussion of the reasons for this vulnerability (Niemelä and Mattson 1996), the environmental and economic risks posed by alien invasions are mostly documented as individual case studies. Only limited summary information is available for Canadian forests (CFS 1999).

This paper first reviews some case studies of alien fungal pathogens. It then describes some of the many species of alien insects that have become established on woody plants in Canada, and examines why Canada's forests are so vulnerable to them. Some of the alien plants and vertebrate animals in Canada's forests are more briefly discussed. The paper concludes with some observations concerning the need for new resources to deal with invasive alien species in forests.

Alien Fungal Pathogens

Fungal pathogens have had arguably the most devastating economic and environmental impacts on Canada's forests of any group of alien species. Impacts have not been limited to mortality of individual trees, but have involved major shifts in composition of forest ecosystems, virtual elimination of once-dominant tree species, and local extirpation or even extinction of associated native insects. This section describes some of the most serious fungal diseases introduced to date.

Beech bark disease was introduced to Halifax in 1890. It is caused by an alien fungal pathogen, *Nectria coccinea* var. *faginata* Lohm., Wats. & Ayers, together with an alien scale insect, *Cryptococcus fagisuga* Lind. (Houston 1994, Houston and O'Brien 1998). The disease has spread southward to the Great Smoky Mountains National Park in the United States and westward to Ontario. It often kills more than half of the larger beech trees (more than 25 cm in diameter) in an infected stand. As the top parts of these older trees die, the roots send up dense clusters of sprouts, resulting in a new stand that is overly rich in beech and impoverished in associated species. Beech sprouts are also infected by the disease, and most show poor form and growth. Compared with the mature stands they replace, the diseased beech stands originating from sprouts have little value for wildlife species such as black bear (*Ursus americanus* Pallas).

American chestnut once dominated the forests of eastern North America as far north as southern Ontario. Beginning in the 1870s, Japanese chestnuts (*Castanea crenata* Sieb. & Zuuc.) were widely sold by mail order for ornamental plantings (Anagnostakis 1995). Chinese chestnuts (*C. mollissima* Blume) were first imported in 1900. Both species are carriers of chestnut blight, first recorded on native chestnut trees in New York City in 1904. The disease spread at a rate of about 40 km/year. Within a few decades it essentially eliminated the American chestnut, and with it the large crops of nuts eaten by wildlife and by Aboriginal

American people. Several insect species that specialized on chestnuts were driven to extinction (Opler 1978). Oaks (*Quercus* spp.), hickories (*Carya* spp.), and other species that replaced chestnut have less food value and form less stable forests. Although the American chestnut continues to sprout from roots, most sprouts quickly succumb to disease and the future of this species lies with experimental breeding programs involving crosses with other species, and with introduction of less virulent strains of the *Cryphonectria* fungal pathogen.

The history of butternut canker (*Sirococcus clavignenti-juglandacearum* Nair, Kost. & Kuntz) is less well known. It is thought to be an alien pathogen because of its sudden appearance and rapid spread, and to have established in the southeastern United States about 40 years ago (Schlarbaum et al. 1997). It was first reported in Quebec in 1990, Ontario in 1991, and New Brunswick in 1997. Limited genetic resistance is observed in butternut (*Juglans cinerea* L.). All wild populations are at risk of extirpation. Unlike chestnut, butternut does not sprout after stem death. The nuts themselves carry fungal spores, complicating the work of conserving populations through ex-situ means. The causal agent of butternut canker has no known sexual stage. Lack of knowledge of its physiology and genetics hinders the development of a comprehensive strategy for saving the butternut.

Dutch elm disease (*Ophiostoma ulmi* (Buis.) Nannf. and *O. novo-ulmi* Brasier) (Figure 1) was first isolated from dying white elms (*Ulmus americana* L.) in Cleveland in May 1930 (Hubbes 1999). A new and more virulent strain of the pathogen was detected in Quebec in 1944, linked to shipments of elm crates from France. The disease is now found in most of North America, having reached Alberta in 1998. It was introduced and spread by the smaller European elm bark beetle (*Scolytus multistriatus* Marsh). All three native elms in Canada are at risk. Loss of white elm is particularly tragic because of its widespread use as an urban shade tree. Control of Dutch elm disease is possible, although costly. The urban elms threatened by this alien species are worth about $2.5 billion within Canada (Hubbes 1999), based on their value for insurance purposes.

Harvesting of eastern white pine (*Pinus strobus* L.) was fundamental to Canada's economy during its early years as a nation. The detection of white pine blister rust (*Cronartium ribicola* J.C. Fisch.) (Figure 2) in 1917, following its introduction to the United States around 1910, was a formative event in the development of Canada's forestry service (Johnstone 1991). It led to the merger of scientific and economic aspects of forestry in a single agency, and spawned a national program of forest insect and disease survey that survived until severe

Figure 1. Mature white elm with early symptoms of Dutch elm disease. Photo by C. Monnier, CFS, LFC, Sainte-Foy, QC.

Figure 2. White pine blister rust on western white pine (*Pinus monticola* Dougl. ex D. Don). Photo courtesy of CFS, PFC, Victoria, BC.

funding cuts were made to federal science in the 1990s. All native North American white pines are at risk from white pine blister rust (Hoff et al. 1980). The most susceptible species are whitebark pine (*Pinus albicaulis* Engelm.) and limber pine (*P. flexilis* James), both of which have high value as wildlife habitat. The disease also has greatly inhibited the development of commercial plantations of white pine.

Alien Invertebrates

Alien Insect Introductions

At least 180 alien insects that feed on woody plants have become established in Canada (Tables 1 and 2). As with fungal pathogens, their impacts extend beyond mortality of host plants to include destabilization of major forest ecosystem types and elimination of

Table 1. Alien insect species feeding on woody plants in Canada.

Order	Family	Species name
Coleoptera	Anobiidae	*Anobium punctatum* (De Geer), *Ernobius mollis* (L.), *Stegobium paniceum* (L.), *Xestobium rufovillosum* (De Geer)
	Buprestidae	*Agrilus cyanescens* Ratz.
	Cerambycidae	*Tetropium fuscum* (Fabricius)
	Chrysomelidae	*Lina tremulae* Fabricius, *Plagiodera versicolora* (Laich), *Pyrrhalta luteola* (Mueller), *P. viburni* (Paykull)
	Curculionidae	*Cryptorhynchus lapathi* (L.), *Otiorhynchus ligustici* (L.), *O. ovatus* (L.), *O. raucus* Fabricius, *O. rugosostriatus* (Goeze), *O. scaber* (L.), *O. singularis* (L.), *O. sulcatus* (Fabricius), *Phyllobius intrusus* Kono, *Polydrusus cervinus* (L.), *P. impressifrons* Gyllenhal, *Sciaphilus asperatus* Bonsdorff, *Strophosoma melanogrammum* (Forster)
	Lyctidae	*Lyctus brunneus* (Stephens)
	Oedemeridae	*Nacerdes melanura* (L.)
	Scarabaeidae	*Popillia japonica* Newman, *Rhizotrogus majalis* (Razoumowsky)
	Scolytidae	*Crypturgus pusillus* (Gyllenhal), *Scolytus mali* (Bechstein), *S. multistriatus* (Marsham), *S. rugulosus* (Mueller), *Tomicus piniperda* (L.), *Xyleborinus saxeseni* (Ratz.), *X. dispar* (Fabricius), *Xylosandrus germanus* (Blandford)
Diptera	Agromyzidae	*Paraphytomyza populicola* (Walker)
	Cecidomyiidae	*Contarinia baeri* (Prell), *C. pyrivora* (Riley), *Dasineura mali* (Keiffer), *Semudobia betulae* (Winnertz), *S. tarda* Roskam
Hemiptera	Miridae	*Orthotylus viridinervis* Kirschbaum, *Pilophorus confusus* (Kirschbaum)
Homoptera	Adelgidae	*Adelges abietis* (L.), *A. laricis* Vallot, *A. nusslini* (Borner), *A. piceae* (Ratz.), *A. tsugae* Annand
	Aleyrodidae	*Dialeurodes chittendeni* Laing
	Aphididae	*Acyrthosiphon caraganae* (Cholodkovsky), *Chaetoporella aceris* (L.), *Elatobium abietinum* (Walker), *Euceraphis punctipennis* (Zetterstedt), *Hyadaphis tataricae* (Aizenberg), *Periphyllus californiensis* (Shinji), *P. testudinacea* (Fernie)
	Cercopidae	*Aphrophora alni* (Fallen)
	Cicadellidae	*Aguriahana stellulata* (Burmeister), *Allygus mixtus* (Fabricius), *Empoasca bipunctata* (Oshanin), *E. luda* Davidson & DeLong, *E. populi* Edwards, *E. smaragdula* (Fallen), *Fieberiella florii* (Stal), *Idiocerus stigmaticalis* Lewis, *Japananus hyalinus* (Osborn), *Macropsis fuscula* (Zetterstedt), *M. graminea* (Fabricius), *M. mendax* (Fieber), *M. notata* (Prohaska), *M. ocellata* Provancher, *M. vicina* (Horvath), *Oncopsis tristis* (Zetterstedt), *Opsius stactogalus* Fieber, *Orientis ishidae* (Matsumura), *Pediopsis tillae* (Germar), *Rhytidodus decimasquartus* (Schrank), *Ribautiana tenerrima* (Herrich-Schaeffer), *R. ulmi* (L.), *Typhlocyba avellanae* Edwards, *T. barbata* Ribaut, *T. candidula* Kirschbaum, *T. froggatti* Baker, *T. frustrator* Edwards, *T. hippocastani* Edwards, *T. lethierryi* Edwards,

(Continued)

Table 1 *(Concluded)*

Order	Family	Species name
		T. nigriloba Edwards, *T. plebeja* Edwards, *T. prunicola* Edwards, *T. quercus* (Fabricius), *Zygina flammigera* (Fourcroy)
	Diaspididae	*Dynaspidiotus britannicus* (Newstead)
	Eriococcidae	*Cryptococcus fagisuga* Lindinger, *Gossyparia spuria* (Modeer)
	Eriosomatidae	*Eriosoma ulmi* (L.), *Pemphigus bursarius* (L.)
	Psyllidae	*Psyllopsis fraxinicola* (Forster)
Hymenoptera	Argidae	*Arge ochropa* (Gmelin)
	Diprionidae	*Diprion similis* (Hartig), *Gilpinia frutetorum* (Fabricius), *G. hercyniae* (Hartig), *G. viminalis* (Fallen), *Neodiprion sertifer* (Geoffroy)
	Pamphiliidae	*Acantholyda erythrocephala* (L.)
	Siricidae	*Sirex juvencus* (L.)
	Tenthredinidae	*Allantus basalis* (Klug), *A. cinctus* (L.), *Caliroa cerasi* (L.), *Caulocampus acericaulis* (MacGillivray), *Croesus varus* (Villaret), *Eriocampa ovata* (L.), *Fenusa dohrnii* (Tischbein), *F. pusilla* (Lepeletier), *F. ulmi* Sundevall, *Hemichroa crocea* (Geoffroy), *Heterarthrus nemoratus* (Fallen), *Hoplocampa brevis* (Klug), *H. testudinea* (Klug), *Macrophya punctum-album* (L.), *Messa nana* (Klug), *Nematus ribesii* (Scopoli), *N. salicisodoratus* Dyar, *Pontania proxima* (Lepeletier), *Pristiphora abbreviata* (Hartig), *P. erichsonii* (Hartig), *P. geniculata* (Hartig), *Profenusa thomsoni* (Konow), *Trichiocampus viminalis* (Fallen)
Lepidoptera	Choreutidae	*Choreutis (Eutromula) pariana* (Clerck)
	Coleophoridae	*Coleophora fuscedinella* (Zeller), *C. laricella* (Hubner), *C. serratella* (L.), *C. ulmifolliela* McDunnough
	Gelechiidae	*Anacampsis populella* (Clerck), *Anarsia lineatella* Zeller, *Dichomeris marginella* (Fabricius), *Exoteleia dodecella* (L.), *Recurvaria nanella* Denis & Schiff.
	Geometridae	*Chloroclystis retangulata* (L.), *Erannis defoliaria* Clerck, *Hemithea aestivaria* Hubner, *Operophtera brumata* (L.), *Thera juniperata* (Linnaeus)
	Gracillariidae	*Caloptilia negundella* (Chambers), *C. (Gracillaria) syringella* (Fabricius), *Phyllonorycter blancardella* (Fabricius)
	Lymantriidae	*Euproctis chrysorrhoea* (L.), *Leucoma salicis* (L.), *Lymantria dispar* (L.), *Orgyia antiqua* (L.)
	Noctuidae	*Amphipyra tragopoginis* L., *Peridroma saucia* (Hubner), *Syngrapha interrogationis* (L.)
	Oecophoridae	*Cheimophila salicella* (Hubner)
	Plutellidae	*Homadaula anisocentra* Meyrick
	Pyralidae	*Eurrhypara hortulata* L.
	Saturniidae	*Sarnia cynthia* (Drury)
	Tortricidae	*Acleris comariana* (Zeller), *A. variegana* (Denis & Schiff.), *Aethes rutilana* (Hubner), *Archips podana* (Scopoli), *A. rosana* (L.), *Cnephasia longana* (Haworth), *Croesia holmiana* (L.), *Cydia pomonella* (L.), *Ditula angustiorana* (Haworth), *Epiblema cynosbatella* (L.), *Epinotia nanana* (Treitschke), *E. solandriana* (L.), *Grapholita molesta* (Busck), *Hedya nubiferana* (Haworth), *Pandemis cerasana* (Hubner), *P. heparana* (Denis & Schiff.), *Rhopobota naevana* (Hubner), *Rhyacionia buoliana* (Denis & Schiff.), *Spilonota lariciana* (Heinemann), *S. ocellana* (Denis & Schiff.)
	Yponomeutidae	*Ocnerostoma piniariella* Zeller, *Yponomeuta malinellus* Zeller
Thysanoptera	Thripidae	*Taeniothrips inconsequens* Uzel, *Thrips calcaratus* Uzel

Source: Mattson et al. 1994, updated with new Canadian records. See the original reference for date and location of introduction, distribution, pest status, host plant(s), feeding behavior, and literature citations.

native species. Evidence suggests that European insects have wholly displaced their North American counterparts in certain niches, characterized as a "hostile takeover" by Niemelä and Mattson (1996). Some alien insects are serious economic pests, including gypsy moth (*Lymantria dispar* (L.)), balsam woolly adelgid (*Adelges piceae* (Ratz.)), pine false webworm (*Acantholyda erythrocephala* (L.)), pine shoot beetle (*Tomicus piniperda* (L.)), introduced pine sawfly (*Diprion similis* Hartig), and birch casebearer (*Coleophora serratella* L.).

Most invading insects are in the orders Homoptera (aphids, scale insects, leafhoppers, cicadas, and others), Lepidoptera (moths and butterflies), Coleoptera (beetles),

and Hymenoptera (wasps, bees, ants, and sawflies). There are large gaps in knowledge about when and where alien species were first introduced, and how widely they have spread. But it is clear that the rate of introduction has been well over one species per year for the past century (Table 3), and that new introductions are continuing. For example, the European brown spruce longhorn beetle (*Tetropium fuscum* (Fabricius)) (Figure 3) was first detected in Halifax in 1999. Its entry can be dated to 1990 from specimens that were originally misidentified as other species. It belongs to the Cerambycidae, a group of large beetles whose larvae bore holes in trees. It is the first alien species of this

Table 2. Alien insects feeding on woody plants in North America.

Order	US only	Canada only	US + Canada	Unknown	Total
Coleoptera	49	3	32	20	104
Diptera	6	2	4	1	13
Hemiptera	8	2	0	3	13
Homoptera	44	11	43	16	114
Hymenoptera	5	3	28	2	38
Isoptera	1	0	0	0	1
Lepidoptera	10	14	37	19	80
Orthoptera	1	0	0	0	1
Psocoptera	1	0	0	0	1
Thysanoptera	1	0	2	1	4
Total	**126**	**35**	**146**	**62**	**369**

Summarized from Mattson et al. 1994.

Table 3. North American introduction of alien insects feeding on woody plants in Canada. Order totals may be less than in Table 2 because some introduction dates are unknown.

Order	<1800	1800–19	1820–39	1840–59	1860–79	1880–99	1900–19	1920–39	1940–59	1960–79
Coleoptera	0	1	2	1	4	3	5	3	4	1
Diptera	0	0	0	0	0	0	0	1	1	1
Hemiptera	0	0	0	0	0	0	0	1	0	1
Homoptera	0	0	0	0	1	7	10	5	8	9
Hymenoptera	1	0	0	0	1	5	2	7	1	3
Lepidoptera	2	0	0	1	5	4	8	9	2	6
Thysanoptera	0	0	0	0	0	0	1	1	0	0
Total	**3**	**1**	**2**	**2**	**11**	**19**	**26**	**27**	**16**	**21**

Summarized from Mattson et al. 1994.

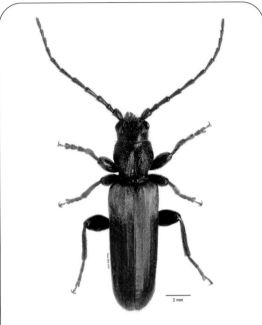

Figure 3. Male brown spruce longhorn beetle. Photo by Klaus Bolte, CFS, Science Branch, Ottawa.

Figure 4. Trunk of a red spruce (*Picea rubens* Sargent) with resin pouring from numerous wounds caused by brown spruce longhorn beetles. Photo courtesy of K.J. Harrison, CFS, AFC, Fredericton, NB.

family to become established in Canada, and it has triggered a major eradication effort to protect spruces (*Picea* spp.), all species of which are commercially important (Figure 4).

A lag of a decade or more between introduction and detection of an alien species is not uncommon. Failure to detect introductions promptly makes eradication of harmful alien species far more difficult if not impossible. Ongoing monitoring for new arrivals is essential. Another harmful alien cerambycid, the Asian longhorned beetle (*Anoplophora glabripennis* Mots.), was detected in New York City in 1996 and Chicago in 1998. Cutting of thousands of street trees has failed to control the spread of this species to date. Its preferred hosts are the widely planted sugar maple (*Acer saccharum* Marsh.) and Norway maple (*A. platanoides* L.), but it also attacks horsechestnuts (*Aesculus* spp.), birches (*Betula* spp.), willows (*Salix* spp.), poplars (*Populus* spp.), ashes (*Fraxinus* spp.), black locust (*Robinia pseudoacacia* L.), apples (*Malus* spp.), mulberries (*Morus* spp.), elms, and others.

Behavior of Alien Insect Pests

Gypsy moth attacks a wide range of tree species and other plant hosts (over 500 different species). It is well established from Ontario east to the Maritime provinces (see Nealis, this publication, p. 151). Its recent introduction to Vancouver Island, British Columbia, led to imposition of quarantine restrictions there. Larval feeding in June can lead to complete defoliation of infested trees in severe outbreaks, killing conifers such as pines and reducing growth in hardwoods such as oaks. Gypsy moth populations typically show rapid increases to epidemic levels, followed by sudden declines and prolonged periods of scarcity.

Adelgids are members of a family of wingless, plant-sucking insects that feed exclusively on conifers. They are related to aphids, and these two families include many of the most damaging alien pests in North America. The balsam woolly adelgid is a serious pest of balsam fir in eastern Quebec and the Atlantic provinces. It has caused widespread death of Fraser fir (*Abies fraseri* (Pursh) Poir.) forests in the southern Appalachians of the United States, and also attacks amabilis fir (*A. amabilis* (Dougl. ex Loud.) Dougl. ex J. Forbes) and subalpine fir (*A. lasiocarpa* (Hook.) Nutt.) in British Columbia, where it is subject to quarantine regulations. Planting of amabilis fir was suspended in British Columbia in 1966 because of its susceptibility to attack by balsam woolly adelgid (Carrow 1973). It feeds on tree stems, causing severe swelling and decreased wood fiber quality. In a second type of attack known as gout, adelgids mass in the tree crowns and feed on young shoots, causing swelling and distortion. Either type of feeding can lead to tree death.

The behavior of alien insect species that feed on trees is less predictable than that of native insects. For example, the pine false webworm, a European sawfly, has been present in Ontario since 1961. Around 1994 it shifted its feeding preference from small trees to trees of all sizes. Formerly limited to eastern North America, it recently appeared in Edmonton, Alberta. Another alien species showing dramatic range expansion and changing food preferences is the pine shoot beetle (Figure 5). Introduced to Cleveland, Ohio, in 1992, it spread rapidly, appearing in Ontario in 1993 and Quebec in 1998. It was first thought to damage only Christmas tree plantations of alien Scots pine (*Pinus sylvestris* L.). But in 1998, considerable damage, including tree mortality, was found in white pine, red pine (*P. resinosa* Ait.), and jack pine (*P. banksiana* Lamb.) stands in Ontario. All affected stands were close to Scots pine, and it is possible that this alien tree species must be present for pine shoot beetle populations to damage healthy trees of other pine species (Ministry of Natural Resources 2000).

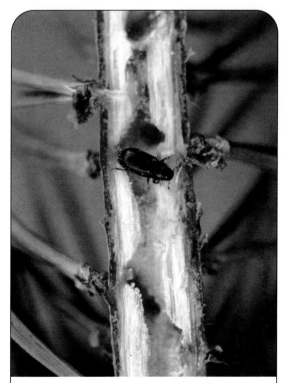

Figure 5. Pine shoot beetle on damaged shoot. Photo courtesy of CFS, GLFC, Sault Ste. Marie, ON.

The introduced pine sawfly is another alien species that feeds preferentially on Scots pine but can attack native pine species. Niemelä and Mattson (1996) have suggested that an abundance of alien plant species near ports of entry and in disturbed habitats in North America may contribute to the success of alien insect species, which feed on nectar and foliage of alien plants before laying eggs in native host plants.

Alien insects may have replaced their North American counterparts in some niches. As noted above, Niemelä and Mattson (1996) characterize this as a "hostile takeover". Birch casebearer, an alien leaf-mining moth, together with four species of alien leaf-mining sawflies, now dominate leaf-feeding on white birch (*Betula papyrifera* Marsh.) throughout much of its range. Although their feeding is generally not a direct cause of mortality, it destabilizes stands of birch, one of Canada's dominant deciduous tree species, by decreasing their drought resistance and predisposing them to fatal attacks from wood-boring insects and fungi.

Alien Soil Invertebrates

Another large group of little-studied alien insects abundant in North American forests is the root-feeding weevils (for example, various species of *Otiorhynchus*, *Polydrusus*, and *Phyllobius*) (Mattson 1998). Both adults and larvae of root weevils can seriously damage seedlings. Studies in British Columbia tree nurseries have identified the strawberry root weevil (*Otiorhynchus ovatus* L.), the rough strawberry root weevil (*O. rugosostriatus* Goeze), and the black vine weevil (*O. sulcatus* Fabr.) as major pests causing stem girdling and death of seedlings. Larvae of the strawberry root and black vine weevils are soil inhabitants. They feed on, and seriously damage, seedling roots. Mattson (1998) suggests that "these inconspicuous, unstudied immigrants may be having important, though unappreciated, ecological impacts" in native forests as well as in nurseries.

In general, little is known about alien organisms in forest soils compared with forest canopies. But Parkinson and coworkers have documented extensive impacts of invading alien earthworms on trembling aspen (*Populus tremuloides* Michx.) and lodgepole pine (*Pinus contorta* Dougl. ex Loud. var. *latifolia* Engelm.) forests in Alberta, including increased growth of understory plants (Scheu and Parkinson 1994), decreased diversity and richness of fungi, decreased availability of nutrients for microorganisms, and increased turnover of litter (McLean and Parkinson 1997, 2000). Although the rate of spread of alien earthworms is slow compared with the spread of insects and fungi, their ecological impacts are profound.

Biological Control Agents

Alien biological control organisms have reduced the numbers and ecological and economic impacts of a small group of alien insect species that formerly caused major damage in North American forests (Mattson 1998). These include three defoliators—larch casebearer (*Coleophora laricella* Hbn.), European spruce sawfly (*Gilpinia hercyniae* Hartig), and larch sawfly (*Pristiphora erichsonii* Hartig)—and one shoot borer, European pine shoot moth (*Rhyacionia buoliana* Denis & Schiff.). For example, the European spruce sawfly was a serious defoliator of spruces until a viral pathogen providing biological control was introduced into Canada (Clark et al. 1973). Forest birds were the likely means for spread of this biological control agent, as the virus remains highly infective after passing through their guts (Entwistle et al. 1978).

Classical biological control is discussed in depth by Corrigan (this publication, p. 279). It is not a panacea. Developing safe and effective biological controls is expensive and time consuming. Biological control agents often fail; furthermore, as alien species themselves, they pose risks to native flora and fauna that must be carefully studied. Of 13 parasite species introduced into Canada for control of pine shoot moth, 10 failed to become established, and several of these would not have been introduced had more careful screening been conducted (Schroder 1974). Nonetheless, biological control offers the greatest potential for mitigating damages caused by alien pests in natural forests while minimizing impacts on nontarget organisms.

Competitive Advantage of Alien Insect Pests

Sagoff (2000) has suggested that the distinction between native and nonnative species is "irrelevant" and "does not predict a species' economic or ecological effect". But there is strong evidence that this distinction does matter in the case of insects. Niemelä and Mattson (1996) examined the "negative balance of trade" in insects between Europe and North America. About 300 of 400 woody-plant-feeding alien insect species in North America are from Europe, but only 34 species have made the reverse journey. These authors propose two major explanations for this imbalance: greater ecological opportunities in North America, and greater competitive ability of European insect species.

Greater ecological opportunities come in the form of higher numbers of potential host tree species in North America, with less fragmented distributions. While Europe lost many tree species during the last ice age, European insects may retain an ability to colonize North American relatives of these "lost species". Furthermore, European trees such as birches generally support higher numbers of insect species than their North American counterparts. Translocated European insects may find the relatively low number of insect species on Canadian trees to their advantage.

Greater competitive ability of European insects may stem from strong selection pressure created by fragmentation and disturbance. Several factors contributed to a high frequency of fragmented and disturbed forest habitats in Europe: more rugged topography, greater impacts of glaciation, and clearing of forests by human populations. High rates of population increase of European insects are facilitated by asexual reproduction (parthenogenesis) in several major insect groups (adelgids, scale insects, bark beetles, and sawflies). Furthermore, the Gulf Stream allows equivalent forest types to grow at higher latitudes in Europe (for instance, in Scandinavia) than in North America. European insects adapted to high-latitude forests and short days readily occupy lower-latitude forests in North America. Their overwintering state (diapause) is triggered by a much wider range of day lengths than occurs in insects adapted to lower latitudes, allowing them to survive cold Canadian winters.

European insects also have more flexibility in their day length requirements for breaking diapause in the spring. Gypsy moth and pine shoot beetle, two European species now established as major pests in Canada, exploit this advantage by occupying choice feeding habitats before their native competitors emerge. Early spring feeding is also characteristic of other alien moth species and the two members of the order Thysanoptera (thrips) that are established in Canada (Niemelä and Mattson 1996).

Alien Plants

Direct impacts on Canadian forests from alien vascular plants and vertebrate animals have been considerably less serious than from alien insects and diseases. Whereas the latter have displaced native species in certain habitats and successfully colonized the vast, publicly owned timber-producing forests of Canada, the former are mainly restricted to disturbed and early successional habitats (Haber, this publication, p.43). It is worth emphasizing, however, that shipments of alien higher plants (or parts derived from them) have been a pathway for entry to Canada of many damaging alien insects and diseases (Allen 1998; Dawson, this publication, p. 243).

As forests become more fragmented—particularly in southern Canada—the impacts of alien higher plants and animal species become more evident. Of particular concern is the management of forest remnants in urbanized areas, which can become foci for multiplication and spread of invasive species such as common (or European) buckthorn (*Rhamnus cathartica* L.). Road development and human travel assist the spread of weedy species from modified urban landscapes into formerly intact forests (Haber, this publication, p. 43).

Scotch broom (*Cytisus scoparius* (L.) Link) illustrates this phenomenon. Widely planted for ornamental purposes and stabilization of road cuts, it is now invading the drier Douglas-fir (*Pseudotsuga menziesii* (Mirb.) Franco var. *menziesii*) forests on the southern part of Vancouver Island. Spreading into the forest from access roads, Scotch broom is particularly successful when harvesting activities open up the stand. Its rapid regeneration and growth interfere with establishment of a new crop of Douglas-fir seedlings (Peterson and Prasad 1998). Diffuse knapweed (*Centaurea diffusa* Lam.) is another alien weedy species that may affect survival and growth of planted conifer stock in British Columbia (Powell et al. 1997).

To date, however, invasive higher plants pose more of a concern for conservation of rare and endangered native plants in Canada than for commercial forestry (Table 4). Scotch broom is invading the Garry oak (*Quercus garryana* Dougl.) woodlands of Vancouver Island, threatening to extirpate a number of plant species that are listed federally as being at risk and occur only in these naturally rare habitats. Garlic mustard (*Alliaria petiolata* (Bieb.) Cavara and Grande) is an invasive weed that threatens rare native plants in the Carolinian forest of southern Ontario. It is one of the few weeds that thrives in the full shade of an intact forest canopy (Nuzzo and McKnight 1993) and represents an exception to the generalization that invasive alien plants are confined to disturbed areas.

Alien Vertebrate Animals

When the topic of alien species is mentioned, many people think of animals that share our urban environments: rats (*Rattus norvegicus* Berkenhout), starlings (*Sturnus vulgaris* L.), house sparrows (*Passer domesticus* L.), and pigeons (*Columba livia* Gmelin). Alien birds have caused major reductions in populations of many Canadian forest birds by competing for cavity nesting sites and food resources. Cats (*Felis catus* L.) are a direct source of mortality for forest birds in suburban environments. Globally, alien vertebrate animal species have had the most devastating impacts on the biodiversity of geographically and evolutionarily isolated islands, and have been responsible for many species extinctions in these areas. Relatively little attention has been paid to transfers of alien species to isolated islands within Canada.

Following deglaciation, the island of Newfoundland had a much more limited mammal fauna than mainland Canada. A whole suite of nonnative mammals has been introduced over time (Table 5), with mixed results. There is concern that introductions of small mammals will increase fox populations and increase predation by this species on the endangered Newfoundland pine marten (*Martes americana* Turton). Also somewhat problematic is the explosion in populations of moose (*Alces alces* L.), first introduced in 1878, to more than 100 000 individuals. Although this increase is welcomed by hunters, balsam fir (*Abies balsamea* (L.) Mill.) is a preferred food of moose (Crete and Bedard 1975) as well as being Newfoundland's most important commercial tree species. Increased pressure from moose browsing generally impedes balsam fir regeneration in harvested areas, and adds a degree of unpredictability to the results of management treatments such as precommercial thinning.

Implications for Science and Information Management

This overview of alien species in Canadian forests points to a need for increased efforts in prevention and control of alien invasions. There are significant gaps in Canada's ability to address issues related to alien species. New alien species such as the brown spruce longhorn beetle often go undetected for lengthy periods of time, making control measures more difficult, expensive, and controversial. The capacity to monitor insects, diseases, and weeds has been greatly eroded, along with the taxonomic capacity to identify alien species. Federal support for research into biological control options for alien forest pests has been virtually eliminated.

Table 4. Invasive alien plant species in Canadian forests.

Species	Scientific name	Comments
Amur maple	*Acer ginnala*	Widely planted and spreading, southern Ontario
Norway maple	*Acer platanoides*	Local impact, urban ravines, natural areas, Ontario
Garlic mustard	*Alliaria petiolata*	Major problem, threatens endangered wood poppy and American ginseng, Ontario and Quebec
European white birch	*Betula pendula*	Local impact, Ontario
Siberian peashrub	*Carragana arborescens*	Invades woodlands near shelterbelts, Alberta
Diffuse knapweed	*Centaurea diffusa*	Interferes with conifer survival and growth in mid-elevation montane forests of interior British Columbia
Spotted knapweed	*Centaurea maculosa*	Similar to previous species
Bull thistle	*Cirsium vulgare*	Established in lodgepole pine clearcuts, Saskatchewan
Scotch broom	*Cytisus scoparius*	Major problem in threatened Garry oak habitats, British Columbia
Winged euonymus	*Euonymus alatus*	Widely planted, invades urban parks, Ontario
European euonymus	*Euonymus europaeus*	Similar to previous species
Ground ivy	*Glechoma hederacea*	Forms carpets in riparian woodlands and aspen groves, Saskatchewan
English ivy	*Hedera helix*	Kills mature trees in the wild, British Columbia
Dame's rocket	*Hesperis matronalis*	Threatens native plants similarly to *Alliaria petiolata* but only moderate impact, Ontario and Quebec
English holly	*Ilex aquifolium*	Invades closed forests in greater Vancouver, British Columbia
Privet	*Ligustrum* sp.	Invades woodlands near Hamilton, Ontario
Tartarian honeysuckle	*Lonicera tatarica*	Major problem in southern Ontario forest edges
White mulberry	*Morus alba*	In forest edges, threatens endangered native red mulberry by hybridization, Ontario
Scots pine	*Pinus sylvestris*	Moderate impact, Ontario
European white poplar	*Populus alba*	Local impact, Ontario, forms hybrids with native poplars
English oak	*Quercus robur*	Species of concern in Nova Scotia
Common buckthorn	*Rhamnus cathartica*	Major problem, highly invasive in forest edges, floodplains, in Ontario, Quebec, and Maritimes
Glossy buckthorn	*Rhamnus frangula*	Moderate impact, swamps and wet habitats, Ontario and Quebec; local impact in Maritimes
Black locust	*Robinia pseudoacacia*	Local impact, Ontario
Common lilac	*Syringa vulgaris*	Local impact in Ontario but does not spread much from point of introduction
Common gorse	*Ulex europaeus*	Occupies large patches in southern Vancouver Island, British Columbia, source of increasing concern
Highbush-cranberry	*Viburnum opulus*	(Or European cranberry), widely planted, spreading in southern Ontario

Erich Haber, National Botanical Services, Ottawa, personal communication.

Community involvement and public awareness are important elements in mitigating the impacts of alien plant species such as garlic mustard and Scotch broom. For these well-established species, control (including hand weeding) is the only option. Public awareness campaigns can also complement government efforts to detect and limit the spread of insect pests targeted for eradication.

Table 5. Some alien terrestrial vertebrate species in Newfoundland.

Species	Scientific name	Comments
Deer mouse	*Peromyscus maniculatus*	Accidentally introduced—possibly in imported hay from Maritimes—now widespread across the island. First-order effect: increased food supply for native predators fox and marten. Second-order effect: fox populations increase and prey on marten or arctic hare.
Masked shrew	*Sorex cinereus*	Introduced in 1958 from New Brunswick stock to combat the larch sawfly. Dispersed across island over the next decade. Used as prey by marten but impacts largely unknown.
Red squirrel	*Tamiasciurus hudsonicus*	Introduced in 1963–64. First-order effect: increased food supply for native predators fox and marten. Second-order effect: fox populations increase and prey on marten or arctic hare.
Eastern chipmunk	*Tamias striatus*	Introduced in 1962 by government to provincial parks for aesthetic reasons. First-order effect: increased food supply for native predators fox and marten. Second-order effect: fox populations increase and prey on marten or arctic hare.
Ruffed & spruce grouse	*Bonasa umbellus* and *Dendragapus canadensis*	Introduced by government in 1960s. First-order effect: increased food supply for native predators fox and marten. Second-order effect: fox populations increase and prey on marten or arctic hare.
Coyote	*Canis latrans*	Dispersed naturally to island in early 1980s from Cape Breton. First recorded in 1986 or 1987. Increased predation on native species. Marten and arctic hare—two rarest native species—of particular concern. Preys on caribou calves. Will displace and kill native red fox.
Snowshoe hare	*Lepus americanus*	Introduced starting in 1864 from Nova Scotia to supplement game populations. First-order effect: increased small-mammal diversity and prey choice for native predators (fox, marten). Second-order effect: fox populations increase and prey on marten or arctic hare.
Moose	*Alces alces*	Introduced in 1878 and again in 1904. Second introduction thought to be successful. Browsing has shifted forests from fir to black spruce. Calves are eaten by black bears during first weeks of life and influence bear population dynamics to an unknown extent.
Mink	*Mustela vison*	Introduced in early 1930s for fur ranching. Escaped/released from fur farms in 1938. Unknown influence on system.
Norway rat	*Rattus norvegicus*	Associated primarily with human settlement—garbage dumps, logging camps, etc. Used by native predators marten and fox.
House mouse	*Mus musculus*	Associated primarily with human settlement—garbage dumps, logging camps, etc. Used by native predators marten and fox.

Brian Hearn, NRCan, CFS, Atlantic Forestry Centre, Corner Brook, NF, personal communication.

There has never been a comprehensive information system for tracking alien species in Canada, nor even recognition of the benefits this could bring. Key information sources used in the present overview were developed in the United States. Although a high level of cooperation with our neighbor to the south is essential, Canada is not doing enough in the information management area. Given the importance of knowledge management to the Canadian economy, and the rapid technological development of systems for accessing and integrating biological information (often online), new programs and investments in biological information management will be essential.

Building capacity in taxonomy, monitoring, control, and information management is challenging. It will require multiagency approaches. For invasive alien species in forests, the Canadian Forest Service and the Canadian Food Inspection Agency must take the lead, but other agencies—including the Canadian Wildlife Service, Agriculture and Agri-Food Canada, Parks Canada, and the Canadian Museum of Nature—can play important supporting roles. Taxonomic expertise must be restored in critical areas such as tree diseases, and key reference collections must be refurbished. New investments in federal science capacity—both human resources and physical infrastructure—will be needed in a range of areas.

An internal assessment done by the Canadian Forest Service (Bowers et al. 2000) identified gaps that hinder efforts to limit the introduction and spread of invasive alien species in Canada's forests. Fungi represent one of the least-known components of global biodiversity, with less than 5% of species described. From a quarantine perspective, a high priority should be placed on developing taxonomic expertise in wood-staining ophiostomatoid fungi, as well as their insect vectors (wood-boring and bark beetles). Also important is building biosystematics capacity, including use of molecular tools, for other fungal groups (rusts, cankers, root and butt rots, etc.) that include serious pathogens that can be spread by human activities. Regarding alien insect pests, a broad strategy is needed to rebuild the capacity for rapid diagnosis of newly detected alien species, knowledge of potential biocontrol agents (for example, parasitic wasps), and management of collections and associated databases.

The pressure to take such steps is growing. The International Plant Protection Convention is examining an expansion of its traditional mandate of controlling economic pests to address broader environmental issues. The Convention on Biological Diversity is urging nations to take steps to prevent the introduction of alien species that harm the environment, and to mitigate their impacts. Risk assessment for deliberate introductions of both alien species and genetically modified organisms is a focus of both these international treaties. Global efforts are under way to address gaps in taxonomic capacity and biological information management.

References

Allen, E.H. 1998. Exotic insect interceptions from wooden dunnage and packing material. Natural Resources Canada, Canadian Forest Service, Pacific Forestry Centre, Victoria, BC. http://www.pfc.cfs.nrcan.gc.ca/biodiversity/exotics/dunnage_e.html.

Anagnostakis, S.L. 1995. The pathogens and pests of chestnuts. Pages 125–145 in J.H. Andrews and I. Tommerup, eds. Advances in botanical research, Vol. 21. Academic Press, New York.

Bowers, W.; Hendrickson, O.; Humble, L.; Ottens, H.; Moody, B.; Huber, J. 2000. Biosystematics–bioinformatics needs assessment. Unpublished report available from W. Bowers, Natural Resources Canada, Canadian Forest Service, Atlantic Forestry Centre, Corner Brook, NF.

Carrow, J.R. 1973. Establishment and survival of balsam woolly aphid on second growth amabilis fir at intermediate elevations. Department of the Environment, Ottawa, ON. Bi-monthly Research Notes 29(2):10–11.

[CFS] Canadian Forest Service, Natural Resources Canada. 1999. Alien forest pests: context for the Canadian Forest Service's science program. Science Branch, Canadian Forest Service, Natural Resources Canada, Ottawa, ON.

Clark, R.C.; Clarke, L.J.; Pardy, K.E. 1973. Biological control of the European spruce sawfly in Newfoundland. Department of the Environment, Ottawa, ON. Bi-monthly Research Notes 29(1):2–3.

Crete, M; Bedard, J. 1975. Daily browse consumption by moose in the Gaspé peninsula, Quebec. J. Wildl. Manag. 39:368–373.

Entwistle, P.F; Adams, P.H.W.; Evans, H.F. 1978. Epizootiology of a nuclear polyhedrosis virus in European spruce sawfly (Gilpinia hercyniae): the rate of passage of infective virus through the gut of birds during cage tests. J. Invertebr. Pathol. 31:307–312.

Gibbs, J.N.; Wainhouse, D. 1986. Spread of forest pests and pathogens in the northern hemisphere. Forestry 59:141–153.

Hoff, R.; Bingham, R.T.; McDonald, G.I. 1980. Relative blister rust resistance of white pines. Eur. J. For. Pathol. 10:307–316.

Houston, D.R. 1994. Major new disease epidemics: beech bark disease. Annu. Rev. Phytopathol. 32:75–87.

Houston, D.R.; O'Brien, J.T. 1998. Beech bark disease. USDA, Forest Service. Forest Insect & Disease Leaflet 75. Northeastern Forest Experiment Station, Hamden, CT. http://www.na.fs.fed.us/spfo/pubs/fidls/beechbark/fidl-beech.htm

Hubbes, M. 1999. The American elm and Dutch elm disease. For. Chron. 75:265–273.

Johnstone, K. 1991. Timber and trauma: 75 years with the federal forestry service, 1899–1974. Forestry Canada, Ottawa, ON.

Mattson, W.J. 1998. Exotic insects in North American forests: ecological systems forever altered. Pages 187–193 *in* K.O. Britton, ed. Exotic pests of eastern forests. Tennessee Exotic Pest Plant Council and USDA, Forest Service, Asheville, NC.

Mattson, W.J.; Niemelä, P.; Millers, I.; Inguanzo, Y. 1994. Immigrant phytophagous insects on woody plants in the United States and Canada: an annotated list. USDA, North Central Forest Experiment Station. Gen. Tech. Rep. NC–169.

McLean, M.A.; Parkinson, D. 1997. Soil impacts of the epigeic earthworm *Dendrobaena octaedra* on organic matter and microbial activity in lodgepole pine forest. Can. J. For. Res. 27:1907–1913.

McLean, M.A.; Parkinson, D. 2000. Field evidence of the effects of the epigeic earthworm *Dendrobaena octaedra* on the microfungal community in pine forest floor. Soil Biol. Biochem. 32:351–360.

Ministry of Natural Resources. 2000. Pine shoot beetle. Forest Health Alert–2. Queen's Printer for Ontario, Toronto, ON. http://www.mnr.gov.on.ca/MNR/forests/foresthealth/pineshoot/beetle.htm

Niemelä, P.; Mattson, W.J. 1996. Invasion of North American forests by European phytophagous insects: legacy of the European crucible? BioScience 46:741–753.

Nuzzo, V; McKnight, B.N. 1993. Distribution and spread of the invasive biennial *Alliaria petiolata* (garlic mustard) in North America. Pages 137–145 *in* Biological pollution: the control and impact of invasive exotic species. Indiana Academy of Science, Indianapolis, IN.

Opler, P.A. 1978. Insects of American chestnut: possible importance and conservation concern. Pages 83–85 *in* J. McDonald, ed. The American chestnut symposium. West Virginia University Press, Morgantown, WV.

Peterson, D.J.; Prasad, R. 1998. The biology of Canadian weeds, 109. *Cytisus scoparius* (L.) Link. Can. J. Plant Sci. 78:497–504.

Powell, G.W.; Wikeem, B.M.; Sturko, A; Boateng, J. 1997. Knapweed growth and effect on conifers in a montane forest. Can. J. For. Res. 27:1427–1433.

Sagoff, M. 2000. Why exotic species are not as bad as we fear. The Chronicle of Higher Education. 23 June 2000.

Scheu, S.; Parkinson, D. 1994. Effects of invasion of an aspen forest (Canada) by *Dendrobaena octaedra* (Lumbricidae) on plant growth. Ecology 75:2348–2361.

Schlarbaum, S.E.; Hebard, F.; Spaine, P.C.; Kamalay, J.C. 1997. Three American tragedies: chestnut blight, butternut canker, and Dutch elm disease. *In* K.O. Britton, ed. Exotic pests of eastern forests. Tennessee Exotic Pest Plant Council and USDA, Forest Service. Asheville, NC. http://www.srs.fs.fed.us/pubs/rpc/1999-03/rpc_99mar_33.htm

Schroder, D. 1974. A study of the interactions between the internal larval parasites of *Rhyacionia buoliana* (Lepidoptera:Olethreutidae). Entomophaga 19:145–171.

Introduction and Transfer of Alien Aquatic Species in the Great Lakes– St. Lawrence River Drainage Basin

Yves de Lafontaine and Georges Costan

The introduction and spread of alien species, whether deliberate or accidental, has become a global problem threatening the diversity and integrity of ecosystems in all parts of the world (Carlton and Geller 1993; Cohen and Carlton 1998; Sala et al. 2000). Species introductions in aquatic systems are mainly caused by human activities, which have practically eliminated the natural geographic barriers to dispersion and gene flow of species across otherwise isolated drainage basins (Drake et al. 1989; Mills et al. 1993; Mills et al. 1997). With regard to biodiversity, the introduction of species leads to homogenization of the biota (Rahel 2000), and introduced species occasionally become the dominant life-forms in an ecosystem (Cohen and Carlton 1998; Galatowitsch et al. 1999).

In North American waters, the introduction of alien species began with European settlements and the associated development of economic activities. The first species introductions occurred through deliberate releases of imported plants and through stocking of fish (Dextrase and Coscarelli 1999). Alien species have received much attention over the past 15 years after the unintentional introduction, spread, and subsequent economic and ecological impacts of both zebra mussel (*Dreissena polymorpha* (Pallas)) and quagga mussel (*D. bugensis*) (Nalepa and Schloesser 1993; Claudi and Mackie 1994). Ironically, in response to the increasing scientific and public awareness of the problem, the Great Lakes now represent one of the best, if not the best, documented aquatic systems with regard to alien species. For example, in their extensive review, Mills et al. (1993) listed 139 species introduced into the Great Lakes up to 1991.

The Great Lakes–St. Lawrence River system (Figure 1) is the largest and most economically important drainage basin in Canada (Government of Canada 1991). However, human activities such as agriculture, shoreline development, urbanization, and industrialization have

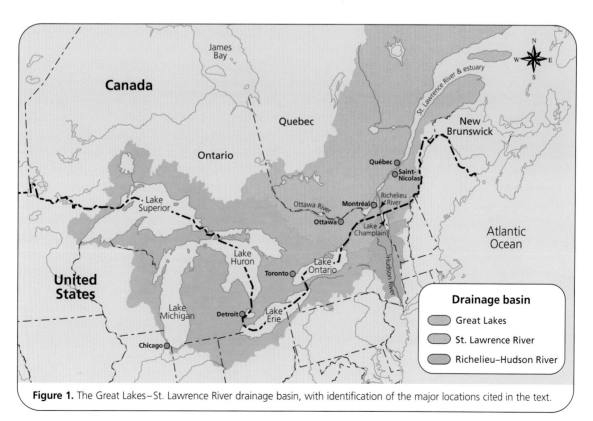

Figure 1. The Great Lakes–St. Lawrence River drainage basin, with identification of the major locations cited in the text.

had severe impacts on this ecosystem (Shear 1996). Since the explorations of Jacques Cartier, who sailed the St. Lawrence River up to Montréal in 1535, many thousands of foreign and local vessels have traveled into the St. Lawrence–Great Lakes corridor, contributing to the region's economic development. To facilitate the trade of goods across the continent, the Great Lakes were artificially connected to the Hudson River drainage basin by the Erie Canal in 1825 and to the Illinois–Mississipi River drainage basin by the Chicago Canal at the southern end of Lake Michigan in 1848 (Mills et al. 1999). These environmental changes led to the introduction, and subsequent transfer, of various alien species (Mills et al. 1993; Mills et al. 1999; Wiley and Claudi 1999).

Despite the natural link between the Great Lakes and the St. Lawrence River, very little is known about alien species in the St. Lawrence River. Because of its geographic position at the end of the drainage basin, the St. Lawrence River is the natural outflow of water from the Great Lakes and, as such, is continuously exposed to downstream transport of and colonization by organisms from upstream sources. The St. Lawrence River also represents the gateway for both local and foreign ships traveling into the Great Lakes. Between 1978 and 1996, the number of ships from foreign countries that went up the river as far as Montréal averaged 1050 per year, but only 250 vessels each year moved up into the Great Lakes to their first port of entry (Bourgeois et al. 2001). In terms of ballast capacity, the volume of water discharged into the St. Lawrence River is four times higher than that entering the Great Lakes. Montréal is by far the most important harbor in the system for foreign shipping, and each year it receives, on average, nearly three times more foreign vessels and ballast water than the entire Great Lakes system. Therefore, the St. Lawrence River is definitely subject to the introduction of alien species from outside the country, as well as to the transfer of organisms from upstream sources either by natural drift or assisted by ship transport. Equally, the St. Lawrence River may act as a potential source of alien species for the Great Lakes through upstream transfer by shipping or other assisted mechanisms. These scenarios are only hypotheses, as there has been no assessment of species transfer encompassing the whole drainage basin of the Great Lakes and the St. Lawrence River.

This chapter presents an overview of the current status of alien species in the Great Lakes–St. Lawrence River ecosystem, providing the first such assessment for the St. Lawrence River. It also evaluates the importance of downstream relative to upstream transfer of alien species between the Great Lakes and the St. Lawrence River. More precisely, this analysis has the following aims:

- to list the species introduced and established in the Great Lakes and in the St. Lawrence River in the past 200 years,
- to examine the relative proportion of introduced species now found in each region, and
- to assess and compare the historic and present rate of species introductions in each region and thereby determine the extent to which the St. Lawrence River represents a potential source of alien species for the Great Lakes and other tributary drainage basins.

For convenience, our inventory follows that of Mills et al. (1993) in including only freshwater aquatic species and excluding strictly terrestrial plants and large vertebrates such as reptiles, birds, and mammals.

Data Collection

Data were obtained through an extensive search of various documents and other resources, including scientific papers, books, technical reports, computerized databases, and Web sites. For the St. Lawrence River, museum and herbarium collections were also examined. Relevant information on the presence, distribution, and abundance of alien species was compiled in a database. Data included the scientific and common names of the species, the date and site of introduction into the Great Lakes–St. Lawrence River drainage basin, the date and location of first report of the species in the St. Lawrence River (if present), the geographic origin of the species, and the identified vector of introduction. When in doubt, we consulted scientific experts to validate the data. Following the definition adopted by Mills et al. (1997), the date of introduction corresponds to the date of the first recorded release, observation, or collection. In the few cases where the date of first publication was the only information available, the date of introduction was identified as before (<) the date of publication. The vectors of introduction were grouped and coded as in Mills et al. (1993). Deliberate introduction was defined as that occurring through agriculture or fish-stocking activities, and unintentional introduction was defined as that occurring through aquarium releases, aquaculture escapes, bait release, ship fouling, ship ballast, or canals.

Alien Species in the Great Lakes– St. Lawrence Basin

A total of 163 species have been introduced in the entire Great Lakes–St. Lawrence River drainage basin (Table 1, Figure 2). These species belong to various taxonomic groups (algae, vascular plants, invertebrates, and fish), but alien amphibians have not been reported (Benson 1999). Of that total, 160 have been reported from the Great Lakes. This number includes an additional 21 new species since Mills et al. (1993): 1 algal species, 1 vascular plant, 13 invertebrate species, and 6 fish species. Of this group, the vascular plant, eight invertebrate species, and two fish species were reported after 1990 and are considered recent introductions. One mollusk species (*Pisidium moitessierianum* Paladilhe),

Table 1. Alien species introduced into the Great Lakes and the St. Lawrence River.[a]

Taxon / Species	Origin	Vector[b]	Great Lakes Date[c]	Great Lakes Site[d]	St. Lawrence River Date[c]
Algae					
Class Bacillariophyceae					
Actinocyclus normanii f. *subsalsa* (Juhl.-Dannf.) Hust.	Northern Europe	S(BW)	1938	LO	
Biddulphia laevis Ehr.	Africa	S(BW)	1978	LM	
Chaetoceros hohnii Graebn. & Wujek	Unknown	S(BW)	1978	LH	
Cyclotella atomus Hust.	Widespread	S(BW)	1964	LM	
Cyclotella cryptica Reimann, Lewin & Guillard	Widespread	S(BW)	1964	LM	
Cyclotella pseudostelligera Hust.	Widespread	S(BW)	1946	LM	<1998
Cyclotella wolterecki Hust.	Widespread	S(BW)	1964	LM	
Diatoma ehrenbergii Kütz.	Widespread	S(BW)	1937	LM	Unknown
Skeletonema potamos (Weber) Hasle	Widespread	S(BW)	1963	LE	1996
Skeletonema subsalsum (A. Cleve) Bethge	Baltic Sea	S(BW)	1973	LE	1995
Stephanodiscus binderanus (Kütz) Kreig.	Eurasia	S(BW)	1938	LM	1955
Stephanodiscus subtilis (Van Goor) A. Cleve	Eurasia	S(BW)	1946	LM	
Terpsinoe musica Ehrenb.*	Unknown	Unknown	1978	LM	
Thalassiosira guillardii Hasle	Widespread	S(BW)	1973	LE	Unknown
Thalassiosira lacustris (Grunow) Hasle	Widespread	S(BW)	<1978	LE	
Thalassiosira pseudonana Hasle & Heim	Widespread	S(BW)	1973	LE	1994
Thalassiosira weissflogii (Grunow) Fryxell & Hasle	Widespread	S(BW)	1962	LE	Unknown
Family Bangiaceae					
Bangia atropurpurea (Roth) C. Agardh	Coast of North Atlantic Ocean	S(BW), S(F)	1964	LE	IND
Family Characeae					
Nitellopsis obtusa	Eurasia	S(BW)	1983	LSC	1978

(Continued)

Symbols: *Species not listed in Mills et al. (1993).   [†]Introduced into the Richelieu River.

[a] For each of the two regions, the date is the reported date of introduction. For the Great Lakes, the site is the lake of the first report.

[b] R(D) = release, deliberate; R(AQ) = release from aquarium; R(C) = release resulting from cultivation; R(F) = release of organisms with bait or other fish; R(A) = release, accidental; RH = railways and highways; S(BW) = shipping, with ballast water; S(SB) = shipping, with solid ballast; S(F) = shipping, with fouling; C = canals.

[c] Date of first publication was the only information available, so date of introduction is identified as before (<) the date of publication.

[d] LO = Lake Ontario, LE = Lake Erie, LSC = Lake St. Clair, LH = Lake Huron, LM = Lake Michigan, LS = Lake Superior, WID = widespread, IND = indigenous.

[e] This family is also commonly known as Moronidae.

Table 1 *(Continued)*

Taxon / Species	Origin	Vector[b]	Great Lakes Date[c]	Great Lakes Site[d]	St. Lawrence River Date[c]
Family Haptophyceae					
Hymenomonas roseola	Eurasia	S(BW)	1975	LH	
Family Porphyridiaceae					
Chroodactylon ramosus	Atlantic Ocean	S(BW)	1964	LE	<1982
Family Sphacelariaceae					
Sphacelaria fluviatilis	Asia	S(BW)	1975	LM	
Sphacelaria lacustris	Unknown	S(BW)	1975	LM	
Family Ulvaceae					
Enteromorpha intestinalis (L.) Nees	Atlantic Ocean	R(A)	1926	LO	1995
Enteromorpha prolifera (O.F. Müller) J. Agardh	Atlantic Ocean	Unknown	1979	LSC	1999
Plants					
Family Apiaceae					
Conium maculatum L.	Eurasia	R(C)	<1843		1832
Family Araceae					
Pistia stratiotes L.*	Southeast United States	R(C)	2000	LE	
Family Asteraceae					
Cirsium palustre (L.) Scop.	Eurasia	Unknown	<1950	LS	1821
Pluchea odorata (L.) Cass. var. *purpurescens*	Atlantic Ocean	R(A)	1916	LE	
Pluchea odorata (L.) Cass. var. *succulenta* (Fern.) Cronq.	Atlantic Ocean	Unknown	<1950	LO	
Solidago sempervirens L.	Atlantic Ocean	R(A)	1969	LM	IND
Sonchus arvensis L.	Eurasia	R(A)	1865	LO	1862
Sonchus arvensis L. var. *glaberescens*	Eurasia	R(A)	1902	LE	
Family Balsaminaceae					
Impatiens glandulifera Royle	Asia	R(C)	1912	LH	1943
Family Betulaceae					
Alnus glutinosa (L.) Gaertn.	Eurasia	R(C)	<1913		
Family Boraginaceae					
Myosotis scorpioides L.	Eurasia	R(C)	1886	LO	1903
Family Brassicaceae					
Rorippa nasturtium-aquaticum (L.) Hayek	Eurasia	R(C)	1847	LO	1970
Rorippa sylvestris (L.) Bess.	Eurasia	S(SB), R(C)	1884	LO	1934
Family Butomaceae					
Butomus umbellatus L.	Eurasia	S(SB)	1930	LM	1905
Family Cabombaceae					
Cabomba caroliniana Gray	Southern United States	R(AQ), R(A)	1935	LM	
Family Caryophyllaceae					
Stellaria aquatica (L.) Moench	Eurasia	Unknown	1894	LSC	1965
Family Chenopodiaceae					
Chenopodium glaucum L.	Eurasia	RH	1867	LO	1904
Family Cyperaceae					
Carex acutiformis Ehrh.	Eurasia	Unknown	1951	LM	
Carex disticha Hudson	Eurasia	S(SB)	1866	LO	1927
Carex flacca Schreb.	Eurasia	Unknown	1896	LE	1975

(Continued)

Table 1 (Continued)

| Taxon / Species | Origin | Vector[b] | Great Lakes | | St. Lawrence River |
			Date[c]	Site[d]	Date[c]
Family Haloragaceae					
Myriophyllum spicatum L.	Eurasia	R(AQ), S(F)	1949	LE	1945
Family Hydrocharitaceae					
Hydrocharis morsus-ranae L.	Rideau Canal	R(AQ), R(D)	1972	LO	1932
Family Iridaceae					
Iris pseudacorus L.	Eurasia	R(C)	1886	LO	1943
Family Juncaceae					
Juncus compressus Jacq.	Eurasia	R(A)	1895	LE	1904
Juncus gerardii Loisel.	Atlantic Ocean	S(SB)	1862	LM	IND
Juncus inflexus L.	Eurasia	Unknown	1922	LO	
Family Lamiaceae					
Lycopus asper Greene	Mississippi River basin	R(A)	1892	LE	1942
Lycopus europaeus L.	Eurasia	S(SB)	1903	LO	1964
Mentha gentilis L. = *Mentha arvensis* L.	Eurasia	R(C)	1915	LO	1890
Mentha ×*piperita*	Eurasia	R(C)	1933	LH	1935
Mentha spicata L.	Eurasia	R(C)	<1843	WID	1821
Family Lythraceae					
Lythrum salicaria L.	Eurasia	S(SB), C	1869	LO	1865
Family Marsileaceae					
Marsilea quadrifolia L.	Eurasia	R(C)	1925	LE	
Family Menyanthaceae					
Nymphoides peltata (Gmel.) Kuntze	Eurasia	R(A)	1930	LE	1950
Family Najadaceae					
Najas marina L.	Eurasia	S(BW)	1864	LO	1901
Najas minor All.	Eurasia	R(D)	1934	LE	
Family Onagraceae					
Epilobium hirsutum L.	Eurasia	R(A), S(SB)	1874	LO	1940
Epilobium parviflorum Schreb.	Eurasia	Unknown	1966	LM	
Family Poaceae					
Agrostis gigantea Roth	Eurasia	R(C)	1884	LS	1981
Alopecurus geniculatus L.	Eurasia	R(C)	1882	LE	1899
Echinochloa crus-galli (L.) Beauv.	Eurasia	R(C), S(SB)	<1843	WID	1862
Glyceria maxima (Hartman) Holmb.	Eurasia	R(C), S(SB)	1940	LO	
Poa trivialis L.	Eurasia	R(C), S(SB)	<1843	WID	1899
Puccinellia distans (Jacq.) Parl.	Eurasia	S(SB), RH	1893	LO	1984
Family Polygonaceae					
Polygonum caespitosum Blume var. *longisetum* (de Bruyn) A.N. Steward	Asia	Unknown	1960	LE	
Polygonum persicaria L.	Unknown	Unknown	<1843	WID	1945
Rumex longifolius DC.	Eurasia	R(C)	1901	LS	1960
Rumex obtusifolius L.	Eurasia	Unknown	<1840	WID	1821
Family Potamogetonaceae					
Potamogeton crispus L.	Eurasia	R(D), S(F)	1879	LO	1932
Family Primulaceae					
Lysimachia nummularia L.	Eurasia	R(C)	1882	LO	1895
Lysimachia vulgaris L.	Eurasia	R(C)	1913	LO	

(Continued)

Table 1 (Continued)

Taxon / Species	Origin	Vector[b]	Great Lakes Date[c]	Great Lakes Site[d]	St. Lawrence River Date[c]
Family Rhamnaceae					
Rhamnus frangula L. = *Frangula alnus* P. Mill.	Eurasia	R(C)	<1913	LO	1970
Family Salicaceae					
Salix alba L.	Eurasia	R(C)	<1886	WID	1945
Salix fragilis L.	Eurasia	R(C)	<1886	WID	1945
Salix purpurea L.	Eurasia	R(C)	<1886	WID	1943
Family Scrophulariaceae					
Veronica beccabunga L.	Eurasia	S(SB), R(C)	1915	LO	1905
Family Solonaceae					
Solanum dulcamara L.	Eurasia	R(C)	<1843	WID	1891
Family Sparganiaceae					
Sparganium glomeratum (Laestad.) L. Neum	Eurasia	Unknown	1941	LS	1931
Family Trapaceae					
Trapa natans L.[†]	Eurasia	R(A), R(AQ)	<1959	LO	1998
Family Typhaceae					
Typha angustifolia L.	Eurasia	C, R(A)	1880s	LO	<1935
Invertebrates					
Family Argulidae					
Argulus japonicus Thiele	Asia	R(F), R(AQ)	<1988	LM	
Family Bithyniidae					
Bithynia tentaculata (L.)	Eurasia	S(SB), R(D)	1871	LM	1914
Family Bosminidae					
Eubosmina coregoni	Eurasia	S(BW)	1966	LM	1994
Family Brachyura					
Eriocheir sinensis Milne-Edwards*	Asia	S(BW)	1965	LO	
Family Cambaridae					
Orconectes limosus (Rafinesque)	North America	Unknown			<1970
Orconectes rusticus (Girard)*	Mississippi River basin	Unknown	1960	LS	
Family Cercopagidae					
Bythotrephes cederstroemi (Schoedler)	Eurasia	S(BW)	1984	LH	
Cercopagis pengoi (Ostroumov)*	Eurasia	S(BW)	1998	LO	
Family Clavidae					
Cordylophora caspia (Pallas)	Eurasia	R(A)	1956	LE	
Family Corbiculidae					
Corbicula fluminea (Müller)	Asia	R(A), R(AQ)	1980	LE	
Family Corophiidae					
Corophium mucronatum Sars*	Ponto-Caspian	Unknown	1997	LSC	
Family Curcolionidae					
Tanysphyrus lemnae Fabricius	Eurasia	Unknown	<1943	?	
Family Daphnidae					
Daphnia lumholtzi Sars*	Australia	Unknown	1999	LE	
Family Diaptomidae					
Skistodiaptomus pallidus (Herrick)	Mississippi River basin	R(A), R(F)	1967	LO	

(Continued)

Table 1 *(Continued)*

| Taxon / Species | Origin | Vector[b] | Great Lakes | | St. Lawrence River |
			Date[c]	Site[d]	Date[c]
Family Dreissenidae					
Dreissena bugensis	Eurasia	S(BW)	1989	LO	1992
Dreissena polymorpha (Pallas)	Eurasia	S(BW)	1986	LSC	1989
Family Gammaridae					
*Echinogammarus ischnus**	Eurasia	S(BW)	1995	LE	1997
Gammarus fasciatus	Atlantic Ocean	S(SB), S(BW)	<1940	?	IND
Family Hydrobiidae					
Gillia altilis (Lea)	Atlantic Ocean	C	1918	LO	
Potamopyrgus antipodarum (Gray)*	New Zealand	Unknown	1991	LO	
Family Lophopodidae					
Lophopodella carteri (Hyatt)*	Asia	S(F)	1934	LE	1989
Family Lymnaeidae					
Radix auricularia (L.)	Eurasia	R(AQ), R(A)	1901	LM	1996?
Family Naididae					
Ripistes parasita	Eurasia	S(BW)	1980	LH	1983
Family Petasidae					
Craspedacusta sowerbyi Lankester	Asia	R(A)	1933	LE	
Family Planariidae					
Dugesia polychroa (Schmidt)	Eurasia	S(BW)	1968	LO	1968
Phylum Platyhelmintha					
Ichthyocotylurus pileatus (Rudolphi)*	Europe	R(F)	1994	LSC	
Family Pleuroceridae					
Elimia virginica (Say)	Atlantic Ocean	C	1860	LE	
Phylum Protozoa					
Glugea hertwigi	Eurasia	R(F)	1960	LE	1980
Myxobolus cerebralis (Hofer)	Europe	R(F)	1968	LE	
Sphaeromyxa sevastopoli Naidenova*	Black Sea	R(F)	1994	LSC	
Family Pseudomonadaceae					
Aeromonas salmonicida (Lehmann & Neumann)	Unknown	R(F)	<1902	WID	Unknown
Family Pyralidae					
Acentropus niveus (Oliver)	Eurasia	R(A)	1950	LE, LO	
Family Sphaeriidae					
Pisidium amnicum (Müller)	Eurasia	S(SB)	1897	LO	1978
Pisidium henslowanum (Sheppard)*	Europe	Unknown	1905	WID	<1980
Pisidium moitessierianum Paladilhe*	Europe	S(SB)	<1894	LE	
Pisidium supinum Schmidt*	Europe	Unknown	1959	LO	
Sphaerium corneum (L.)	Eurasia	Unknown	1924	LO	1977
Family Temoridae					
Eurytemora affinis (Poppe)	Widespread	S(BW)	1958	LO	1992
Family Tubificidae					
Branchiura sowerbyi Beddard	Asia	R(A)	1951	LM	
Phallodrilus aquaedulcis Hrabe	Eurasia	S(BW)	1983	LO	
Family Unionidae					
Lasmigona subviridis (Conrad)	Atlantic Ocean	C	<1959	LE	

(Continued)

Table 1 (Continued)

| Taxon / Species | Origin | Vector[b] | Great Lakes | | St. Lawrence River |
			Date[c]	Site[d]	Date[c]
Family Valvatidae					
Valvata piscinalis (Müller)	Eurasia	S(SB)	1897	LO	1991
Family Viviparidae					
Cipangopaludina chinensis malleata (Reeve)	Asia	R(AQ)	1931	LO	<1980
Cipangopaludina japonica (Martens)	Asia	R(D)	1940s	LE	
Viviparus georgianus (Lea)	Mississippi River basin	R(AQ)	<1906	LM	<1977
Fishes					
Family Centrarchidae					
Enneacanthus gloriosus (Holbrook)	Eastern coast of United States	R(AQ), R(F)	1971	LO	
Lepomis humilis (Girard)	Mississippi River basin	R(A), R(AQ)	1929	LE	
Lepomis microlophus (Günther)	Mississippi River basin	R(D), R(AC)	1928	LM	
Family Clupeidae					
Alosa pseudoharengus (Wilson)	Coast of North Atlantic Ocean	C	1873	LO	IND
Alosa aestivalis ((Mitchill)*	Coast of North Atlantic Ocean	C	1995	LO	
Dorosoma cepedianum (Lesueur)*	Mississippi River basin	C	1848	LE	1944
Family Cobitidae					
Misgurnus anguillicaudatus (Cantor)	Easthern Asia	R(A)	1939	LH	
Family Cyprinidae					
Carassius auratus (L.)	Asia	R(D), R(AQ)	<1878	WID	Unknown
Ctenopharyngodon idella (Valenciennes)*	Asia	R(D)	1986	LE	
Cyprinus carpio L.	Eurasia	R(C), R(D)	1879	LE	1908
Hypophthalmichthys nobilis (Richardson)*	Asia	R(C)	1995	LE	
Notropis buchanani Meck	Mississippi River basin	R(F)	1979	LSC	
Phenacobius mirabilis (Girard)	Mississippi River basin	R(F)	1950	LE	
Scardinius erythrophthalmus (L.)	Caspian and Aral seas	R(F)	1950s	LE	1990
Tinca tinca (L.)[†]	Europe	R(A)			1991
Family Gasterosteidae					
Apeltes quadracus (Mitchill)	Coast of North Atlantic Ocean	S(BW)	1986	LS	IND
Gasterosteus aculeatus L.*	Coast of North Atlantic Ocean	C	1980	LH	IND
Family Gobiidae					
Neogobius melanostomus (Pallas)	Eurasia	S(BW)	1990	LSC	1997
Proterorhinus marmoratus (Pallas)	Eurasia	S(BW)	1990	LSC	
Family Ictaluridae					
Noturus insignis (Richardson)	Coast of North Atlantic Ocean	C, R(F)	1928	LO	1971
Family Osmeridae					
Osmerus mordax (Mitchill)	Coast of North Atlantic Ocean	C, R(F)	1912	LM	IND
Family Perchichthyidae[e]					
Morone americana (Gmelin)	Coast of North Atlantic Ocean	C	1950	LO	IND

(Continued)

Table 1 *(Concluded)*

Taxon / Species	Origin	Vector[b]	Great Lakes Date[c]	Great Lakes Site[d]	St. Lawrence River Date[c]
Family Percidae					
Gymnocephalus cernuus (L.)	Eurasia	S(BW)	1986	LS	
Family Petromyzontidae					
Petromyzon marinus L.	Coast of North Atlantic Ocean	C, S(F)	1835	LO	IND
Family Pleuronectidae					
Platichthys flesus (L.)*	Europe	Unknown	1974	LE	
Family Poeciliidae					
Gambusia affinis (Baird & Girard)	Mississippi River basin	R(D)	1923	LM	
Family Salmonidae					
Oncorhynchus gorbuscha (Walbaum)	Coast of North Pacific Ocean	R(A), R(F)	1956	LS	
Oncorhynchus kisutch (Walbaum)	Coast of North Pacific Ocean	R(D)	1933	LE	1972
Oncorhynchus mykiss (Walbaum)	Coast of North Pacific Ocean	R(D)	1876	LH	1950
Oncorhynchus nerka (Walbaum)	Coast of North Pacific Ocean	R(D)	1950	LO	
Oncorhynchus tshawytscha (Walbaum)	Coast of North Pacific Ocean	R(D)	1967	LM, LS	1983
Oncorhynchus clarki (Richardson)*	Coast of North Pacific Ocean	R(A)			1941
Salmo trutta L.	Eurasia	R(D)	1883	LO, LM	1890

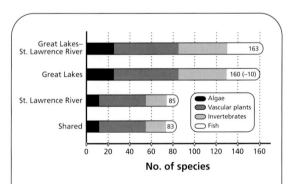

Figure 2. Number of alien species reported in the Great Lakes–St. Lawrence River drainage basin. Ten species introduced into the Great Lakes are endemic to the St. Lawrence River.

which was reported only recently, in 1997, was apparently introduced during the 19th century and might have been misidentified or confused with another species since then (Grigorovich et al. 2000). The remaining nine species were reported before 1990 and were probably missed by Mills et al. (1993).

Of the 160 species introduced into the Great Lakes, 10 are native to the St. Lawrence River and other rivers of the northeastern North American coast (Table 1). This group consists of one algal species, two vascular plants, one invertebrate species, and six fish species. Rainbow smelt (*Osmerus mordax* (Mitchill)) was deliberately introduced into the Lake Michigan system in 1912, but the introductions of the other species into the Great Lakes were due to shipping activities. Solid and liquid ballast releases are believed to have been responsible for the transfer of the single algal species (*Bangia atropurpurea* (Roth) C. Agardh), one of the vascular plants (*Juncus gerardii* Loisel.), the invertebrate (*Gammarus fasciatus*), and one fish species (*Apeltes quadratus* (Mitchill)). Ship canals are indicated as the source of entry for four fish species. The threespine stickleback (*Gasterosteus aculeatus* L.) reached Lake Huron in 1980 via the Nipissing Canal (Fuller et al. 1999), whereas alewife (*Alosa pseudoharengus* (Wilson)), white perch (*Morone americana* (Gmelin)), and sea lamprey (*Petromyzon marinus* L.) presumably invaded the Great Lakes via the Erie Canal

(Mills et al. 1993). However, upstream migration of these species from the St. Lawrence River cannot be ruled out (Scott and Crossman 1973).

Given that these 10 species are native along the North American Atlantic coast, it is difficult to ascertain precisely whether they originated from the St. Lawrence River or from other sources. Studies on the population genetic structure of these species would provide further clues. In theory, native species would consist of several genetically distinct local populations, whereas introduced species would be characterized by less genetic variability. As a consequence, the analysis of genetic distance among populations of species introduced into the Great Lakes and those from sites within their native ranges in North America would identify the populations of origin and the routes of entry. For example, Hogg et al. (1999) recently compared the population structure of two species of amphipods within the Great Lakes–St. Lawrence River drainage basin. Their results showed much higher levels of genetic differentiation for the native amphipod *Hyalella azteca* (Saussure) than for the introduced species *Gammarus fasciatus* (from Lake Superior to Québec).

Eighty-seven alien species have been introduced into the St. Lawrence River and its tributaries. Eighty-five species have been observed in the St. Lawrence itself (Figure 2), and two species recently invaded the Richelieu River, a major tributary of the St. Lawrence. Overall, only three alien species currently found in the St. Lawrence River drainage basin have not yet been reported in the Great Lakes. These are the spinycheek crayfish (*Orconectes limosus* (Rafinesque)), the cutthroat trout (*Oncorhynchus clarki* (Richardson)), and the very recently introduced tench (*Tinca tinca* (L.)). The spiny-cheek crayfish was presumably introduced into the river in the late 1960s from southern New York via the Lake Champlain–Richelieu River waterways. It is uncertain whether these relatively new records are the result of natural expansion or unintentional introductions (Hamr 1998). This intruder is abundant in the downstream sector of the St. Lawrence River where it has displaced and almost eliminated the native crayfish *Orconectes virilis* (Hagen) (Jean Dubé, Société de la Faune et des Parcs du Québec, personal communication, November 2000). Sampling surveys conducted during summer 2000 confirmed that *O. limosus* is the dominant crayfish downstream of Montréal but is very rare upstream, where *O. virilis* is still common (de Lafontaine, unpublished data). The presence of cutthroat trout in the St. Lawrence River is the result of fish stocking that took place in some tributaries along the north shore of the river in the 1940s.

The introduction of tench into the upper Richelieu River was confirmed in October 1999 from specimens captured in commercial fisheries (Dumont et al., this publication, p. 169). The species had escaped from fish farming ponds in 1991, following its unauthorized import from Germany in 1986. Although introduced and established in many states of the United States (Fuller et al. 1999), this is only the second record of tench in Canadian waters, the first being from British Columbia lakes (Dumont et al., this publication, p. 169). Given the highly invasive character of this species, it is expected that tench will eventually move downstream into the St. Lawrence River. Similarly, the invasive water chestnut (*Trapa natans* L.) was reported in the upper Richelieu River for the first time in 1998 (Gratton 1998). The source of introduction is unknown but was probably an accidental transfer by pleasure boats and trailers, a release from cultivation, or an input from southern Lake Champlain and New York populations (Ann Bove, Vermont Department of Environmental Conservation, Waterbury, VT, personal communication, November 2000). Unless it is rapidly eradicated, the species will spread farther downstream along the Richelieu River and eventually invade the shoreline habitats and wetlands of the St. Lawrence River. Although water chestnut has been observed at some locations around the Great Lakes (Mills et al. 1993), it is still absent from the St. Lawrence River.

A total of 83 alien species occur in both the Great Lakes and the St. Lawrence River (Figure 2). About 55% (83 of 150) of the species introduced into the Great Lakes and not originally present in the St. Lawrence River have now been reported from the river. Although the number of introduced species in the Great Lakes is twice that for the St. Lawrence River, the relative proportion of the various taxonomic groups differs between the two systems. There are between 2.0 and 2.3 times more algal, invertebrate, and fish species, but only 1.3 times more vascular plant species in the Great Lakes. Alien vascular plant species are more numerous in the St. Lawrence River (51%) than in the Great Lakes (38%).

The alien species common to the Great Lakes and St. Lawrence River are not from the same geographic origins as those found only in the St. Lawrence River (Table 2). Species from Eurasia dominate in the river (66%), whereas they account for only half (47%) of the species in the entire basin. Conversely, the

Table 2. Origin of alien species introduced into the Great Lakes drainage basin and the St. Lawrence River.

Origin	Great Lakes and St. Lawrence River		St. Lawrence River	
	n	(%)	n	(%)
Eurasia	76	(47)	56	(66)
Europe	11	(7)	4	(5)
Asia	15	(9)	4	(5)
North America				
West coast	5	(3)	4	(5)
East coast	23[a]	(14)	5	(6)
Mississippi basin	11	(7)	3	(4)
Other point of origin or unknown	20	(12)	9	(11)

[a] Includes the nine species that are endemic to the St. Lawrence River.

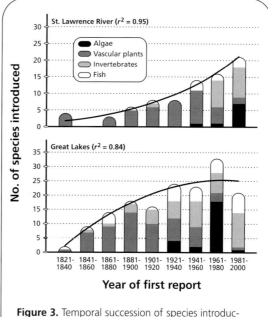

Figure 3. Temporal succession of species introductions in the St. Lawrence River (*top*) and the Great Lakes (*bottom*).

number of species from the Atlantic coast, the Mississippi River basin, and Asia are proportionally higher in the Great Lakes than in the river.

Rate of Species Introduction and Transfer

The numbers of alien species introductions over time follow different patterns in the Great Lakes and the St. Lawrence River (Figure 3). In the Great Lakes, the numbers of species introduced in 20-year periods gradually increased after 1820, levelling off at about 20 to 25 species every two decades since 1921 (Mills et al. 1993). This translates to an average rate of introduction of about one species per year. Plant introductions dominated in the early years, with some invertebrate and fish introductions reported in the late 1800s. Introductions peaked during the period from 1961 to 1980 because of the numerous reports of new algae. During the past 20 years, 21 new species, mostly invertebrates (12) and fish (7), have been introduced.

In contrast, since 1820, species introductions in the St. Lawrence River have increased almost exponentially (Figure 3). Introductions peaked during the last 20-year period (1980–2000), with a total of 21 new species recorded, the same number as observed in the Great Lakes for the same period. Until 1960, introduced species were mainly vascular plants, but since then reported species have been mostly invertebrates.

Comparison of the dates of introduction for the species common to the two regions reveals that 65 (83%) of the 78 species with known dates of introduction were reported in the Great Lakes before being found in the St. Lawrence River. This pattern suggests downstream transfer via either natural or anthropogenic dispersal. For each species, the time required for transfer was estimated by calculating the difference (in years) between the date of the first report from the Great Lakes and that from the St. Lawrence River (see Table 1). Values vary greatly within and between taxonomic groups (Table 3). On average, downstream transfer has been most rapid for algae (mean 31.5 years, median 21 years) and slowest for vascular plants (mean 52.0 years, median 56 years). Transfer of fish and invertebrates has usually been slow, averaging 40 years. These average estimates are based solely on species common to the two regions and do not account for the temporal variation in the proportion of species in each group that have reached the St. Lawrence River. The proportion of species first observed in the Great Lakes and later reported in the St. Lawrence River has decreased with time (Figure 4). Nearly all species that were introduced more than 100 years ago have been transferred and reported in the river. Only up to 35% of the species introduced during the past 40 years had been reported in the river by 2000. The pattern is relatively independent of taxonomic group.

Table 3. Estimated times for alien species to transfer between the Great Lakes and the St. Lawrence River.

Taxonomic group	No. of species	Transfer time (years)[a]			
		Mean ± SD	Median	Minimum	Maximum
Algae	8	31.5 ± 19.1	21	17	69
Vascular plants	31	52.0 ± 28.4	56	2	123
Invertebrates	17	41.7 ± 33.5	43	1	95
Fishes	10	38.4 ± 30.0	35	7	96
Vascular plants: upstream transfer	12	−25.2 ± 34.5	−15	−3	−129

[a] Difference in date of first report (reports from Great Lakes precede those from the St. Lawrence River, except as noted otherwise).

Note: SD = standard deviation.

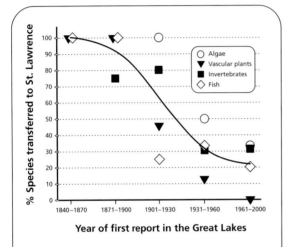

Figure 4. Proportion of species transferred from the Great Lakes into the St. Lawrence River as a function of year of first report in the Great Lakes.

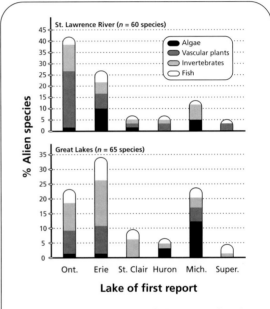

Figure 5. Relative proportion of alien species found in the St. Lawrence River (top) and in the Great Lakes only (bottom) as a function of the lake of first introduction. Ont. = Ontario; Mich. = Michigan; Super. = Superior.

Conversely, 13 (17%) of the species with known dates of introduction were first discovered in the St. Lawrence River before being observed in the Great Lakes. This suggests some upstream transfer of species between the river and the lakes. Twelve vascular plants were introduced in the late 1800s and early 1900s, and one alga (*Nitellopsis obtusa*) was first discovered in the river in 1978. The calculated upstream transfer time for vascular plants was 25 years (median 15 years). Adding the two species (spinycheek crayfish and cutthroat trout) present only in the St. Lawrence River yields a total of 15 alien species (out of 152 [10%]) first reported in the St. Lawrence River. For these species, the river might have been the first site of introduction in the Great Lakes–St. Lawrence River drainage basin or even in North America.

The majority of alien species introduced into the Great Lakes were first reported in Lake Ontario (*n* = 46), Lake Erie (*n* = 38), or Lake Michigan (*n* = 23). This is not surprising, given that these three lakes have been, and still are, subject to many more human activities and much more anthropogenic stress than the others. Important harbor facilities accommodating maritime traffic and large cargo ships are located on these lakes. The list of alien species in the St. Lawrence River is dominated by species first introduced into Lake Ontario (42%) followed by those first introduced into Lake Erie (27%) (Figure 5). This differs from the pattern observed for species found only in the Great Lakes, which is characterized by a relatively high proportion of species first introduced into Lake Erie and Lake Michigan. Species introduced into Lake Michigan are largely underrepresented in the St. Lawrence River.

Spatial Distribution of Alien Species in the St. Lawrence River

A complete description of the spatial distribution and relative abundance of alien species in the St. Lawrence River is beyond the scope of this chapter. Evidence of the spatial distribution of alien species along the St. Lawrence River was determined by compiling information on the presence and reports of each species (irrespective of abundance) in 13 arbitrarily defined sectors between Cornwall, Ontario, and the saltwater edge near Montmagny, Quebec, downstream of Québec. Half of the species (42 of 83 [51%]) have been observed in fewer than a quarter of the sectors, and only one-third (26 of 83 [31%]) have been reported in more than half of the sectors. The most widely distributed species are the diatom *Stephanodiscus binderanus* (Kütz) Kreig., 14 vascular plants (including purple loosestrife, *Lythrum salicaria* L., and flowering rush, *Butomus umbellatus* L.), three invertebrates (the faucet snail, *Bithynia tentaculata* (L.); the zebra mussel; and the quagga mussel), and five fish species (including common carp, *Cyprinus carpio* L.; rainbow trout, *Oncorhynchus mykiss* (Walbaum); and brown trout, *Salmo trutta* L.). Given the dynamic flow regime and the relatively short length of the river (about 300 km), the level of spatial heterogeneity for the alien species along the river is surprising. Two factors may contribute to this apparent patchiness. First, the high diversity of habitats along the river may help to maintain some level of spatial heterogeneity in the distribution of various species for which life-history characteristics and habitat requirements differ. Second, many introduced species may occur at very low densities in the river and are therefore not frequently encountered or sampled. Data for most species are too scant at present to adequately evaluate these possibilities.

Studies to quantify the ecological effect of alien species have generally dealt with specific cases of invasion (mostly for the Great Lakes), but the global impact of alien species on the Great Lakes–St. Lawrence River ecosystem has been relatively more difficult to assess (Claudi and Leach 1999). With the exception of a study of the impact of zebra mussels on native unionid mussels (Ricciardi et al. 1996), little has been done to assess the relative impact of alien species in the St. Lawrence River. River and lake ecosystems are very different in their structure and function, so it would not be legitimate to extrapolate and apply the results of lake studies to the St. Lawrence River. The ratio of alien to native species can provide a basic index of the potential impact of introduced species on the biodiversity of a system (Gido and Brown 1999; Whittier and Kincaid 1999; Prieur-Richard and Lavorel 2000; Rahel 2000). Such an index, based on species richness, has been particularly useful for documenting the effect of alien species in terrestrial plant communities, but not aquatic systems. The index requires an intensive and detailed inventory of both alien and native species, which may represent an enormous and often tedious task for some aquatic communities (for example, benthic or planktonic communities).

According to the most recent and very extensive account of the St. Lawrence River phytoplankton by Paquet et al. (1998), who reported 364 taxa, the number of introduced algae ($n = 12$; see Table 1) represents only 3% of the overall phytoplanktonic community. Hall and Mills (2000) reported that alien fish species represented between 11% and 17% of the fish species richness in each of the five Great Lakes. Given an estimated total number of 93 fish species in the St. Lawrence River (Bernatchez and Giroux 1996), the relative proportion of alien fish species ($n = 11$; see Table 1) is 12%, similar to that reported for the Great Lakes. However, these estimates are less than those calculated for small northeastern lakes, where the proportion of alien species often exceeded 25% of the overall fish assemblage (Whittier and Kincaid 1999).

To further estimate fishery impacts in the St. Lawrence River, fish catch data collected daily since 1971 at the experimental trap fishery of the Aquarium du Québec, located at Saint-Nicolas, near Québec, were examined. Given that the alien fishes present in the river were introduced a long time ago (Table 1), an attempt was made to assess their relative importance to the structure and diversity of the fish community in the St. Lawrence River. In terms of species richness, alien species accounted for 7% to 14% (mean 10%) of the total number of species (40–48 species) captured at the experimental trap, with no significant trend over the past 30 years (Figure 6). The percentage of alien fish in the total catch was, however, more variable and exhibited three definite peaks, reaching up to 22%. No temporal trend was evident, and the peaks in relative abundance indicate the level of variability in recruitment and population dynamics of these alien species.

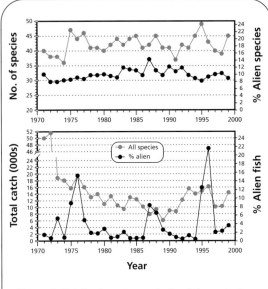

Figure 6. Relative importance of alien fish species in the fish community of the St. Lawrence River at Saint-Nicolas between 1971 and 1999.

Common carp (first observed in the river in 1908) and gizzard shad (*Dorosoma cepedianum* (Lesueur), first reported in 1944) are the two numerically dominant alien fish species in that fishery, but the proportion of introduced salmonids has increased over time. This increase is attributed to the recent stocking programs in several lakes and tributaries within the St. Lawrence River drainage basin (Dumont et al. 1988). The present situation with regard to alien fish species in the St. Lawrence River may change dramatically in the near future with the introduction of the round goby (*Neogobius melanostomus* (Pallas)), into the St. Lawrence River. Downstream extension of Great Lakes distribution of the goby is expected (Table 1). First reported in a fall 1997 commercial trap fishery near Québec, the species was reported again on the south shore of Lake St. François (near Massena, New York) and at Saint-Nicolas in 2000. Our results further suggest that species richness is not sufficient to describe the potential impact of alien species in an ecosystem; an index based on relative abundance or biomass of alien relative to native species should also be used to determine ecosystem properties and responses to species introduction.

Discussion

The count of 163 alien species in the entire Great Lakes–St. Lawrence River drainage basin is considered a conservative estimate, as the list (Table 1) is certainly not complete. As pointed out by Benson (1999), introductions of small organisms and those for which taxonomic classification is difficult have received much less attention and are less well documented. In fresh waters, taxonomic difficulties are particularly important for planktonic organisms, bryozoans, benthic worms, parasites, fungi, and other pathogens. Introduced species can carry cryptic species, which may not be easily recognized by nonexperts (Carlton 1999; Grigorovich et al. 2000). They can also act as disease vectors for some native species (see examples cited in Dextrase and Coscarelli 1999; Goodchild 1999). A notable example is the introduction of the spinycheek crayfish to Europe, where it decimated native crayfish populations through the transfer of a pathogenic fungus (Lodge et al. 2000). Although these factors may impede the capacity to detect new species within these numerically abundant groups, it will not be surprising if, in the future, other alien species are added to the current list as a result of improved diagnostic and identification methods.

The rate of species introductions in the Great Lakes has been approximately one per year since 1920. The lack of similar indexes for other aquatic systems precludes any comparison, but intuitively this value would exceed by far the rate of species expansion due to natural causes. It should therefore be considered indicative of a serious problem. The slightly lower number of new alien species reported during the past 10 years (Table 4) tends to confirm a decline in species introductions, as anticipated by Mills et al. (1993). Transport by ships and through canals has been identified as a major vector of introductions into the Great Lakes (Locke et al. 1993; Wiley 1997; Wiley and Claudi 1999) and is implicated as a primary or secondary cause of introductions for nearly half of the species (Table 1). The significant increase in the number of introduced species during the 20th century was primarily a result of the change from solid ballast to water ballast in cargo ships and, probably more importantly, the opening of the Great Lakes St. Lawrence Seaway in 1959 (Mills et al. 1993; Mills et al. 1999). The latter event would have caused the peak in species introductions between 1960 and 1980. It is worth noting that this peak was largely due to the reporting of 18 new algal species and coincided with the period of high eutrophication in the Great Lakes (Government of Canada 1991). This environmental crisis has contributed to scientific interest and led to increased sampling effort for phytoplankton and algae, which may have favored the discovery and identification of new species.

Table 4. Numbers of alien species reported per decade since 1900 traced to shipping-related vectors, canals, other vectors, and unknown sources.

Decade	Shipping	Canals	Other vectors	Unknown	Total
1901–1910	2		5		**7**
1911–1920		1	8		**9**
1921–1930	1		7	2	**10**
1931–1940	5		9		**14**
1941–1950	1	1	5	4	**11**
1951–1960	2	1	6	3	**12**
1961–1970	10		4	1	**15**
1971–1980	11	1	4	2	**18**
1981–1990	9		2		**11**
1991–2000	5	1	1	2	**9**

Guidelines for regulating the ballast discharged by ships entering the fresh waters of the Great Lakes–St. Lawrence River ecosystem were put forward by the Canadian government in 1989 (Wiley and Claudi 1999) in response to the severe impacts of zebra mussel introductions in the mid-1980s and in an attempt to reduce the number of species introductions by this means. The rate of compliance with these guidelines exceeded 90% after 1993 (Wiley 1995). It is interesting that the number of new species reported in the Great Lakes during the decade 1991–2000 (nine species) is the lowest for a 10-year period since 1920 (Table 4). Species introductions attributed to ships' ballast over the past 10 years have also dropped, to 5 from 9 or 10 per decade between 1960 and 1990. Although we do not maintain that the establishment of guidelines for ballast control has effectively contributed to the recent reduction in species introductions into the Great Lakes, these results tend to support the view that the guidelines for ships' ballast control, along with other control methods, may help to minimize the risk of new introductions of alien species into Canadian waters. Consequently, guidelines for ballast water exchange should be rigorously enforced along the St. Lawrence River.

More than half of the species that were introduced into the Great Lakes have been reported in the St. Lawrence River to date. In comparison, the Hudson River has more alien species (n = 113) than the St. Lawrence River but shares a lower percentage of species with the Great Lakes (48 [34%] of 139) (Mills et al. 1996). This indicates that the strategic position of the St. Lawrence River, the downstream end of the Great Lakes continuum, favors exchange and transfer of organisms, which in turn results in similarity of introduced species between the two regions. The majority (90%) of species introduced into the St. Lawrence River were first introduced into the Great Lakes, particularly Lake Ontario (Figure 5). Irrespective of the mechanisms involved, the St. Lawrence River appears to be highly exposed and vulnerable to the downstream transfer of and invasion by alien species introduced into the Great Lakes.

The introduction and presence of alien species in the river does not necessarily imply the existence of established or self-perpetuating populations. As shown for zebra mussels in the Rhine River (Kern et al. 1994), river populations may be entirely dependent on annual recruits from reproducing populations in upstream lakes. A similar conclusion was reached by de Lafontaine et al. (1995) and by de Lafontaine and Cusson (1997), who observed that zebra mussel larvae in the St. Lawrence River may have drifted from reproductive sources located as far as 250 to 500 km upstream in Lake Ontario. Comparative studies of the population dynamics of alien species in lakes and rivers would be very useful to determine the extent to which similar mechanisms exist for the alien species in the St. Lawrence River.

Our results suggest that the river may represent a potential source of entry for alien species in Canada and North America. Approximately 10% of the alien species reported in the Great Lakes were first found in and reported from the St. Lawrence River. Species first recorded from the river were vascular plants, introduced in the 1800s as a result of cultivation release or the discharge of solid ballast (Mills et al. 1994) in harbors of the St. Lawrence River. Although the contribution of the river as a primary receiving system for alien species seems to have been more important in the past, it is not negligible and it represents an active potential source of new introductions. The upstream transfer of these species, against the natural direction of water flow, implies that active or human-assisted mechanisms are responsible. Both foreign and domestic shipping activities are considered the most probable vectors for such transport (Niimi 2000). Similar upstream transfer of organisms (for example, the zebra mussel, the round goby) within the Great Lakes has also occurred, as numerous species first introduced in the lower Great Lakes (Lake Ontario and Lake Erie) have spread into the upper lakes within a relatively short time (Wiley and Claudi 1999). These lines of evidence call for the development and implementation of adequate controls to reduce the active transfer of organisms within the drainage basin.

In theory, the likelihood that a species will be successfully transferred increases with time. Indeed, this analysis suggests that species transfer within the Great Lakes–St. Lawrence drainage basin is primarily a function of time elapsed since the first sighting (Figure 4) and distance from the original site of entry (Figure 5). The finding that the proportion of species common to both the lakes and the river increases with time since the first report implies that, once introduced, species will eventually spread and be distributed throughout the entire drainage basin. The results indicating that geographic distance influences the probability of species transfer within the basin (Figure 5) support the hypothesis that species may invade and establish themselves in communicating adjacent waters more rapidly and more successfully than in more distant locations (Johnson and Carlton 1996). Given that 62 species introduced into the Great Lakes have not yet been reported in the river, it is expected that the number of alien species reported in the St. Lawrence River will continue to increase in the near future. The exponential trend in species introductions in the river may well be maintained for another decade. In addition, species may also invade the St. Lawrence River from its tributaries. The Richelieu River, which connects to Lake Champlain and the Hudson River drainage basin, has been identified as a source of species alien to the St. Lawrence River (for example, the spinycheek crayfish) and may well be the route for future invasions by the tench and water chestnut, which have recently become established in its upper reaches.

Implications for Management

The above analysis depends entirely on the nature and the quality of the information available. To a large extent, this information is a function of the research efforts and number of studies conducted in a given region. If the probability of introducing a species is considered ecological roulette (sensu Carlton and Geller 1993), the discovery and confirmation of a new species is a matter of chance and sampling effort. Despite the fact that the introduction reports used to develop the present synthesis originated from many different sources representing various levels of expertise, the proportion of species transferred over time and estimates of transfer times were relatively similar among the various taxonomic groups. The reasons for this similarity are not obvious, but it would suggest that differences in transfer mechanisms between taxonomic groups are less important than the hydrological, ecological, and anthropogenic forces assisting the dispersion of organisms, in particular within the Great Lakes–St. Lawrence River drainage basin. With species introductions being essentially a human-related activity, it is not surprising that first reports of alien species were often from the areas of greatest anthropogenic impact, such as Lake Ontario, Lake Erie, and Lake Michigan (Figure 5). As a consequence, large harbor areas and canals would represent priority monitoring sites for species introductions and transfer in the Great Lakes and St. Lawrence River. Given the number of introductions associated with disposal of live bait (Litvak and Mandrak 1999), important fishing sectors permitting the use of live bait also warrant inspection and monitoring.

The spread of alien species throughout the Great Lakes and the St. Lawrence River has been relatively well described, and monitoring is already in place for a few species. Overall, however, very little information is available on the distribution and relative abundance of the vast majority of alien species. The lack of adequate monitoring programs for freshwater biodiversity in Canada is largely responsible for this situation. Such information is a prerequisite to assessing the relative importance, and the eventual impact, of alien species on Canadian ecosystems. Information systems in the United States (Benson 1999) and elsewhere (Ricciardi et al. 2000) have proven useful for compiling and synthesizing information (for example, Fuller et al. 1999; Galatowitsch et al. 1999; Gido and Brown 1999; Rahel 2000).

Attempts to control and manage the problem at the species level may look promising, but the problem calls for a more holistic approach. Exemplifying the species-level approach are programs for chemical control of sea lamprey in the Great Lakes. The programs have involved enormous costs and effort over the past 50 years, and millions of dollars will continue to be spent in the future (Mills et al. 1999). Despite the harvesting programs developed to counteract the northward progression of another species, water chesnut, in Lake Champlain (Hauser and Bove 1999), the species has found its way into the Richelieu River (Gratton 1998), where it is now expanding rapidly. Shifting away from species management, effort and legislation to manage the human activities that contribute to species dispersal and transfer should be enhanced and strongly supported. Emphasis should be placed on the vectors of introduction, and the arbitrary distinction between deliberate and accidental introductions should be dismissed.

The dynamic and open nature of aquatic systems, as well as their natural continuity within a drainage basin, allows species to distribute widely within a given system. In recent years much emphasis has been dedicated to the introduction of species, but much less attention has been directed to their subsequent transfer. The present analysis of the Great Lakes–St. Lawrence River drainage basin reveals that these two aspects of the problem are equally important.

Acknowledgments

We wish to acknowledge the generous contribution of numerous colleagues who patiently devoted time and effort to reviewing and validating various information and details of this work. Our sincere thanks to Fanny Delisle, who compiled most of the information and assisted in validating information on vascular plants; Christiane Hudon and Chantal Vis for their algal data; and Paul Harrison, Gerald Mackie, Premek Hamr, Ed Crossman, and Pierre Dumont for their help with algae, mollusk, crayfish, and fish information. Denise Séguin and François Boudreault prepared the map.

References

Benson, A. 1999. Documenting over a century of aquatic introductions in the United States. Pages 1–31 *in* R. Claudi and J.H. Leach, eds. Nonindigenous freshwater organisms. Vectors, biology, and impacts. Lewis Publishers, Boca Raton, FL.

Bernatchez, L.; Giroux, M. 1996. Guide des poissons d'eau douce du Québec et leur distribution dans l'Est du Canada. 2nd ed. Éditions Broquet, L'Acadie, QC.

Bourgeois, M.; Gilbert, M.; Cusson, B. 2001. Évolution du trafic maritime en provenance de l'étranger dans le Saint-Laurent de 1978 à 1996 et implications pour les risques d'introduction d'espèces aquatiques non indigènes. Rapp. tech. can. sci. hallieut. aquat. [Can. Tech. Rep. Fish. Aquat. Sci.] 2338. 34 p.

Carlton, J.T. 1999. Molluscan invasions in marine and estuarine communities. Malacologia 41(2):439–454.

Carlton, J.T.; Geller, J. 1993. Ecological roulette: the global transport and invasion of nonindigenous marine organisms. Science 261:78–82.

Claudi, R.; Leach, J.H., eds. 1999. Nonindigenous freshwater organisms: vectors, biology, and impacts. Lewis Publishers, Boca Raton, FL. 480 p.

Claudi, R.; Mackie, G.L., eds. 1994. Practical manual for zebra mussel monitoring and control. Lewis Publishers, Boca Raton, FL. 227 p.

Cohen, A.N.; Carlton, J.T. 1998. Accelerating invasion rate in a highly invaded estuary. Science 279:555–558.

de Lafontaine, Y.; Cusson, B. 1997. Veligers of zebra mussels in the Richelieu River: an intrusion from Lake Champlain. Pages 30–41 *in* Proceedings of the Second Northeast Conference on Nonindigenous Aquatic Nuisance Species, Burlington, VT, 18–19 April 1997. Connecticut Sea Grant College Program, University of Connecticut, Groton, CT.

de Lafontaine, Y.; Lapierre, L.; Henry, M.; Grégoire, Y. 1995. Abondance des larves de Moule zébrée (*Dreissena polymorpha*) et de Quagga (*Dreissena bugensis*) aux abords des centrales hydroélectriques de Beauharnois, Les Cèdres et Rivière-des-Prairies. Environment Canada, Quebec Region, Montréal, QC. Rapp. sci. tech. [Sci. Tech. Rep.] ST-14. 52 p.

Dextrase, A.J.; Coscarelli, M.A. 1999. Intentional introductions of nonindigenous freshwater organisms in North America. Pages 61–98 *in* R. Claudi and J.H. Leach, eds. Nonindigenous freshwater organisms: vectors, biology, and impacts. Lewis Publishers, Boca Raton, FL.

Drake, J.A.; Mooney, H.A.; di Castri, F.; Groves, R.H.; Kruger, F.J.; Rejmanek, M.; Williamson, M., eds. 1989. Ecology of biological invasions: a global perspective. John Wiley & Sons, New York, NY.

Dumont, P.; Bergeron, J.F.; Dulude, P.; Mailhot, Y.; Rouleau, A.; Ouellet, G.; Lebel, J.-P. 1988. Introduced salmonids: Where are they going in Quebec watersheds of the Saint-Laurent River? Fisheries 13:9–17.

Fuller, P.L.; Nico, L.G.; Williams, J.D. 1999. Nonindigenous fishes introduced into inland waters of the United States. Am. Fish. Soc. Spec. Publ. 27. 613 p.

Galatowitsch, S.M.; Anderson, N.O.; Ascher, P.D. 1999. Invasiveness in wetland plants in temperate North America. Wetlands 19:733–755.

Gido, K.B.; Brown, J.H. 1999. Invasion of North American drainages by alien fish species. Freshwater Biol. 42:387–399.

Goodchild, C.D. 1999. Ecological impacts of introductions associated with the use of live baitfish. Pages 181–195 in R. Claudi and J.H. Leach, eds. Nonindigenous freshwater organisms: vectors, biology, and impacts. Lewis Publishers, Boca Raton, FL.

Government of Canada. 1991. The state of Canada's environment. Ottawa, ON.

Gratton, L. 1998. Espèces végétales exotiques envahissantes du milieu riverain. Pages 13–16 in Compte rendu atelier sur les espèces exotiques envahissantes, Saint-Jean-sur-Richelieu, 23 novembre 1998. Parks Canada, Ecosystem Conservation Service, Québec, QC.

Grigorovich, I.A.; Korniushin, A.V.; MacIsaac, H.J. 2000. Moitessier's pea clam Pisidium moitessierianum (Bivalvia, Sphaeriidae): a cryptogenic mollusc in the Great Lakes. Hydrobiologia 435:153–165.

Hall, S.R.; Mills, E.L. 2000. Exotic species in large lakes of the world. Aquat. Ecosyst. Health Manage. 3:105–135.

Hamr, P. 1998. Conservation status of Canadian freshwater crayfishes. World Wildlife Fund and Canadian Nature Federation, Toronto, ON. 87 p.

Hauser, M.W.; Bove, A.E. 1999. Importance of consistent, adequate resources for aquatic nuisance species management: a case study of water chesnut (Trapa natans) in Lake Champlain [abstract]. Page 44 in Proceedings of the 9th International Zebra Mussel and Aquatic Nuisance Species Conference, Duluth, MN, 26–30 April 1999. The Professional Edge, Pembroke, ON.

Hogg, I.D.; Eadie, J.M.; De Lafontaine, Y. 1999. Passive dispersal among fragmented habitats: the population genetic consequences for freshwater and estuarine amphipods. Pages 307–326 in F.R. Schram and J.C. von Vaupel Klein, eds. Crustaceans and the biodiversity crisis. Proceedings of the 4th International Crustacean Congress, Amsterdam, 20–24 July 1998. Brill Publishing, Boston, MA.

Johnson, L.E.; Carlton, J.T. 1996. Post-establishment spread in large-scale invasions: dispersal mechanisms of the zebra mussel Dreissena polymorpha. Ecology 77:1686–1690.

Kern, R.; Borcherding, J.; Neumann, D. 1994. Recruitment of a freshwater mussel with a planktonic life-stage in running waters—studies on Dreissena polymorpha in the River Rhine. Arch. Hydrobiol. 131:385–400.

Litvak, M.K.; Mandrak, N.E. 1999. Baitfish trade as a vector of aquatic introductions. Pages 163–180 in R. Claudi and J.H. Leach, eds. Nonindigenous freshwater organisms: vectors, biology, and impacts. Lewis Publishers, Boca Raton, FL.

Locke, A.; Reid, D.M.; van Leeuwen, H.C.; Sprules, W.G.; Carlton, J.T. 1993. Ballast water exchange as a means of controlling dispersal of freshwater organisms by ships. Can. J. Fish. Aquat. Sci. 50:2086–2093.

Lodge, D.M.; Taylor, C.A.; Holdich, D.M.; Skurdal, J. 2000. Nonindigenous crayfishes threaten North American freshwater biodiversity: lessons from Europe. Fisheries 25:7–20.

Mills, E.L.; Chrisman, J.R.; Holeck; K.T. 1999. The role of canals in the spread of non-indigenous species in North America. Pages 347–379 in R. Claudi and J.H. Leach, eds. Nonindigenous freshwater organisms: vectors, biology, and impacts. Lewis Publishers, Boca Raton, FL.

Mills, E.L.; Leach, J.H.; Carlton, J.T.; Secor, C.L. 1993. Exotic species in the Great Lakes: a history of biotic crises and anthropogenic introductions. J. Great Lakes Res. 19:1–54.

Mills, E.L.; Leach, J.H.; Carlton, J.T.; Secor, C.L. 1994. Exotic species and the integrity of the Great Lakes. Lessons from the past. Bioscience 44(10): 666–676.

Mills, E.L.; Scheuerell, M.D.; Carlton, J.T.; Strayer, D. 1997. Biological invasions in the Hudson River basin. N.Y. State Mus. Circ. 57. 51 p.

Mills, E.L.; Strayer, D.L.; Scheuerell, M.D.; Carlton, J.T. 1996. Exotic species in the Hudson River basin: a history of invasions and introductions. Estuaries 19(4):814–823.

Nalepa, T.F.; Schloesser, D.W., eds. 1993. Zebra mussels: biology, impacts and control. Lewis Publishers, Boca Raton, FL. 810 p.

Niimi, A.J. 2000. Role of vessel transit patterns on exotic species introductions to the Great Lakes. Dreissena 11(1):1–10.

Paquet, S.; Jarry, V.; Hudon, C. 1998. Phytoplankton species composition in the St. Lawrence River. Verh. Int. Verein. Limnol. 26:1095–1105.

Prieur-Richard, A.-H.; Lavorel, S. 2000. Invasions: the perspective of diverse plant communities. Austral Ecol. 25:1–7.

Rahel, F.J. 2000. Homogenization of fish faunas across the United States. Science 288:854–856.

Ricciardi, A.; Steiner, W.W.M.; Mack, R.N.; Simberloff, D. 2000. Toward a global information system for invasive species. BioScience 50:239–244.

Ricciardi, A.; Whoriskey, F.G.; Rasmussen, J.B. 1996. Impact of the Dreissena invasion on native unionid bivalves in the upper St. Lawrence River. Can. J. Fish. Aquat. Sci. 53:1434–1444.

Sala, O.E.; Chapin, F.S., III; Armesto, J.J.; Berlow, E.; Bloomfield, J.; Dirzo, R.; Huber-Sannwald, E.; Huenneke, L.; Jackson, R.B.; Kinsig, A.; Leemans, R.; Lodge, D.M.; Mooney, H.A.; Oesterheld, M.; Poff, N.L.; Sykes, M.T.; Walker, B.H.; Walker, M.; Wall, D.H. 2000. Biodiversity scenarios for the year 2010. Science 287:1770–1774.

Scott, W.B.; Crossman, E.J. 1973. Freshwater fishes of Canada. Fish. Res. Board Can. Bull. No. 184. 966 p.

Shear, H. 1996. The development and use of indicators to assess the state of ecosystem health in the Great Lakes. J. Ecosyst. Health 2:241–258.

Whittier, T.R.; Kincaid, T.M. 1999. Introduced fish in northeastern USA lakes: regional extent, dominance, and effect on native species richness. Trans. Am. Fish. Soc. 128:769–783.

Wiley, C.J. 1995. Ballast water control: overview of the Canadian approach. Pages 489–494 in Proceedings of the 5th International Zebra Mussel and Other Aquatic Nuisance Organisms Conference, Toronto, ON, 14–21 February 1995. The Professional Edge, Pembroke, ON.

Wiley, C.J. 1997. The aquatic nuisance species: nature, transport and regulation. Pages 55–64 in F.M. D'Itri, ed. Zebra mussels and aquatic nuisance species. Ann Arbor Press, Chelsea, MI.

Wiley, C.J.; Claudi, R. 1999. The role of ships as a vector of introduction for non-indigenous freshwater organisms, with focus on the Great Lakes. Pages 203–213 in R. Claudi and J.H. Leach, eds. Nonindigenous freshwater organisms: vectors, biology, and impacts. Lewis Publishers, Boca Raton, FL.

Photo with chapter title: Spinycheek crayfish. Photo courtesy of Environment Canada, St. Lawrence Centre, Montréal, QC.

Alien Aquatic Species in the Great Lakes–St. Lawrence River Drainage Basin **91**

Alien Aquatic Species in Manitoba: Present and Threatening

Wendy Ralley

Manitoba is unique in that all surface water entering the province eventually flows north as part of the Hudson Bay drainage basin. Moreover, all its major waterways, such as the Assiniboine, Red, Winnipeg, and Saskatchewan Rivers, originate in other jurisdictions. Authorities in Manitoba must therefore be alert to alien species occurrences in adjacent jurisdictions because of the direct influence such species may have on the province's watersheds. All these major Manitoba river systems discharge into Lake Winnipeg (Figure 1).

An examination of river basins in Manitoba reveals a great number of possible routes through which aquatic alien species from other areas can find their way into the province. The Assiniboine River basin drains about 154 176 km² and much of the basin is in Saskatchewan. The headwaters originate in eastern and central Saskatchewan and eventually discharge into the Red River within the City of Winnipeg. The Red River originates

at Lake Traverse, South Dakota, on the northeastern border with South Dakota and Minnesota. The Red River basin is about 121 932 km², excluding the Assiniboine River. The Winnipeg River originates in northwestern Ontario at Lake of the Woods, with contributions from the Rainy River and English River systems. The Saskatchewan River basin is one of the most diverse in North America, draining 420 000 km² across the three Prairie provinces. The river crosses the Manitoba–Saskatchewan border near The Pas and discharges into the north basin of Lake Winnipeg at Grand Rapids.

Manitoba is fortunate in that relatively few of the aquatic alien species that have become established in the Great Lakes region of Ontario and the St. Lawrence River area of southern Quebec have colonized its lakes, rivers, and wetlands. Common carp (*Cyprinus carpio* L.) and purple loosestrife (*Lythrum salicaria* L.), which were the first aliens to be introduced into Manitoba, have

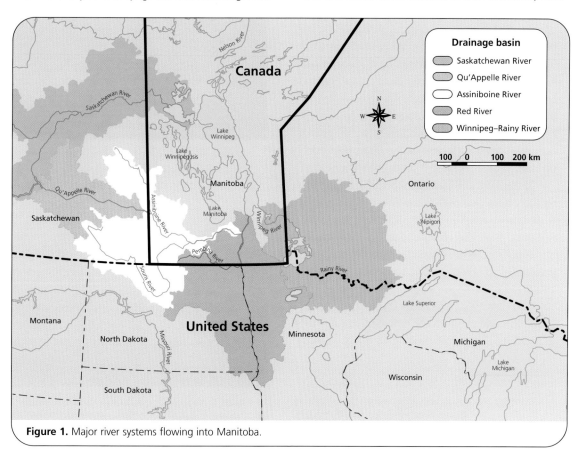

Figure 1. Major river systems flowing into Manitoba.

caused ecological damage within the province. Ecological effects of other alien species, such as rainbow smelt (*Osmerus mordax* (Mitchill)), white bass (*Morone chrysops* (Rafinesque)), and the recently discovered cladoceran, *Eubosmina coregoni* (Baird), are not as well known and documented. The potential for accidental introduction of other invasive and damaging species, such as zebra mussels (*Dreissena polymorpha* (Pallas)), into Manitoba remains high. Efforts to combat further introductions into the province include heightening public awareness to the issue of alien species, monitoring waterways, and filling gaps in legislation.

Aquatic Alien Species Present in Manitoba

Manitoba's few aquatic alien species are of concern for ecological, economic, and social reasons. They are described in the following sections.

Common Carp

As in other areas of Canada, common carp (Figure 2) was introduced into Manitoba in the late 1800s for commercial purposes. These early introductions into lakes and rivers in central and western Manitoba were apparently unsuccessful (Atton 1959). The first official record of carp caught in Manitoba was from the Red River at Lockport in 1938. Carp probably moved downriver from stocking events in the Sheyenne and Red Rivers in North Dakota during the late 1800s (K. Stewart, personal communication). At present, carp have become widely distributed throughout the province and have spread as far north as the Hayes River estuary on Hudson Bay (A. Derksen, personal communication).

The ecological impacts of carp on the aquatic environment have been well documented since the 1930s (King and Hunt 1967; Crivelli 1983; King et al. 1997; Robertson et al. 1997; Lougheed et al. 1998; Wrubleski and Anderson 1999). During feeding and spawning activities, carp uproot aquatic vegetation, causing an overall reduction in rooted aquatic plants (Robel 1961; King and Hunt 1967), a reduction in cover for waterfowl, young fish, and other aquatic organisms (Swain 1979; K. Stewart personal communication), and an increase

in water turbidity (Roberts et al. 1995; Lougheed et al. 1997). In addition to consuming and destroying roots of aquatic plants, carp are also thought to feed on benthic organisms and impact other fish species by consuming eggs and destroying spawning beds (Swain 1979).

The effects of carp are being assessed in the Delta Marsh, Manitoba. Delta Marsh is a 22 000-ha wetland of connected shallow bays located along the south shore of Lake Manitoba (Shay et al. 1999). It is one of the largest and best-known freshwater marshes in North America (Figure 3). In 1982, Delta Marsh was included in the List of Wetlands of International Importance under the Ramsar Convention on Wetlands[1], and in 1996, designated a Manitoba Heritage Marsh. Delta Marsh is also an important component of Environment Canada's Ecological and Monitoring Assessment Network (Goldsborough 1999).

Delta Marsh is largely separated from Lake Manitoba by a forested sand bar created about 2500 years ago and is connected to the lake through four channels (Figure 4). This allows free movement of water and fish

Figure 2. Common carp. Photo © John G. Shedd Aquarium, Chicago, IL.

Figure 3. Aerial photograph of Delta Marsh, 1999. Photo courtesy of G. Goldsborough, University of Manitoba Field Station, Delta Marsh, MB.

---

[1] The Convention on Wetlands, signed in Ramsar, Iran, in 1971, is an intergovernmental treaty that provides the framework for national action and international cooperation for the conservation and wise use of wetlands and their resources. There are at present 124 Contracting Parties to the Convention.

into and out of the marsh. Historically, water levels of the marsh fluctuated in accordance with those of Lake Manitoba. Since 1961, water levels in Lake Manitoba and Delta Marsh have become stable due to control structures regulating inflow and outflow. Part of this effort included a diversion channel from the Assiniboine River to Lake Manitoba. The quality of this diverted water is characteristic of a primarily agricultural watershed and is rich in nutrients and suspended sediments.

The first evidence of carp in the marsh was recorded in 1960. At this time, use of the marsh by migrant and breeding waterfowl decreased due to a reduction in the abundance of aquatic macrophytes, which provide food and nesting material for the birds (Swain 1979). Although there are no data for carp numbers and density, it is estimated that carp abundance in the marsh peaked during 1960 and 1962 (Wrubleski 1998). About this time, carp exclusion screens were placed at the mouths of channels that connected the marsh with Lake Manitoba. Increased macrophyte growth was observed following their placement; however, no supporting data are available (Wrubleski and Anderson 1999). The exclusion screens were not maintained and were eventually destroyed by storms; the carp are now firmly established in the marsh (G. Goldsborough, personal communication). Wrubleski and Anderson (1999) have summarized the interacting processes

believed to have caused habitat destruction and water quality degradation in Delta Marsh (see Figure 5).

Stabilized lake levels in the Delta Marsh have worked in concert with the destructive behavior of carp. The erosion properties of wind and waves, augmented by the rooting behavior of carp, have effectively reduced the number of small islands in the larger bays of the marsh. The coalescence of bays and smaller waterbodies into larger open lakes has resulted in significant habitat loss for waterfowl (Goldsborough 1999). Over a 30-year period, habitat has been mapped in the Delta Marsh through a series of aerial photos and ground surveys to identify surface area and species composition. During this time, there has been a displacement of major plant species, with fewer species becoming more widely dispersed. Increased turbidity, and thus reduced light penetration, is largely caused by algal blooms and has resulted in the loss of submerged macrophytes. In all of the large bays studied, there were major reductions of submerged macrophytes, and an overall loss of islands and shoreline emergent vegetation (Wrubleski and Anderson 1999). This loss of marsh habitat has likely resulted in the decline of nesting waterfowl. In addition, habitat loss in the marsh, which acts as a nursery for fishes, may also be contributing to the decline of large, commercially valuable fish in Lake Manitoba (Goldsborough 1999).

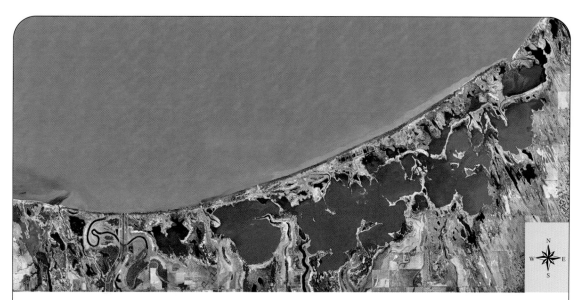

Figure 4. Composite of digital, infrared, aerial photographs of Delta Marsh, MB, taken 15 August 1997. Turbidity is shown by lighter shades of blue with black indicating water that is low in suspended sediments; cover types of marsh vegetation reflect different shades of red; and agricultural crops are indicated by shades of green to the south. Photo courtesy of Ducks Unlimited Canada; Institute for Wetland and Waterfowl Research; Delta Marsh Field Station (University of Manitoba); Delta Waterfowl and Wetlands Research Station; and Manitoba Conservation.

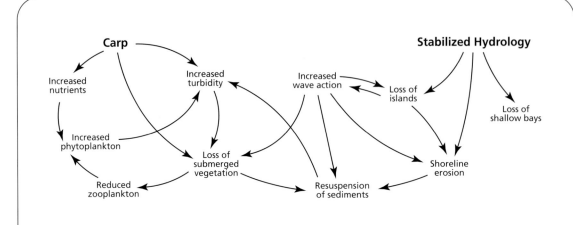

Figure 5. Conceptual model of interacting processes affecting Delta Marsh over the past 30 years (from Wrubleski and Anderson 1999).

Rainbow Smelt

Rainbow smelt were first discovered in Manitoba in 1990 when one was caught in the gill nets of a commercial fishing boat in the south basin of Lake Winnipeg (Campbell et al. 1991). Earlier that same year, the remains of rainbow smelt had been detected in the stomach contents of commercially caught walleye (*Stizostedion vitreum* (Mitchill)). Anecdotal evidence suggests that rainbow smelt appeared in the Red River at Lockport in 1975 (K. Stewart, personal communication). The route of entry of smelt into Lake Winnipeg is unknown. Campbell et al. (1991) discussed possible scenarios, such as downstream dispersal from Ontario or, most likely, direct introduction into the Red River by humans. Smelt soon began to appear in more northern locations along the Nelson River (Franzin et al. 1994; Remnant et al. 1997), and in 1998, rainbow smelt were reported from the Nelson River estuary (Zrum 1999). The species may have experienced a long lag period during which populations slowly increased, accounting for the gap between anecdotal evidence of first observations in Manitoba and their present distribution (K. Stewart, personal communication).

The ecological and social impacts of smelt populations in Manitoba are speculative and may include the following:

- a qualitative decline in palatability of walleye and lake trout (*Salvelinus namaycush* (Walbaum));

- a decrease in the population sizes of cisco (*Coregonus artedi* Lesueur) and lake whitefish (*C. clupeaformis* (Mitchill));

- an increase in mercury levels due to increased foraging and higher mercury levels in stored body fat; and

- a loss of income to commercial fisheries, as all of these species are harvested (Remnant 1991; Wain 1993; Franzin et al. 1994).

Many of these negative impacts have occurred in other waters in which smelt has been introduced, but have not yet been witnessed in Lake Winnipeg.

At present, population parameters, feeding, and predation dynamics of Lake Winnipeg smelt are being studied (W. Franzin, personal communication). There is evidence that the larger predatory fish in Lake Winnipeg are feeding primarily on a smelt diet. This will likely result in walleye and pike growing more rapidly and having a greater fat content than if they were feeding on native forage species (Stewart 2000). Walleye feeding on smelt decline in quality, developing a greasy blandness to their flesh (Stewart 2000). Smelt are also predatory, consuming and competing with juvenile stages of other larger species, many of which are commercially caught in Lake Winnipeg. This could have an effect on the annual value of the commercial fisheries in this region, which accounts for 50% of the commercial fish harvest from Manitoba.

White Bass and the Cladoceran *Eubosmina coregoni*

Like the common carp, white bass found their way into Manitoba from North Dakota, where in 1953, they had been deliberately introduced into Lake Ashtabula, a reservoir on the Sheyenne River (a Red River tributary). White bass first appeared in Manitoba in the south basin of Lake Winnipeg in 1963. By 1994, white bass had been found over the entire north-south extent of the lake and had become the most abundant spiny-rayed fish in the south basin of Lake Winnipeg. Currently there is no evidence of any ecological damage caused by white bass, but they may be in the process of displacing yellow perch (*Perca flavescens* (Mitchill)) from the offshore area of the south basin (K. Stewart, personal communication). There is also no evidence that white bass have extended their range into any other of Manitoba's major lakes. Populations of their main food source, emerald shiners (*Notropis atherinoides* Rafinesque), appear to be unaffected. Although there are no apparent ecological effects from the establishment of white bass in Manitoba waters, fishery resource managers remain concerned about their long-term impacts on the Lake Winnipeg and Red River fisheries.

A new cladoceran, *Eubosmina coregoni* (Baird), was discovered in Lake Winnipeg during the open-water season of 1999 (A. Salki, personal communication). All previous records of distribution in Canada were confined to the Great Lakes region (Patalas 1972; Patalas et al. 1994). *Eubosmina coregoni* was introduced into the Great Lakes from Europe likely through the release of ballast water from oceangoing vessels during the early 1960s. It was not found during intensive sampling of Lake Winnipeg during 1994, 1996, and 1998. However, in 1999, this species was the most dominant cladoceran found in the north basin of Lake Winnipeg. Although *E. coregoni* was also found in the south basin and narrows area of Lake Winnipeg, the density and range of dispersion were not as pronounced as in the north basin (A. Salki, personal communication).

It is not known how or when *E. coregoni* was introduced into Lake Winnipeg, or from which body of water the species was introduced. At this time, *E. coregoni* is being regarded as an invasive alien species, and as such, concerns regarding its impacts to the trophic status and food-web dynamics of Lake Winnipeg and implications to the lake's overall health are being studied by Fisheries and Oceans Canada.

Alien Aquatic Species Threatening Manitoba

Future introductions of aquatic alien species into Manitoba waters are likely to occur. Each year the risk of such introductions, primarily through transport on recreational watercraft or intentional releases as live bait by anglers, grows. The sheer number of anglers from other areas who trailer recreational watercraft into Manitoba and into its contributing watersheds greatly increases the potential for new introductions. Land barriers to the south and east separating Manitoba's waters (that is, the Hudson Bay drainage basin) from other watersheds that contain alien species are relatively small. For example, only 180 km separates the Great Lakes drainage basin from the headwaters of the English–Winnipeg River basin and less than 5 km separates the headwaters of the Red River from the headwaters of the Minnesota River (upper Mississippi River basin). Round goby (*Neogobius melanostomus* (Pallas)), ruffe (*Gymnocephalus cernuus* L.), rusty crayfish (*Orconectes rusticus* Girard), spiny waterflea (*Bythotrephes cederstroemi*), zebra mussel, and a variety of other aquatic alien species have not been reported from Manitoba waters, but they occur in adjacent watersheds. It is likely that one or more of these species may already occur in the province (rusty crayfish was reported from Lake of the Woods in 1960 [P. Hamr, personal communication]). Easy accessibility, recreational opportunities, and the general aesthetics of northwestern Ontario and eastern Manitoba attract national and international boaters. Lake of the Woods is also a body of water shared by Canada and the United States. Alien species that come into Manitoba via watercraft would be extremely difficult to regulate.

Interbasin transfer of untreated or insufficiently treated water is another means by which alien species could be accidentally transferred to Manitoba. Several projects are proposed that would move water from the Missouri River basin, across the Continental Divide, to the Hudson Bay basin (for example, the Garrison Diversion). The waters of these basins have been hydrologically isolated from each other for nearly 10 000 years, with each basin containing a unique assemblage of organisms. A number of alien species are present in the Missouri River basin that are not yet present in the Hudson Bay basin. In addition, other projects, such as the Devils Lake (North Dakota) stabilization project, propose to move water from a system that has been hydrologically isolated from the remainder of the Hudson Bay basin for nearly 1500 years and has the potential to contain organisms not present elsewhere in the basin.

Zebra Mussels

Zebra mussels have become widely distributed in eastern North America since their introduction into Lake St. Clair in 1986. Interconnected waterways have become especially vulnerable to invasion, whereas isolated watersheds, such as Manitoba's, are afforded some protection. The Hudson Bay drainage basin, which flows through Manitoba, is separated from the mussel-infected watersheds that flow south (Mississippi River) and east (Great Lakes) (Figure 6). Since 1989, Manitoba has been involved in diverse activities to prevent the introduction of zebra mussels into the province. To date, zebra mussels have not been reported from Manitoba waters or from any of the watersheds that flow into the province.

When zebra mussels became established in the Great Lakes, invasion into Manitoba waters became highly probable. In 1989, the province established the Zebra Mussel Advisory Committee, comprising representatives from four provincial government departments, utilities such as Manitoba Hydro, municipalities including the City of Winnipeg, and private industry. The major goals of the advisory committee were to use all reasonable means to attempt to slow the westward migration of zebra mussels into Manitoba; and, given that a zebra mussel invasion was inevitable, to properly prepare all major water-using sectors likely to be affected.

To meet these goals, the Zebra Mussel Advisory Committee maintained an information network and secured funding for various activities. Although these goals have been met over the last several years, the province continues to be involved in a number of initiatives to heighten the awareness of the general public and target audiences to the zebra mussel issue. Similar to the activities in neighboring jurisdictions, Manitoba produces a variety of written materials on aquatic alien species for wide distribution. Recognizing that the issue of alien species crosses political boundaries, Manitoba has been working cooperatively with the Province of Ontario, the State of Minnesota, and the US Fish and Wildlife Service in the cost-sharing of highway billboard signs directed at traffic heading west and north into Manitoba.

Manitoba is actively represented on the Western Regional Panel on Aquatic Nuisance Species, whose focus is to stop the spread of aquatic alien species into the 17 western US states, the 4 western Canadian provinces, and western Mexico. The panel was formed by a provision in the US *National Invasive Species Act* of 1996. To date, 49 members represent Canadian federal and provincial agencies and US federal, state, tribal, academic, and private organizations with marine and freshwater interests. One initiative is to stop the spread of zebra mussels across the 100th meridian. Although all efforts to prevent zebra mussels from becoming established in Manitoba are aimed at the watershed

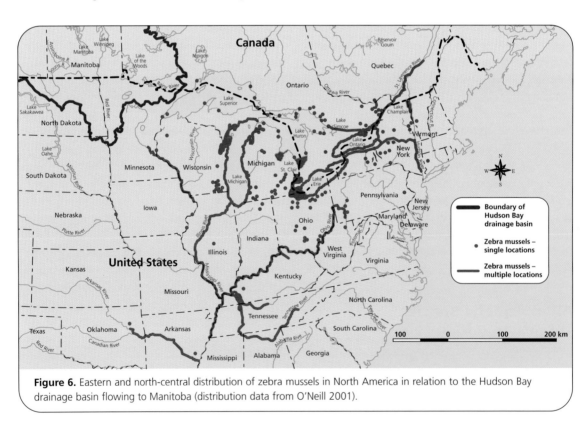

Figure 6. Eastern and north-central distribution of zebra mussels in North America in relation to the Hudson Bay drainage basin flowing to Manitoba (distribution data from O'Neill 2001).

borders, the province is directly involved with this initiative because the 100th meridian transects the province just west of Brandon.

Determining boater awareness of aquatic alien species is important in the development of pertinent public education and information campaigns. In 1994, Fish Futures Inc., in conjunction with the Provinces of Ontario and Manitoba and Canada Customs, conducted an inspection of boats and a survey of boater awareness aimed at visitors trailering watercraft across the international border and other key sites. All interviews and inspections were carried out in watersheds that contribute surface water to Manitoba. Travelers were surveyed about their general knowledge of zebra mussels, and their watercraft and trailers were inspected for evidence of mussels. About 1600 interviews were conducted, with the following results: 93% of the boats originated in jurisdictions that had waters known to have zebra mussels; 5% of the boats had been in water with zebra mussels within the last five days; and 60% of the travelers interviewed knew that zebra mussels were present in their jurisdiction of origin. No zebra mussels were found. The level of zebra mussel knowledge was the highest among travelers from Minnesota and Wisconsin (Fish Futures Inc.1994).

North Dakota conducted a similar survey in 1999; it assessed the potential of introducing aquatic alien species into the state by recreational watercraft. Again boaters from Minnesota and Wisconsin were the most knowledgeable about alien species, and they were careful about inspecting their own equipment for such (Grier and Sell 1999). About half of the boaters from North Dakota that were interviewed were uninformed about aquatic alien species. Out-of-state boaters from jurisdictions with zebra mussels launched their boats almost exclusively in Devils Lake. The report of the survey results concluded that the overall risk of alien species introductions into the state was low.

In 1999, the Manitoba Purple Loosestrife Project conducted a survey largely of shore anglers (Lindgren and Simpson 1999) and some boaters. Approximately 350 anglers were interviewed about their general knowledge of aquatic alien species in Manitoba. Overall, boaters were more aware than shore anglers. Most respondents were unfamiliar with aquatic alien species and the study identified a clear need for greater public awareness. Results also indicated that 20% of anglers disposed of their live unused bait into surface water.

On 30 June 1999, zebra mussels were found on a pleasure boat that was purchased five days earlier in

Orillia, Ontario (Lake Simcoe), and trailered to a yacht club on the Red River just north of Winnipeg. All zebra mussels were dead, and no veligers were found. As a precaution, however, the owner was ordered to scrape the boat and wash it down with water containing bleach. At present, the Province of Manitoba surveys and inspects watercraft trailered across the international borders at Emerson and Sprague, Manitoba, as well as, when practical, at the Manitoba–Ontario provincial border. Of the 850 inspections conducted on boats and trailers during 2000, no evidence of zebra mussels was found. Most visitors that were surveyed originated from Minnesota and, similar to the 1994 survey, they were the most knowledgeable about aquatic alien species.

Monitoring for zebra mussels in waterways is carried out by three agencies in Manitoba: the City of Winnipeg, Manitoba Hydro, and Manitoba Conservation. The City of Winnipeg draws its drinking water from Shoal Lake, located 140 km east of the city on the Manitoba–Ontario border. Water is gravity fed from the lake and travels to Winnipeg through a large aqueduct. Infestation of the aqueduct and related pumping equipment by zebra mussels would be extremely costly. The City of Winnipeg monitors for zebra mussels using artificial-substrate samplers placed close to the aqueduct intake and in larger bays of the lake. It combines engineering, operational, and chemical initiatives in a comprehensive plan to protect the aqueduct from zebra mussel colonization.

Manitoba Hydro operates 11 hydroelectric and 2 thermoelectric stations in the province. About half of these stations are at risk of zebra mussel colonization due to their location along recreational rivers. Manitoba Hydro monitors for zebra mussels by placing artificial-substrate samplers close to the intakes of these stations and in nearby bays. The samplers are checked once per month during open-water season. A study was also undertaken to assess which areas of these stations are likely to be damaged by zebra mussel colonization. This information will be valuable in assisting and directing mitigation activities once colonies become established.

At the end of each boating season, Canadian Coast Guard navigational buoys pulled from the Red River and the south and north basin of Lake Winnipeg are thoroughly inspected by Manitoba Conservation staff for zebra mussels. In addition, marker buoys from waters where there is heavy recreational use and a high probability of boater traffic from outside the province are inspected. At present, no monitoring or inspection of water equipment is conducted west of Winnipeg or north of the 52nd parallel.

In addition to yearly monitoring efforts, the potential for zebra mussels to colonize in Manitoba waters was assessed. Manitoba Environment sampled 580 locations, representing146 bodies of water (Sorba and Williamson 1997). Following methods outlined in O'Neill (1996), researchers used water quality criteria to rate the colonization potential from very low to high. The lowest potential represented the limiting variable for zebra mussel colonization at a location. Manitoba watercourses with high colonization potential were confined to the Prairies and Boreal Plains Ecozones. About 25%, or 146 individual sites, rated a high colonization potential and 34% rated very low potential. The remaining sites were evenly distributed with about 20% in each of the moderate and low potential categories (Sorba and Williamson 1996). Of the three major watercourses evaluated, the Red River had the highest risk of zebra mussel colonization, followed by the Assiniboine River. The Winnipeg River and other waterbodies on the Canadian Shield area of eastern Manitoba were evaluated at low or very low risk of successful zebra mussel colonization because of the low concentration of calcium (necessary for mollusk shell development) that is characteristic of these waters.

Legislative Framework

The issue of aquatic alien species within Manitoba remains the responsibility of the provincial government. Legislation to reduce the risk of accidental introduction of alien species is in place. In 1992, zebra mussels were added to the list of prohibited species identified in the Manitoba Fisheries Regulations under the federal *Fisheries Act*. This action not only made it illegal to transport zebra mussels into the province, but also afforded authority to Manitoba Natural Resources officers (Manitoba Conservation) and officials representing Canada Customs to stop and inspect trailered watercraft. The provincial Fisheries Regulations prohibit the importation of live bait without a permit, and in only a few areas of the province is fishing with live bait permitted. The live bait industry is growing in Manitoba, and there is concern that this will create a potential for alien species, diseases, and parasites to be introduced into waterways. A Live Aquatic Bait Plan has been developed with the bait industry for an "environmentally friendly" approach to maintaining a viable industry while reducing the potential for alien species introductions (Manitoba

Conservation 1999). Manitoba, along with Alberta, Saskatchewan, Ontario, and Fisheries and Oceans Canada, has developed a risk assessment protocol for the transfer and introduction of alien aquatic species. Fisheries and Oceans Canada, in conjunction with the provinces and territories, has developed a national code for the introduction and transfer of aquatic species that will govern what species may be brought into Canada.

In spite of the above, legislative gaps and weaknesses exist in the efforts to control the introductions of alien aquatic species into Manitoba. For example, the provincial *Wildlife Act*, which controls the importation, harvest, and use of amphibians for bait (or other uses), only puts minimum restrictions on their harvest and use. As well, with respect to importing alien species, the *Wildlife Act* is reactive because it is based on species-specific lists; it should be proactive and restrict all potentially new importations. Similarly, regulations that restrict pet trade importations are limited in scope. In many cases, the public's perception that alien pet species are not harmful is misguided. The importation of species for the live food industry, as well as mercy releases of live food and alien pet species, are not regulated. Provincial government departments responsible for the various acts and regulations governing aquatic alien species must coordinate their approaches to ensure consistency in alien species prevention and management.

Acknowledgments

Maps of Manitoba watersheds and zebra mussel distribution were originally created in ArcView GIS (ver. 3.2) by Geoff Jones, Manitoba Conservation. Appreciation is extended to Dr. Bill Franzin and Alex Salki of the Freshwater Institute (Department of Fisheries and Ocean) in Winnipeg for sharing their unpublished data and observations. Appreciation is also extended to Drs. Gordon Goldsborough and Ken Stewart, University of Manitoba, and Dr. Dale Wrubleski of Ducks Unlimited Canada for sharing their observations, and to Art Derksen, Manitoba Conservation for his review and comments.

References

Atton, M. 1959. The invasion of Manitoba and Saskatchewan by carp. Trans. Am. Fish. Soc. 88:203–205.

Campbell, K.B.; Derksen, A.J.; Remnant, R.A.; Stewart, K.W. 1991. First specimens of the rainbow smelt, *Osmerus mordax*, from Lake Winnipeg, Manitoba. Can. Field-Nat. 105(4):568–570.

Crivelli, A.J. 1983. The destruction of aquatic vegetation by carp. Hydrobiologia 106:37–41.

Fish Futures Inc. 1994. Zebra mussel survey of boaters and inspection of boats, summer 1994, border crossings and other key sites, Manitoba watershed. Unpublished report. Available from Manitoba Environment, Winnipeg, MB. 10 p.

Franzin, W.G.; Barton, B.A.; Remnant, R.A.; Wain, D.B.; Pagel, S.J. 1994. Range extension, present and potential distribution and possible effects of rainbow smelt in Hudson Bay drainage waters of northwestern Ontario, Manitoba, and Minnesota. N. Am. J. Fish. Manage. 14:65–76.

Goldsborough, G. 1999. What is happening to the Delta Marsh and why? Manitoba Environment, Winnipeg, MB.

Grier, J.W.; Sell, J.D. 1999. Potential of introducing aquatic nuisance species to North Dakota by boats. Unpublished report. Available from the North Dakota Game and Fish Department, Fargo, ND. 38 p.

King, A.J.; Robertson A.I.; Healey M.R. 1997. Experimental manipulations of the biomass of introduced carp (*Cyprinus carpio*) in billabongs. I. Impacts on water-column properties. Mar. Freshw. Res. 48:435–443.

King, D.R.; Hunt G.S. 1967. Effect of carp on vegetation in a Lake Erie marsh. J. Wildl. Manage. 31(1):181–188.

Lindgren, C.J.; Simpson C.M. 1999. The 1999 Manitoba aquatic nuisance species survey. What is the level of awareness in Manitoba? Manitoba Purple Loosestrife Project Report. 31 p. Unpublished report. Available from the Manitoba Purple Loosestrife Project, Winnipeg, MB.

Lougheed, V.L.; Crosbie B.; Chow-Fraser P. 1998. Predictions on the effect of common carp (*Cyprinus carpio*) exclusion on water quality, zooplankton, and submergent macrophytes in a Great Lakes wetland. Can. J. Fish. Aquat. Sci. 55:1189–1197.

Manitoba Conservation. 1999. Manitoba fisheries. Five year report to the legislature. Year ending 31 March 1999. Manitoba Conservation, Winnipeg, MB. 50 p.

O'Neill, C.R., Jr. 1996. Zebra mussel environmental tolerances: variables vs colonization potential. Dreissena! 6(5): 9. [Print and online]. http://sgnis.org/publicat/newsltr/drv6_5.pdf

O'Neill, C.R., Jr. Editor. 2001. North American range of zebra mussel. Dreissena! 11(4): 6–7.

Patalas, K. 1972. Crustacean plankton and the eutrophication of the St. Lawrence Great Lakes. J. Fish. Res. Board Can. 29:1451–1462.

Patalas, K.; Patalas J.; Salki A. 1994. Planktonic crustaceans in lakes of Canada (distribution of species, bibliography). Can. Tech. Rep. Fish. Aquat. Sci. 1954. v+218 p.

Remnant, R.A. 1991. An assessment of the potential impact of rainbow smelt on the fishery resources of Lake Winnipeg. M.Sc. thesis, University of Manitoba, Winnipeg, MB. 170 p.

Remnant, R.A; Graveline, P.G.; Brutecher, R.L. 1997. Range extension of the rainbow smelt, *Osmerus mordax*, in the Hudson Bay drainage of Manitoba. Can. Field-Nat. 111(4):660–662.

Robel, R.J. 1961. The effects of carp populations on the production of waterfowl food plants on a western waterfowl marsh. Trans. N. Am. Wildl. Conf. 26:147–159.

Roberts, J.; Chick, A.; Oswald, L; Thompson, P. 1995. Effect of carp, *Cyprinus carpio* L., an exotic benthivorous fish, on aquatic plants and water quality in experimental ponds. Mar. Freshw. Res. 46:1171–1180.

Robertson, A.I.; Healey M.R.; King A.J. 1997. Experimental manipulations of the biomass of introduced carp (*Cyprinus carpio*) in billabongs. II. Impacts on benthic properties and processes. Mar. Freshw. Res. 48:445–454.

Shay, J.M.; de Geus P.M.J.; Kapinga M.R.M. 1999. Changes in shoreline vegetation over a 50-year period in the Delta Marsh, Manitoba in response to water levels. Wetlands 19(2):413–435.

Sorba, E.A.; Williamson D.A. 1997. Zebra mussel colonization potential in Manitoba, Canada. Water Quality Management Section, Manitoba Environment. Rep. 97–07.

Stewart, K.W. 2000. Rainbow smelt has negative effects. The Winnipeg Free Press, 17 July 2000.

Swain, D.P. 1979. Biology of the carp (*Cyprinus carpio* L.) in North America and its distribution in Manitoba, North Dakota and neighbouring US waters. Manitoba Department of Mines, Natural Resources and Environment. MS Rep. 79–73. 36 p.

Wain, D.B. 1993. The effects of introduced rainbow smelt (*Osmerus mordax*) on the indigenous pelagic fish community of an oligotrophic lake. M.Sc. thesis, University of Manitoba, Winnipeg, MB. 131 p.

Wrubleski, D.A. 1998. The fish community of Delta Marsh: a review. Institute for Wetland and Waterfowl Research/ Ducks Unlimited Canada, Winnipeg, MB. 48 p.

Wrubleski, D.A.; Anderson M.G. 1999. The submersed aquatic macrophytes of east Delta Marsh, 1974 and 1997. University of Manitoba Field Station (Delta Marsh) Annu. Rep. 33.

Zrum, L. 1999. Abundance and species composition of zooplankton in the Nelson River estuary: baseline monitoring program 1998–year III. Report prepared for Manitoba Hydro by North/South Consultants Inc, Winnipeg, MB.

Photo with chapter title: Common carp. Courtesy Denis Rochon.

Alien Species in Saskatchewan: Impacts, Pathways, and Possible Solutions

*Richard H.M. Espie, Paul C. James,
and Kevin M. Murphy*

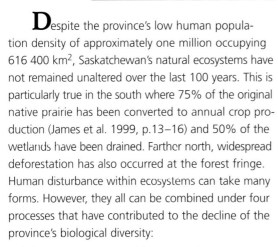

Despite the province's low human population density of approximately one million occupying 616 400 km², Saskatchewan's natural ecosystems have not remained unaltered over the last 100 years. This is particularly true in the south where 75% of the original native prairie has been converted to annual crop production (James et al. 1999, p.13–16) and 50% of the wetlands have been drained. Farther north, widespread deforestation has also occurred at the forest fringe. Human disturbance within ecosystems can take many forms. However, they all can be combined under four processes that have contributed to the decline of the province's biological diversity:

- habitat destruction and fragmentation,
- alien species invasion,
- pesticides and pollution, and
- overexploitation.

Of the four, most contemporary ecologists agree that the first two constitute the greatest threats to biodiversity, particularly when they act together. For example, most of Saskatchewan's native prairie now exists on small, highly isolated parcels surrounded by a matrix of agricultural lands in which many alien species thrive. The native parcels are therefore highly susceptible to invasion by these species, which in turn, lowers the ecological integrity of the invaded parcels. In Saskatchewan, little research has been conducted on the numbers, distribution, and impacts of alien species. However, many conclusions can be drawn from research carried out elsewhere on the problem in other regions with similar ecosystems. We will first consider the most important alien species threats to Saskatchewan's native biodiversity within its four major ecosystem types: aquatic, wetland, grassland, and boreal forest ecosystems. Consideration will then be given to the most important pathways of aliens into the province. Finally, a synthesis of the problem is presented together with some recommendations for further action. The threats identified in this paper are by no means an all-encompassing list of the problems associated with alien species in Saskatchewan; however, they are some of the most pressing issues.

Aquatic and Wetland Ecosystems

The movement of potentially invasive fishes and other aquatic organisms in North America continues to increase at an alarming rate (Courtenay 1993). Those who purposefully transfer and introduce alien aquatic organisms often claim that there has been relatively little environmental damage demonstrated from such releases. Of course, not all fish introductions will be bad, but with time each introduction will result in impacts to native biota, which may range from almost nil to major, including extinctions of native species. No natural ecosystem can accept an alien species without some change (Courtenay 1993). In aquatic biota, however, these impacts are often more difficult to detect and measure than in more familiar terrestrial habitats. In Saskatchewan and the rest of North America, millions of dollars have been, and are, annually expended by agencies and industry to import, culture, and directly introduce alien fishes; yet very little money is allocated to examine post-introduction impacts. Quite often, those who introduce fishes deliberately are more interested in impacts on fishes considered immediately useful to humans and not impacts on the overall native fish fauna or on aquatic and wetland biota in general.

Most introductions of alien fishes into Saskatchewan have stemmed from the desire to introduce potential sport fishes. Typically, these are predators that have a high capacity to affect the populations of aquatic organisms at lower trophic levels. Because so little is known of the natural workings of aquatic ecosystems, most potential impacts are based on assumptions about their cause and effect (Bright 1998). Because the changes were not determined and measured while they were occurring, little effect is assumed. Testing expected impacts before making an introduction is a far safer and more worthwhile approach than has characterized the history of fish introductions in Saskatchewan.

There are 57 known species of native fishes in Saskatchewan and 24 alien fish species have been introduced into the province over the last century. Currently, 11 species of alien fishes (16% of the total fish fauna) are thought to occur in Saskatchewan waters. Based on these numbers, the proportion of established aliens is very high when compared to other regions in North America. However, we have little information regarding the impacts of these introductions on the native aquatic biodiversity. There is some indication, though, that the effects of alien fish in some aquatic systems have been enormous.

For example, recent test netting in Last Mountain Lake has indicated that the alien common carp (*Cyprinus carpio* L.) constitutes the majority of fish biomass in the near-shore waters of the lake. In 1998, catches from trap nets yielded 20 000 common carp but only 20 bigmouth buffalo (*Ictiobus cyprinellus* (Valenciennes)) (Saskatchewan Environment and Resource Management, SERM, Regina, SK, unpublished data). It is believed that the population explosion of common carp in Last Mountain Lake has had a direct impact on the decrease in the bigmouth buffalo in the lake. As a result of this, along with other factors, the bigmouth buffalo is soon to be listed as an endangered species in the province. Saskatchewan's latest fish arrival, the grass carp (*Ctenopharyngodon idella* (Valenciennes)) was introduced in 1999 for weed control purposes in Cypress Hills Provincial Park. Should it ever establish in the natural waters of the province, it is likely to cause extensive ecological damage, as it has in the lower Mississippi River region of the United States.

Another problem involves the transfer of native fish from different parts of their range in Saskatchewan. This is common practice in fisheries management throughout North America and constitutes a form of genetic invasion. It could compromise the locally adapted gene complexes of the resident fishes, but little research on this problem has been conducted in the province. One case is the impact of transferring of walleye (*Stizostedion vitreum* (Mitchill)) which was investigated at the genetic level: variation in the mitochondrial DNA of this species was found to be similarly distributed throughout Saskatchewan. This means that two distant populations are likely to share most of their genes. Therefore, the within-province movement of walleye is considered to be acceptable and ecologically benign, but to what extent these results could be applied to other species remains unknown.

Intentional fish introductions are not the only problem. Aquaculture, if not properly regulated, represents perhaps the greatest source for future introductions of invasive fishes and fish diseases into North American waters, including Saskatchewan (Courtenay and Williams 1992). Aquaculturalists are attracted by species of foreign origin, possibly thinking that they will

provide higher financial returns. Some of the potential problems associated with aquaculture such as nutrition, disease, parasites, and water quality can be dealt with. A more significant challenge, however, is how to prevent escape or deliberate release into natural waters. Aquaculture uses natural stocks of organisms that have the potential to survive on their own should they escape or be released elsewhere. The ideal solution might be to ensure that only sterile fish are involved (Courtenay 1993). However, even sterile fish can cause ecological damage for several years before they die. In June 2000, 400 000 rainbow trout (*Oncorhynchus mykiss* (Walbaum)) escaped from an aquaculture operation on Lake Diefenbaker and are predicted to have a significant ecological impact on the system. Despite this, no new management practices were adopted and the normal fishing limits for this species were maintained.

In addition to fish, other taxa threaten Saskatchewan's aquatic ecosystems. For example, a significant threat comes from various aquatic weeds such as purple loosestrife (*Lythrum salicaria* L.) and alien invertebrate species that are currently expanding their ranges. Ducks Unlimited and other agencies have created the Saskatchewan Purple Loosestrife Eradication Project that is trying to pinpoint and eliminate this invader of wetlands. The most serious potential invertebrate alien is the zebra mussel (*Dreissena polymorpha* (Pallas)), which has made its way into the Missouri River system by hitchhiking on boating equipment. It is therefore just a matter of time until it arrives in Saskatchewan. Zebra mussels are detrimental to native mollusks through direct competition and are extremely costly to remove from infrastructure such as water intake pipes and pumping stations. They multiply rapidly and will completely encrust any available surface, including themselves. SaskPower, Saskatchewan's electrical utility, has already begun discussions with SERM concerning the potential impact of zebra mussels on its operations.

Grassland Ecosystems

Over the last 100 years, Saskatchewan's native grasslands have been heavily altered by agriculture and, for the most part, people in the southern portion of the province live in an artificial prairie of domesticated and wild alien plants. After the success of these has come the success of numerous other alien species. Throughout the history of human settlement in the south, there has been a prevailing philosophy of remedying the symptoms of poor land management, rather than their causes, by introducing alien species (Romo and Grilz 1990). The literature suggests that alien plants and arthropods present the grassland region with the greatest threats to its biodiversity and ecosystem integrity. Hundreds of alien plants in the south have become established by deliberate introduction to increase forage production. Unfortunately, we have little data other than a few anecdotal reports regarding the spread of many alien plants into native adjacent grassland areas in the province. The Saskatchewan Conservation Data Center is currently compiling data on the distribution of alien plants. For arthropods, recent research on native grasslands has revealed that of 157 beetle species recorded, 12 (8%) were alien (Pepper 1999). Even though there are limited data on the invasions of plants and arthropods in the grassland region, some general conclusions can still be drawn.

Alien invasions in the south are a permanent process of large-scale agricultural disturbance in Saskatchewan. The grassland region contains so many potential sources of disturbance to both the agricultural landscapes and to the adjacent native ones that the prospect for long-term stability is low. There are several dimensions to this instability from the perspective of an alien species. First, the reproductive boundary between many crops and weed species is porous. Most crops are members of "complexes", groups of closely related species with similar habitat requirements that can often interbreed. For example, all 12 species in the oat genus *Avena* will interbreed, including domestic oats and wild oats. This interbreeding may allow a newly introduced crop variety to pass some of its genes on to the crop's undesirable relatives (that is, genetic invasion). This may allow an invasion by alien hybrids into areas where they have not occurred before. Second, some aliens may move from agricultural lands to native prairie and thereby produce results that are damaging to the native ecosystems. There are many alien plants that could be included in this scenario.

One alien plant that is prevalent in both agricultural and native grassland areas is smooth brome (*Bromus inermis* Leyss.) (Romo and Grilz 1990). Smooth brome is native to southern Europe but has been widely introduced into Canada for forage production and erosion control, beginning in the late 1800s. The greatest invasions of smooth brome appear to be in moister areas of short grass and mixed prairie, as well as aspen parkland regions (Romo and Grilz 1990). Little attention appears to have been paid to controlling it in natural areas because this grass is widely used in agriculture.

Driver (1987) found that as brome-dominated grasslands establish, their use by native birds declined from 10 species to 2. Other work has shown that alien vegetation influences native bird communities by causing a change in the species composition (Wilson and Belcher 1989).

Another plant making inroads into the province's grassland region is leafy spurge (*Euphorbia esula* L.). First noted in Saskatchewan in 1928, it has become a prevalent alien plant in native grassland. Use of this plant by native herbivores is very limited due to the production of sticky latex within the plant that exudes when the surface of the plant is damaged. Because of its persistence and difficulty in eradication, leafy spurge control in areas of high infestation is extremely costly and difficult. Also, leafy spurge has become dominant in some mixed-grass prairie and changed the abundance and diversity of native plant and animal species because of its superior competitive advantages of rapid population growth, and allelopathic effects on other species (Steenhagen and Zimdahl 1979; Belcher and Wilson 1989).

Boreal Forest Ecosystems

The boreal forest region of the province is currently being affected by a growing number of human activities as a result of rapid economic expansion. These include oil and gas exploration and extraction, mining, forest harvesting, and their attendant road building. Current invasion of the forests by alien species is limited mostly to small herbaceous plants, such as the Canada thistle (*Cirsium arvense* (L.) Scop.). However, potentially important invasions are looming just over the horizon. Of particular concern is the potential invasion of alien forest pests and diseases. Another is plantation style or agroforestry, which could cause ecological damage to the northern forests in the same way that agriculture has affected the southern grasslands.

Agroforestry for commercial production of short-rotation woody crops has been in development in the southern hemisphere and China for about the last 40 years. Between 1965 and 1990, tropical plantation forestry area increased five- to sixfold and most of the countries involved have announced plans to double their plantation areas by 2010 (Bright 1998). North America is well behind in the development of agroforestry; Saskatchewan is one jurisdiction planning a major expansion. Quite often the use of alien tree species or hybrid crosses of alien and native trees is seen as a panacea to agroforestry. From a biological invasion standpoint, this is of considerable concern because some alien trees can become invasive. Generally, the use of hybrid plants increases the threat of a genetic invasion through crossbreeding with native species (Williamson 1996). Genetic considerations are also important because available studies conclude that the critical difference between invasion success and failure will often come from differences centered around 10 or fewer genes (Williamson 1996).

Native forest insects are an important part of the cycle of forest renewal and thus an integral part of the boreal ecosystem. The spread of alien forest insects is a growing threat to Canada's forests (CFS 1999). In the past century, they have had substantial impacts on forest health and biodiversity in different regions (CFS 1999). A recent arrival in Canada, and one of potential concern in Saskatchewan, is the Asian long-horned beetle (*Anoplophora glabripennis* (Mots.)). The beetle arrived in wood used as packing material for Asian imports. This beetle is well established in the United States and has already been the target of control campaigns in New York and Chicago where millions of dollars have been spent to cut down thousands of infected trees (CFS 1999).

Of particular concern to Saskatchewan is that the beetle attacks poplar (*Populus* spp.) plantations in China. If this beetle makes its way to Saskatchewan, the results could be disastrous for the aspen forests. Another alien beetle of potential concern is the eight-spined spruce bark beetle (*Ips typographus* (L.)). This spruce beetle is one of the most serious pests of spruce in its native range in Europe and Asia (Humphreys and Allen 1999). Adults have already been detected in British Columbia, Ontario, Quebec, and the Maritimes. It prefers to attack mature stands of spruce, and potentially all spruce stands across Canada are now at risk. The beetle is also a known vector of several fungi that are pathogenic to conifers (Humphreys and Allen 1999).

Although many of the alien pests and diseases listed by the Canadian Forest Service are not known to occur in Saskatchewan now, shifts in global climate, increased human disturbance and movement, and other factors could enable several pests to invade the province's forests at great ecological and economic cost. Currently, there is no estimate for Saskatchewan, or Canada, of timber losses due to invasive species in our forests (CFS 1999). However, losses due to alien forest pests in the United States are estimated to be about US$4 billion annually (Pimentel et al. 1999), which does not include the significant ecological costs to native forest biodiversity.

Pathways of Alien Species into Saskatchewan

The movement of goods globally contributes significantly to the spread of alien species around the Earth. It appears to be a universal feature of human culture to provide pathways to convey organisms far beyond their natural ranges. These pathways can be found in almost every economic industry in the province including agriculture, forestry, horticulture, interprovincial and international trade, fish and wildlife introductions, mining, oil and gas development, and the pet trade. In addition, organisms can invade Saskatchewan on their own from adjacent jurisdictions if they are not being controlled there. Saskatchewan's "biopollution" problems cannot be isolated to any one particular industry or human activity. Of course, some species are more likely to arrive here, either intentionally or accidentally, through certain pathways. Following is an examination of the invasion risks from four pathways that are important because of their currency and the challenges they pose due to their inherent regulatory and policy complexities: biological control, horticulture, game farming, and aquaculture. Although other pathways exist (for example, game fish introductions), these are controlled by established regulatory and policy mechanisms.

Biological Control

There are many types of biological control, but all focus on using biological agents to control undesirable species. Biological control almost always involves a predator, parasitoid, or pathogen. Two very different types of biological control are classical and inundative (Williamson 1996). In classical biological control, the target species is normally an arthropod or plant pest that attacks crops and does so partly because it has been introduced without its natural enemies, and thus has reached a high population density. The strategy of classical biocontrol is to search the target species' region of origin for suitable enemies, grow them in quarantine to rid them of their enemies and to test their host range, and then to release those species that are approved. The intention is to establish one or more control species that will reduce the pest at no further cost. Ideally both pest and control agent will then persist at low densities. Corrigan discusses this method extensively in this publication, page 279.

Inundative control uses a control agent as if it were a chemical pesticide, spraying it on the pest and getting a rapid kill (Williamson 1996). *Bacillus thuringiensis* is a native bacterium that produces a protein that is toxic to insects and is often used in this way. The advantage over ordinary chemicals is that the agent is usually more specific and shorter lived. It has been widely used in northern Saskatchewan to control spruce budworm (*Choristoneura fumiferana* (Clem.)). Pure inundative control does not usually involve the establishment of new species (although it could), but strategies that are between inundative and classical biological control usually do. Other recent examples of biological control in Saskatchewan include the use of grass carp (*Ctenopharyngodon idella*) and *Tilapia* spp. to control aquatic macrophytes and the use of flea beetles (assorted alien species) against the widespread leafy spurge. We believe the establishment of alien species as biological control agents should be used only as a last-resort management option.

Horticulture

Despite being a relatively minor industry in Saskatchewan, horticulture has globally been responsible for widespread distribution of some of the world's worst plant invaders. One survey of 1060 woody plant invasions globally found that of the 624 for which the origin of the invasion could be ascertained, 59% came from botanical gardens, landscaping, or other similar activities (Binggeli 1996). In North America, garden introductions are estimated to account for about 50% of the 300 or so serious pest plants in natural areas (Binggeli 1996). Many species that are known to be invasive remain on the market. For example, more than 60% of North America's worst weeds are still being sold by nurseries (Bright 1998). Plant breeders are also continually combing the genome of established garden plants for new varieties. In addition to escaped garden plants, horticulturalists and gardeners release many alien insects, such as ladybugs. For example, during the summer of 1999, large numbers of Australian ladybugs (unknown species) were released in Regina by well-meaning school children. The species does not appear to have established a permanent population. However, several alien species of ladybug are now established in Saskatchewan and although it has been speculated that native species are on the decline (J. Pepper, SERM, Regina, SK, personal communication), there has been no research directed at the problem.

Game Farming and Aquaculture

Game farming and aquaculture are rapidly developing industries in Saskatchewan and both use wild or only recently domesticated species, many of which are alien. The threats to Saskatchewan's biodiversity from game farming and aquaculture center mostly on the importation of alien animals into the province, ungulates and salmonids being paramount. These animals could escape and some could become invasive. Also, some alien ungulates likely will hybridize with native species, for example, the European red deer with elk (*Cervus elaphus* L.). Game farming and aquaculture practices also make possible the establishment of alien diseases and parasites when alien animals are brought into Saskatchewan. For instance, chronic wasting disease has been found in several domestic elk herds and in two wild mule deer (*Odocoileus hemionus* (Rafinesque)). There was no reported evidence of this disease in Saskatchewan before the advent of game farming. Increasing aquaculture activities in the province also increases the risk of establishing whirling disease, caused by the parasite *Myxobolus cerebralis* (Hofer), in farmed and wild salmonids. Whirling disease is not present in Saskatchewan now, but it has been found in bordering states. In this regard, game farming and aquaculture are no different than other forms of agriculture dealing with the domestication and use of alien species.

Possible Solutions

Alien species are now a common feature of the landscape and this is partly why they have attracted so little attention. For example, southern Saskatchewan is dominated by alien species and we have become used to living with their presence. In addition, the human lifespan is short compared to the scale of time on which natural systems operate, so that most people cannot perceive these impacts. As a result, we tend to minimize the process of invasion by calling established alien populations naturalized, as we do with the house sparrow (*Passer domesticus* L.). However, this is a mistake because it encourages people to view every invader as simply a native in the making (Bright 1998).

We also tend to view biological invasion as an isolated problem, yet we know that habitat fragmentation and bioinvasion work together. Less is known, however, about how global climate change may exacerbate the problem of invasive species. Changes in temperature and rainfall patterns are likely to stimulate many new invasions or accelerate invasions already under way. For example, the mild wet winters and dry summers predicted for western North America are likely to favor some of the worst weeds such as Russian thistle (*Salsola kali* L.).

Also, alien weeds such as cheatgrass or downy brome (*Bromus tectorum* L.), which is currently not a problem in Saskatchewan, may invade as the climate changes. Fast growing, highly invasive plants like cheatgrass may also benefit from the increased carbon content in the atmosphere, while slower growing natives, unable to use the carbon as quickly, may be replaced by the invaders (Bright 1998). Warmer waters are also likely to invite additional invasions in the province by warm water alien species.

There is little or no chance that the problems associated with alien species in Saskatchewan will solve themselves within any reasonable time frame without direct intervention. Also, invasive species in Saskatchewan, as elsewhere, are tightly bound to the economy and society. Thus, anyone addressing the problem of aliens through policy, legislation, and education must be cognizant of the local or regional situation. The following is a proposed framework for action concerning alien species within Saskatchewan. It includes monitoring, management, cooperation, legislation, and education.

Monitoring

Currently, there is very little information available on the number, abundance, dispersal, distribution, and spread of alien species in Saskatchewan. It might be best to begin with better known, extremely detrimental invasive species like leafy spurge. The monitoring of alien species should receive at least the same level of concern and staffing that endangered species receive, because the impact of aliens is certainly greater than the loss of a few native endangered species. These programs could dovetail, as with common carp and bigmouth buffalo discussed earlier. As new problem alien species arrive, we need a tracking process to control and eradicate them if discovered early enough, as aliens are often much more vulnerable in their initial stages of establishment. Overall though, the cheapest solution to controlling invasive aliens is to keep them out altogether. Specifically, a monitoring program could:

- establish standardized field protocols and a tracking process for alien species, in cooperation with the Saskatchewan Conservation Data Center;
- conduct research on, and monitor, alien species distribution and dispersal;
- locate and control the pathways of entry into the province; and
- establish and document the ecological impacts of aliens.

Management

Historically, the response to the arrival and dispersal of invasive aliens in Saskatchewan has been immediate and thorough when the species in question threatened agriculture; otherwise, the response has been limited. Alien species continue to be allowed entry simply because they are thought to pose no danger to agricultural enterprises.

Attempts by agencies and organizations to limit and/or eradicate harmful introductions should focus on the worst offenders first (for example, common carp, leafy spurge, etc.). Currently, the typical pattern of management is reactive rather than proactive, a situation that should be reversed. Ongoing evaluation of management programs would provide feedback that would allow for adjustment or abandonment of failing courses of action. The management of alien species should be an adaptive process that would incorporate the results of previous actions and adjust future recommendations accordingly. A cycle of data collection, management, evaluation, and analysis would facilitate this approach. Specifically, a management program could:

- identify the worst offenders for management action;
- incorporate the best information into control programs;
- focus on limiting the range and population control of existing aliens;
- take a proactive approach to the management of alien species; and
- use adaptive management to provide for adjustment of control measures.

Cooperation

Alien species are a societal concern yet we approach the issue piecemeal. There must be an increase in communication between all agencies and organizations. In many cases, these groups often work at cross-purposes, or retain information important to others. For example, the range condition of native grasslands is routinely conducted by federal and provincial pasture agencies in Saskatchewan. In the process, information is collected on the incidence of alien plants. This information should be shared so that possible strategies for their monitoring and/or control can be formulated with other agencies. Finally, control efforts of alien species should be coordinated among the various partners to be fully effective. Specifically, cooperation could:

- improve communication between all stakeholders;

- establish common goals and methods for the monitoring and control of alien species; and

- discuss and coordinate control measures among stakeholders.

Legislation

The biggest problem with existing legislation concerning alien species is its often imprecise and contradictory nature. Currently, there is a considerable amount of federal legislation in place. One shortcoming of the current federal legislation (in particular the *Wild Animal and Plant Protection and Regulation of International and Interprovincial Trade Act* [WAPPRIITA] and the *Plant Protection Act*) is its use of a list of undesirable aliens, the blacklist approach. This leaves the door open to any species not on the list and some of these will turn out to be invasive. A better approach is the Department of Fisheries and Oceans draft policy on fish introductions and transfers that puts the onus on the proponent to demonstrate that an introduction or transfer will have minimal ecological impact. The best approach is the white list approach, that is, permit entry only to those species that have been shown to have negligible impacts. Perhaps the proponent of an alien introduction that becomes invasive and destructive should be required to pay damages or to provide some sort of performance bond before the introduction.

Provincial legislation in Saskatchewan uses the same blacklist approach with many acts, such as the *Noxious Weeds Act*, *Pest Control Act*, and *Diseases of Animals Act*. Perhaps the strongest provincial legislation concerning alien species is the *Fisheries Act*, which includes almost all aquatic organisms. No one can import or introduce any alien aquatic organism without legal permission. Conversely, the *Wildlife Act* is weaker than the *Fisheries Act* because it focuses almost exclusively on vertebrates, except for endangered species. As discussed previously, the most threatening alien species are not vertebrates. Finally, the introduction of a new alien species into Saskatchewan is currently not subject to an environmental review process. Specifically, legislation could:

- establish consistent policy and legislative positions within governments regarding alien species;

- work with the federal government to extend WAPPRIITA to include more than just endangered species;

- work with governments to consider a white list approach to alien species;

- revise the *Wildlife Act* to include all alien species and not just vertebrates;

- require environmental assessment for the release of new alien species; and

- apply and enforce current legislation concerning alien species to the fullest extent.

Education

Unless society in general better understands the threats of alien species, all attempts to control them will fail. We need a more ecologically literate society that understands the risks, dangers, and costs of introducing these species. Statements like "they are hardy, disease-free, have few if any insect pests, and reproduce or propagate easily" often promote alien species. The general public needs to understand that these characteristics are precisely what make aliens such a serious ecological problem. Specifically, an education program could:

- prepare and distribute educational materials concerning the impacts of alien species, and

- work with industry to promote the use of native species in ecological restoration.

In addition, the control of alien species is both necessary and cost effective. Any delay in control only raises the price later, whether ecological or economic. The benefits of prompt action are often difficult to ascertain because they are measured mostly in terms of damage avoided. In the long term, the only hope against the impacts of ecological invasions is a public that values species being where they belong.

References

Belcher, J.W.; Wilson, S.D. 1989. Leafy spurge and the species composition of a mixed-grass prairie. J. Range Manag. 42:212–215.

Binggeli, P. 1996. A taxonomic, biogeographical and ecological overview of invasive woody plants. J. Veg. Sci. 7:121–124.

Bright, C. 1998. Life out of bounds: bioinvasion in a borderless world. W.W. Norton & Company, Inc. New York, NY.

[CFS] Canadian Forest Service. 1999. Alien forest pests [print and online]. Natural Resources Canada. Ottawa, ON.

Courtenay, W.R. 1993. Biological pollution through fish introductions. Pages 35-61 *in* B.N. McNight, ed. Biological pollution: The control and impact of invasive exotic species. Indiana Acad. Sci. Indianapolis, IN. 270 p.

Courtenay, W.R.; Williams, J.D. 1992. Dispersal of exotic species from aquaculture sources, with emphasis on freshwater fishes. Pages 49–81 *in* A. Rosenfield and R. Mann, eds. Dispersal of living organisms into aquatic ecosystems. Maryland Sea Grant Program, College Park, MD. 496 p.

Driver, E.A. 1987. Fire on the grasslands—friend or foe? Blue Jay 45:217–225.

Humphreys, N.; Allen, E. 1999. Eight-spined spruce bark beetle—*Ips typographus* [print and online]. Exotic Forest Pest Advisory 3, Natural Resources Canada, Canadian Forest Service, Pacific Forestry Centre, Victoria, BC. 4 p.

James, P.C.; Murphy, K.M.; Beek, F.; Seguin, R. 1999. The biodiversity crisis in southern Saskatchewan: A landscape perspective. Natural History Occasional Paper 24. Provincial Museum of Alberta, Edmonton, AB.

Pepper, J. 1999. Diversity and community assemblages of ground-dwelling beetles and spiders on fragmented grasslands of southern Saskatchewan. M.Sc. thesis, University of Regina, Regina, SK.

Pimentel, D.; Lach, L.; Ziniga, R.; Morrison, D. 1999. Environmental and economic costs associated with non-indigenous species in the United States. College of Agriculture & Life Sciences, Cornell University, Ithaca, NY.

Romo, J.T.; Grilz, P.L. 1990. Invasion of the Canadian prairies by an exotic perennial. Blue Jay 48:130–135.

Russo, E.; Cove, D. 1995. Genetic engineering. Dreams and nightmares. W.H. Freeman, London.

Samways, M.J. 1994. Insect Conservation Biology. Chapman and Hall, London.

Simberloff, D. 1996. Impacts of introduced species in the United States. U.S. Global Change Research Information Office. Palisades, NY. Saginaw Valley State University, University Center, MI. Consequences 2(2):12–22.

Simberloff, D.; Stiling, P. 1996. How risky is biological control? Ecology 77:1965–1974.

Steenhagen, D.A.; Zimdahl, R.L. 1979. Allelopathy of leafy spurge (*Euphorbia esula*). Weed Sci. 27:1–3.

Williamson, M. 1996. Biological invasions. Chapman and Hall, London.

Wilson, S.D.; Belcher, J.W. 1989. Plant and bird communities of native prairie and introduced Eurasian vegetation in Manitoba. Conserv. Biol. 3:39–44.

Photo with chapter title: Brome grass. Photo by A.A. Stillborn, Saskatchewan Environment and Resource Management, Regina, SK.

Marine and Estuarine Alien Species in the Strait of Georgia, British Columbia

Colin Levings, Dorothee Kieser,
Glen S. Jamieson, and Sarah Dudas

The Strait of Georgia, located in southwestern British Columbia between Vancouver Island and the mainland (Figure 1), is an important inland sea used for seafood production, recreation, and maritime industry. The human population around the strait is growing rapidly, and this trend is projected to continue well into the 21st century. Concern over the sustainability of marine and estuarine ecosystems in the strait has been documented in a number of reports (summarized in Wilson et al. 1994). In this paper we discuss a relatively new concern, the presence and role of alien species in the Strait of Georgia ecosystem. This topic has been investigated in detail for the Great Lakes–St. Lawrence River basin, where 157 species have been introduced in the past two centuries (de Lafontaine 2000). Preliminary information suggests that at least 17 species of introduced invertebrates have been recorded from Nova Scotian waters, but there have been no formal surveys for marine or estuarine alien species in the coastal regions of Atlantic Canada (Gretchen Fitzgerald, Dalhousie University, personal communication), nor do there appear to be any summaries or comprehensive studies for those areas.

A workshop (Tunnicliffe 1996) and collaboration with US scientists under the auspices of the British Columbia/Washington Georgia Basin Task Force (see Wilson et al. 1994) have focused attention on problems related to alien species in the strait. The biodiversity and

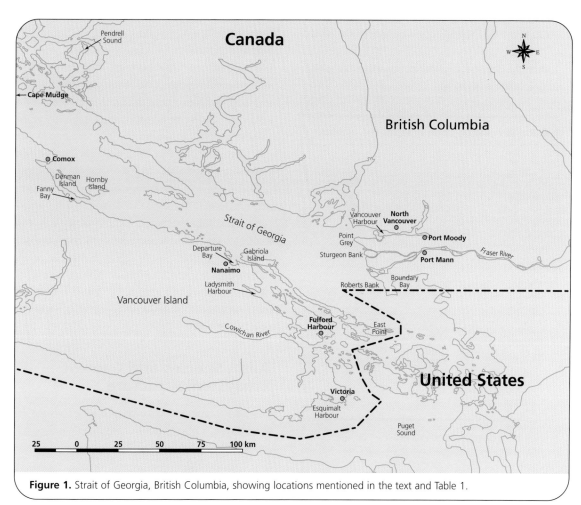

Figure 1. Strait of Georgia, British Columbia, showing locations mentioned in the text and Table 1.

community ecology of the plants and animals found there, as well as the presence of alien species, provide indices of the marine environmental quality of the strait. This information is important for implementation of Canada's *Oceans Act*, such as measurement of marine environmental quality. The arrival of pathogens or parasites can threaten aquaculture, as well as commercial fisheries, and the productive capacity of fish habitat can also be modified by intertidal plant species, such as purple loosestrife (*Lythrum salicaria* L.) (Grout et al. 1997) and cordgrass (*Spartina* spp.) (Simenstad et al. 1996). It is therefore important to document the baseline situation for alien species in the strait so that meaningful monitoring programs and ecological assessment projects can be developed.

Oceanographic and Geological Setting

Lying between about 49°N and 50°N, the Strait of Georgia could be classified as a temperate high-latitude marine ecosystem. Some of its important physical and oceanographic characteristics are presented in Table 1.

Table 1. Physical and oceanographic features of the Strait of Georgia.

Physical or oceanographic feature[a]	Value
Surface area	6800 km^2
Volume	1050 km^3
Mean depth	155 m
Mean yearly runoff	5800 m^3/s
Basin flushing time	
Summer	50–75 d
Winter	100–200 d
Representative annual temperature range	
Warm water (Ladysmith Harbour)[b]	5.5–20.6°C
Cool water (East Point)[b]	7.1–11.6°C
Representative annual surface salinity range	
Estuarine (Sturgeon Bank)[b]	0–25 ppt
(Cape Mudge)[b]	27.1–29.1 ppt
Shoreline length	
Rock and gravel beaches	2668 km
Sand and mud beaches	1053 km

[a] For the Strait of Georgia as a whole, except as otherwise indicated. Data from Levings et al. (1983) and references therein, except as otherwise indicated.

[b] Thomson 1994.

Note: ppt = parts per thousand; d = days.

The main body of the strait is relatively warm and brackish, with the oceanographic characteristics of a stratified estuary. In fact, the strait is an example of a classic northeast Pacific estuarine system. Most of the freshwater is contributed by the Fraser River, which has about 100 km of tidal freshwater in its lower reaches. There is considerable spatial variation in the properties of the water (especially temperature and salinity), and microhabitats can be found in particular tidal passes, embayments, and fjords (Thomson 1994). There is also significant spatial variation in substrates along the shoreline, pocket beaches of sand and mud being interspersed along a generally rocky shoreline on the east side of the strait north of Vancouver and around the Gulf Islands. The shoreline on the west side of the strait north of Nanaimo is mostly loose substrate, with extensive areas suitable for culture of intertidal bivalves.

Native Species and Original Ecosystem Structure

Both traditional ecological knowledge and early natural history data support the concept that the strait was recognizable as an ecosystem distinct from other parts of the British Columbia coast. Data from 1955 surveys enabled Bousfield (1957) to classify the shoreline invertebrate fauna into a distinct zoogeographic and ecological group that he called "reproductively warm–stenothermal brackish-water forms of the Strait of Georgia." This description correlates with the oceanographic regime described above. Traditional ecological knowledge provides insight into the diverse and productive ecosystems that sustained First Nations along the strait. Almost all of the estimated 350 native plants and animals gathered as food or medicine by coastal peoples had specific names (Turner 1997). In addition, earlier natural history specialists provided detailed descriptions of the intertidal algae (Collins 1913) and invertebrates (e.g., McLean-Fraser 1932), as summarized in Levings et al. (1983).

Alien Species and Current Ecosystem Structure

The number of alien invertebrate species reported from the Strait of Georgia increased exponentially in the last half of the 20th century (Figure 2), a trend that may also have extended to algae and vascular plants. The reasons for this increase are not known, and it may well be an artifact related to the greater effort expended in

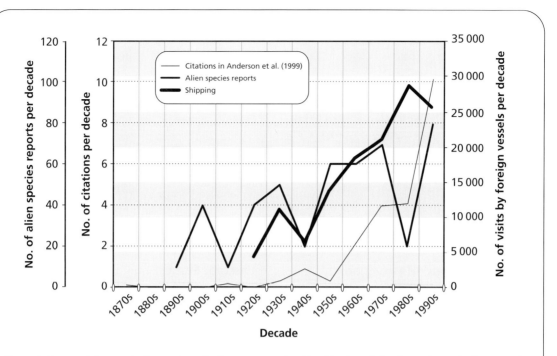

Figure 2. Temporal changes in the number of references reporting identification of alien invertebrates in the Strait of Georgia published in each decade, as cited in Anderson et al. (2000); the number of alien species of marine invertebrates reported from the Strait of Georgia in each decade, and the number of foreign vessels arriving in the Port of Vancouver in each decade.

ecological surveys. For example, it is possible that some of the hitchhiker species now being detected in surveys were actually introduced with oysters decades ago (see below). However, the increase may be real, influenced by increases in human activity in the region. There have been few regular, systematic ecological surveys in the strait, so identification of alien species has been spotty, with the best first-sightings data available for macroscopic species that are readily observable by fishers or lay persons.

The current provisional listing of alien species (including cryptogenic species, that is, a species that is not demonstrably native or introduced; Carlton 1996) for the Strait of Georgia is given in the Appendix. This list is based mainly on three internal reports, for algae (Lindstrom 1999), vascular plants (Taylor 1999), and invertebrates (Anderson et al. 2000), which have been archived and are available from the first author. The list also incorporates data from a more recent survey of published information (Dudas 2000), supplemented by the authors' personal knowledge. Preliminary results of a field survey (the Rapid Assessment Survey [RAS]) in February and March 1999 (Biologica Environmental Services 2000) at 33 locations in the strait are also included.

Methods for the literature and specimen searches differed somewhat between taxa. For algae and vascular

plants, the collection records in the University of British Columbia herbarium were reviewed. Distinctions were made between alien species and cryptogenic species for invertebrates and macroalgae but not for vascular plants. Authoritative local references and checklists were also used. For invertebrates, references and checklists were reviewed, but museum material was not consulted. In some cases, experienced taxonomists were consulted to ensure that relevant personal knowledge was considered. There were some differences among the three published reports in the criteria used to define a species as alien. The invertebrate report (Anderson et al. 2000) stipulated that to qualify as alien, the species must have been absent, as shown by ecological survey in a study area at a baseline time, and reported later as an established, isolated, self-propagating population. On the basis of this criterion, range extensions by themselves do not confer alien species status. This criterion was not always applied to the algae and vascular plant data (Lindstrom 1999; Taylor 1999). Because of timing and seasonality problems, the RAS did not effectively sample all habitats, nor did it necessarily involve sufficient effort for detailed identification of the flora and fauna collected. However, results that complement or extend the literature review are presented below. Data on fish, birds, and mammals were obtained from the literature or from previously unpublished work.

The total number of alien algae and invertebrate species reported here (89; see Appendix) is relatively high compared with the number reported from other temperate high-latitude marine ecosystems, where between 32 and 80 introduced species of these taxa have typically been recorded (Hines and Ruiz 2000). If all taxa (nonvascular and vascular plants, invertebrates, fish, birds, and mammals) are included, 118 alien species are known to have been reported from the strait. However, as mentioned above, there is considerable uncertainty in the data because of taxonomic identification problems and the lack of comprehensive biological surveys.

Phytoplankton and Macroalgae

Lindstrom (1999) found that 23 alien species of phytoplankton and macroalgae had been recorded in the strait, but this list is provisional because of taxonomic identification problems.

As far as is known, no species of alien phytoplankton have been introduced in the strait. However, taxonomic experts have speculated that some species of the dinoflagellate genus *Alexandrium* may have arrived with ballast water released into Vancouver Harbour (F.J.R. Taylor, personal communication *in* Lindstrom 1999).

The brown seaweed *Sargassum muticum* (Yendo) Fensholt, introduced from Japan with oysters, has been recorded at numerous locations in the strait since the 1940s. Two species of red algae, *Lomentaria hakodatensis* Yendo and *Gelidium vagum* Okamura, are cryptogenic but may also have arrived with oysters. *Lomentaria hakodatensis* was discovered at Gabriola Island in the 1960s and *G. vagum* at Hornby and Denman islands in the 1980s (Figure 1). Both may have been present for some time before they were found. It is likely that at least one species of *Ceramium* in local waters is introduced, as indicated by successful hybridization of this organism with North Atlantic *Ceramium*. A species frequently found in association with docks and harbors and occurring nearly worldwide in temperate waters is *Antithamnionella spirographidis*. It is assumed that the populations found in British Columbia, including those in Vancouver Harbour, are introduced. Several other species have been identified as possible introductions, although they should more correctly be called cryptogenic. For example, the red alga *Caulacanthus ustulatus* is likely a relictual endemic species on the west coast. The red alga *Porphyra mumfordii* and the brown alga *Scytothamnus* sp. or *Scytothamnus* cf.

fasciculatus are known only from southern British Columbia (Barkley Sound and the Strait of Georgia) and Oregon.

Other species of cryptogenic algae may represent examples of recent introductions. These include species of *Enteromorpha* and *Ulva*, *Capsosiphon fulvescens*, *Gayralia oxysperma*, *Percursaria percursa*, *Ulothrix implexa*, and *Ulothrix speciosa* among the green algae; *Colpomenia peregrina*, *Fucus spiralis*, *Melanosiphon intestinalis*, *Petalonia fascia*, and *Scytosiphon lomentaria* among the brown algae; and *Chondria dasyphylla* and *Grateloupia doryphora* among the red algae. At present there are no data to confirm where populations of these species occurring in the strait originated.

Vascular Plants

Taylor (1999) estimated that 21 species of alien vascular plants have been recorded in the tidal waters of the strait or adjacent to the intertidal zone. In addition, records of an additional 33 alien species from freshwater marshes close to tidal influence were found.

Some of these plants are well established and are strongly influencing the native species in their ecosystems. For most species, the date of first introduction is unknown. The six species listed below from freshwater tidal habitats represent a subsample of those recorded by Taylor (1999) and are the plants most likely to be adapted to tidal changes.

Saline tidal habitats

Dwarf eelgrass (*Zostera japonica* Ascherson & Graebner), possibly introduced with Pacific, or Japanese, oysters (*Crassostrea gigas* Thunberg) (Harrison and Bigley 1982), is fairly widespread on sand and gravel beaches in the strait. It has been recorded from Boundary Bay, from Roberts Bank, and near Comox. Saltmeadow cordgrass (*Spartina patens* (Ait.) Muhl.) has been located in marsh habitat at three locations: Comox (Buffet 1999), North Vancouver, and Port Moody (Williams 1999).

Freshwater tidal habitats

The most obvious example of an aggressive alien species is purple loosestrife, which is widespread in the brackish parts of the Fraser River estuary. The success of this plant appears to be increased by soil disturbance. The origin of the purple loosestrife in the strait is unknown, but accidental releases from nurseries are likely. There is an indication that yellow flag (*Iris pseudacorus* L.) may also be spreading; this plant merits monitoring because of its potential to outcompete native wetland species. The yellow flag is also probably a horticultural introduction. Reed canarygrass (*Phalaris arundinacea* L.), thought by some workers to be an introduced plant, is the dominant grass on sand beaches in the upper Fraser River estuary and appears capable of outcompeting the native sedges (*Carex* spp.) that live in these habitats. Lesser cattail (*Typha angustifolia* L.) is well established near Point Grey and shows every indication of expanding its range. This species is capable of hybridizing with the native species *Typha latifolia* L. The eastern mosquitofern (*Azolla caroliniana* Willd.) likely escaped from garden ponds. Taylor (1999) reported a large stand of this species in a drainage ditch near Sturgeon Bank.

Invertebrates

The list of 49 species presented by Anderson et al. (2000) has been augmented by the RAS and personal communications with experts, and we now estimate that 66 alien invertebrate species are present in the tidal waters of the strait. This estimate is conservative, given that the list does not include insects. The current list must still be considered provisional because some of the reports are incomplete and some of the taxonomic identifications are subject to change.

The majority of the alien species are gastropod and bivalve mollusks, tunicates, and amphipod crustaceans (see Appendix). The Atlantic oyster (*Crassostrea virginica* (Gmelin)) was intentionally brought into the strait between 1906 and 1933 (Elsey 1933). Intentional introductions of live Pacific oysters (Figure 3) from Asia

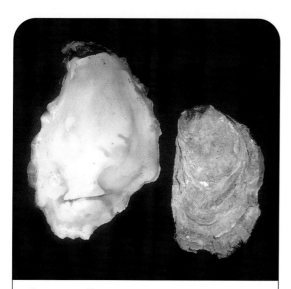

Figure 3. Pacific, or Japanese, oyster. Photo © Rick Harbo, Marine Images, Nanaimo, BC.

were conducted from 1912 or 1913 to about 1980 (Ketchen et al. 1983), although the first records of this species in the region date back to 1893 (Carlton 1979). During those years, numerous invertebrate "hitchhikers", such as the eastern drill (*Urosalpinx cinerea* (Say)) and the Manila clam (*Venerupis philippinarum* (A. Adams & Reeve)), were introduced along with the Atlantic and Pacific oysters.

The preliminary RAS found a number of species not reported in the literature, especially polychaetes. Another alien species of interest found in the RAS was the foraminiferan *Trochammina hadai* Uchio, which is normally found along the coast of northeast Asia (McGann et al. 2000). Its populations have recently expanded dramatically in San Francisco Bay, and the current report is the first record of this species from the strait.

Fishes

Five alien fish species have been recorded in the tidal waters of the strait, three of them from freshwater tidal habitats of the Fraser River estuary. McPhail and Carveth (1992) reported 11 alien fish species in the lower Fraser River, which included tidal and nontidal river habitat.

Saline tidal habitats

To date, no alien species of marine or anadromous fish are known to have established populations in the strait, although feral juvenile Atlantic salmon (*Salmo salar* L.) have been reported in Amor de Cosmos Creek, just north of the Strait of Georgia in Johnstone Strait (Volpe et al. 2000). Whether the presence of juveniles indicates a feral population is currently being debated (Andrew J.L. Thomson, Fisheries and Oceans Canada, Pacific Biological Station, personal communication), as returning feral adults have yet to be observed. Since 1987, 95 adults have been captured in the marine waters of the strait. In addition, since 1991, 48 adult Atlantic salmon have been captured or sighted in 13 different river systems draining into the strait. These were probably escaped specimens from the aquaculture industry (Thomson and Candy 1998) in Puget Sound and the inlets off the north end of the strait.

The American shad (*Alosa sapidissima* (Wilson)) is an Atlantic fish species periodically recorded from the Fraser River estuary (McPhail and Carveth 1992). As far as is known, shad have not become established in the strait, and the individuals found there may be infrequent migrants from alien populations elsewhere in the Pacific.

Freshwater tidal habitats

Three species of cyprinid fish, all native to either east of the Rocky Mountains or Asia, are well established in the tidal lower Fraser River: carp (*Cyprinus carpio* L.), brown bullhead (*Ameiurus nebulosus* (Lesueur)), and black crappie (*Pomoxis nigromaculatus* (Lesueur)). These three species were reported in surveys of tidal marshes near Port Mann on the Fraser River estuary (Whitehouse et al. 1993).

At the request of sportfishers, several trout species (Atlantic salmon, rainbow trout [*Oncorhynchus mykiss* (Walbaum)], brown trout [*Salmo trutta* L.], brook trout [*Salvelinus fontinalis* (Mitchill)], and lake trout [*Salvelinus (=Cristivomer) namaycush*]) were introduced into the Cowichan River in the 1930s. Brown trout have become established in the river, with natural reproduction first recorded in 1937 (Neaves 1949). Current river surveys indicate that on rare occasions (less than 5% of swim surveys), brown trout are found in the tidal area of the river (George Reid, British Columbia Ministry of Environment, Lands and Parks, personal communication).

Birds

The mute swan (*Cygnus olor* (Gmelin)), native to Europe, has established populations in the strait (Baron and Acorn 1997) at both the Cowichan River estuary and Fulford Harbour. The Canada goose (*Branta canadensis* (L.)), commonly found in nearshore habitats of the strait, is also an alien species, as its natural range is Ontario (Rob Butler, Canadian Wildlife Service, personal communication). As far as is known, these are the only alien marine or estuarine bird species in the strait.

Mammals

One semiaquatic alien mammal species is known from the strait, the Norway rat (*Rattus norvegicus* (Berkenhout)). This species is common in the intertidal zone near Vancouver Harbour, where populations originated from oceangoing ships. Brown et al. (1977) showed that the Norway rat was part of an intertidal food web involving mussels (*Mytilus* spp.) and the snowy owl (*Nyctea scandiaca* L.) on the Fraser River estuary.

Effects of Alien Species on Ecosystem Structure and Function

There are few detailed reports of ecosystem changes in the strait relating to alien species, which suggests that most introductions to date have been considered benign or have resulted in functional changes that have gone undetected. The main exceptions are Pacific oysters and Manila clams, which were introduced or arrived through the 20th century, and dark mahogany, or varnish, clams (*Nuttallia obscurata* (Reeve)), which became established more recently, in the 1990s (Gillespie 1995). The Manila clam is sufficiently abundant that it has become the main species both in the wild intertidal clam fishery (over the past two decades) and in clam culture. However, concern has recently been expressed that in the upper intertidal zone, dark mahogany clams, which are considerably bigger in British Columbia than in their natural habitat in Korea and Japan, may be displacing, or at least competing strongly with, Manila clams. A fishery is now being considered for the dark mahogany clam as well (Gillespie et al. 1999). Pacific oysters are also well established, and in parts of the strait they form extensive populations, increasing the availability of epibenthic shelter. These bivalves have extensively altered the intertidal ecology of nearshore areas, and, where they are being farmed, associated practices (e.g., removal of rocks and covering of the ground with netting) have an additional impact. There is no research on the effects of intensive raft culture of oysters on phytoplankton dynamics in the strait, but in other parts of the world intensive bivalve culture has modified local productivity (Grant et al. 1998).

A complete analysis of the effects of alien species would require detailed data on a variety of ecological processes, including competition, habitat change, predation, herbivory, hybridization, parasitism, toxicity, and bioturbation, as shown by Ruiz et al. (1999) for Chesapeake Bay. To date, ecologists have not observed widespread ecosystem changes, such as major shifts in predatory species or changes in the productive capacity of the strait, that could be related to the arrival of alien species; however, there have been no focused research projects on these topics.

The following are a few examples of effects suggesting that certain ecosystems and ecological processes in the strait are vulnerable to change caused by alien species.

The brown seaweed *Sargassum muticum* is the most obvious alien algal species in the strait. Some authors, working in the north Atlantic, have speculated that this species may compete for space with eelgrass (*Zostera marina* L.) (Den Hartog 1997). There are no local data on this topic.

According to De Wreede (1983), *S. muticum* may have negatively influenced the distribution and abundance of the native alga *Rhodomela larix* in the strait. De Wreede (1996) concluded that this was the only documented effect of an introduced algal species in British Columbia. However, in certain areas *S. muticum* has become a significant substrate for the deposition of spawn by Pacific herring (*Clupea pallasi* Valenciennes) (Humphreys and Hourston 1978, who use *C. harengus* for Pacific herring) and so is affecting the ecology of other species. There are anecdotal reports (Joe Stanhope, Qualicum Beach, BC, personal communication) that in parts of the strait in the 1940s and 1950s, *Sargassum* was so abundant that it affected fishing and nearshore boat usage. Today, it is not nearly so abundant, which suggests that local herbivores and other species are now cropping it sufficiently to maintain it in some degree of equilibrium with other species. Alternatively, oceanographic conditions in the strait may be constraining production of this alga at this time.

In estuarine or marine intertidal zones, dwarf eelgrass is the most widespread alien vascular plant species (Harrison and Bigley 1982). It lives at higher elevations than native eelgrass (*Z. marina*) and fosters local increases in invertebrate diversity (Posey 1988). Dwarf eelgrass is also used as food by waterfowl (Baldwin and Lovvorn 1994).

In freshwater tidal habitats, as well as ponds and lakes, purple loosestrife has the potential to dominate in the high intertidal zone, perhaps to the detriment of the natural detritus-based ecosystem, which depends on native sedges (Grout et al. 1997). Cordgrass (especially smooth cordgrass, *Spartina alterniflora* Loiset) has the potential to modify intertidal habitats by increasing sedimentation on sand and mud flats, to the detriment of native fauna as well as oyster rearing, as has been shown in Washington (Simenstad et al. 1996).

The Pacific oyster was imported as seed from Japan between 1912 or 1913 and 1980. The annual number of oysters imported peaked in 1951 at about 81 million (Elsey 1933; Ketchen et al. 1983). Over this 68-year period, the Pacific oyster had successful spatfalls in specific, widely separated areas in a number of very warm years, which resulted in intertidal communities completely dominated and structured by this species (e.g., Pendrell Sound and Ladysmith Harbour). Lewis and Quayle (1972) noted that because the Pacific oyster has no obvious predators except starfish (*Pisaster ochraceus* (Brandt) and *Evasterias* sp.) at lower intertidal levels, smaller invertebrates (e.g., barnacles, limpets, and littorinids) were unable to competitively displace

the oyster and, in fact, used oyster shells as substrates in the same way they would natural rock. The authors noted that in cooler regions of the strait (e.g., Departure Bay) the settlements of Pacific oysters were intermittent and relatively small, so other species could occur in greater abundance.

The introduction of Pacific oysters may have reduced harvesting pressure on certain native intertidal mollusks. However, even if harvesting was a factor in the decline of the native Olympia oyster (*Ostrea conchaphila* (Carpenter)), increased harvesting of the alien species was ineffective in halting that decline, and the endemic oyster is now rare in the strait. The reason or reasons for the decline remain unknown, but Gillespie (1999) has discussed issues related to this change.

The Japanese oyster drill (*Ceratostoma inornatum* (Recluz)), a gastropod, was introduced with oysters from Japan. Quayle (1988) recognized this drill as a major predator on cultured Pacific oysters, but its effects on native fauna are not well described.

The European green crab (*Carcinus maenas* L.) was found in 1999 and 2000 in Esquimalt Harbour, near Victoria, and on the west coast of Vancouver Island. To date, this alien species has not been recorded from the strait (see Department of Fisheries and Oceans green crab Web site <http://www.pac.dfo–mpo.gc.ca/ops/fm/shellfish/Green_Crab/default.HTML>), but it will likely extend its range into that area. There, it will become the first large intertidal predator introduced into the region and will compete with native crab species (Jamieson et al. 1998). The green crab is recognized as an able colonizer with the potential to significantly alter any ecosystem it invades.

Manila clams are extensively harvested in the region (Gillespie et al. 1999). The flesh of these clams is readily detached from the shell after cooking. This feature, coupled with a large stock biomass, ease of capture, strong market demand, and a relatively rapid purging of paralytic shellfish poison toxins from this species, has facilitated the development of new markets. Dark mahogany clams, because of their high abundance and their marketing characteristics, which are similar to those of Manila clams, are now being proposed for harvest as well. In this instance, the arrival of the alien species has had a significant economic effect. Ecosystem effects have not been studied, and because the different species have different habitat preferences and biological characteristics, the ecological consequences of these introductions are not clear.

Modes of Introduction and Control

Aquaculture

Aquaculture has historically been considered one of the most important avenues of importing alien species, and to date, seven species of algae, invertebrates, and fish have been intentionally brought into the Strait of Georgia from elsewhere in the world by the aquaculture industry (Table 2). However, the situation in British Columbia has now shifted. In earlier years, a "Johnny Appleseed mentality" allowed, if not encouraged,

Table 2. Species intentionally brought into the Strait of Georgia by the aquaculture industry and known associated or hitchhiker organisms that have become established.

Intentional introduction	Years stock was reared in the strait	Hitchhiker organisms
Pacific oyster (*Crassostrea gigas*)	1912 or 1913 to present (Elsey 1933; Ketchen et al. 1983)[a]	Manila clam (*Venerupis philippinarum*), Japanese oyster drill (*Ceratostoma fournieri*, now known as *Ceratostoma inornatum*), *Mytilicola orientalis* (a copepod), oyster-eating flatworm (*Pseudostylochus ostreaphagus*), Atlantic gribble (*Limnoria tripunctata*) (Quayle 1988); Japanese horn snail (*Batillaria cumingi*, now known as *Batillaria attramentaria*) (Quayle 1964); dwarf eelgrass (*Zostera japonica*) (Harrison and Bigley 1982); *Sargassum muticum* (De Wreede 1996)
Atlantic oyster (*Crassostrea virginica*)	1903 to about 1933 (Elsey 1933)	Eastern drill (*Urosalpinx cinerea*) (Elsey 1933); eastern mudsnail (*Nassarius obsoletus*, now known as *Ilyanassa obsoleta*) (Quayle 1964); softshell clam (*Mya arenaria*)[b] (Quayle 1964)
Blue mussel complex (*Mytilus edulis, M. trossulus, M. galloprovincialis*)	Considered introduced (Harbo 1997); part of complex that could involve two other species[c] (Coan et al. 2000)	Unknown
Atlantic salmon (*Salmo salar*)	1985 to present	Unknown
Kumamoto oyster (*Crassostrea sikamea*)	1999 to present (Coan et al. 2000; D. Kieser, unpublished data)	Unknown
Japanese weathervane scallop (*Mizuhopecten* [*Patinopecten*] *yessoensis*)	1985 to present (Harbo 1997); quarantined, then F_1 progeny cultured[d]	Unknown
Red algae (*Porphyra yezoensis*)	Late 1980s	Unknown (Sandra Lindstrom, personal communication)

[a] Since the publication of Ketchen's article in 1983, a total of 571 lots of oysters have been brought in from sources along the Pacific coast of North America. More recently, imports have also come from Hawaiian production facilities.

[b] Secondary introduction from Atlantic oysters transplanted into San Francisco Bay in 1874 (Quayle 1964; Coan et al. 2000).

[c] Twelve imports in recent years, 11 from the Pacific Northwest and 1 from Prince Edward Island, went into quarantine at the Pacific Biological Station, Nanaimo, BC. First-generation (F_1) progeny were later cultured in the Strait of Georgia.

[d] Four imports from Japan between 1989 and 1993 went into quarantine at the Pacific Biological Station, Nanaimo, BC. First-generation (F_1) progeny were later cultured in the Strait of Georgia.

importation of any alien species of interest to aquaculture, sport-fishing groups, and other interested parties, but there is now a well-regulated procedure for the importation of new species. Before a new species is licensed for introduction, the risks must be reviewed, to evaluate and prevent any unacceptable biological effects on local stocks and their environment. It must be determined, on the basis of biological characteristics, whether the species to be introduced has the potential to become established in the area of introduction, whether it could have genetic effects on local stocks (e.g., through interbreeding or through impact on survival), and whether it might have negative ecological impacts (e.g., through displacement, predation, or competition for food). Another major aspect to be considered is the potential for other species, either disease agents or hitchhikers that might become established in local waters, to accompany the introduced species and to affect local stocks.

In British Columbia, the body that carries out the review of risks and makes recommendations to the licensing agencies is the federal–provincial Fish Transplant Committee. This committee consists of members from the Department of Fisheries and Oceans (DFO), which has jurisdiction over the release of live fish into fish habitat and the transfer of live fish into fish-rearing facilities (sections 55 and 56 of the Fishery [General] Regulations [DFO 1993], which apply in most provinces); the provincial Ministry of Agriculture, Fisheries and Food, the agency that issues aquaculture licenses; and the Ministry of Environment, Lands and Parks, which issues licenses under the *Wildlife Act* for transporting, possessing, and trafficking in live fish. This committee evaluates the risks, taking into account the components related to genetic impact, disease transfer, and ecological alterations outlined above. Importations are recommended for approval only if the risk to local species is considered minimal (Stephen 1998).

British Columbia's Fish Transplant Committee and equivalent committees in other provinces and territories will be integral components of the risk review process proposed in the National Code on Introductions and Transfers of Aquatic Organisms (DFO 2002). The concept of a thorough risk assessment, similar to the process carried out by British Columbia's Fish Transplant Committee and the process proposed by the national code of conduct, is well tested in other policy areas and should minimize negative impacts on local species, provided transfers and importations are permitted only if the risks are determined to be minimal. There are

two main problems with risk assessment: the scientific information available for the assessment is often limited and unforeseen events may occur. However, such assessments represent the best avenue available for considering and minimizing potential impacts on local stocks.

Importation of Salmon and Other Finfish

The Canadian Fish Health Protection Regulations (DFO 1984) govern the importation of fish in the family Salmonidae. These regulations were developed in the 1970s to prevent the importation of fish disease agents, which could seriously affect native stocks in areas where fish are imported. To prevent the importation of alien disease agents, imported fish must originate from fish farms or stocks that have been certified as free of certain diseases (Schedule II of the regulations). To become certified, a farm must undergo a series of at least four inspections, along with laboratory testing of samples of all stocks on site. To remain certified, the farm must undergo two inspections and laboratory testing of fish each year.

Atlantic salmon are not native to British Columbia. However, in the early 1900s an effort was made to establish this species in the province, along with other sport fish such as brown trout (Neaves 1949). Millions of Atlantic salmon eggs were introduced into rivers draining into the strait. In contrast to the situation for brown trout, which became established in one river system (the Cowichan River, as described above), there is no indication that any self-sustaining populations of Atlantic salmon have become established. In the 1980s, the aquaculture industry became interested in Atlantic salmon because of its market value and its suitability for aquaculture (it has a high food-conversion efficiency), and Atlantic salmon now make up about 75% of the salmon cultured in British Columbia (Ann McMullin, British Columbia Salmon Farmers Association, personal communication). In the 1980s, many aquaculture operations were located in the inlets of the strait, but almost all farms have now been relocated outside the strait. Table 3 lists importations of Atlantic salmon eggs since 1995 (Fish Transplant Committee, unpublished data).

Before the first importation of Atlantic salmon by the aquaculture industry, regulatory agencies recognized the risk of potential introductions of disease agents. Regional policies were developed to complement the national Fish Health Protection Regulations. For instance, for the importation of any salmon species into British Columbia, shipments must not only be licensed under

Table 3. Importations of Atlantic salmon eggs, 1995–1999.

Year	No. of eggs imported (millions)
1995	0.775
1996	1.5
1997	1.6
1998	2.4
1999	2.4

the regulations but must also meet the following policy requirements for regional salmonid importation. 1) The health of all stocks at the source facility has been certified according to Canadian Fish Health Protection Regulations. 2) The importation involves only surface-disinfected eggs. Live fish are not permitted because of a greater risk of hitchhiker species, including fish pathogens. An example of inadvertent transfer of a fish parasite with movement of Atlantic salmon juveniles was the dispersal of the trematode *Gyrodactylus salmonis* to Norwegian rivers, where it affected the survival of local salmon stocks (Johnsen and Jensen 1986). Another well-known example of parasites being transferred with live fish is the spread of trout whirling disease throughout North America. The causative parasite, *Myxobolus cerebralis* (Hofer), is thought to be the cause of the decline of trout populations in major fishing rivers such as the Madison River in Montana (Nickum 1999). Such parasites cannot accompany eggs. 3) The source facility must be able to demonstrate reliable management of fish health both at the specific site and in the watershed where the facility is located. 4) Once transferred to British Columbia, imported eggs must be held in a federally approved quarantine system until their health has been tested repeatedly. Only after meeting the conditions of quarantine can smolts be transferred to sea cages.

For other fish species being considered for introduction into aquaculture operations or natural fish habitat, the Fish Transplant Committee evaluates applications on a case-by-case basis. The license requirements are usually modeled on the federal Fish Health Protection Regulations.

Numerous fish species have been introduced into freshwater habitats for purposes of recreational fishing (Crossman and Cudmore 2000), but there are no instances of intentional fish releases into the tidal waters of the strait for recreational purposes.

Importation of Shellfish

The oyster industry in British Columbia was originally based on the native Olympia oyster (*Ostrea conchaphila*). For example, between 1913 and 1915, a total of 1843 barrels of the native oyster were harvested (Elsey 1933). However, other species were quickly introduced for culture. Atlantic oysters were imported first, with limited success, and in 1912 or 1913, the Pacific oyster was introduced into Ladysmith Harbour and Fanny Bay. By 1925, the latter species was reproducing in British Columbia waters (Quayle 1988). The British Columbia shellfish farming industry has since grown considerably and now produces in excess of 53 000 t (tonnes) of oysters annually. It also produces 7000 t annually of Manila clams (Ruth Salmon, British Columbia Shellfish Growers Association, personal communication), a species that arrived as a hitchhiker with Pacific oysters (as described above). The Manila clam itself is now cultured, but other hitchhiker species, such as the Japanese oyster drill and the flatworm *Pseudostylochus ostreaphagus* (Hyman), are less desirable. Table 2 lists other hitchhiker species thought to have accompanied early oyster shipments. At present, there is some seed production in the strait, but British Columbia bivalve farmers currently import most of the seed needed for culture from the United States. To limit introduction of new alien species, including shellfish pathogens and parasites, all importations of shellfish for culture into British Columbia are now permitted only under license, and a license is issued only if conditions to prevent the introduction of pathogens and hitchhikers are met. A bilateral system between Canada and the United States limits the sources of imports of bivalve seed for intertidal culture to facilities that are certified for shellfish health. Only bivalve larvae or seed can be shipped, which also reduces the likelihood of importing epiphytes and other hitchhiker species.

DFO policy requires that proposals for imports of new species of shellfish be reviewed in detail and that a risk assessment be undertaken before approval is granted. As an example, a recent assessment of Kumamoto oysters (*Crassostrea sikamea* (Amemiya)) for import indicated that because the source of the oysters was a health-certified farm, the main concern was the possible establishment of this species and its potential to interbreed with other introduced oyster species already in the area. On comparison of the temperature and salinity requirements of the Kumamoto oyster for spawning with local oceanographic conditions in the strait, it was concluded that these oysters would be unlikely to reproduce in British Columbia waters, and approval was ultimately given to import Kumamoto oyster seed.

Ballast Water and Shipping

Shipping activity has the potential to bring organisms into the region by either hull fouling or ballast water. Figure 2 shows that the number of ships arriving in Vancouver Harbour has increased exponentially over the past few decades. However, even before shipping records were being maintained, alien species were probably arriving as fouling organisms on ship hulls or possibly in solid ballast.

A preliminary survey by Levings et al. (1998) showed that ballast water in ships using Vancouver Harbour and other ports around the strait contained up to about 13 000 invertebrates/m^3. The arrival and rapid spread of some alien invertebrate species in recent years may be attributed to ballast water. The oligochaete *Tubificoides benedii*, normally found in the Atlantic, is now established in Vancouver Harbour, in an area where major volumes of ballast water are discharged each year. Between June and September 1999, the inner Vancouver Harbour received about 4.9 Mt of ballast water (Vancouver Port Authority, unpublished data).

The mandatory ballast-water exchange protocol imposed by the Vancouver Port Authority is an example of a short-term progressive measure to reduce the arrival of alien species through shipping (Levings 1999). Unfortunately, mid-ocean exchanges do not eliminate all coastal organisms and their efficiency can vary widely. In one of the few estimates available, efficiency of exchange was assessed at only about 67% (Locke et al. 1993). As an example, the Asian copepod *Pseudodiaptomus marinus* was recently found in the ballast water of a vessel in Vancouver Harbour after ballast-water exchange (Levings et al. 1998). Furthermore, ships from the west coast of North America north of Cape Mendocino in California are exempt from the Vancouver Port Authority protocol, as are cruise ships and vessels carrying less than 1000 t of ballast. In the long term, treatment procedures to kill alien species in ballast water on all vessels will be required. Collaborative research and development projects on new treatment options are currently under way (Sutherland et al. 2001).

International agreements are being developed that could decrease the use of tributyl tin compounds in antifouling paint for ships' hulls (Evans and Smith 1999). However, if effective alternative coatings are not used, perhaps for economic reasons, increases in alien fouling species may result.

The Norway rat probably established populations in the strait in the 1800s, arriving on ships from elsewhere in the world. Rodent barriers on mooring lines and other measures by Canadian public health officials have almost eliminated the prospect of rodent populations moving ashore from vessels and vice versa.

Live Seafood and Fish

The live seafood trade also offers possibilities for the introduction of alien species into the strait, because most such importations are not reviewed according to the risk assessment process administered by the federal–provincial Fish Transplant Committee.

Federal regulations currently require licenses only for the intentional introduction of live fish, shellfish, and crustaceans into fish-bearing waters or fish-rearing facilities (Sections 55 and 56 of the DFO Fishery [General] Regulations [DFO 1993]). In addition, the importation of live fish of certain species in a total of 48 genera is prohibited under Section 5 of the Pacific Fishery Regulations (DFO 1993). Although some of these "prohibited" species are licensed for sale in seafood markets, most of the species imported for the live seafood trade are not listed in the regulations and hence are not subject to risk assessment.

As an example, all eel species (*Anguilla* spp.) are listed as prohibited for intentional live importation, and no anguillids are native to the Pacific coast of North America, yet there are reports that anguillid eels have been caught in San Francisco Harbor. The route of introduction is thought to have been shipments of live seafood (Williamson and Tabeta 1991). Although the likelihood of live seafood finding its way into fish-bearing waters may seem limited, there are examples from the strait where this has occurred. There have been several newspaper reports of Atlantic lobsters, probably *Homarus americanus*, being found by divers near both Vancouver Harbour and Victoria Harbour. This species is routinely shipped live to seafood markets. In the past, religious groups have released into the strait a variety of live food fish species available from British Columbia suppliers. There are no documented examples of such releases leading to the establishment of alien species, but the potential exists. Through an educational program, such groups are now encouraged to release only food fish that were harvested by local commercial fisheries (Fish Transplant Committee, unpublished data).

Plant Nurseries, Algae Culture, and the Aquarium Trade

Plant nurseries and suppliers are another likely source for introduction of alien aquatic vascular plants. Long-recognized problem species such as purple loosestrife continue to be sold by unaware new suppliers, even though environmental agencies and fish and wildlife groups have undertaken intensive educational campaigns to reduce their spread. Little information is available on intentional introductions of algae. However the red alga *Porphyra yezoensis* Ueda, introduced from the northwest Pacific in the 1980s as a potentially harvestable species, has not become established in the strait (Sandra Lindstrom, University of British Columbia, personal communication).

There is limited aquarium trade in temperate marine fish species. A small survey of some major wholesale aquarium suppliers in the Vancouver area indicated that marine ornamental species consistuted a relatively small proportion of their imports (D. Kieser, unpublished data) These fish are considered an expensive specialty, and importers stated that all species currently being sold came from tropical areas. Deliberate releases of marine aquarium fish into the strait seem unlikely, and because of their tropical origins such fish would be unlikely to survive and establish self-sustaining populations. However, large numbers of ornamental temperate freshwater fishes are imported annually, including thousands of ornamental carp (koi) (*Cyprinus carpio*) for aquariums and backyard ponds. Their importation into British Columbia is controlled, and the health status of imported fish is monitored when they are first brought in, but there are no controls on their distribution after an initial three-week isolation period. Ponds may be in locations subject to periodic natural flooding, and birds and other predators could inadvertently transfer pond fish into natural fish habitats, including tidal habitats in the lower reaches of rivers draining into the strait.

Research and Teaching

The potential spread of alien species through accidental or intentional release by government researchers has been reduced through the review mechanisms of the federal–provincial Fish Transplant Committee. There is limited information on controls implemented by educational institutions to reduce the spread of alien species by academic researchers and teaching laboratories. However, special precautions have been put in place at the University of British Columbia (UBC n.d.).

Control or Eradication of Established Alien Species

As experience elsewhere in the world has shown, control or eradication of an alien species once it has become established can be extremely costly and difficult, if indeed it is even possible. Control is effectively impossible for species with pelagic larval stages that are dispersed by ocean currents, such as the green crab (see green crab Web site <http://www.pac.dfo–mpo.gc.ca/ops/fm/shellfish/Green_Crab/default.HTML>) and for vascular plants with copious seed production, such as purple loosestrife. Although a variety of measures have been undertaken to control some alien species found in the strait, documentation of their efficacy is often lacking. For example, trapping (Quayle 1988) and freshwater immersion (Mueller and Hoffman 1999) have been used in the past to control the spread of oyster drills, but this species persists. Physical removal and biological control with insects have been used in attempts to reduce the spread of purple loosestrife in the Fraser River estuary, but success has not been documented for either technique (Grout et al. 1997). Physical removal to eradicate cordgrass has been conducted in the adjacent waters of Puget Sound (Reeves 1999), but this technique has not been attempted in the strait.

Summary and Conclusions

This review of alien species in the Strait of Georgia shows that this important inland sea has more alien species than have typically been recorded in other temperate (40°N to 60°N) marine ecosystems. Because of the estuarine nature of the strait and the presence of the Port of Vancouver, the southeast portion of the strait may be particularly vulnerable to the introduction of alien species from brackish coastal waters elsewhere in the world. Alien species with broad tolerances for temperature and salinity, such as the dark mahogany clam and the green crab, are likely to spread from there throughout the rest of the strait.

Because of the variety of pathways by which alien species can enter the strait, it is difficult to implement effective control mechanisms to minimize or prevent introductions. However, programs already in place, such as quarantine procedures, ballast-water control and management, and public education, could be expanded to help reduce the risk. Research to identify the alien species that are poised to invade the strait from elsewhere in the world is needed, to ensure that attention is focused on appropriate control mechanisms. A species profile approach, building on the comprehensive surveys of alien species for nearby waters (e.g., Puget Sound, Washington [Cohen et al. 1998], and Prince William Sound, Alaska [Hines and Ruiz 2000]), may be most useful here.

For established species for which control or eradication may be possible, an adaptive management approach is needed because of the inherent natural variability of marine ecosystems. In aquaculture, identification of potentially harmful disease organisms that could be introduced is important. An international network of disease specialists can provide assistance. Current import regulations and policies have stringent control procedures to minimize inadvertent importation of fish pathogens. If such organisms do arrive in British Columbia with fish intended for aquaculture, it may be possible to control some of them with medication and quarantine provided the introduced fish species are first maintained in land-based containment systems. On the other hand, species that create structure in certain ecosystems (e.g., smooth cordgrass in estuaries) are typically almost impossible to control once they have gained a "beachhead"; such species can cause irreversible changes to habitat or ecosystem function (Ruiz et al. 1999).

Acknowledgments

Funding for major portions of the work reported here was provided by the DFO Oceans Act Implementation Fund and the DFO Environmental Sciences Strategic Research Fund. We are grateful to Edward Anderson, Sheila Byers, Sandra Lindstrom, and Terry Taylor for their assistance with literature surveys and expertise on particular taxa. Thanks are also owed to Valerie MacDonald (Biologica Environmental Services), and Beth Piercey (Science Branch, DFO) for fieldwork during the Rapid Assessment Survey in the Strait of Georgia. Officials from the Vancouver Port Authority helped obtain archived data on shipping. Deborah Koo, Canadian Food Inspection Agency, provided information on the importation of live seafood.

References

Anderson, E.A.; Austin, W.C.; Byers, S.; Lipovsky, S. 2000. Literature review on nonindigenous invertebrates of the Strait of Georgia. Edward Anderson Marine Sciences, Sidney, BC. Unpublished report prepared for Fisheries and Oceans Canada, West Vancouver Laboratory, West Vancouver, BC. 96 p.

Baldwin, J.R; Lovvorn, J.R. 1994. Expansion of seagrass habitat by the exotic Zostera japonica, and its use by dabbling ducks and brant in Boundary Bay, British Columbia. Mar. Ecol. (Prog. Ser.) 103:119–127.

Baron, N.; Acorn, J. 1997. Birds of coastal British Columbia. Lone Pine Publishing, Vancouver, BC. 240 p.

Biologica Environmental Services. 2000. Report on preliminary rapid assessment survey of the Strait of Georgia, February and March 1999. Victoria, BC. Unpublished report prepared for Fisheries and Oceans Canada, West Vancouver Laboratory, West Vancouver, BC. 22 p.

Bousfield, E.L. 1957. Ecological investigations on shore invertebrates of the Pacific Coast of Canada, 1955. Bull. Natl. Mus. Can. 147:104–113.

Brown, D.A.; Bawden, C.A.; Chatel, K.W.; Parsons, T.R. 1977. The wildlife community of Iona Island jetty, Vancouver, BC and heavy-metal pollution effects. Environ. Conserv. 4:213–216.

Buffet, D., for Ducks Unlimited. 1999. Records of Spartina in the Strait of Georgia. In Minutes of the Spartina workshop held at Canadian Wildlife Service offices, Delta, BC, 4 October 1999.

Carlton, J.T. 1979. History, biogeography, and ecology of the introduced marine and estuarine invertebrates of the Pacific coast of North America. Ph.D. thesis, University of California, Davis, Davis, CA. 904 p.

Carlton, J.T. 1996. Biological invasions and cryptogenic species. Ecology 77:1653–1655.

Coan, E.V.; Scott, P.V.; Bernard, F.R. 2000. Bivalve seashells of western North America. Santa Barbara Mus. Nat. Hist. Monogr. No. 2. 764 p.

Cohen A.; and 17 others. 1998. Puget Sound expedition. A rapid assessment survey of nonindigenous species in the shallow waters of Puget Sound. Unpublished report prepared for Washington State Department of Natural Resources and United States Fish and Wildlife Service. 37 p.

Collins, F.S. 1913. The marine algae of Vancouver Island. Can. Geol. Surv. Victoria Mem. Mus. Bull. 99–137.

Crossman, E.J.; Cudmore, B.C. 2000. Summary of fishes intentionally introduced in North America. Pages 99–112 in R. Claudi and J.H. Leach, eds. Nonindigenous freshwater organisms. Lewis Publishers, Boca Raton, FL. 464 p.

de Lafontaine, Y. 2000. Species introduction in the St. Lawrence River: how does it compare to the Great Lakes? Page 306 *in* Proceedings of the 10th International Aquatic Nuisance Species and Zebra Mussel Conference, Toronto, ON, 13–17 February 2000. The Professional Edge, Pembroke, ON.

Den Hartog, C. 1997. Is *Sargassum muticum* a threat to eelgrass beds? Aquat. Bot. 58:37–41.

De Wreede, R.E. 1983. *Saragassum muticum* (Fucales, Phaeophyta): regrowth and interaction with *Rhodomela larix* (Ceramiales, Rhodophyta). Phycologia 22:153–160.

De Wreede, R.E. 1996. The impact of seaweed introductions on biodiversity. Global Biodiversity 6(3):2–9.

[DFO] Department of Fisheries and Oceans. 1984. Fish health protection regulations: manual of compliance. Fish. Mar. Serv. Misc. Spec. Publ. 31 (Rev.). 43 p.

[DFO] Department of Fisheries and Oceans. 1993. Fishery (general) regulations SOR/93-52, amended to 31 December 2000. Ottawa, ON. Available from: http://laws.justice.gc.ca/en/F-14/SOR-93-53 (cited 22 November 2001).

[DFO] [Department of] Fisheries and Oceans Canada. 2002. National code on introductions and transfers of aquatic organisms [print and online]. Ottawa, ON. http://www.dfo-mpo.gc.ca/science/OAS/aquaculture/nationalcode/codedefault_e.htm

Dudas, S. 2000. Data base on literature searches for non-indigenous species in the Strait of Georgia. Unpublished report on file at Fisheries and Oceans, West Vancouver Laboratory, West Vancouver, BC.

Elsey, C.R. 1933. Oysters in British Columbia. Biol. Bd. Can. Bull. 34. 34 p.

Evans, S.M.; Smith, R. 1999. The effects of regulating the use of TBT-based antifouling paints on TBT contamination. Session 5G *in* Proceedings of Oceans 99: Annual Meeting of Marine Technology Society and Institute of Electrical and Electronics Engineers, Seattle, WA, 12–17 September 1999.

Gillespie, G.E. 1995. Distribution and biology of the exotic varnish clam, *Nuttallia obscurata* (Reeve 1857), in the Strait of Georgia, British Columbia. J. Shellfish Res. 14:578.

Gillespie, G.E. 1999. Status of the Olympia oyster, *Ostrea conchaphila*, in Canada. Fisheries and Oceans Canada, Ottawa, ON. Canadian Stock Assessment Secretariat Research Document 99/150. 36 p.

Gillespie, G.S.; Parker, M.; Merilees, W. 1999. Distribution, abundance, biology and fisheries potential of the exotic varnish clam (*Nuttallia obscurata*) in British Columbia. Fisheries and Oceans Canada, Ottawa, ON. Canadian Stock Assessment Secretariat Research Document 99/193. 16 p.

Grant, J.; Stenton–Dozey, J.; Monteiro, P.; Pitcher, G.; Heasman, K. 1998. Shellfish culture in the Benguela system: a carbon budget of Saldanha Bay for raft culture of *Mytilus galloprovincialis*. J. Shellfish Res. 17:41–49.

Grout, J.; Levings, C.D.; Richardson, J.S. 1997. Decomposition rates of purple loosestrife (*Lythrum salicaria*) and Lyngbyei's sedge (*Carex lyngbyei*) in the Fraser River estuary. Estuaries 20:96–102.

Harbo, R.M. 1997. Shells and shellfish of the Pacific northwest: a field guide. Harbour Publishing, Madeira Park, BC. 270 p.

Harrison, P.G.; Bigley, R.E. 1982. The recent introduction of the seagrass *Zostera japonica*, Aschers. and Graebn., to the Pacific coast of North America. Can. J. Fish. Aquat. Sci. 39:1642–1648.

Hines, A.H.; Ruiz, R.M. 2000. Biological invasions of coldwater ecosystems: ballast-water mediated introductions in Port Valdez/Prince William Sound, Alaska. Final project report. Regional Citizens' Advisory Council of Prince William Sound, Valdez, AK.

Humphreys, R.D.; Hourston, R.H. 1978. British Columbia herring spawn deposition survey manual. Fish. Mar. Serv. Misc. Spec. Publ. 38. 40 p.

Jamieson, G.S.; Grosholz, E.D.; Armstrong, D.A.; Elner, R.W. 1998. Potential ecological implications from the introduction of the European green crab, *Carcinus maenas* (Linneaus), to British Columbia, Canada, and Washington, USA. J. Nat. Hist. 32:1587–1598.

Johnsen, B.O.; Jensen, A.J. 1986. Infestations of Atlantic salmon, *Salmo salar*, by *Gyrodactylus salaris* in Norwegian rivers. J. Fish Biol. 29:233–241.

Ketchen, K.S.; Bourne, N.; Butler, T.H. 1983. History and present status of fisheries for marine fishes and invertebrates in the Strait of Georgia, British Columbia. Can. J. Fish. Aquat. Sci. 40:1095–1119.

Levings, C.D. 1999. Review of current practices to reduce the risk of introducing non-indigenous species into the Pacific region via ballast water. Fisheries and Oceans Canada, Ottawa, ON. Canadian Stock Assessment Secretariat Research Document 99/211. 13 p. Available: http://www.dfo-mpo.gc.ca/csas/CSAS/English/Research_Years/1999/a99_211e.htm (cited 12 December 2001).

Levings, C.D.; Foreman, R.E.; Tunnicliffe, V.J. 1983. A review of the benthos of the Strait of Georgia and contiguous fjords. Can. J. Fish. Aquat. Sci. 40:1120–1141.

Levings, C.D.; Piercey, G.E.; Galbraith, M.; Jamieson, G. 1998. Analyses of invertebrate fauna in ballast water collected in ships arriving at British Columbia ports, especially those from the western north Pacific. Pages 111–124 *in* Proceedings of the 8th International Zebra Mussel and Aquatic Nuisance Species Conference, Sacramento, CA, 16–18 March 1998. The Professional Edge, Pembroke, ON.

Lewis, J.R.; Quayle, D.B. 1972. Some aspects of the littoral ecology of British Columbia. Fish. Res. Bd. Man. Rep. Ser. 1213. 23 p.

Lindstrom, S. 1999. Literature review of introduced algae and seagrasses in the Strait of Georgia. Unpublished document prepared for Fisheries and Oceans Canada, West Vancouver Laboratory, West Vancouver, BC. 22 p.

Locke, A.; Reid, D.M.; van Leeuwen, H.C.; Sprules, W.G.; Carlton, J.T. 1993. Ballast water exchange as a means of controlling dispersal of freshwater organisms by ships. Can. J. Fish. Aquat. Sci. 50:2086–2093.

McGann, M.; Sloan, D.; Cohen A.M. 2000. Invasion by a Japanese marine microorganism in western North America. Hydrobiologia 421:25–30.

McLean-Fraser, C. 1932. A comparison of the marine fauna of the Nanaimo region with that of the San Juan archipelago. Trans. R. Soc. Can. Sect. 5:49–70.

McPhail, J.D.; Carveth, R. 1992. A foundation for conservation: the nature and origin of the freshwater fish fauna of British Columbia. Fish Museum, Department of Zoology, University of British Columbia, Vancouver, BC. 39 p.

Mueller, K.W.; Hoffman, A. 1999. Effect of freshwater immersion on attachment of the Japanese oyster drill, *Ceratostoma inornatum* (Recluz 1851). J. Shellfish Res. 18:597–600.

Neaves, F. 1949. Game fish populations of the Cowichan River. Bull. Fish. Res. Bd. Can. 84. 32 p.

Nickum, D. 1999. Whirling disease in the United States: a summary of progress in research and management. Trout Unlimited, Arlington, VA. 35 p.

Posey, M.H. 1988. Community changes associated with the spread of an introduced seagrass, *Zostera japonica*. Ecology 69:974–983.

Quayle, D.B. 1964. Distribution of introduced marine Mollusca in British Columbia waters J. Fish. Res. Bd. Can. 21:1155–1178.

Quayle, D.B. 1988. Pacific oyster culture in British Columbia. Can. Bull. Fish. Aquat. Sci. 218:1–241.

Reeves, B., for Washington Department of Agriculture. 1999. *Spartina* in Puget Sound. *In* Minutes of the *Spartina* workshop held at Canadian Wildlife Service offices, Delta, BC, 4 October 1999.

Ruiz, G.M.; Fofonoff, P.; Hines, A.H.; Grosholz, E.D. 1999. Nonindigenous species as stressors in estuarine and marine communities: assessing invasion impacts and interactions. Limnol. Oceanogr. 44:950–972.

Simenstad, C.A.; Cordell, J.R.; Tear, L.; Weitkamp, L.A.; Paveglio, F.L.; Kilbride, K.M.; Fresh, K.L.; Grue, C.E. 1996. Use of Rodeo registered and X–77 registered spreader to control smooth cordgrass (*Spartina alterniflora*) in a southwestern Washington estuary: 2. Effects on benthic microflora and invertebrates Environ. Toxicol. Chem. 15:969–978.

Stephen, C. 1998. Outline of the decision making process used by the British Columbia Federal–Provincial Fish Transplant Committee. Unpublished report prepared for the federal–provincial Fish Transplant Committee, Nanaimo, BC.

Sutherland, T.F.; Levings, C.D.; Elliott, C.C.; Hesse, W.W. 2001. The effect of a ballast water treatment system on the survivorship of natural populations of marine plankton. Mar. Ecol. (Prog. Ser.) 210:139–148.

Taylor, T. 1999. Preliminary study of introduced vascular plants growing within tidal influence along the shores of Georgia Strait. Unpublished report prepared for Fisheries and Oceans Canada, West Vancouver Laboratory, West Vancouver, BC. 22 p.

Thomson, A.J.; Candy, J.R. 1998. Summary of reported Atlantic salmon (*Salmo salar*) catches and sightings in British Columbia and adjacent waters in 1997. Can. Manuscr. Rep. Fish. Aquat. Sci. 2467. 39 p.

Thomson, R.E. 1994. Review of the marine environment and biota of Strait of Georgia, Puget Sound and Juan de Fuca Strait. Pages 36–100 *in* R.C.H. Wilson, R.J. Beamish, F. Aitkens, and J. Bell, eds. Proceedings of the BC/Washington Symposium on the Marine Environment, Vancouver, BC, 13–14 January 1994. Can. Tech. Rep. Fish. Aquat. Sci. 1948.

Tunnicliffe, V.J., ed. 1996. Introduction of exotic species—the marine perspective in British Columbia. Unpublished proceedings of a workshop, University of Victoria, Victoria, BC, 14 March 1996. 58 p.

Turner, N.J. 1997. Traditional ecological knowledge. Pages 275–298 *in* P.K. Schoonmaker, B. van Hagen, and E.C. Wolf, eds. Proceedings of a Conference on the Environment and People of the Coastal Temperate Rain Forest, Whistler, BC, 28–30 August 1994. Island Press, Washington, DC.

[UBC] University of British Columbia, Department of Health, Safety and Environment. n.d. Non-indigenous species. University of British Columbia, Vancouver, BC. Available: http://www.hse.ubc.ca/v.2/innerPubsAndProcs.php?ct=pb (cited 12 December 2001).

Volpe, J.P.; Taylor, E.B.; Rimmer, D.W.; Glickman, B.W. 2000. Evidence of natural reproduction of aquaculture-escaped Atlantic salmon in a coastal British Columbia river. Conserv. Biol. 14:889–903.

Whitehouse, T.R.; Boyle, D.E.; Levings, C.D.; Newman, J.; Black, J. 1993. Fish distribution within a tidal freshwater marsh in the lower Fraser River. Can. Data Rep. Fish. Aquat. Sci. 917. 49 p.

Williams, G.L., for Department of Fisheries and Oceans, Habitat and Enhancement Branch. 1999. *Spartina* in Vancouver Harbour. *In* Minutes of the *Spartina* work-

shop held at Canadian Wildlife Service offices, Delta, BC, 4 October 1999.

Williamson, G.R.; Tabeta, O. 1991. Search for *Anguilla* eels on the West Coast of North America and the Aleutian Islands. Jpn. J. Ichthyol. 38(3):315–317.

Wilson, R.C.H.; Beamish, R.J.; Aitkens, F.; Bell, J., eds. 1994. Review of the marine environment and biota of Strait of Georgia, Puget Sound and Juan de Fuca Strait. Proceedings of the BC/Washington Symposium on the Marine Environment, Vancouver, BC, 13–14 January 1994. Can. Tech. Rep. Fish. Aquat. Sci. 1948. 390 p.

Appendix

Provisional list of alien and cryptogenic algae, vascular plants, invertebrates, finfish, birds, and mammals reported in the Strait of Georgia, British Columbia.

Taxonomic group	Scientific name[a] [synonym]	Source[b]	Species designation[c]
Algae			
Division Chlorophyta			
Family Ulotrichaceae	Ulothrix speciosa	Eastern North Atlantic	3
	Ulothrix implexa	Eastern North Atlantic	3
Family Ulvaceae	Gayralia oxysperma [=Monostroma oxysperma, M. oxyspermum]	Hawaii	3
	Enteromorpha sp.		3
	Ulva sp.		3
Family Capsosiphonaceae	Capsosiphon fulvescens	Western North Atlantic	3
Family Chlorophyceae	Percursaria percursa	Western North Atlantic	3
Division Phaeophyta			
Family Phaeophyceae	Melanosiphon intestinalis		3
	Fucus spiralis	Eastern North Atlantic	3
	Sargassum muticum (Yendo) Fensholt	Western North Pacific (Japan)	1
	Colpomenia peregrina	West Mexico	3
	Petalonia fascia	Western North Atlantic	3
	Scytosiphon lomentaria	Eastern North Atlantic	3
Family Scytothamnaceae	Scytothamnus or S. cf. fasciculatus	New Zealand	3

(Continued)

[a] Taxonomic authorities for algae are not presented here if they did not appear in Lindstrom (1999).

[b] Suspected area of origin. If blank, origin of species is unclear or unknown.

[c] Key to species designations: 1 = confirmed as an alien species, 2 = probably an alien species, 3 = cryptogenic species, dash = unassigned as an alien species, investigation of historical records required.

Appendix (Continued)

Taxonomic group	Scientific name[a] [synonym]	Source[b]	Species designation[c]
Division Rhodophyta			
Family Rhodophyceae	*Porphyra mumfordii*		3
	Gelidium vagum Okamura	Japan	1
	Grateloupia doryphora		3
	Antithamnionella spirographidis	Western North Pacific	2
Family Lomentariaceae	*Lomentaria hakodatensis* Yendo	Japan	1
Family Ceramiaceae	*Ceramium* sp.	North Atlantic	1
	Ceramium (cf. *C. rubrum*)		1
Family Caulacanthaceae	*Caulacanthus ustulatus*		3
Family Rhodomelaceae	*Chondria dasyphylla*	Middle Western Atlantic	3
Vascular Plants[d]			
Family Salviniaceae	*Azolla caroliniana* Willd.	Middle Western Atlantic	1
Family Caryophyllaceae	*Spergularia marina* (L.) Griseb.	Eurasia	1
Family Brassicaceae	*Cardamine pratensis* L.	Western Europe	–
Family Haloragaceae	*Myriophyllum spicatum* L.	Eurasia	1
Family Lythraceae	*Lythrum salicaria* L.	Eurasia	1
Family Callitrichaceae	*Callitriche stagnalis* Scop.	Europe	1
Family Plantaginaceae	*Plantago coronopus* L.	Eurasia	1
Family Asteraceae	*Cotula coronopifolia* L.	South Africa	1
	Sonchus arvensis var. *arvensis* L.	Europe	1
Family Alismataceae	*Alisma lanceolatum* Withering	Europe	1
Family Zosteraceae	*Zostera japonica* Ascherson & Graebner	Japan	1
Family Juncaceae	*Juncus gerardii* Loisel.	Eurasia	1
Family Poaceae	*Agrostis stolonifera* L.	Europe	1
	Ammophila arenaria (L.) Link	Europe	1
	Festuca arundinacea Schreb.	Europe	1
	Phragmites australis (Cav.) Trin. ex Steud.[e]	Eurasia	2
	Spartina patens (Ait.) Muhl.	East coast North America	1
	Phalaris arundinacea L. [=*P. roseau*]	Europe	–
Family Typhaceae	*Typha angustifolia* L.	Eurasia	1
Family Iridaceae	*Iris pseudacorus* L.	Europe	1
	Iris germanica L.	Europe	1

(Continued)

[d] Includes only species that Taylor (1999) reported as growing within tidal conditions.

[e] Listed by Taylor (1999) on the basis of a personal communication from Dr. V. Brink.

Appendix *(Continued)*

Taxonomic group	Scientific name[a] [synonym]	Source[b]	Species designation[c]
Invertebrates			
Phylum Foraminifera			
Family Trochamminidae	*Trochammina hadai* Uchio	Western North Pacific (Japan)	1
Phylum Porifera			
Family Sycettidae	*Scypha* spp.	Eastern North Atlantic	1
Family Leucosoleniidae	*Leucosolenia nautilia* de Laubenfels		3
Family Halichondridae	*Halichondria bowerbanki* Burton [=*H. coatlita*]	North Atlantic	1
Family Clionidae	*Cliona* spp.	North Atlantic, western North Pacific (Japan)	–
Phylum Cnidaria			
Class Hydrozoa			
Family Clavidae	*Cordylophora caspia* (Pallas) [=*C. lacustris*]	Black Sea, Caspian Sea	1
Family Tubulariidae	*Tubularia crocea* (Agassiz) [=*T. elegans, Parypha microcephala*]	Western North Atlantic	2
Class Anthozoa			
Family Diadumenidae	*Haliplanella lineata* (Verrill) [=*H. luciae, Diadumene lineata, D. luciae, Sagartia luciae*]	Pacific coast of Asia	1
Phylum Platyhelminthes			
Family Callioplanidae	*Koinstylochus ostreophagus* [=*Pseudostylocus ostreophagus*]	Western North Pacific (Japan)	1
Phylum Annelida			
Class Polychaeta			
Family Syllidae	*Autolytus* cf. *tsugarus*[f]	Western North Pacific (Japan)	2
	Syllis (*Syllis*) *spongiphila* Verrill	Atlantic, western North Pacific (Japan)	1
	Trypanosyllis (*Trypanedenta*) *gemmipara* Johnson	Western Pacific	3
	Typosyllis alternata[f]	Western North Pacific	3
	Typosyllis pulchra	Western North Pacific, Bering Sea	3
Family Nereididae	*Neanthes succinea* (Frey & Leuckart)[f]	North Atlantic, North Sea	3
	Platynereis bicanaliculata (Baird)[f]	Western North Pacific (Japan)	3
Family Spionidae	*Polydora cornuta* Bosc [=*P. amarincola, P. ligni*]	North Atlantic	1
	Polydora websteri Harman	Atlantic	1
	Polydora limicola Annenkova[f]	Western North Pacific (Japan), Bering Sea	1

(Continued)

---

[f] Polychaete species for which further taxonomic investigation is required to distinguish morphologically similar species (S.C. Byers, Environmental Services, Vancouver, BC, personal communication).

Taxonomic group	Scientific name[a] [synonym]	Source[b]	Species designation[c]
	Boccardia columbiana (E. Berkeley)	Western North Pacific (Japan)	3
	Pseudopolydora kempi (Southern) [=*Neopygiospio laminifera*]	India, Mozambique, Japan	1
Family Cirratulidae	*Dodecaceria concharum* Oersted[f]	Western North Atlantic	3
Family Capitellidae	*Heteromastus filiformis* (Claparède)	North Atlantic	1
Family Ampharetidae	*Hobsonia florida* (Hartman) [=*Amphicteis gunneri floridus*]	Western North Atlantic, Gulf of Mexico	1
Class Oligochaeta			
Family Tubificidae	*Tubificoides benedii* [=*Tubifex benedii*]	North Atlantic	2
Phylum Mollusca			
Class Gastropoda			
Family Potamididae	*Batillaria attramentaria* (Sowerby) [=*B. cumingi, B. zonalis*]	Western North Pacific	1
Family Calyptraeidae	*Crepidula fornicata* (L.)	Western North Atlantic	1
Family Muricidae	*Thais clavigera* (Kuster) [=*T. tumulosa, Nucella clavigera, Purpura (Mancinella) clavigera*]	Western North Pacific	1
	Ocenebra japonica Dunker	Western North Pacific (Japan), northern China Sea	1
	Ceratostoma inornatum (Recluz) [=*C. fournieri, Ocenebra japonica, O. inornatum*]	Western North Pacific (Japan), northern China Sea	1
	Urosalpinx cinerea (Say)	Western North Atlantic	1
Family Nassariidae	*Ilyanassa obsoleta* (Say) [=*Nassarius obsoletus*]	North Atlantic	1
Family Melampidae	*Ovatella myosotis* (Draparnaud) [=*Myosotella myosotis, Phytia myosotis*]	Eastern North Atlantic, Mediterranean Sea	1
Class Bivalvia			
Family Mytilidae	*Mytilus edulis* L.	North Atlantic	2
	Mytilus galloprovinicialis Lamarck	North Atlantic, southern California	1
	Musculista senhousia (Benson) [=*Modiolus senhousia*]	Western North Pacific	1
Family Ostreidae	*Crassostrea gigas* (Thunberg) [=*Ostrea laperousii*]	Western North Pacific (Japan)	1
	Crassostrea virginica (Gmelin)	Western North Atlantic	1
Family Psammobiidae	*Nuttallia obscurata* (Reeve) [=*Soletellina obscurata, Psamma olivacea*]	Western North Pacific (Korea, Japan)	1
Family Trapezidae	*Trapezium liratum* (Reeve) [=*T. japonica*]	Western North Pacific (Japan and Indo-Pacific areas)	1

(Continued)

Appendix *(Continued)*

Taxonomic group	Scientific name[a] [synonym]	Source[b]	Species designation[c]
Family Veneridae	*Venerupis philippinarum* (A. Adams & Reeve) [=*V. japonica*, *Ruditapes philippinarum*, *Paphia bifurcata*, *Tapes philippinarum*]	Western North Pacific	1
	Gemma gemma (Totten) [=*G. purpurea*]	Western North Atlantic	1
Family Myidae	*Mya arenaria* L.	Western North Atlantic	1
Family Teredinidae	*Teredo navalis* L. [=*T. beachi*, *T. novangliae*]	Western North Atlantic	1
	Lyrodus takanoshimensis (Roch)	Western North Pacific	1
Phylum Arthropoda **Subphylum Crustacea** **Subclass Copepoda** Family Mytilicolidae	*Mytilicola orientalis* Mori [=*M. osteae*]	Western North Pacific	1
Order Isopoda Family Limnoriidae	*Limnoria tripunctata* Menzies	Western North Pacific	1
Subclass Cirripedia Family Balanidae	*Balanus improvisus* Darwin	Western North Atlantic	2
Order Amphipoda Family Ampithoidae	*Ampithoe valida* Smith [=*A. shimizuensis*]	Western North Atlantic	1
	Ampithoe lacertosa	Eastern North Atlantic	–
Family Aoridae	*Grandidierella japonica* Stephenson	Western North Pacific	1
Family Corophiidae	*Monocorophium acherusicum* (Costa) [=*Corophium acherusicum*]	Eastern North Atlantic	2
	Monocorophium insidiosum (Crawford) [=*Corophium insidiosum*]	North Atlantic	2
Family Gammaridae	*Melita nitida* [=*M. oregonensis*]	Western North Atlantic	1
Family Talitridae	*Allorchestes angusta* group	Western North Atlantic	–
Order Cumacea Family Levconidae	*Nippolevcon hinumensis*[g]	Western North Pacific	1
Phylum Bryozoa Family Alcyonidiidae	*Alcyonidium polyoum* (Hassall) [=*A. gelatinosum*]	Eastern North Atlantic	–
Family Vesiculariidae	*Bowerbankia gracilis* Leidy	Western North Atlantic	2
Family Schizoporellidae	*Schizoporella unicornis* (Johnston in Wood) [=*Lepralia unicornis*]	Western North Pacific	2
Family Cryptosulidae	*Cryptosula pallasiana* (Moll) [=*Lepralia pallasiana*]	North Atlantic	2
Phylum Chordata **Subphylum Urochordata** Family Cionidae	*Ciona savignyi* Herdman	Western North Pacific	2
Family Goniodorididae	*Botrylloides violaceus* Oka	Western North Pacific	1

(Continued)

[g] Jeff Cordell, Fishery Sciences, University of Washington, Seattle, WA, personal communication

Taxonomic group	Scientific name[a] [synonym]	Source[b]	Species designation[c]
Family Styelidae	*Styela clava* Herdman	Western North Pacific	1
Family Goniodorididae	*Botryllus schlosseri* Pallas	Eastern North Atlantic	1
	Molgula manhattensis (DeKay)	Western North Atlantic	1
Finfish			
Phylum Chordata			
Class Osteichthyes			
Family Cyprinidae	*Cyprinus carpio* L.	Asia	1
Family Ictaluridae	*Ameiurus nebulosus* (Lesueur)	East of Rocky Mountains	1
Family Centrarchidae	*Pomoxis nigromaculatus* (Lesueur)	East of Rocky Mountains	1
Family Salmonidae	*Salmo salar* L.	Atlantic Ocean	1
Family Clupeidae	*Alosa sapidissima* (Wilson)	Atlantic Ocean	1
Birds			
Phylum Chordata			
Class Aves			
Family Anatidae	*Cygnus olor* (Gmelin)	Europe	1
	Branta canadensis (L.)	Ontario	1
Mammals			
Phylum Chordata			
Class Mammalia			
Family Muridae	*Rattus norvegicus* (Berkenhout)	Europe	1

Species Introductions and Changes in the Marine Vegetation of Atlantic Canada

Annelise S. Chapman, Robert E. Scheibling, and Anthony R.O. Chapman

Although invasion ecology is still in its infancy in the marine realm, evidence is emerging that alien species can alter marine ecosystems significantly (for example, Ribera and Boudouresque 1995; Ruiz et al. 1999; Grosholz et al. 2000). Relatively few species of bottom-dwelling invertebrates and seaweeds have invaded Atlantic Canada, in contrast to the situation in other parts of the world (Wallentinus 1992, unpublished manuscript; Carlton 2000, unpublished manuscript; Table 1 and Appendix, this chapter). However, given the long seafaring tradition of the region and the lack of historical species inventories, some of the so-called native biota in Atlantic Canada are likely unidentified travellers from other shores. The recorded invasive species of Atlantic Canada have had major impacts on native communities. This has been well documented along the central Atlantic coast of Nova Scotia, an area intensively studied for more than three decades.

This chapter reports on the current status of alien species invasions into vegetated marine habitats of the Atlantic coast of Canada, including seaweed, salt marsh, and seagrass communities. It provides detailed information on three invertebrate aliens from Europe: the common periwinkle (*Littorina littorea* (L.)), the bryozoan *Membranipora membranacea* (L.), and the green crab (*Carcinus maenas* (L.)). It also presents results of new research on recent invasions that have altered or replaced kelp bed communities on Canada's Atlantic coast. Data show that successful invasions by bottom-dwelling species (hereafter called benthic species) took place in the lower Gulf of St. Lawrence in the mid- to late 19th century. Knowledge of the general ecology of these species elsewhere in the western North Atlantic allows inferences about the effects of species invasions in the Gulf region.

Native Plant and Algal Communities

In this chapter, Atlantic Canada refers to Newfoundland, the Gulf of St. Lawrence (bounded by the Gaspé peninsula of Quebec and the northern shores of New Brunswick), Nova Scotia, Prince Edward Island,

and the Atlantic and Bay of Fundy shores of Nova Scotia and New Brunswick (Figure 1). Although the coast of Labrador could be considered part of Atlantic Canada, it is not included in the study. The text concentrates on marine benthic species in ecosystems dominated by macrophytes (large plants, such as cordgrasses, sea-grasses, and seaweeds) of the shore zone between the high and low tide marks (intertidal) to the shore zone below the low tide mark (subtidal).

The rocky intertidal zones of the Atlantic and Fundy shores of Nova Scotia and New Brunswick are generally not ice-scoured in winter and support a dense cover of brown rockweeds (fucoid algae, for example, *Fucus* spp.

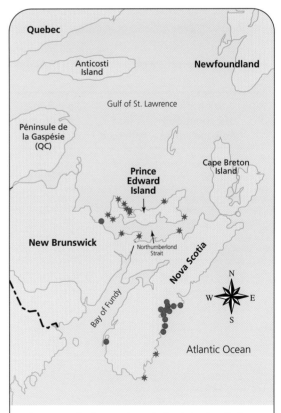

Figure 1. Atlantic Canada, excluding Labrador. *Codium fragile* subsp. *tomentosoides* distribution on the southern shore of Nova Scotia from a quantitative diving survey (unpublished) by R.E. Scheibling and T. Balch in 2000 (●), and from beach cast presence/absence records (unpublished) by D.J. Garbary et al. in 1999–2000 (✱).

and *Ascophyllum nodosum* (L.) Le Jolis) at mid-intertidal levels and a zone of Irish moss (*Chondrus crispus* Stackhouse) on the low shore. Ice-scoured shores elsewhere in Atlantic Canada have more patchy vegetation, and in some areas, all macrophytes are removed by ice each winter. In clear coastal waters, the vegetated zone extends to at least 20 m and rocky bottoms support extensive forests of kelps (large brown seaweeds, such as *Laminaria* spp.), except where sea urchin grazing is intensive. The unpolluted waters of the western Atlantic are low in nutrients (Chapman and Craigie 1977), and low phytoplankton production limits populations of invertebrate filter feeders, allowing luxuriant growth of seaweed beds. Only polluted areas, such as Halifax Harbour, support large populations of filter-feeding mussels and barnacles, instead of seaweeds.

The sedimentary shores of Atlantic Canada are characterized by salt marshes in areas with sufficient shelter from ocean waves to allow sediment accumulation (Davis and Browne 1996). Often, these salt marshes grade into intertidal and subtidal seagrass meadows. In addition to flowering plants of terrestrial origin, Atlantic salt marshes support a large biomass of fucoid algae growing in mats around the stems of cordgrasses (*Spartina* spp.).

The lush stands of vegetation in Atlantic Canada contain remarkably few species. South (1984) lists 346 species of seaweeds, only about half of the number found in the eastern Atlantic Ocean (Parke and Dixon 1976). Monospecific canopies of seaweed are common, especially in the subtidal kelp forests, and it appears that most species play a unique ecological role.

Alien Seaweeds

Origin and Introduction

Five species of alien seaweed appear to have invaded Atlantic Canada, representing only 1.5% of the algal flora (Table 1). By comparison, 4–5% of seaweed species in the Mediterranean and 2–3% in Atlantic Europe and in Australasia are introduced (Ribera and Boudouresque 1995). Although few species have invaded Atlantic Canada, all but one (*Colpomenia peregrina* (Sauvageau) Hamel) have

Table 1. Alien seaweeds in Atlantic Canada.[a]

Scientific and common[b] names (division)	Year first collected	Location first collected	Origin	Present occurrence	Abundance (qualitative)	Reference
Bonnemaisonia hamifera (Rhodophyta)	1948	Lower Gulf of St. Lawrence	Indo-Pacific	All waters but St. Lawrence estuary	Abundant throughout	McLachlan et al.1969
Furcellaria lumbricalis (Rhodophyta)	1853	NF	European	Lower Gulf of St. Lawrence	Abundant	Harvey 1853
				Atlantic NS	Locally abundant	
				Southern NF	Locally abundant	
Codium fragile subsp. *tomentosoides,* oyster thief (Chlorophyta)	1991	Mahone Bay, Atlantic NS	Indo-Pacific	Central Atlantic NS	Very abundant	Bird et al. 1993; Garbary et al. 1997; this paper
				Lower Gulf of St. Lawrence	Locally abundant	
				Bay of Fundy approaches, NS	Uncommon	
Colpomenia peregrina, oyster thief (Heterokontophyta)	1960	Atlantic NS	? Indo-Pacific	Atlantic NS	Uncommon	Blackler 1964
				NF	Uncommon	
Fucus serratus, serrated wrack (Heterokontophyta)	1869	Pictou on the Lower Gulf of St. Lawrence	European	Lower Gulf of St. Lawrence	Very abundant	Dale 1982; Novaczek and McLachlan 1989
				Atlantic shores of NS	Locally abundant	

[a] NF=Newfoundland; NS=Nova Scotia.

[b] If available.

become abundant, resulting in large changes in community structure.

Algal invaders of Atlantic Canada in the 19th century originated in Europe (Table 1). At that time, the most likely vectors would have been ships' hulls. Subsequent invading seaweed species are of Indo-Pacific origin (Table 1), although they initially invaded Europe in the late 19th century before reaching the western shores of the Atlantic. Two species (*Bonnemaisonia hamifera* Hariot and *Codium fragile* subsp. *tomentosoides* (van Goor) P.C. Silva)[1] likely moved into Atlantic Canada from initial points of introduction on the New England coast of the United States earlier in the 20th century (Villalard-Bohnsack 1998). *Codium* was first recorded in the western North Atlantic at Long Island Sound in 1957 (Carlton and Scanlon 1985) and reached Nova Scotia by 1989 (Bird et al. 1993). Possible mechanisms of introduction of *Codium* to Nova Scotia include transport via yachts and other small craft, importation on commercial shellfish or as aquaculture packaging material, and delivery of drifting fragments of the alga by ocean currents (Bird et al. 1993). A third species of Indo-Pacific origin (*Colpomenia peregrina*) only occurs in few and very small populations in Atlantic Canada, and it has not been reported from other areas of the western North Atlantic (Bird and Edelstein 1978).

In addition to other hard surfaces, all of the seaweed species of Indo-Pacific origin can also be found growing on the shells of bivalve mollusks, especially where hard and soft substrata are interspersed. Indeed, both *Codium* and *Colpomenia peregrina* are commonly called "oyster thief" because their gas-filled bodies (thalli) can float, and thus carry away the oysters to which they are attached. *Colpomenia peregrina* was introduced to European shores with Pacific (Japanese) oysters, *Crassostrea gigas* Thunberg (Ribera and Boudouresque 1995), but it is not known whether shellfish were vectors of introduction for any of the alien seaweeds of Atlantic Canada. Similarly, whether transportation on ships' hulls was responsible for any particular introduction remains uncertain.

Invasion Biology

The widespread and abundant alien seaweeds of Atlantic Canada (Table 1) share few life-history characteristics that may account for their invasiveness. *Fucus serratus* L. relies fully on the dispersal of sexually produced offsprings, whereas *Bonnemaisonia hamifera*

disperses primarily through vegetative fragmentation and subsequent reattachment. *Furcellaria lumbricalis* (Hudson) Lamouroux and *Codium* appear to spread both through vegetative fragmentation and production of asexual cells (Fralick and Mathieson 1972; Sharp et al. 1993). High growth rate, a weedy characteristic that often typifies successful invaders (Lodge 1993), is exhibited by *Codium*, but not *Fucus serratus* or *Furcellaria lumbricalis*, which are slow-growing species characteristic of late succession. *Bonnemaisonia hamifera* occurs primarily in the filamentous diploid life-history phase ("Trailliella"),[2] often in early stages of succession. It is also abundant as an epiphyte on leathery macrophytes such as Irish moss. All five alien species are perennial or pseudoperennial (for example, *Codium* can overwinter as a microscopic filamentous stage, Fralick and Mathieson 1972). In sum, the alien seaweeds of Atlantic Canada are a functionally and taxonomically diverse group. Their establishment and invasion success are more likely related to the properties of the invaded communities than of the invaders themselves.

The invasion of *Codium* on the Atlantic coast of Nova Scotia was facilitated by the prior introduction of the European bryozoan *Membranipora membranacea*, which contributed to the disappearance of extensive areas of kelp. The loss of kelp may also account for the recent spread of *Fucus serratus* on this coast (R.E. Scheibling and T. Balch, unpublished data), where it occurs in only a few dispersed populations (Novaczek and McLachlan 1989). While kelp communities of Atlantic Nova Scotia appear to have resisted invading *C. fragile* (and possibly *F. serratus*) as long as kelp canopies were intact, native communities in the lower Gulf of St. Lawrence were unable to withstand these invaders at any time. The friable and unstable sandstone of the lower Gulf is unsuitable for dense populations of large kelps that are dislodged by waves. Consequently, the kelps there are small (less than 1 m long) and canopy cover rarely exceeds 60% (Novaczek and McLachlan 1989). *Codium*, *Fucus serratus*, and *Furcellaria lumbricalis* established and formed luxuriant beds in the lower Gulf, possibly because of limited competition with the native kelps. Thus, the presence of a dense kelp canopy appears to be a major factor in determining how vulnerable native seaweed communities in Atlantic Canada are to invasion.

---

[1] Hereafter "*Codium*".

[2] *B. hamifera* = *Trailliella intricata* Batters; this seaweed's two morphologically different life phases ("Bonnemaisonia" and "Trailliella") were originally thought to be two different species; hence two names.

All of the invading seaweeds in Atlantic Canada occur primarily in subtidal regions where the sea urchin *Strongylocentrotus droebachiensis* (O.F. Müller) is the dominant grazer. During outbreaks of this voracious herbivore in Atlantic Nova Scotia, all foliose macrophytes on rocky substratum, including alien species, are removed from all but the most wave-exposed refugia (Chapman 1981). Only encrusting coralline seaweeds are able to persist under such severe grazing pressure. Apart from sea urchins, there are many other species of generalist invertebrate grazers, including periwinkles, chitons, limpets, amphipods, and isopods, which could potentially limit invasive seaweeds. Two genera of sea slugs, *Placida* and *Elysia*, feed on *Codium fragile*. However, there is no evidence that grazing regulates *C. fragile* populations anywhere within its global range (Trowbridge 1998). In Atlantic Europe, invading *C. fragile* is largely absent from the subtidal zone, though it is widespread in the intertidal. The factor(s) determining its absence below the low tide mark remain unknown, but biotic interactions could well play an important role. Higher species richness at all trophic levels might account for the presence of potential competitors or grazers, which collectively limit the invasion success of *C. fragile* (Chapman 1999). In contrast, the seaweed communities of the western North Atlantic are not only less diverse than those of the eastern North Atlantic, but the component species have not yet, during their evolution within the community, experienced the full range of challenges by potential predators and competitors. Both features are thought to make a community more prone to biological invasions (Lodge 1993; Stachowicz et al. 1999).

Ecological Impacts

The most abundant and conspicuous of the seaweed invaders, *Codium*, is discussed in the section on the kelp bed ecosystem. However, even inconspicuous species are bound to have ecological effects, albeit perhaps on small scales. For example, *Bonnemaisonia hamifera* and *Colpomenia peregrina* occur as epiphytes in Atlantic Canada, mostly on turf-forming seaweeds in the subtidal zone. The delicate filamentous structure of *B. hamifera*, in particular, increases small-scale spatial heterogeneity, which may enhance the abundance of small fauna living on the seaweed (epifauna) by providing microhabitat refuges from predators. Amphipods and isopods, for example, are particularly abundant on *B. hamifera* (A.S. Chapman, personal observation). The occurrence of halogen-containing gland cells in

B. hamifera (Wolk 1968), which may function in defence against herbivores (Fenical 1975), suggests an additional form of protection by association with a chemically defended alga (cf. Hay et al. 1990). On the other hand, *B. hamifera* might accumulate sediments at higher rates than adjacent surfaces, a mechanism that could interfere with recruitment of other seaweeds (Devinny and Volse 1978; Albrecht 1998). The precise indirect effects of *B. hamifera* on small-scale community structure remain to be investigated.

Changes in macrophyte assemblages through species invasions may negatively impact commercial species that rely on marine vegetation for food or habitat. Loss of kelp beds, for example, is expected to have a detrimental impact on the fishery for sea urchin roe (Scheibling 2000) and possibly also on the lobster fishery (Steneck et al. 2001), which at present accounts for 40% of dollar earnings for East Coast fishers (DFO 1998). Displacement of native seaweeds by alien species may also impact seaweed harvesting in Atlantic Canada. *Furcellaria lumbricalis*, through very large increases in population densities in the lower Gulf of St. Lawrence over the last three decades, significantly reduced the quality of commercially harvested Irish moss on Prince Edward Island (Sharp et al. 1993). Subsequently, the alien seaweed itself became sufficiently abundant to allow commercial harvesting for marine gums in this region (G. Sharp, Department of Fisheries and Oceans, Dartmouth, NS, personal communication).

Alien Invertebrates

Invertebrate invasive species have the potential to severely affect marine vegetation because they interact with marine plants in many ways, for example, by feeding (as grazers or filter feeders), by fouling, or by changing light and nutrient regimes. However, only a few examples exist of food web interactions between invertebrate invaders with phytoplankton (see, for example, Alpine and Cloern 1992 and Greve 1993), and there is even less documentation of alien invertebrate impacts on benthic marine vegetation. One notable exception is the interference of the invasive green mussel (*Musculista senhousia* (Benson)) with rhizome growth and vegetative propagation of native eelgrass (*Zostera marina* L.) in southern California (Reusch and Williams 1999).

Although a dozen alien species of invertebrates are known to have invaded the Atlantic shores of Canada (see Appendix), this analysis concentrates on the three most abundant invertebrate invaders whose ecological interactions and effects have been well studied: the common periwinkle (*Littorina littorea*), the bryozoan *Membranipora membranacea*, and the green crab (*Carcinus maenas*).

Common Periwinkle

Common periwinkle was introduced from Europe to North America in the 1840s, near Pictou on the Northumberland Strait (Bequaert 1943). Archaeological records of several periwinkle specimens from Nova Scotia and New Brunswick suggest a much earlier, but post-glacial, introduction 1000–500 years ago, possibly with exploring European vessels (Reid 1996). However, there are no records for the last 500 years prior to the 1840s introduction (Carlton 2000, unpublished manuscript). More recent genetic evidence is contradictory in suggesting that current *Littorina littorea* populations of the western North Atlantic have been separated from eastern North Atlantic ones for at least 50 000 years (C. Cunningham, Duke University, Durham, NC, *in verbis*). Hence, the issue of the common periwinkle as an invasive species in eastern North America continues to be debated and is as yet unresolved. The species is now distributed from Atlantic Canada, through

New England to Virginia and occurs in abundance in rocky shore and salt marsh vegetation. There is likely no ecological analog to the common periwinkle in the recipient native community and it probably entered a vacant niche (Bertness 1984).

The effects of the common periwinkle have been studied extensively in the salt marshes (Bertness 1984) and on the rocky shores of New England (Lubchenco 1978, 1982, 1983, 1986). There are no comparable studies of effects in the salt marshes of Atlantic Canada, so extrapolation to more northerly waters remains tentative. For rocky shores, however, results of experimental work in Nova Scotia are available (reviewed in Chapman 1986, 1995 and Chapman and Johnson 1990).

The role of common periwinkle in the experimental interaction web for the low intertidal zone of New England is shown in Figure 2 (after Menge and Sutherland 1987). There is a strong negative effect of this grazer on ephemeral algae. Ephemeral algae, primarily green algae in the genera *Enteromorpha* and *Ulva*, occur in the middle of a competitive hierarchy of filter feeders and seaweeds (> signifies competitive dominance):

blue mussels > barnacles > ephemeral algae > Irish moss > fucoids (rockweeds)

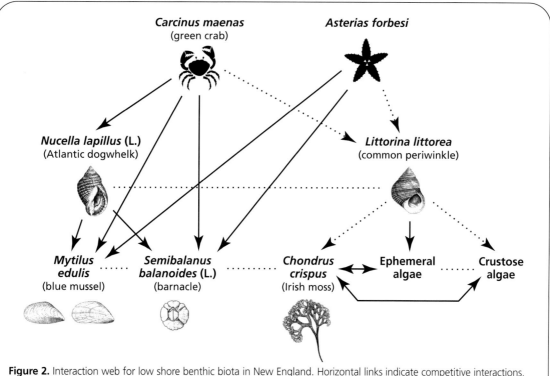

Figure 2. Interaction web for low shore benthic biota in New England. Horizontal links indicate competitive interactions. Other links connect consumer species to prey. Solid lines indicate strong interactions; dashed lines weak interactions. Links determined experimentally. A ➤ B: A has a strong negative effect on B. Modified from Menge and Sutherland (1987).

In New England, the two top competitors for space on wave-exposed rocky shores, blue mussels (*Mytilus edulis* L.) and barnacles, occupy contiguous zones in the intertidal zone. However, these filter feeders are not abundant on sheltered shores, which are dominated by Irish moss and rockweed species. The authors of a number of studies suggest that abundant vegetation occurs where carnivores control the abundance of competing filter feeders and propose that the efficacy of those carnivores is reduced on wave-exposed shores, so that filter feeders are able to occupy space to the exclusion of vegetation (Figure 2; Lubchenco 1978, 1980, 1983, 1986; Lubchenco and Menge 1978; Menge and Lubchenco 1981). They also suggest that common periwinkle reduces the abundance of fast-growing ephemeral algae, allowing the development of slow-growing stands of Irish moss on the low shore and rockweeds on the mid-shore. Therefore, the overall community morphology of sheltered rocky shores in New England may have been fundamentally different before the mid-1800s, when common periwinkle was introduced. Is a similar phenomenon occurring in Atlantic Canada?

Common periwinkle was not abundant on mid-Atlantic intertidal emergent rock surfaces of exposed shores in the 1980s (Barker and Chapman 1990; McCook and Chapman 1997). However, in tide pools on the upper shore, where *Fucus distichus* L. dominates the vegetation, densities of periwinkle often exceeded 1000/m^2 in summer months, while other species of snails were rare (loc. cit.). Findings of studies in these high-shore tide pools agree with those on intertidal rocky surfaces of New England: early successional species (ephemeral green seaweeds in New England and blue-green algal mats in Atlantic Canada) inhibited development of a fucoid vegetation, unless common periwinkles grazed on early successional forms (Parker et al. 1993; Parker and Chapman 1994).

In contrast, on emergent rock of the mid-shore in Atlantic Canada, early successional blue-green algal mats appeared to facilitate, rather than inhibit, juveniles of late successional fucoids, possibly by ameliorating desiccation stress (McCook and Chapman 1993). At yet other (mid-shore, wave exposed) sites in Atlantic Nova Scotia, the common periwinkle was very rare and played no role in vegetation dynamics (McCook and Chapman 1997). In the mid-1990s, high densities of periwinkle were found in the fucoid zone on exposed shores of central Nova Scotia, averaging about 100/m^2 (Worm and Chapman 1998). On the lower shore, in

the Irish moss zone, periwinkle densities were nearly twice as high and constituted most of the grazer biomass (loc. cit.). Grazers readily consumed fucoid recruits on the low shore, and in combination with competitive pressure from the Irish moss canopy, effectively prevented the development of a rockweed canopy in the low intertidal zone.

Hence, population densities of common periwinkle are highly variable in space and time, but this species has major demonstrable effects on the uppermost and lowermost intertidal vegetation of wave-exposed rocky shores in Nova Scotia.

In salt marshes of New England, common periwinkles cause erosion by disturbing the sediment (Bertness 1984). The snails also graze on the shoots and rhizomes of marsh cordgrasses. Experimental removal of periwinkles resulted in expansion of the littoral area occupied by smooth cordgrass (*Spartina alterniflora* Loisel). Salt marshes may therefore have been more extensive before the invasion of periwinkle. The snail may have similar effects in Atlantic Canada where it occurs in abundance in swards of cordgrass. However, this extrapolation awaits experimental verification.

The Bryozoan *Membranipora membranacea*

Membranipora membranacea is a European species first observed in the western North Atlantic off New Hampshire and southern Maine in 1987 (Berman et al. 1992). Within two years, the bryozoan became the dominant epiphyte on kelps in the Gulf of Maine. Its introduction to the region was most likely by larval transport in ballast water (Schwaninger 1999). *Membranipora* probably invaded eastern Canada from the Gulf of Maine; it was first reported on kelps in Mahone Bay, Nova Scotia, in 1992 (Scheibling et al. 1999).

Although *M. membranacea* colonizes various benthic macroalgae, it is particularly abundant on kelps of the genus *Laminaria* (Berman et al. 1992). In the Gulf of Maine, large blades of these kelps were more heavily encrusted than small ones, and kelps from exposed sites were more infested than conspecifics from protected sites (loc. cit.). Encrustation with *M. membranacea* may affect both the nutrient metabolism (Hurd et al. 1994) and light physiology of its algal host (Molina et al. 1991). However, the large-scale defoliation of kelp beds by *M. membranacea* observed in New England (Lambert et al. 1992) and Nova Scotia (Scheibling et al. 1999) is attributed primarily to a change in flexibility of encrusted fronds, which increases fragmentation rate during wave surges and storm disturbance. Localized growth tissues are often lost with fragmenting blades, precluding subsequent regrowth. Similar processes caused defoliation of giant kelp (*Macrocystis pyrifera* (L.) C. Agardh) in California (Dixon et al. 1981). Whether *M. membranacea* encrustations of kelp blades also reduce spore release and hence affect recruitment is currently unknown.

In Europe, *M. membranacea* and other bryozoan species frequently occur on various kelp species, but there are no records of large-scale destructive effects. Berman et al. (1992) suggest that the absence of nudibranch[3] predators during the early outbreaks of *M. membranacea* in New England accounts for these differences between the native and invaded habitats. At present, in Nova Scotia, we frequently observe nudibranch predators (for example, fuzzy onchidoris, *Onchidoris muricata* (Müller)) feeding on *M. membranacea*, both on kelp blades and on turfs. The interaction dynamics of *Membranipora* with potential predators and higher-level consumers await further experimental clarification.

Green Crab

Within Canada, green crabs (*Carcinus maenas*) were first observed in the early 1950s (Glude 1955), after the species had been present in New England for over a hundred years (Grosholz and Ruiz 1996). The green crab originates from Europe and represents one of the most successful marine invertebrate invaders, with almost worldwide distribution (Grosholz and Ruiz 1996). In Atlantic Canada, green crab occurs on rocky and sandy littoral and sublittoral habitats including sandy beaches, tidal flats, and salt marshes.

Mollusks (especially bivalves), small crustaceans, and polychaetes comprise most of the green crab's diet, with only slight changes in composition worldwide (Grosholz and Ruiz 1996). Although green crab predation can markedly reduce populations of invertebrate prey (Grosholz et al. 2000), crab feeding likely has little direct effect on benthic vegetation. Plants generally represent only a minor fraction of their diet (Ropes 1968; Elner 1981; Rangeley and Thomas 1987; Grosholz and Ruiz 1996; Grosholz et al. 2000), except in one study in North Wales (Elner 1977). Menge and Sutherland (1987) found no strong direct or indirect effects of green crabs on seaweeds in the low rocky intertidal zone in New England (Figure 2). However, this result is inconsistent with previous studies by the same authors, which indicate a strong interaction between filter feeders (mussels and barnacles) and the seaweeds mentioned above.

On tidal flats, green crabs burrow in surface sediments to escape desiccation and bird predation at low tide (Reise 1985), and this activity may affect the roots and rhizomes of sea grasses and marsh grasses. In New England salt marshes, burrowing Atlantic marsh fiddler crabs (*Uca pugnax* (Smith)) alter the physical environment through soil aeration and soil drainage and consequently enhance production of smooth cordgrass (Bertness 1985). Similar changes to marsh vegetation may arise if green crab attains high population densities in salt marshes in Atlantic Canada.

Kelp Bed Ecosystem of Atlantic Nova Scotia

Kelp bed communities represent one of the major vegetation types in sublittoral Atlantic Canada, especially on rocky shores. Also, they are among the best studied coastal ecosystems in the region. This section examines the known effects of bio-invaders into kelp communities of Atlantic Canada.

Disruption of Sea Urchin–Kelp Dynamics

Before 1995, the rocky subtidal ecosystem of Nova Scotia's Atlantic coast exhibited cyclical alternations between two stable states driven by large-scale fluctuations in sea urchin (*Strongylocentrotus droebachiensis*) abundance (reviewed by Chapman and Johnson 1990 and Elner and Vadas 1990). In areas where urchins were rare, luxuriant kelp beds (mainly *Laminaria longicruris* De La Pylaie and *L. digitata* (Hudson) Lamouroux) covered the shallow (less than 20 m) seabed forming a dense and highly productive canopy. As sea urchin numbers increased, however, urchins destructively grazed kelps and other seaweeds, creating "barrens" dominated by encrusting coralline algae. These barrens persisted until sea urchin populations were eliminated by disease, which in turn enabled kelp beds to reestablish. Since the pioneering studies of this ecosystem by K.H. Mann and coworkers in the 1970s, alternations between the two states have occurred at decadal time scales (Scheibling et al. 1999). Anecdotal evidence suggests similar changes in community state have taken place along this coast throughout much of the last century (Miller 1985).

A pathogenic amoeba, *Paramoeba invadens* Jones, has been identified as the causal agent of

---

[3] Marine gastropod mollusks (sea slugs) in the order Nudibranchia.

disease outbreaks (technically paramoebiasis epi-zootics) that drive the transition from barrens to kelp beds (Jones 1985; Jones and Scheibling 1985). Several lines of evidence suggest *P. invadens* is an alien species periodically introduced to the Nova Scotian coast by ocean currents:

- It is consistently isolated from tissues of diseased urchins, but has not been found in healthy urchins, or in coastal waters and sediments, in areas or years without epizootics (Jones et al. 1985; Jellett et al. 1989).

- It is waterborne and can be cultured on marine bacteria, indicating it is a facultative parasite of urchins with a free-living existence (Jones and Scheibling 1985).

- It is unable to survive at or below 2°C, which is above the winter temperature minimum in coastal waters off Nova Scotia (0 to -2°C), suggesting it originates from warmer regions (Jellett and Scheibling 1988).

- Disease outbreaks have been correlated with large-scale oceanographic and meteorological events, which may serve to transport a waterborne agent (Scheibling and Hennigar 1997).

The cause of paramoebiasis remains poorly known, but a non-indigenous origin for the pathogenic agent suggests random events play an important role in the disease outbreaks.

In recent years, synergistic interactions between two other invasive species have disrupted sea urchin–kelp dynamics off Nova Scotia and shifted the subtidal ecosystem to a new alternative state. The epiphytic bryozoan *Membranipora membranacea* (Figure 3) has decimated kelp beds since the early 1990s (see above). Loss of kelp canopy facilitated the establishment of the siphonaceous green alga *Codium fragile* subsp. *tomentosoides*, which expanded rapidly over the past decade to become the dominant macroalga in shallow rocky habitats along hundreds of kilometres of Atlantic coastline (R.E. Scheibling and T. Balch, unpublished data).

Marked changes in community structure resulting from interactions between these recent invaders and the native kelps have been documented in a study monitoring ecological changes at Little Duck Island in Mahone Bay, Nova Scotia (Scheibling et al. 1999; Scheibling 2000). When this study began in 1992, the community was in transition. Dense aggregations (fronts) of urchins, moving onshore from deeper water, were destructively grazing kelp beds and forming barrens

Figure 3. Infestation of kelp blades (*Laminaria* spp.) with colonies of the alien bryozoan *Membranipora membranacea*. *Upper:* Close-up. Frame size is 10 × 7 cm. *Lower:* Complete cover of *L. longicruris* blade (about 60 cm long) with *M. membranacea*. Photos by A. S. Chapman.

in their wake. Within the remaining kelp beds, a major outbreak of *M. membranacea* in the fall of 1993 caused widespread loss of *Laminaria* canopy the following winter. This defoliation likely facilitated the establishment of *Codium* at this site, primarily in shallow and wave-swept nearshore areas (less than 5 m below mean water). Recurrent outbreaks of *M. membranacea* over the next three years enabled *Codium*

Figure 4. Transition of a sublittoral (4 m deep) kelp bed to a *Codium fragile* subsp. *tomentosoides* meadow at Little Duck Island, central Atlantic coast of Nova Scotia. *Upper:* Initially *Codium* plants became established in canyons and crevices. The kelp plant in the foreground (*Laminaria longicruris*) is about 1 m long. April 1996. Photo by A.R.O. Chapman. *Lower:* Late stage *Codium* meadow with average plant size about 60 cm. September 2000. Photo by R. E. Scheibling.

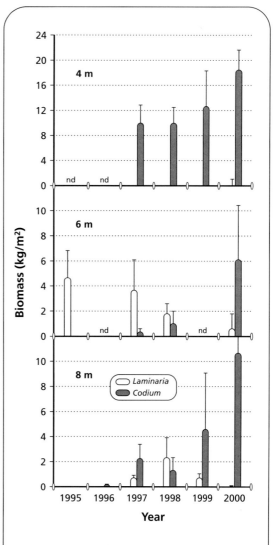

Figure 5. Biomass (fresh weight, mean + SD) of kelp (>95% *Laminaria longicruris*) and *Codium fragile* subsp. *tomentosoides* in 1-m² quadrats sampled at three depths off Little Duck Island between 1995 and 2000. At 4 m, five quadrats were sampled within patches of *Codium* (as part of a manipulative experiment) between 1997 and 1999. At 6 m and 8 m during those years, and at 4 m in 2000, 8–10 quadrats were sampled randomly within a 2 × 50 m belt transect at each depth. In 1995, the transect at 6 m sampled a mature kelp bed and at 8 m a recently formed urchin barrens. *Codium* was first observed at the site in 1996.

to gradually replace kelp as the dominant macroalga (Figure 4). Further offshore (6–8 m depth), a widespread outbreak of paramoebiasis eliminated sea urchins in the fall of 1995 (Scheibling and Hennigar 1997) and *C. fragile* was among the first seaweeds to colonize the former barrens. In the succession that followed, *Codium* gradually surpassed *Laminaria* spp. in terms of biomass within four years (Figure 5). Manipulative experiments at Little Duck Island confirmed that a dense canopy of *Laminaria* suppresses *C. fragile*, presumably through shading (Scheibling 2000 and unpublished data). Removal of that canopy, either experimentally or through bryozoan infestations, enables *Codium* to expand within kelp beds. Once dense stands of the invasive alga are established, they appear to inhibit recruitment of kelp and eventually displace it.

Sea urchins could potentially control populations of both *M. membranacea* (Nestler and Harris 1994) and *Codium* (Prince and LeBlanc 1992; Scheibling and Anthony 2001), but urchin numbers have remained low after the mass mortality in 1995 and a subsequent die-off in 1999 (R.E. Scheibling, personal observations). A resurgence of sea urchin grazing fronts would likely destroy all erect macroalgae (including less palatable forms such as *C. fragile*) and reinstate barrens. However, the shift from kelp to *Codium* dominance may disrupt positive feedbacks to sea urchin reproduction or recruitment, which drive urchin population outbreaks in Nova Scotia (Meidel and Scheibling 2001). Laboratory studies showed that production of reproductive organs is significantly reduced when urchins are fed *Codium* rather than kelp (Scheibling and Anthony 2001). Bryozoan infestations, on the other hand, probably act synergistically with urchin outbreaks in that they accelerate destruction of kelp beds (Scheibling et al. 1999). Other known grazers of *Codium* include sacoglossan (for example, spanish tenor, *Placida* [= *Hermaea*] *dendritica* (Alder and Hancock)) and littorinid (for example, common periwinkle) gastropods, but these appear to cause only limited or superficial damage (Trowbridge 1998; R.E. Scheibling, unpublished data). The small nudibranch, fuzzy onchidoris (mentioned previously), which feeds on *M. membranacea* in Nova Scotia, reaches seasonally high population densities, but it too appears to have minimal impact on its introduced prey (A.S. Chapman and R.E. Scheibling, personal observations).

Replacement of Kelp by *Codium*

A survey of the southwestern shore of Nova Scotia (about a 100-km straight-line distance from Halifax to Port Medway) in late 2000 revealed dense meadows of *C. fragile* throughout Mahone Bay and adjacent St. Margarets Bay, suggesting this area was the epicenter of the *Codium* invasion (R.E. Scheibling and T. Balch, unpublished data; see Figure 1). Densities of the alga declined beyond these large embayments, particularly towards Halifax Harbour to the east. The dispersal of *Codium* via microscopic planktonic propagules or macroscopic drifting vegetative fragments (Carlton and Scanlon 1985) may be governed by the residual southwesterly flow of the coastal current. Spatial patterns of distribution and abundance of *Codium* across its range

in southwestern Nova Scotia in 2000 reflect the temporal pattern observed at Little Duck Island in the 1990s, suggesting a chronosequence of invasion and community change. Only scattered kelps were observed within *Codium* meadows; residual kelp beds near the limits of the survey range, or in highly wave-exposed locations, generally were encrusted with *M. membranacea*. *Codium* also has become established in the Northumberland Strait along the northern shores of Nova Scotia (Garbary et al. 1997) and New Brunswick (Milewski and Chapman 2002), and in tidepools near the mouth of St. Margarets Bay (R.E. Scheibling, unpublished data).

Habitat modification by dense stands of *Codium* (for example, changes in biogenic structure, water flow, light penetration, or sedimentation rate) is expected to alter benthic assemblages of invertebrates and fish. At Little Duck Island, Scheibling et al. (unpublished data) have observed a marked increase in sedimentation and concomitant decreases in numbers of small, cryptic, and sedentary species (for example, limpets, chitons, brittle stars) during the transition from kelp beds or barrens to *Codium* meadows. Such changes in habitat and prey populations could have significant cascading effects on larger, ecologically and economically important species, such as finfish, lobsters, and sea urchins, that use kelps as food, habitat, or nursery areas.

Future studies should address biological and physical factors that influence the establishment and spread of *M. membranacea* and *Codium*, such as reproductive and dispersal mechanisms and potential controls by predation or grazing (Chapman 1999). Further work is also required in understanding the causes of *Paramoeba invadens* outbreaks. However, given the random occurrence of this disease and the complexity of interactions among invading and native species (Scheibling 2000), the likelihood of predicting community dynamics at relevant ecological and economical scales seems slight. We may be witnessing a system, disrupted by centuries of overfishing of large finfish and invertebrate predators (Pringle et al. 1982), that has become increasingly more vulnerable to further perturbations, such as the introduction of invasive species. Along the Atlantic coast of Nova Scotia, recent multiple invasions appear to be acting synergistically in driving the system towards a new state in which *Codium* is replacing kelp as the dominant macrophyte. Evaluating alterations in the structure and function of the rocky subtidal ecosystem, and the stability of the *Codium* state, are major challenges for future research.

Protecting Coastal Waters from Biological Invasions

At present, there is no single piece of federal legislation regulating the introduction and transfer of aquatic, let alone marine, organisms in Canada. Instead, various international, national, and provincial policies and guidelines (without penal authority for noncompliance) deal primarily with the intentional introduction of aquatic organisms into Canadian waters, generally for economic exploitation. Thus, the federal Department of Fisheries and Oceans in the National Code on Introductions and Transfers of Aquatic Organisms (NCITAO) (DFO 2002) justifies the need for a national code based on the increasing demand "to introduce or transfer fish to restock stocks, improve fishing opportunities and to expand enhancement programs and to obtain new culture species for diversification (of the aquaculture industry)." Aquatic environments are viewed primarily as "habitats" housing economic resources rather than as ecosystems with intrinsic value, independent of human utilization. Consequently, all guiding principles, recommendations, and assessments are provided in the context of present and future exploitation of these resources.

Canada ratified the United Nations Convention on Biological Diversity in 1992 and is committed therefore to "prevent the introduction of, control or eradicate those alien species which threaten ecosystems, habitats or species" (Article 8h of the convention). The World Conservation Union identifies species invasions globally as the second largest threat to biodiversity, after habitat destruction (Glowka et al. 1994). Any guidelines and policies referring to the prevention, management, and eradication of aliens in natural ecosystems should therefore prioritize the protection of biodiversity and should include accidental as well as intentional introductions.

Existing international "best practice" recommendations, as provided by the Global Invasive Species Programme (GISP), include monitoring of coastal habitats for early detection of potential invaders, risk assessment procedures to identify likely "next" pests, and eradication and control measures where invasions have already occurred. Generally, the preferred strategy is prevention of invasions wherever possible.

Despite international advances on this issue, prioritization to protect biodiversity in Canada is being compromised by socioeconomic aspects, among others, and likely will be in the future. For example, ballast water is a major vector of alien species and their attendant ecological impacts (Carlton and Geller 1993; Lavoie et al. 1999; Ruiz et al. 2000). The Canadian Ballast Water Management Guidelines[4] are designed to implement recommendations on ballast water management by the International Maritime Organization (IMO), but contain various exceptions to accommodate safety and, ultimately, economic concerns. The guidelines should be regarded as a first step in the right direction. However, they should be open to change in accordance with current scientific evidence and should work towards the principle of protecting biodiversity as a main priority.

Similarly, the assessment procedure for applications to intentionally introduce or transfer organisms into aquatic systems (as outlined in the NCITAO) should require independent scientific evaluation, based on original research, before permission is granted. However, as exemplified by the *Codium* invasion in the western North Atlantic, it may be impossible, even with a solid knowledge of the life history and ecology of an invasive organism in its native (or previously invaded) habitat, to predict its impacts in a novel environment. Invasion success and impact depend on the respective qualities of the alien species and the recipient native community, on modes and rates of introduction, and on physical environmental conditions. Sensible decisions can only be made case by case with local scientific evidence and the overarching application of the precautionary principle.

Acknowledgments

We would like to thank Jim Carlton for the provision of his unpublished manuscript on faunal invasions into the western North Atlantic region, and Inger Wallentinus for unpublished information on seaweed invaders in the Northern Hemisphere. David Garbary readily shared unpublished distributional data of *Codium fragile*, mainly from the Gulf of St. Lawrence, which significantly complemented our own. Glyn Sharp offered discussion and information on commercial seaweed harvest in Atlantic Canada, and Derek Davis gave helpful advice in the context of marine invertebrate invaders. Thanks to all of them and to the constructive comments of an independent reviewer.

References

Albrecht, A.S. 1998. Soft bottom versus hard rock: community ecology of macroalgae on intertidal mussel beds in the Wadden Sea. J. Exp. Mar. Biol. Ecol. 229:85-109.

---

[4] See http://www.tc.gc.ca/MarineSafety/Tp/Tp13617/Tp13617e.htm

Alpine, A.E.; Cloern, J.E. 1992. Trophic interactions and direct physical effects control phytoplankton biomass and production in an estuary. Limnol. Oceanogr. 37:946–955.

Barker, K.M.; Chapman, A.R.O. 1990. Feeding preferences of periwinkles among four species of *Fucus*. Mar. Biol. 106:113–118.

Bequaert, J. 1943. The genus *Littorina* in the western Atlantic. Johnsonia 1:1–28.

Berman, J.; Harris, L.; Lambert, W.; Buttrick, M.; Dufresne, M. 1992. Recent invasions of the Gulf of Maine: three contrasting ecological histories. Conserv. Biol. 6:435–442.

Bertness, M.D. 1984. Habitat and community modification by an introduced herbivorous snail. Ecology 65:370–381.

Bertness, M.D. 1985. Fiddler crab regulation of *Spartina alterniflora* production on a New England salt marsh. Ecology 66:1042–1055.

Bird, C.J.; Dadswell, M.J.; Grund, D.W. 1993. First record of the potential nuisance alga *Codium fragile* ssp. *tomentosoides* (Chlorophyta, Caulerpales) in Atlantic Canada. Proc. N.S. Inst. Sci. 40:11–17.

Bird, C.J.; Edelstein, T. 1978. Investigations of the marine algae of Nova Scotia XIV. *Colpomenia peregrina* SAUV. (Phaeophyta: Scytosiphonaceae). Proc. N.S. Inst. Sci. 28:181–187.

Blackler, H. 1964. Some observations on the genus *Colpomenia* (Endlicher) Derbes et Solier 1851. Proc. Int. Seaweed Symp. 4:50–54.

Bleakney, J.S.; Mustard, M.E. 1974. Sponges of the Minas Basin, Nova Scotia. Can. Field-Nat. 88:93–95.

Carlton, J.T. 1992. Introduced marine and estuarine molluscs of North America: an end-of-the-20th-century perspective. J. Shellfish Res. 11:489–505.

Carlton, J.T. 2000. Marine bioinvasions of the northwestern Atlantic Ocean: introduced and cryptogenic species from the Bay of Fundy to Long Island Sound. Unpublished manuscript. Available from James Carlton, Maritime Studies Program, Williams College, Mystic Seaport, Mystic, CT.

Carlton, J. T.; Geller, J.B. 1993. Ecological roulette: the global transport of nonindigenous marine organisms. Science 261:78–82.

Carlton J.T.; Scanlon, J.A. 1985. Progression and dispersal of an introduced alga: *Codium fragile* spp. *tomentosoides* (Chlorophyta) in New England. Phycologia 11:67–70.

Chapman, A.R.O. 1981. Stability of sea urchin dominated barren grounds following destructive grazing of kelp

in St. Margaret's Bay, eastern Canada. Mar. Biol. 62:307–311.

Chapman, A.R.O. 1986. Population and community ecology of seaweeds. Adv. Mar. Biol. 23:1–161.

Chapman, A.R.O. 1995. Functional ecology of fucoid algae: twenty-three years of progress. Phycologia 34:1–32.

Chapman, A.R.O.; Craigie, J.S. 1977. Seasonal growth of *Laminaria longicruris*: relations with dissolved inorganic nutrients and internal reserves of nitrogen. Mar. Biol. 40:197–205.

Chapman, A.R.O.; Johnson, C.R. 1990. Disturbance and organization of macroalgal assemblages in the northwest Atlantic. Hydrobiologia 192:77–121.

Chapman, A.S. 1999. From introduced species to invader: what determines variation in the success of *Codium fragile* ssp. *tomentosoides* (Chlorophyta) in the North Atlantic Ocean? Helgoländer Meeresunters. 52:277–289.

Clare Carver, Mallet Research Services Ltd., 4 Columbo Drive, Dartmouth, NS, Canada, B2X 3H3

Dale, M. 1982. Phytosociological structure of seaweed communities and the invasion of *Fucus serratus* in Nova Scotia. Can. J. Bot. 60:2652–2658.

Davis, D.S.; Browne, S. 1996. The Natural History of Nova Scotia. Vol. 1: Topics and habitats. Nova Scotia Museum, Halifax, NS. 518 p.

Devinny, J.S.; Volse, L.A. 1978. Effects of sediments on the development of *Macrocystis pyrifera* gametophytes. Mar. Biol. 48:343–348.

[DFO] Department of Fisheries and Oceans. 1998. 1999 Atlantic Coast commercial landings, by region. Canadian Landings Information Web Page. http://www.ncr.dfo.ca/communic/statistics/landings/S1999aqe.htm

[DFO] [Department of] Fisheries and Oceans Canada. 2002. National Code on Introductions and Transfers of Aquatic Organisms [print and online]. Ottawa, ON. http://www.dfo-mpo.gc.ca/science/OAS/aquaculture/nationalcode/code default_e.htm

Dixon, J.; Schroeter, S.C.; Kastendiek, J. 1981. Effects of the encrusting bryozoan, *Membranipora membranacea*, on the loss of blades and fronds by the giant kelp, *Macrocystis pyrifera* (Laminariales). J. Phycol. 17:341–345.

Elner, R. 1981. Diet of green crab, *Carcinus maenas* (L.) from Port Hebert, southwestern Nova Scotia. J. Shellfish Res. 1:89–94.

Elner, R.W. 1977. The predatory behaviour of *Carcinus maenas* (L.). PhD thesis, University College of North Wales [now University of Wales], Bangor, UK. 91 p.

Elner, R.W.; Vadas, R.L.S. 1990. Inference in ecology: the sea urchin phenomenon in the northwestern Atlantic. Am. Nat. 136:108–125.

Fenical, W. 1975. Halogenation in the Rhodophyta—a review. J. Phycol. 11:245–259.

Fralick, R.A.; Mathieson, A.C. 1972. Winter fragmentation of *Codium fragile* (Suringar) Hariot ssp. *tomentosoides* (van Goor) Silva (Chlorophyceae, Siphonales) in New England. Phycologia 11:67–70.

Garbary, D. J.; Vandermeulen, H.; Kim, K.Y. 1997. *Codium fragile* ssp. *tomentosoides* (Chlorophyta) invades the Gulf of St. Lawrence, Atlantic Canada. Bot. Mar. 40:537–540.

Glowka, L.; Burhenne Guilmin, F.; Synge, H. 1994. A guide to the Convention on Biological Diversity. IUCN (World Conservation Union), Gland, Switzerland. 97 p.

Glude, J.B. 1955. The effects of temperature and predators on the abundance of the soft-shell clam, *Mya arenaria*, in New England. Trans. Am. Fish. Soc. 84:13–26.

Gould, A.A. 1841. Report on the Invertebrata of Massachusetts, comprising the Mollusca, Crustacea, Annelida and Radiata. Folsom, Wells, and Thurston, Cambridge, UK. 373 p.

Greve, W. 1993. German Bight ecosystem responses to the invasion of a siphonophore. ICES, Copenhagen, Denmark. 7 p.

Grosholz, E.D.; Ruiz, G.M. 1996. Predicting the impact of introduced marine species: lessons from the multiple invasions of the European green crab *Carcinus maenas*. Biol. Conserv. 78:59–66.

Grosholz, E.D.; Ruiz, G.M.; Dean, C.A.; Shirley, K.A.; Maron, J.L.; Connors, P.G. 2000. The impacts of a nonindigenous marine predator in a California bay. Ecology 81:1206–1224.

Harvey, W.H. 1853. Nereis Boreali Americana. Part II. Rhodospermae. Smithson. Contrib. Knowl. 5:1–258.

Hay, M.E.; Duffy, J.E.; Fenical, W. 1990. Host-plant specialization decreases predation on a marine amphipod: a herbivore in plant's clothing. Ecology 71: 733–743.

Hurd, C.L.; Durante, K.M.; Chia, F.S.; Harrison, P.J. 1994. Effect of bryozoan colonization on inorganic nitrogen acquisition by the kelps *Agarum fimbriatum* and *Macrocystis integrifolia*. Mar. Biol. 121:167–173.

Jellett, J.F.; Novitsky, J.; Cantley, J.; Scheibling, R.E. 1989. Non-occurrence of *Paramoeba invadens* in the water column and sediments off Halifax, Nova Scotia. Mar. Ecol. Prog. Ser. 56:205–209.

Jellett, J.F.; Scheibling, R.E. 1988. Effect of temperature and food concentration on the growth of *Paramoeba invadens* (Amoebida: Paramoebidae) in monoxenic culture. Appl. Environ. Microbiol. 54:1848–1854.

Jones, G.M. 1985. *Paramoeba invadens* n. sp. (Amoebida, Paramoebidae), a pathogenic amoeba from the sea urchin, *Strongylocentotus droebachiensis*, in eastern Canada. J. Protozool. 32:564–569.

Jones, G.M.; Hebda, A.J.; Scheibling, R.E.; Miller, R.J. 1985. Histopathology of the disease causing mass mortality of sea urchins (*Strongylocentotus droebachiensis*) in Nova Scotia. J. Invertbr. Pathol. 45:260–271.

Jones, G.M.; Scheibling, R.E. 1985. *Paramoeba* sp. (Amoebida, Paramoebidae) as the possible causative agent of sea urchin mass mortality off Nova Scotia. J. Parasitol. 71:559–565.

Lambert, W.J.; Levin, P.S.; Berman, J. 1992. Changes in the structure of a New England (USA) kelp bed: the effects of an introduced species? Mar. Ecol. Prog. Ser. 88:303–307.

Lavoie, D.; Smith, L.; Ruiz, G. 1999. The potential for inter-coastal transfer of non-indigenous species in ballast water of ships. Estuar. Coast. Shelf Sci. 48:551–564.

Lodge, D.M. 1993. Biological invasions: lessons for ecology. Trends Ecol. Evol. 8:133–137.

Lubchenco, J. 1978. Plant species diversity in a marine intertidal community: importance of herbivore food preferences and algal competitive abilities. Am. Nat.112: 23–29.

Lubchenco, J. 1980. Algal zonation in the New England rocky intertidal community: an experimental analysis. Ecology 61:333–344.

Lubchenco, J. 1982. Effects of grazers and algal competitors on fucoid colonization in tide pools. J. Phycol. 18:544–550.

Lubchenco, J. 1983. *Littorina* and *Fucus*: effects of herbivores, substratum heterogeneity, and plant escapes during succession. Ecology 64:1116–1123.

Lubchenco, J. 1986. Relative importance of competition and predation: early colonization by seaweeds. Pages 537–555 *in* J. Diamond and T.J. Case, eds. Community ecology. Harper and Row, New York, NY.

Lubchenco, J.; Menge, B.A. 1978. Community development and persistence in a low rocky intertidal zone. Ecol. Monogr. 59:67–94.

Mauchline, J. 1980. The biology of mysids. Adv. Mar. Biol. 18:3–369.

McCook, L.J.; Chapman, A.R.O. 1993. Community succession following massive ice-scour on a rocky intertidal shore:

recruitment, competition and predation during early, primary succession. Mar. Biol. 115:565–575.

McCook, L.J.; Chapman, A.R.O. 1997. Patterns and variations in natural succession following massive ice-scour of a rocky intertidal seashore. J. Exp. Mar. Biol. Ecol. 214:121–147.

McLachlan, J.; Chen, L.C.-M.; Edelstein, T. 1969. Distribution and life history of *Bonnemaisonia hamifera* Hariot. Pages 245–249 *in* R. Margalef, ed. Proceedings of the 6th International Seaweed Symposium. Subsecraria de la Marina mercante, Madrid.

Meidel, S.K.; Scheibling, R.E. 2001. Variation in egg spawning among subpopulations of sea urchins (*Strongylocentrotus droebachiensis*): a theoretical approach. Mar. Ecol. Prog. Ser. 213:97–110.

Menge, B.A.; Lubchenco, J. 1981. Community organization in temperate and tropical intertidal habitats: prey refuges in relation to consumer pressure gradients. Ecol. Monogr. 51:429–450.

Menge, B.A.; Sutherland, J.P. 1987. Community regulation: variation in disturbance, competition, and predation in relation to environmental stress and recruitment. Am. Nat. 130:730–757.

Milewski, I.; Chapman, A.S. 2002. Oysters in New Brunswick, more than a harvestable resource. Conservation Council of New Brunswick, Fredericton, NB. 57 p.

Miller, R.J. 1985. Succession in sea urchin and seaweed abundance in Nova Scotia, Canada. Mar. Biol. 84:275–286.

Molina, X.; Cancino, J.M.; Montecino, V. 1991. Cambios en los pigmentos fotosintetizadores de *Gelidium rex* (Rhodophyta) inducidos por el epibionte *Membranipora tuberculata* (Bryozoa). Rev. Chil. Hist. Nat. 61:289–297.

Nestler, E.C.; Harris, L.G. 1994. The importance of omnivory in *Strongylocentrotus droebachiensis* (Müller) in the Gulf of Maine. Pages 813–818 *in* B. David, A. Guille, J.-P. Feral, and M. Roux, eds. Echinoderms through time. A.A. Balkema, Rotterdam, The Netherlands.

Novaczek, I.; McLachlan, J. 1989. Investigation of the marine algae of Nova Scotia XVII. Vertical and geographical distribution of marine algae on rocky shores of the Maritime Provinces. Proc. N.S. Inst. Sci. 38:91–143.

Parke, M.; Dixon, P.S. 1976. Check-list of British marine algae—third revision. J. Mar. Biol. Assoc. UK 56:527–594.

Parker, T.; Chapman, A.R.O. 1994. Separating the grazing effects of periwinkles and amphipods on a seaweed community dominated by *Fucus distichus*. Ophelia 39:75–91.

Parker, T.; Johnson, C.; Chapman, A.R.O. 1993. Gammarid amphipods and littorinid snails have significant but different effects on algal succession in littoral fringe tidepools. Ophelia 38:69–88.

Prince, J.S.; LeBlanc, W.G. 1992. Comparative feeding preference of *Strongylocentotus droebachiensis* (Echinoidea) for the invasive seaweed *Codium fragile* ssp. *tomentosoides* (Chlorophyceae) and four other seaweeds. Mar. Biol. 113:159–163.

Pringle, J.D.; Sharp, G.J.; Caddy, J.F. 1982. Interactions in kelp bed ecosystems in the northwest Atlantic: review of a workshop. Pages 108–115 *in* M.C. Mercer ed. Multispecies approaches to fisheries management advice. National Research Council Press, Ottawa, Canada. Can. Spec. Publ. Fish. Aquat. Sci. 59.

Rangeley, R.W.; Thomas, M.L.H. 1987. Predatory behaviour of juvenile shore crab *Carcinus maenas* (L.). J. Exp. Mar. Biol. Ecol. 108:191–197.

Reid, D.G. 1996. Systematics and evolution of *Littorina*. The Ray Society, Andover, Hampshire, UK. 463 p.

Reise, K. 1985. Tidal flat ecology. Springer-Verlag, Berlin. 191 p.

Reusch, T.B.H.; Williams, S.L. 1999. Macrophyte canopy structure and the success of an invasive marine bivalve. Oikos 84:398–416.

Ribera, M.A.; Boudouresque, C.-F. 1995. Inroduced marine plants, with special reference to macroalgae: mechanisms and impact. Prog. Phycol. Res. 11:217–268.

Rivest, B.; Coyer, J.; Tyler, S. 1999.The first known invasion of a free-living marine flatworm. Biol. Invasions 1:393–394.

Ropes, J.W. 1968. The feeding habits of the green crab, *Carcinus maenas* (L.). Fish. Bull. (US Fish Wildlife Serv.) 67:183–203.

Scheibling, R.E. 2000. Species invasions and community change threaten the sea urchin fishery in Nova Scotia [online]. The Workshop on the Coordination of Green Sea Urchin Research in Atlantic Canada. Fishery. Session V. Moncton, NB. http://crdpm.cus.ca/OURSIN/PDF/SCHEIB.PDF

Scheibling, R.E.; Anthony, S.X. 2001. Feeding, growth and reproduction of sea urchins (*Strongylocentrotus droebachiensis*) on single and mixed diets of kelp (*Laminaria* spp.) and the invasive alga *Codium fragile* ssp. *tomentosoides*. Mar. Biol. 139:139–146.

Scheibling, R.E.; Hennigar, A.W. 1997. Recurrent outbreaks of disease in sea urchins *Strongylocentrotus droebachiensis* in Nova Scotia: evidence for a link with large-scale meteorologic and oceanographic events. Mar. Ecol. Prog. Ser. 152:155–165.

Scheibling, R.E.; Hennigar, A.W.; Balch, T. 1999. Destructive grazing, epiphytism, and disease: the dynamics of sea urchin-kelp interactions in Nova Scotia. Can. J. Fish. Aquat. Sci. 56:2300–2314.

Schwaninger, H.R. 1999. Population structure of the widely dispersing marine bryozoan *Membranipora membranacea* (Cheilostomata): implications for population history, biogeography, and taxonomy. Mar. Biol. 135:411–423.

Sharp, G.J.; Tetu, C.; Semple, R.; Jones, D. 1993. Recent changes in the seaweed community of western Prince Edward Island: implications for the seaweed industry. Hydrobiologia 260/261:291–296.

South, G.R. 1984. A checklist of marine algae of eastern Canada, second revision. Can. J. Bot. 62.680–704.

Stachowicz, J.J.; Whitlatch, R.B.; Osman, R.W. 1999. Species diversity and invasion resistance in a marine ecosystem. Science 286:1577–1579.

Steneck, R.S.; Wahle, R.E.; Incze, L.S. 2001. Potential slowdown in lobster landings [online]. Joint statement. <http://www.penbay.org/lobstersless.html>.

Trowbridge, C.D. 1998. Ecology of the green macroalga *Codium fragile* (Suringar) Hariot 1889: invasive and non-subspecies. Oceanogr. Mar. Biol. Annu. Rev. 36:1–64.

Villalard-Bohnsack, M.L. 1998. Non-indigenous benthic algal species introduced to the northeastern coast of North America. Pages 130–131 *in* J.R. Sears, ed. NEAS Keys to the benthic marine algae of the northeastern coast of North America from Long Island Sound to the Strait of Belle Isle. North East Algal Society, Dartmouth, MA.

Wallentinus, I. 1992. Introductions and transfer of plants. Unpublished manuscript. Available from Inger Wallentinus, Department of Marine Botany, University of Göteborg, Göteborg, Sweden.

Wolk, C.P. 1968. Role of bromine in the formation of the refractive inclusions of the vesicle cells of the Bonnemaisoniaceae (Rhodophyta). Planta 78:371–378.

Worm, B.; Chapman, A.R.O. 1998. Relative effects of elevated grazing pressure and competition from a red algal turf on two post-settlement stages of *Fucus evanescens* C. Ag. J. Exp. Mar. Biol. Ecol. 220:247–268.

Appendix

Benthic alien invertebrates of Atlantic Canada (organized by phylum).[a]

Scientific and common[b] names	Year(s) or century introduced	Origin	Introduction mechanism	Abundance/ ecological importance	Reference for Atlantic Canada
Porifera (sponges)					
Halichondria bowerbanki Burton	19th century (Long Island, NY) 1974 (Minas Basin, NS)	Europe	Unknown	Locally abundant fouling organism	Bleakney and Mustard 1974
Platyhelminthes (flatworms)					
Convoluta convoluta (Abildgaard)	1995	Europe	Likely ballast water	Abundant on algal substrata in the shallow littoral zone, e.g. fucoids and kelps	Rivest et al.
Mollusca (mollusks)					
Littorina littorea (L.), common periwinkle	~1840	Europe	Intentional release of solid ballast	A major herbivore/ omnivore of rock shores, marshes, and tidal flats	Carlton 1992; Reid 1996
Myosotella myosotis (Draparnaud), marsh snail	18th–19th centuries	Europe	Solid ballast?	Unknown	Gould 1841 (referring to *Auricula myosotis*)

(Continued)

Appendix *(Continued)*

Scientific and common[b] names	Year(s) or century introduced	Origin	Introduction mechanism	Abundance/ ecological importance	Reference for Atlantic Canada
Argopecten irradians (Lamarck), bay scallop	1982	US east coast	Intentional release off PEI	A few naturalized populations	Clare Carver, Mallet Research Services Ltd., personal communication[c]
Ostrea edulis L., edible oyster	At least 1980s, possibly 1960s	Europe	Aquaculture	Only individual escapees from oyster farms surviving in the wild	Carlton 1992
Arthropoda (arthropods)					
Carcinus maenas (L.), green crab	1950s	Europe (via Atlantic US, 19th century)	Europe to US: shipping; then range expansion to Atlantic Canada (Bay of Fundy, Atlantic NS, Gulf of St Lawrence, Cape Breton Island)	Locally important carnivore/omnivore affecting native bivalve densities	Glude 1955
Praunus flexuosus (Müller), chameleon shrimp	1960s	Europe (via New England)	Europe to US: ballast water; then range expansion NS	Locally abundant in salt marshes	Mauchline 1980
Corophium volutator Pallas	18th–19th centuries	Europe	Ship fouling or solid ballast	Major food of shorebirds in Bay of Fundy	Kindle 1916
Bryozoa (bryozoans)					
Membranipora membranacea (L.)	1990s	Europe	Ballast water	Severe encrustation of macrophytes, especially kelps, leading to breakage of blades and defoliation	Lambert et al, 1992; Scheibling et al., 1999
Chordata (chordates)					
Styela clava Herdman, clubbed tunicate	1970s (US east coast) 1998 (PEI)	Asia via Europe	Ship fouling	Fouling of bivalve aquacultures in PEI	Carlton 2000, unpublished manuscript
Botryllus schlosseri (Pallas)	19th century (US east coast, then to NS)	Europe; possibly Pacific Ocean	Ship fouling, then probably range expansion	Fouling of benthic vegetation	Carlton, 2000, unpublished manuscript

Source: Collated and modified from Carlton 2000, unpublished manuscript.

[a] NS = Nova Scotia; PEI = Prince Edward Island; US = United States.

[b] If available.

[c] 4 Columbo Drive, Dartmouth, NS, Canada B2X 3H3.

The Canadian experience with invasive alien species is a patchwork of individual experiences varying in time since introduction, perceived or documented impacts, public and governmental response, and other factors. Each of the chapters in this part deals with a species or a group of species from different taxa and habitats: an aquatic plant, a forest insect, a freshwater fish, a crab of coastal waters, and a group of freshwater mollusks. Collectively, the species (or cases) discussed here cover many vectors and pathways, intentional and accidental introductions and spread, and various degrees of environmental and economic impacts; represent a range of research methods and corrective measures and policies; and point to gaps in knowledge, a lack of national coordination and communication among agencies, and ambiguities in regulations.

The fanwort, an aquatic plant from south temperate and subtropical regions of North and South America, was recently discovered in an Ontario lake. It may adversely affect lake ecosystems and potentially spread and establish in other Ontario lakes and rivers. Various stakeholders in the area have responded to the problem, but the approach is piecemeal. This case study illustrates the lack of a national response plan to deal with such introductions while eradication is still feasible. At the other end of the spectrum, the accidentally introduced and high-impact gypsy moth has received considerable attention from scientists and the public. Costly reactive and proactive control measures have been implemented, but with disappointing results. Gypsy moth affects a number of distinct ecological regions under different jurisdictions. A lack of harmonized policies has impeded proactive management. The gypsy moth case study points to the need for policies that can adapt as knowledge evolves.

Tench, a fish intentionally introduced in Quebec from Europe, has recently escaped into the Richelieu River. The now viable population of tench may affect a globally rare and threatened native fish, the copper redhorse. Government agencies could have easily prevented the establishment of tench if they had communicated more effectively and clarified and rigorously enforced existing regulations.

In the case of green crab, a native of the Mediterranean presumed to have been accidentally introduced in both the Atlantic and the Pacific coastal waters, circumstances are very different from those of the tench. Over the past few years, government agencies from California to British Columbia have widely distributed information on how to identify the species, with a request to report any occurrences. As a result, the public and fishers frequently report sightings. However, the lack of data on ecosystem conditions before the establishment of green crab and of subsequent monitoring of these conditions has impeded an evaluation of its full impact. This makes it difficult to implement appropriate control efforts.

A final study deals with predicting which characteristics of an alien species are likely to make them invasive. In the case of alien freshwater mollusks, the most invasive and damaging are those with a relatively short life (two to four years old), high fecundity, life stages with wide ecological and physiological tolerances, and a diversity of vectors for dispersal. Studies such as this one are important in effecting better management and prevention practices.

Gypsy Moth in Canada: Case Study of an Invasive Insect

Vince G. Nealis

The gypsy moth (*Lymantria dispar* (L.)) is a native insect of Eurasia where it feeds on the leaves of broad-leaf trees, especially oaks (*Quercus* spp.). Populations of gypsy moth increase periodically to very high local densities and severely defoliate preferred host trees (Elkinton and Liebhold 1990). In its native range, gypsy moth displays highly variable biological characteristics. The most significant life-history variations relevant to invasiveness are the geographic differences in flight capability of adult females and host food range of the larvae. Female moths from western (European) populations are flightless, while those from eastern (Asian) populations are capable of strong, directed flight. Gypsy moth larvae feed on a wide variety of mostly broadleaf tree hosts throughout their geographic range, but Asian populations also feed on coniferous tree species and therefore are of even greater concern to Canada than the European populations.

A European strain of the gypsy moth escaped from a laboratory near Boston, MA, in 1869. Since then, gypsy moth has spread and become established in the temperate forests of eastern North America, approximately between latitudes 36° and 47°N, and from the Atlantic coast to the Great Lakes basin as far as 90°W. During this same period, there have been repeated interceptions of both European and Asian strains of gypsy moth in western North America but, as yet (2000), neither strain is regarded as established there.

The North American experience with gypsy moth is an instructive case study of an invasive species. There has been a well-documented public and scientific response to the problems caused by gypsy moth that can serve as a historical lesson for managing local and national environments in the global village. Scientific information on gypsy moth is probably as thorough as that on any invasive forest insect. Public policy on managing gypsy moth has ranged from neglect to aggressive mitigative action at considerable public cost and sometimes with dire environmental consequences. We can compare actions in the United States and Canada from distinct historical and legislative perspectives. As a case study in Canada, we can examine the impacts of establishment and spread of this alien species in eastern Canada and analyze the feasibility and benefits of maintaining gypsy moth-free regions by coordinating national and regional management activities. Discussion here emphasizes history and status of the European strain of gypsy moth now widely established in eastern North America and threatening to extend its range. Regulatory agencies now refer to this European strain as the North American gypsy moth, although it remains an alien species. Issues discussed here, however, pertain equally to the Asian strain of gypsy moth.

Attributes of an Invader

The gypsy moth has several biological and ecological attributes that favor its success as an invasive species. Gypsy moth has a broad native geographic range that presents many potential sources of introduction. Also, the insect tolerates a wide range of climatic conditions and feeds on many different tree species. Thus gypsy moth has a high probability of persistence in temperate forests worldwide. The reproductive biology of gypsy moth also favors colonization. Adult females may produce more than 1000 offspring in a single egg mass, so even one female can contribute a sizable founding population.

The greatest limitation of gypsy moth as an invasive species is that it is a poor disperser over long distances. The female adult moth of the European strain is flightless. Natural dispersal is restricted to relatively short-distance ballooning of newly hatched larvae (Elkinton and Liebhold 1990), making gypsy moth's surreptitious association with humans significant. Many of the host plants that gypsy moth favors flourish in habitats associated with human settlement. Further, gypsy moths frequently leave their host plants to lay eggs in sheltered locations and these are often structures associated with humans, such as firewood and outdoor household goods. When these goods are moved, the gypsy moth moves with them. Thus, although some spread of gypsy moth along the margins of its range in North America can be accounted for by natural dispersal of small larvae, inadvertent movement of egg masses, by a mobile human population, is the source of most new infestations in areas remote from the established populations, particularly those in western North America.

History of an Invasion

The gypsy moth was brought intentionally from Europe to North America by a naturalist, Léopold Trouvelot. Following the accidental escape of moths from a laboratory near Boston in 1869, Trouvelot notified authorities. Nothing was done and the infestation grew. By 1890, the situation was serious enough that state authorities in Massachusetts belatedly began an eradication program. The 10-year program was abandoned in 1900 and within five years gypsy moth appeared in four adjacent states. A major control program was resumed, but by 1920 gypsy moth had spread over much of eastern New England. The US government then established a barrier zone along Lake Champlain and the Hudson River to prevent westward movement of gypsy moth. To the east of the zone, populations were to be suppressed by various means while to the west of the barrier zone, all infestations were to be eradicated. Although spread of gypsy moth during maintenance of this barrier zone was slow, relative to its spread in the previous 20 years, spot infestations occurred and persisted in regions west of the zone, probably because of human transport (Doane and McManus 1981).

During the early 1950s, gypsy moth populations throughout New England increased to unprecedented levels and a new barrier zone was established farther west in New York State. This time, however, both suppression and eradication were carried out with massive aerial applications of DDT. By the late 1950s, gypsy moth defoliation had been reduced to its lowest levels in 30 years. Despite this reduction in damage, the range of gypsy moth actually expanded during this period. As gypsy moth continued to spread westward in the United States, any hope of eradication within the generally infested states was abandoned. Defoliation in the eastern United States peaked at 800 000 ha in 1971 and male moths began to be captured frequently in states on the Pacific coast (Doane and McManus 1981).

Gypsy moth was first intercepted in Canada on nursery stock in 1911 in Vancouver, BC. Actual infestations requiring treatment were detected first in southern Quebec in 1924, and New Brunswick in 1936, and were related directly to infestations in the United States. These early infestations in Canada were considered eradicated (Brown 1967).

Throughout the 1960s, male moths were caught regularly in pheromone traps near the St. Lawrence River from Montreal to Kingston. The Department of Agriculture carried out ground and aerial applications of insecticides during this period to eradicate gypsy moth in Canada. After the discovery of numerous egg masses near Kingston in 1969, control programs in Canada shifted their objective to preventing spread, although there apparently remained some hope among authorities that eradication still could be achieved in eastern Canada (Nealis and Erb 1993). For the first time since 1911, an infestation of gypsy moth was detected in Vancouver in 1978. It was eradicated in 1979 (Humble and Stewart 1994).

In 1981, more than 1000 ha of defoliation by gypsy moth was mapped near Kaladar, ON, more than 50 km from the area where eradication efforts had been underway. Over the next four years, moderate-to-severe defoliation increased steadily in Ontario and reached nearly 350 000 ha in 1991 (Nealis and Erb 1993). Although the area of severe defoliation by gypsy moth has declined steadily since then, the total area infested by gypsy moth has increased annually. By 2000, the area infested by gypsy moth in Canada ranged continuously from western New Brunswick and Nova Scotia to Lake Superior in Ontario (Figure 1).

As the area of infestation grew in eastern Canada, the frequency of new introductions increased in British Columbia. Since 1978, gypsy moth males have been captured in more than 75 separate locations, mostly in the lower Fraser River valley and on southern Vancouver Island. In more than 20 cases, assertive eradication programs have been carried out using the bacterial insecticide *Bacillus thuringiensis* var. *kurstaki* (*Btk*). This included a high profile introduction and subsequent eradication of Asian strain of the gypsy moth in Vancouver in 1991 and 1992 (Humble and Stewart 1994).

Impacts of the Invasion

Managing invasive pest insects is often a reaction to anticipated rather than actual negative impacts because the alien organism is either not established yet or has not caused damage. The actual impacts of gypsy moth, however, in both the native and alien ranges have been examined and the benefits of management actions evaluated. This does not mean that a rigorous cost-benefit analysis for gypsy moth management is straightforward. As with most defoliators, the direct impact of gypsy moth is rarely immediate tree mortality. Instead, trees become weakened and growth is retarded. Mortality lags behind actual defoliation and will be contingent on several variables including tree species, their

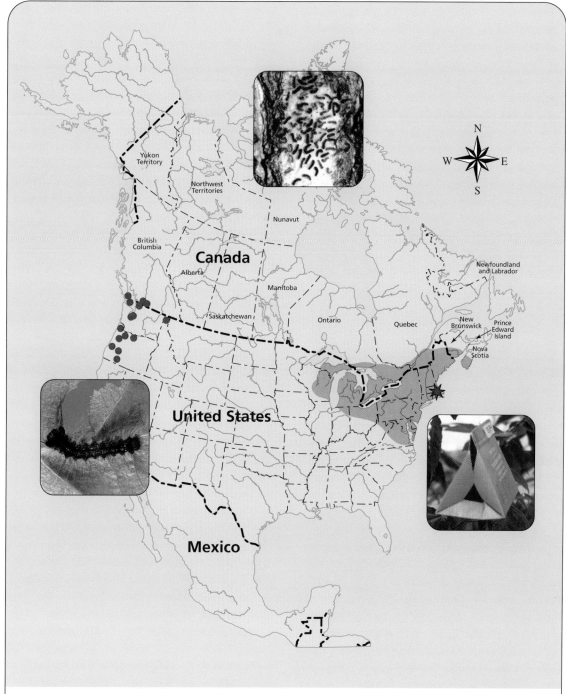

Figure 1. Invasion of North America by the European gypsy moth. Orange shading indicates the current area (2000) regulated for established populations; red star is the point of original introduction in 1869; red dots are points where eradication programs have been carried out since 1990. (*Left*) Gypsy moth larva, (*center*) hatching egg mass, and (*right*) a pheromone trap. Courtesy of CFS, PFC, Victoria, BC.

age and vigor, and the severity and frequency of defoliation (Davidson et al. 1999).

In Canada, information on the direct impact of gypsy moth on the forest resource is sparse. Significant defoliation by gypsy moth is a relatively recent event and the oak species on which it feeds primarily are not inventoried accurately in most provinces so normal growth and mortality rates are poorly understood. Gross et al. (1992) estimate losses from gypsy moth in Ontario between 1982 and 1987 at more than 325 000 m^3 but guess that the rate of mortality responsible for that loss was approximately what would be expected on such poor sites. In the United States, the longer history of gypsy moth and the higher value of the oak resource have resulted in more comprehensive analyses. Stands with a higher proportion of susceptible oaks have been found to suffer the greatest mortality because defoliation is more intense and frequent in those stands. Impacts are significantly greater when gypsy moth first invades an area. As vulnerable trees die, subsequent outbreaks then occur in stands that have become more resistant (Davidson et al. 1999). Translating these losses into a dollar value requires qualifying economic assumptions beyond the scope of this discussion. As an example, however, the Pennsylvania Bureau of Forestry has estimated total losses in Pennsylvania between 1969 and 1987 at US$219 million (Gottschalk 1990).

The indirect ecological impacts associated with defoliation by gypsy moth are broad changes in forest condition ranging from effects on water quality to wildlife habitat (Gottschalk 1990; Nealis and Erb 1993; USDA 1995). These changes in forest condition pose a potential threat to native biodiversity (Krcmar-Nozic et al. 2000). Also, they often involve nonmarket values for which methods of estimation are limited. Nonetheless they must be considered in the context of pest risk assessment. For gypsy moth the biological and ecological information necessary for such an assessment is more complete than for most insects.

A significant impact of the gypsy moth results from the public reaction to infestations. People find the presence of numerous, large, hairy caterpillars abhorrent and defoliation of their trees alarming. Some aspects of human perception, such as a decline in aesthetic and recreational values of property, can be evaluated (Hollenhorst et al. 1992). Others, such as the nuisance factor, are less tractable. Medical studies have confirmed the association of skin rashes with exposure to gypsy moth larvae (Wirtz 1984), but most human reactions may be more a symbolic response to insects in general than a deliberate assessment of gypsy moth as an unwanted invasive species (MacDonald et al. 1997).

These human attitudes do, however, translate to tangible socioeconomic impacts, that is, the public pressure to control gypsy moth and the public and environmental costs that arise from such action. Authorities have always relied on extensive use of pesticides to reduce populations of gypsy moth. Notorious pesticides such as lead arsenate and DDT were developed primarily for use against gypsy moth (Doane and McManus 1981). The environmental damage resulting from extensive use of DDT against gypsy moth was cited specifically as an example of intolerable chemical pollution in *Silent Spring* (Carson 1962), a seminal work of environmental awareness. There has been a continuous search for more environmentally benign pesticides, but the reliance on pesticides remains (Cameron 1991). For example, between 1980 and 1998, more than 4.5 million ha were sprayed in the United States at a cost of US$178.5 million, mostly using the insect growth regulator Dimilin or the bacterial insecticide *Btk* (http://www.fs.fed.us/ne/morgantown/4557/gmoth).

Treatments to suppress gypsy moth populations in Canada have been less extensive. The largest programs were carried out in Ontario between 1986 and 1991 when nearly 250 000 ha were treated almost exclusively with *Btk* at an approximate cost of nearly Can$5 million (van Frankenhuyzen 1990; Nealis and Erb 1993). The per area cost of eradication programs is more expensive than suppression because of costs associated with demands for public reassurance. The cost of eradicating Asian and European gypsy moth from nearly 19 000 ha in Vancouver in 1992, for example, was Can$6.5 million. In 1999, 13 000 ha of south Vancouver Island were treated at a cost of Can$3.7 million (P. Hall, British Columbia Ministry of Forests, personal communication). These are operational costs for the local spray and public relations programs only. The cost of research and monitoring including salaries are extra and difficult to obtain reliably from the accounting methods used. Wallner (1996) considered these latter costs more or less fixed and in the United States they exceeded US$10 million per year. The Canadian research and survey effort on gypsy moth has declined steadily during the 1990s. The principal information gathering activity in Canada now is monitoring in unregulated areas by the Canadian Food Inspection Agency (CFIA). In British Columbia, the CFIA maintains its most extensive pheromone trap network usually of between 8000 and 10 000 traps per year. The cost of deploying these traps and collecting and recording their contents is approximately Can$250 000 (J. Bell, Canadian Food Inspection Agency, personal communication).

In addition to the public pressure for control of gypsy moth is the threat of regulatory restrictions on the shipment of commodities from infested regions. The potential cost of quarantine is the principal incentive for eradicating gypsy moth in British Columbia. The provincial government estimates that if British Columbia was infested with gypsy moth, annual losses would exceed Can$20 million, mostly from the nursery sector. Impact on forestry exports would be primarily on the movement and export of raw logs. Total cost of compliance with regulatory restrictions could be reduced with a system of self-certification. More problematic in permitting gypsy moth to become established in British Columbia is the potential damage in relations between the province and its neighbors and major trading partners in the western United States where there is a commitment to keep gypsy moth out. Increased inspections of private vehicles at border crossings would be an unpopular nuisance.

Public Policy

When Trouvelot first brought gypsy moth to the United States in the 1860s, there was no regulation of his ill-fated interests. This was an era when Europeans were purposefully translocating a lot of plant and animal species around the world for various economic, artistic, and scientific activities. The problems of gypsy moth, however, soon became apparent to the citizens of Massachusetts. Their complaints not only initiated control actions but also precipitated new federal legislation in the United States, the Domestic Plant Quarantine Act (1912). This act marked the beginning of federal–state, multiagency cooperation in regulating and containing gypsy moth. This cooperation extends beyond shared objectives to funding and authority for carrying out operational programs. The result has been significant public funding in the United States for research on all aspects of gypsy moth biology, ecology, and control.

Perhaps because of the vested interest of both federal and state governments, public policy for managing gypsy moth in the United States has strong national and regional components. Not only are new infestations treated with aggressive eradication programs, suppression of populations within or near the generally infested areas of the United States has been an important part of the national management policy by establishing barrier zones or otherwise attempting to slow the spread of gypsy moth. The most recent of these programs is the Slow-the-Spread (STS) program initiated in 1993. Like earlier programs, STS is coordinated by the USDA Forest Service in cooperation with state and county governments.

In Canada, the invasion of gypsy moth lagged almost a century behind the United States and the area

of susceptible forest type and its economic value are significantly less than in the United States. The Canadian reaction has relied on the United States experience. Methods of monitoring and treating infestations developed in the United States have been adopted directly in Canada. As in the United States, managing gypsy moth in Canada has relied on pesticides, and both countries have sought to replace chemical pesticides with microbial insecticides such as *Btk*. Whereas the United States has invested significant resources in the development of alternative controls, including biological and silvicultural approaches, as well as an integrated pest management framework within which to implement these research gains, original research in Canada has been restricted to a few specialized projects on biological control (Nealis et al. 2001).

As in the United States, Canada responded to invasion of the gypsy moth by passing its own Plant Protection Act (1924). Unlike the US act that established joint responsibilities for federal and state governments, the Canadian legislation identified the federal government's primary responsibility for invasive organisms and made no specific provision for cooperative funding or shared responsibility between the federal and provincial governments. In practice, the federal Department of Agriculture assumed complete responsibility for eradication of gypsy moth in Canada. It was not until 1979 that provincial governments undertook operational spray programs, which were only in areas where the federal government was regulating but not reducing populations of the insect. Within these regulated areas, regional trends in defoliation rather than national objectives dictated evolution of the public response. In Quebec, for example, populations of gypsy moth generally declined after 1980 and there has been little subsequent attention paid to the status of populations. In Ontario, a plan to treat the initial area of defoliation in 1981 was canceled because of public opposition to the widespread use of pesticides. As defoliation increased dramatically, the public began to demand action and the provincial government responded with a publicly subsidized spray program for private property. This suppression program peaked at 100 000 ha of treatment before being terminated in 1992 (Nealis and Erb 1993). Throughout this period, gypsy moth infestations in the Maritime provinces were regarded as extensions of the established range in Ontario and Quebec. Eradication was not considered feasible and so affected areas were regulated by the federal government. Provincial officials, however, were not as prepared to concede the point and have continued to carry out control programs to at least curtail further spread of gypsy moth (Carter et al. 1999).

In British Columbia, the federal government carried out all eradication programs until 1998, although there was cost sharing with the provincial government for eradication of the Asian gypsy moth in 1992. A significant precedent was set in British Columbia when the federal government, for matters of public relations, sought a provincial pesticide application permit despite its legislated authority to undertake spray programs for invasive organisms when and where necessary. In 1998, an appeal against such a permit was upheld by a provincial appeal board. The federal government agency that had applied for the permit, the Canadian Food Inspection Agency (CFIA), was limited to carrying out an ineffective ground treatment. Subsequently, the CFIA announced it would no longer eradicate European gypsy moth in British Columbia but would regulate infested areas. The resulting trade restrictions imposed by the United States prompted the government of British Columbia to pass an order-in-council enabling the treatment of more than 13 000 ha of mostly urban land on southern Vancouver Island and the nearby mainland in 1999. A second, smaller area near Vancouver was treated in 2000, once again by the BC provincial government but this time under the authority of a provincial pesticide application permit. An appeal against this permit was lost but not without further emphasis of the growing acrimony between public policy and citizens opposed to sprays.

Current Status and Future Direction

The policy of the CFIA (in 2000) on managing the European strain of gypsy moth, on behalf of the federal government, is to identify and regulate infested areas in Canada. The agency will not carry out eradication programs to maintain gypsy moth-free status in an area. This position has been successfully defended in a recent judicial review, and is the latest development in what has been the gradual withdrawal of federal involvement in managing the gypsy moth in Canada. In 1995, the Canadian Forest Service, which for many years had carried out much of Canada's research effort on gypsy moth and surveys within the infested area, discontinued its Forest Insect and Disease Survey and largely eliminated its modest research program on gypsy moth. Provincial governments may fill some of these gaps but the effort is neither consistent nor comprehensive at the national level. In Ontario and Quebec, populations of gypsy moth have been relatively low in the past five years and so the need for monitoring and management has received less attention. In New Brunswick, the provincial government is on the leading edge of the eastern expansion of gypsy moth, actively monitoring populations in both regulated and unregulated areas and investigating alternative methods of control (Carter et al. 1999). In British Columbia, the provincial government has committed to maintaining gypsy moth-free status in the province and has carried out assertive eradication programs in 1999 and 2000.

Because responsibility for overall management of gypsy moth in regulated areas and eradication of it from unregulated areas are defaulting to provincial governments, new issues arise. For example, the Plant Protection Act gives the federal government broad powers to manage invasive species, including the authority to enter private property to inspect articles, monitor pests, and carry out necessary treatments. Provincial governments, however, generally lack this authority. The federal government may delegate this authority to provincial agencies but the legal implications are as yet untested. More problematic is that once an area becomes regulated, there seems to be little further incentive for controlling or even monitoring gypsy moth. Infested provinces, such as Ontario, that serve as the source of most new residents to British Columbia and, by association, the probable source of most new infestations of gypsy moth to British Columbia (Phero Tech 1994), are not inclined to monitor or manage gypsy moth populations to reduce the risk of new infestations in unregulated areas. Thus, expansion of gypsy moth's range in much of eastern Canada is likely to continue until all ecologically suitable habitats are infested. Maintenance of gypsy moth-free status in susceptible habitats in western Canada depends primarily on the willingness of provincial governments there to react with costly eradication programs, because these provincial governments have little capability to implement a prevention strategy.

A better solution would be to develop multi-agency partnerships like the model that has evolved in the United States and to recognize distinct regional needs within a national context. This does not mean adopting suppression policies used in the United States. For example, the current Slow-the-Spread program in the United States undertakes aggressive control actions in advance of the leading edge of the expanding infestation because of the benefits of even temporarily excluding gypsy moth from high value and uninfested, susceptible forests in the American southeast and Mississippi states. In eastern Canada, however, most of the susceptible forest is infested already, and the remainder is of relatively marginal economic value. Further, experience in both countries indicates that the extremely high densities of insects and associated defoliation that provoked public demands for control programs during the initial invasion are less likely in the aftermath. In view of this, the socioeconomic rationale for suppression programs in eastern Canada seems weak, compared with that in the United States, and the two countries need only follow common regulatory, not suppression, policies.

An argument can be made, however, for a common policy of maintaining gypsy moth-free status in the western regions of both Canada and the United States by prevention and, when that fails, eradication. Several factors contribute to the feasibility of eradicating gypsy moth in western North America: the low natural dispersal rate of gypsy moth, the availability of sensitive pheromone traps to facilitate detection, and the known efficacy of registered pesticides. In addition to the direct environmental benefit of excluding European gypsy moth from the broadleaf forests of western North America is the indirect benefit of facilitating effective detection of the potentially more damaging Asian strain. At present, both strains are detected with the same pheromone traps and their respective identities are confirmed with DNA analysis. When populations of the European strain of gypsy moth increased in British Columbia in 1998 and hundreds of male moths were captured, the CFIA was able to analyze only a subset of the captures (R. Favrin, CFIA, personal communication). Thus, even a relatively low density of European gypsy moth in western Canada would compromise the ability of regulators to detect and eradicate Asian gypsy moth.

Eradication, however, should always be the last resort. It is expensive, intrusive, and has controversial nontarget impacts. In a sense, eradication adds insult to injury by obligating the recipient of an invasive organism to pay financially, politically, and environmentally for extirpation (Wallner 1996). Given the difficulties of carrying out eradication programs using pesticides in urban areas, the gypsy moth is testament to the truism that an ounce of prevention is worth a pound of cure. The sorry developments following failure of authorities to eradicate gypsy moth in 1869 emphasize the enormous benefits of keeping this insect out of susceptible areas. In western Canada, eradication can be justified only if an explicit policy of prevention has been in place. As with so many aspects of gypsy moth

management, this policy can be guided by scientific knowledge. As stated previously, active prevention of the spread of gypsy moth throughout susceptible forests in eastern North America is optimistic at best. Prevention of gypsy moth infestations in western Canada, however, can be rationalized more readily. First, susceptible areas in western Canada are geographically and ecologically isolated from infestations in eastern Canada so that natural dispersal of gypsy moth to western Canada is not likely. Second, the source areas for new infestations are identifiable; they are the areas of eastern Canada where gypsy moth persists and that are points of departure of people and products to western Canada. Third, the high risk routes and times of year for conveying gypsy moth egg masses are well known. Fourth, areas where gypsy moth populations are most likely to persist in British Columbia have been delineated (Régnière and Nealis 2001). Finally and critically, keeping gypsy moth out of western Canada is an entirely domestic issue; Canada has the legal authority and expertise to implement all aspects of prevention. At the risk of oversimplification, there is but one highway through Canada linking infested and uninfested parts of the country.

Prevention measures already exist in Canada by regulating movement of commodities such as nursery stock and Christmas trees and by requesting the military to inspect their own equipment. The weak link in the program is the relative lack of attention paid to one of the highest risk routes of invasion—movement of personal household articles. A comprehensive and ongoing national public information program would decrease human transport of gypsy moth substantially. A more direct component of the prevention strategy would be to obligate moving and vehicle rental companies to inspect and certify outdoor household articles before moving them. This program could be implemented and audited efficiently by maintaining monitoring programs in high risk, regulated areas, so that effort is commensurate with current risk. Development of such a dynamic risk rating system would be based on identification of historical areas of high density gypsy moth populations as revealed by survey information from the 1980s and 1990s (for example, Nealis et al. 1999) and monitoring of current populations with pheromone traps. The prevention program would include the receiving areas with follow-up inspections and deployment of pheromone traps in areas considered ecologically favorable for gypsy moth. Existing regulatory practices would be more effective and so prevention would enhance compliance and quality control.

A program to prevent infestation of western Canada by the gypsy moth is necessarily national in scope and requires federal leadership to be realized. Implementation, however, could be carried out successfully through a partnership among federal and provincial agencies and the private sector. Whereas the federal government has the legislated authority for critical aspects of the program overall, provincial governments and the private sector have the operational capability of supporting the monitoring, inspection, auditing, and information gathering elements of a cooperative program. When prevention fails, provincial governments may need to assume leadership for eradication but look to federal agencies and the private sector for support in this aspect of maintaining gypsy moth-free status in an area. Both the public and private sector would benefit directly from an explicit partnership with this goal.

Conclusions

We are able to make strategic management decisions about gypsy moth because we have a superior knowledge of its biology and the behavior of its populations following invasion. We can assess risk, evaluate impacts, and design mitigative action. In turn, we are able to examine the experience with gypsy moth to determine what critical aspects need to be addressed scientifically when developing policy for managing, or perhaps ignoring, new or threatening cases of invasion.

The gypsy moth case also reminds us that our policies for managing invasive pests, like our scientific knowledge, will evolve and must therefore be open to critical reevaluation and modification. Alien species invade ecosystems not countries. Policy must recognize this and so account for ecological, not political, boundaries. Canada comprises several distinct ecological regions. Some are extensive and contiguous but an increasing number are threatened and fragmented. Because these habitats may belong to different jurisdictions, which affects the authority and/or capability of management action, active harmonization of policies and criteria for management must be addressed for proactive management plans to be implemented.

References

Brown, G.S. 1967. The gypsy moth, *Porthetria dispar* L., a threat to Ontario horticulture and forestry. Proceedings of the Entomological Society of Ontario 98:12–15.

Cameron, E.A. 1991. The gypsy moth: How integrated is pest management? For. Ecol. Manag. 39:113–118.

Carson, R. 1962. Silent Spring. Houghton Mifflin Co., Boston, MA.

Carter, N.; O'Brien, D.; Lavigne, D.; Hartling, L. 1999. Forest pest conditions in New Brunswick in 1999. Pages 104–111 *in* Forest Pest Management Forum 99, 16–17 November, 1999. Ottawa, ON.

Davidson, C.B.; Gottschalk, K.W.; Johnson, J.E. 1999. Tree mortality following defoliation by the European gypsy moth (*Lymantria dispar* L.) in the United States: a review. For. Sci. 45:74–84.

Doane, C.C.; McManus, M.L. eds. 1981. The gypsy moth: research toward integrated pest management. Technical Bulletin 1584. USDA Forest Service, Washington, DC.

Elkinton, J.S.; Liebhold, A.M. 1990. Population dynamics of gypsy moth in North America. Annu. Rev. Entomol. 35:571–596.

Gottschalk, K.W. 1990. Economic evaluation of gypsy moth damage in the United States of America. Pages 235–246 *in* Proceedings, Division 4, IUFRO 19th World Congress. Canadian IUFRO World Congress Organizing Committee, Montréal, QC.

Gross, H.L.; Roden, D.B.; Churcher, J.J.; Howse, G.M.; Gertridge, D. 1992. Pest-caused depletions to the forest resource of Ontario, 1982–1987. Forestry Canada, Ontario Region, Sault Ste. Marie, ON. Joint Report 17. 23 p.

Hollenhorst, S.J.; Brock, S.M.; Freimund, W.A.; Twery, M.J. 1992. Predicting the effects of gypsy moth on near-view aesthetic preferences and recreation appeal. For. Sci. 39:28–40.

Humble, L.; Stewart, A.J. 1994. Gypsy moth. Forest Pest Leaflet 75. Natural Resources Canada, Canadian Forest Service, Pacific Forestry Centre, Victoria, BC. 8 p.

Krcmar-Nozic, E.; van Kooten, G.C.; Wilson, B. 2000. Threat to biodiversity: the invasion of exotic species. Pages 68–87 *in* G.C. van Kooten, E.H. Bulte, and A.E.R. Sinclair, eds. Conserving nature's diversity: Insights from biology, ethics and economics. Ashgate Publishing Ltd., Aldershot, UK.

MacDonald, H.; McKenney, D.W.; Nealis, V. 1997. A bug is a bug is a bug: symbolic responses to contingent valuation questions about forest pest control programs? Can. J. Agric. Econ. 45:145–163.

Nealis, V.G.; Carter, N.; Kenis, M.; Quednau, F.W.; van Frankenhuyzen, K. 2001. *Lymantria dispar* (L.), gypsy moth (Lepidoptera:Lymantriidae). *In* P. Mason and J. Huber, eds. Biological control programmes against insects and mites, weeds, and pathogens in Canada 1981–2000. CABI Publishing, Wallingford, Oxon, UK.

Nealis, V.G.; Erb, S. 1993. A sourcebook for management of the gypsy moth. Forestry Canada, Ontario Region, Great Lakes Forestry Centre, Sault Ste. Marie, ON. 48 p.

Nealis, V.G.; Roden, P.M.; Ortiz, D.A. 1999. Natural mortality of the gypsy moth along a gradient of infestation. Can. Entomol. 131:507–519.

Phero Tech Inc. 1994. A risk assessment of European gypsy moth in British Columbia. Deloitte and Touche Management Consultants, Delta, BC. 73 p.

Régnière, J.; Nealis, V.G. 2001. Evaluating the probability of the persistence of the gypsy moth, *Lymantria dispar* L. in southern British Columbia on the basis of seasonality. Unpublished report available from V.G. Nealis, Natural Resources Canada, Canadian Forest Service, Pacific Forestry Centre, Victoria, BC.

[USDA] United States Department of Agriculture. 1995. Gypsy moth management in the United States: a cooperative approach, final environmental impact statement. Vol. 2. USDA Forest Service, Animal and Plant Health Inspection Branch, Washington, DC.

van Frankenhuyzen, K. 1990. Development and current status of *Bacillus thuringiensis* for control of defoliating forest insects. For. Chron. 67:498–507.

Wallner, W.E. 1996. Invasive pests ('biological pollutants') and US forests: whose problem, who pays? Bulletin OEPP/EPPO Bulletin 26:167–180. Blackwell Science Ltd., Oxford.

Wirtz, R.A. 1984. Allergic and toxic reactions to non-stinging arthropods. Annu. Rev. Entomol. 29:47–69.

Photo with chapter title: Male gypsy moth. Courtesy of CFS, GLFC, Sault Ste. Marie, ON.

Canada's Response to the Introduction of Fanwort in Ontario Waters: A Case Study

Francine MacDonald

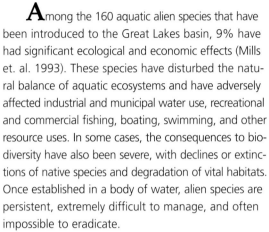

Among the 160 aquatic alien species that have been introduced to the Great Lakes basin, 9% have had significant ecological and economic effects (Mills et. al. 1993). These species have disturbed the natural balance of aquatic ecosystems and have adversely affected industrial and municipal water use, recreational and commercial fishing, boating, swimming, and other resource uses. In some cases, the consequences to biodiversity have also been severe, with declines or extinctions of native species and degradation of vital habitats. Once established in a body of water, alien species are persistent, extremely difficult to manage, and often impossible to eradicate.

In Canada, prevention efforts aimed at alien species have focused on well-known pathways for introduction, such as the ballast water of foreign vessels, often overlooking other equally significant ones, in particular the aquarium and horticultural trades. Disposal of aquarium contents or escapes from cultivation have introduced 17 species of alien invasive aquatic plants to the United States (Benson 1999). In Canada, introductions of aquarium and horticultural species, such as Eurasian water-milfoil (*Myriophyllum spicatum* L.), purple loosestrife (*Lythrum salicaria* L.), and European frog-bit (*Hydrocharis morsus-ranae* L.), may have had significant impact on aquatic ecosystems (White et. al. 1993; Catling et. al. 1988). Despite the known threat that these species pose to aquatic communities, little action has been initiated to prevent introductions from the aquarium and horticultural trades. Furthermore, when an introduction occurs, Canada has no existing framework to identify the ecological risks posed by the species and to implement prevention and control measures. The absence of a national response plan to deal with alien species negates, or significantly impairs, response to an introduction while eradication measures are still feasible.

Recently, the invasion of an Ontario lake by the aquarium plant *Cabomba caroliniana* A. Gray (Cabombaceae), commonly called fanwort or cabomba, has highlighted the failures of existing policy to prevent or control alien species introductions. This chapter presents the current knowledge about the risk this plant poses to Canada's freshwater ecosystems. It points to

an urgent need for a national policy on invasive species that provides an action plan on how to deal with new introductions, prevents their spread, and minimizes the potential impacts of species already present.

Background

Fanwort is a submersed, perennial freshwater plant native to the neotropic and south temperate regions of North and South America (McFarland et al. 1998). In North America, its range has extended to include over 30 states. It has now invaded the northeastern states of New Hampshire, New Jersey, New York, Massachusetts, and Michigan (McFarland et al. 1998) and more recently the northwestern states of Oregon and Washington. Overseas, fanwort has been introduced to Australia, Malaysia, New Guinea, and Japan (McFarland et al. 1998).

Introductions of fanwort to locations beyond its native range are widely believed to be the result of escapes from aquarium cultivation or from the careless disposal of aquarium contents (Holm et.al. 1969; Reimer and Ilnicki 1968; Les and Mehrhoff 1999). Fanwort is commonly sold in aquarium and pet stores across North America. It has also been promoted in the past as a desirable plant for fisheries enhancement in states such as Ohio (Rood 1947). Fanwort was probably introduced to Ontario via the former route, although it may also have arrived on recreational boats from areas of infestation in the United States (A. Dextrase, Ontario Ministry of Natural Resources, Peterborough, ON, personal communication).

The first verified report of an established population of fanwort in Ontario was made in the summer of 1991 (R. Ben-Oliel, Ontario Ministry of Natural Resources, Peterborough, ON, personal communication). It was observed in the North River, immediately downstream of Kasshabog Lake (northeast of Peterborough). Unfortunately, this report was never fully investigated and it was not until nearly eight years later, when the plant was rediscovered in Kasshabog Lake by two Ontario Ministry of Natural Resources biologists, D.A. Sutherland and M.J. Oldham (Oldham 1999), that concerns were raised about its potential impact on aquatic communities. Preliminary monitoring has since found established populations of fanwort in at least four isolated bays on the southeastern side of the lake (Figure 1). Dense populations approaching a hectare in size per site and growing to depths greater than 6 m have been observed. These sites appear to be monocultures, possibly excluding the native plant community.

Figures 1. Fanwort infestation in Kasshabog Lake. Photos by Don Sutherland, Ontario Ministry of Natural Resources, Peterborough, ON.

Potential Impact and Spread of Fanwort

Fanwort has produced serious nuisance growths in other jurisdictions, particularly in New York, New Jersey, Massachusetts, New Hampshire and Connecticut (Les and Mehrhoff 1999; Madsen 1994; Hellquist and Crow 1984; Sheldon 1994). It is considered to be an extremely persistent and aggressive plant. In suitable conditions, it can form dense stands and crowd out previously well-established native plant species (Reimer and Ilnicki 1968; Sheldon 1994). Dense outgrowths of fanwort have also interfered with and restricted recreational uses of invaded bodies of water (Sanders 1979).

The luxuriant growth observed in Kasshabog Lake, and its survival over several seasons, strongly suggest that fanwort populations are well established in the lake and well able to withstand local climatic conditions. Based on its history of invasion elsewhere, fanwort could have adverse effects on the aquatic community of Kasshabog Lake. In addition, the plant could be spread via boat traffic to nearby Stony Lake and thus gain access to all the watersheds in the Trent-Severn

Waterway—a 376-km water system of canals, lakes, and rivers linking Georgian Bay on Lake Huron with the Bay of Quinte on Lake Ontario (see Figure 2).

Fanwort propagates primarily by vegetative multiplication (Reimer and Ilnicki 1968). In the southern areas of its distribution, seed production is also an important means of propagation; however, in northern states such as New Jersey, no evidence of reproduction by seed has been found (Reimer and Ilnicki 1968). At the end of the growing season (usually in late fall), the lower leaves drop and the stems of the plants become brittle and hard, causing the plant to break apart; this facilitates its distribution within the water body. With only a single pair of leaves, these stem sections can produce a new individual if they find a suitable environment. These plant fragments may become entangled on boat motor propellers and trailers, thus spreading the plant to new areas within the lake, to other parts of the water system, and overland to new bodies of water. Les and Mehrhoff (1999) observed that the long, trailing stems of fanwort could easily become entwined on boat trailers and that fanwort populations in Massachusetts and Connecticut abounded in lakes where motor boats were

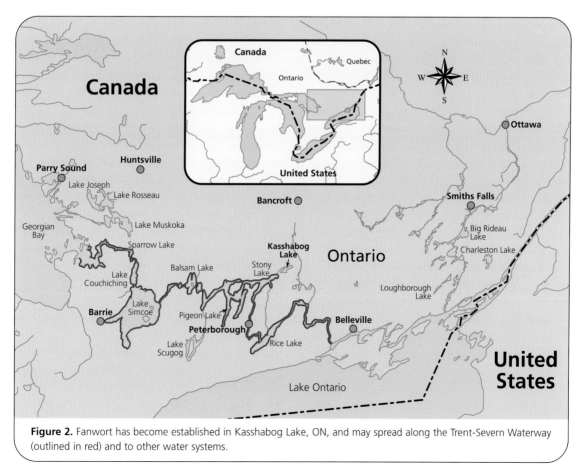

Figure 2. Fanwort has become established in Kasshabog Lake, ON, and may spread along the Trent-Severn Waterway (outlined in red) and to other water systems.

heavily used. Although Kasshabog Lake probably receives only a moderate degree of transient boat traffic, its close proximity to Stony Lake and the rest of the Trent-Severn Waterway greatly increases the opportunity for fanwort to be introduced to numerous southern Ontario water bodies.

As mentioned previously, fanwort's popularity in the aquarium plant trade will also facilitate its introduction and dispersal in Ontario and in Canada. As long as this plant remains widely available to the public, new introductions may be inevitable.

Likelihood of Establishment in Ontario Waters

The potential distribution of fanwort based on its habitat and environmental requirements must still be assessed. Fanwort grows rooted to depths of 10 m, although it prefers shallow areas with soft sediments (1–3 m) in stagnant to slow-flowing waters such as streams, small rivers, lakes, ditches, and ponds (McFarland et al. 1998). Although it grows best in warm, temperate climates at temperatures ranging between 13°C and 27°C, fanwort is cold tolerant and can withstand temperatures dropping below 0°C. Fanwort prefers an acidic environment, with an optimum pH range from 4 to 6 (Tarver and Sanders 1977). Therefore, lakes low in alkalinity, with a relatively early spring warm-up, could be vulnerable to invasion.

Dale (1982) assessed the potential for fanwort to cause nuisance growths in Ontario lakes and suggested that temperature and pH would be the primary factors limiting its distribution. He indicated that southern Ontario lakes low in alkalinity and buffering capacity, such as those in the Haliburton, Muskoka, and Parry Sound areas, would be most vulnerable to invasion. These areas are among the most popular cottage and recreation destinations in Ontario. However, Dale doubted that lakes of this latitude would provide the warm water temperatures of early spring warm-up required for vigorous growth of fanwort. The presence of vigorous stands of fanwort in Kasshabog Lake, and more recent assessments of its success in colder latitudes, suggest that the temperature requirements of fanwort could be met in southern Ontario. McFarland et al. (1998) assessed the possibility of fanwort invading Minnesota as high and predicted that its growth in this state could cause problems. Further, observations of recent fanwort infestations in Wisconsin and Michigan lakes have found fanwort populations not only

surviving but expanding (J. Madsen, Minnesota State University, Mankato, MN, personal communication). These lakes had a similar temperature regime to lakes in Muskoka.

Actions and Obstacles: Preventing the Spread of Fanwort

The potential ecological threat that fanwort poses to aquatic communities, its likelihood of spread, and its capacity to affect the recreational uses of Ontario waterways warrant immediate action to control the species. The Kasshabog Lake fanwort is the only reported established population of this plant in Canada; resource managers therefore have a rare opportunity to prevent new introductions of fanwort, assess its ecological impacts, investigate control options, and contain its spread before it becomes a widespread nuisance. Unfortunately, several obstacles have hindered the implementation of these actions.

The federal government has not taken the lead in developing a strategy to assess the potential impact, spread, and control of fanwort. Instead, stakeholders and agencies affected or concerned by the invasion of fanwort, such as the Kasshabog Lake Residents Association, the Ontario Federation of Anglers and Hunters (OFAH), and the Ontario Ministry of Natural Resources (OMNR), have responded to the problem, although the approach is piecemeal. Their efforts have been mainly aimed at educating the boating public on how to prevent the overland spread of the plant and involve the development and distribution of fact sheets, media releases, and presentations to community groups. Although these efforts are integral to preventing the further spread of fanwort to new waters, activities are still required to contain its spread, assess its impacts, and analyze options for its control. The roles of government departments, nongovernmental agencies, and research institutions must be clearly identified.

Risk Assessment

The risk of fanwort establishment and the scale of its impact must be assessed to determine whether significant financial resources should be invested in control and prevention initiatives. This assessment will also help ensure that control or eradication actions are taken while they are feasible and while this alien species can be contained in its present location.

A risk assessment requires significant resources and the coordination and involvement of numerous government departments because its findings may require approvals for mechanical and chemical control options from Fisheries and Oceans Canada, OMOE, and OMNR. Technical support and advice to obtain data on the impacts of fanwort on aquatic biota and assessment of the efficacy of control options will also be required. The distribution of responsibilities among the various federal and provincial departments and agencies impedes swift action. A single agency responsible for the implementation or coordination of a risk assessment would greatly expedite the process and would better channel input from the various stakeholders.

Regulations and protocols addressing threats to agriculture and forestry are much more developed than those dealing with threats to aquatic ecosystems. The *Plant Protection Act* (S.C. 1990, c. 22), administered by the Canadian Food Inspection Agency, prevents the import, export, and spread of pests injurious to plants and provides for their control and eradication. Its purpose is "…to protect plant life and the agricultural and forestry sectors of the Canadian economy." Traditionally, this act has been used to initiate control and/or eradication measures against agricultural and forest pests as in the case of the recent infestation of the brown spruce longhorn beetle (*Tetropium fuscum* (Fabricius)) in Nova Scotia and the plum pox virus (*Potyvirus: Potyviridae*) outbreak in the Niagara region of Ontario. Under this act, a risk assessment is conducted upon the discovery of a potential pest. Based on this assessment, a control and/or eradication program is implemented.

Unfortunately, although the *Plant Protection Act* prohibits several aquatic plants, such as the European water chestnut (*Trapa natans* L.), and fanwort potentially poses a risk to native plant life, the act does not give to the government the authority to deal with aquatic alien species in general. Its primary focus is the protection of the agricultural and forestry industries. However, based on the economic significance of water resources (recreational and commercial fishery, tourism, recreation, etc.), a similar risk assessment process that provides the regulatory, technical, and financial support to deal with alien aquatic species introductions is warranted. The absence of a national action plan that at least identifies the agencies responsible for dealing with an introduction in the early stages of infestation, while control options may still be feasible, has left Ontario waters vulnerable to further invasions by fanwort as well as other aquatic alien species.

By ratifying the United Nations Convention on Biological Diversity in 1992, Canada recognized at the international level the need to prevent introductions of alien species that threaten ecosystems and economic and recreational activities. Article 8(h) of this convention states:

> Each Contracting Party shall, as far as possible and as appropriate: Prevent the introduction of, control or eradicate those alien species which threaten ecosystems, habitats or species. (UNEP 1992)

In 1995, the federal government, in conjunction with other levels of government and stakeholders such as local and indigenous communities, conservation organizations, and research foundations, developed the Canadian Biodiversity Strategy. It identifies strategic directions to meet the obligations of the convention, including those dealing with harmful alien organisms. These directions include:

> determining priorities for allocating resources for the control of harmful alien species based on their impact to native biodiversity and economic resources and implementing effective control or where possible, eradication measures[1.81a];…and ensuring that there is adequate legislation and enforcement to control introductions or escapes of harmful alien organisms…[1.81e]. (Environment Canada 1995)

The Canadian Biodiversity Strategy should provide the framework for a national policy for dealing with alien species introductions.

Import and Sale

Fanwort is a popular aquarium plant that is easily obtained at aquarium and pet stores across the country. Initiatives aimed at controlling the spread of this plant must thus consider its widespread availability to the public. Once fanwort is sold, control of it is lost. Buyers may release unwanted fanwort specimens into local lakes or streams accidentally along with their aquarium fish or deliberately because they believe the fanwort will enhance lake environments. Inevitably, introductions of fanwort will continue as long as it remains available to the public.

Other alien aquatic plants associated with the horticultural trade, such as European frog-bit, flowering rush (*Butomus umbellatus* L.), and yellow flag (*Iris pseudacorus* L.), have also become established in numerous locations throughout the province (White et al. 1993). Clearly, plant specimens imported by the aquarium and nursery industries should be under greater scrutiny.

Canada's current regulations for the import of plants and animals relies on the *Wild Animal and Plant Protection and Regulation of International and Interprovincial Trade Act* (WAPPRIITA) (S.C. 1992, c. 52) as well as the *Plant Protection Act*. One of the objectives of WAPPRIITA is to "protect Canadian ecosystems from the introduction of listed harmful species." However, despite the establishment of fanwort and numerous other aquatic species in Canadian waters, no plants are currently listed as prohibited by WAPPRIITA. The only aquatic plants prohibited from entry into the country are through the *Plant Protection Act*.[1] The import of all other aquatic plants does not require the importer to demonstrate that the plants are safe and will not adversely affect the environment.

In the absence of any other restrictions on the import of aquatic plants into the country, Ontario's aquatic ecosystems are vulnerable to future invasions by fanwort and a host of additional unknown species. To reduce future introductions of fanwort, the possibility of having this species added to the prohibited list should be investigated. Further assessment needs to be done of the risks presented by other aquatic plants currently being imported into Canada.

Unfortunately, banning the import of fanwort into Canada will not necessarily prevent its sale and distribution within Ontario. Horticultural and aquarium companies can still cultivate populations of aquatic plants such as fanwort from existing stock, although this practice is more prevalent in the southern United States. Listing fanwort as a provincially noxious weed, however, could effectively prohibit its sale and transportation and prevent new introductions from discarded aquarium contents. Although provincial weed acts have traditionally emphasized species that are problematic to agriculture, several provinces list aquatic species in their weed acts—British Columbia includes Eurasian water-milfoil, and Alberta, Manitoba, and Prince Edward Island list purple loosestrife (White et al. 1993).

Increasing the regulation of the aquarium and horticultural trade would probably meet with strong opposition. Species such as fanwort can be economically important to this trade. Since a market has already been established for fanwort, it may be very difficult to have its sale and import banned. An alternative to the regulatory approach would be to involve industry in raising public awareness about the risks of invasion from improper disposal of aquarium contents.

---

[1] They are water-milfoil (*Myriophyllum* spp.); water-thyme or Florida elodea (*Hydrilla verticillata* (L.f.) Royle); Brazilian or South American waterweed (*Elodea densa* (Planch) Casp. = *Egeria densa* Planch.); and water chestnut (*Trapa* spp.).

Public Awareness

In Ontario, and in most other jurisdictions, the direct release of aquarium organisms into the environment is illegal (under the *Fish and Wildlife Conservation Act*). However, as discussed, once these organisms are the property of the public, there is no control over their fate. Organisms are released into the wild for numerous reasons; for example, the hobbyist may no longer be able to care for the organisms or may have lost interest in them; the organisms may seem to be in poor health or have outgrown the aquarium. In all likelihood, the hobbyist does not realize the environmental consequences of such releases.

The Fish Rescue Program is an initiative of organizations concerned about the release of alien aquatic species. Its objective is to provide aquarium, terrarium, and water-garden hobbyists with information on the potential harmful effects of releasing pets and plants into Ontario waters. Organizations involved include the Canadian Association of Aquarium Clubs, the Pet Industry Joint Advisory Council Canada, the Metropolitan Toronto Zoo, the Royal Ontario Museum, the Ontario Federation of Anglers and Hunters, and the Ontario Ministry of Natural Resources (see Dextrase, this publication, p. 219). Increasing public and retail-sector awareness of the issue is key to preventing future introductions of fanwort, and other aquarium organisms, to Ontario waters.

Conclusions

Canada has made international (the Convention on Biological Diversity) and national (Canadian Biodiversity Strategy) commitments to prevent introductions of alien species and to control or eradicate those threatening ecosystems, habitats, or species. The introduction of fanwort to Ontario waters has revealed several major weaknesses in Canada's response to dealing with introduced aquatic nuisance species.

A preliminary risk assessment suggests that fanwort could potentially spread to water bodies throughout southern Ontario, affect native biota, and restrict recreational water uses. However, the absence of a coordinated, expedient response to the introduction of fanwort has left local lakes, rivers, and wetlands vulnerable to possible adverse ecological and economic effects. Fortunately, local stakeholders, some government departments, and nongovernmental agencies are cooperating to prevent the spread of fanwort and hope to develop a strategy for research into its impacts and control and the prevention of its spread.

The fanwort situation has also underscored the need for greater scrutiny of the import of aquarium and horticultural species into Canada. Hundreds of species are imported into the country each year without any legal requirement or responsibility on the part of the importer to provide evidence that these species will not cause harm if released into the environment. This is not in keeping with a precautionary approach to preventing new introductions.

Canada clearly requires a national action plan to deal with introductions of alien species from all sources including aquariums and water gardens. This action plan should identify the agency responsible for assessing the risk posed by the introduction, provide funding mechanisms and technical advice and support for control options, and be capable of functioning in an expedient manner. This is necessary not only to fulfill our national and international commitments, but also to protect Canada's ecosystems from the detrimental effects of future invasions.

References

Benson, A.J. 1999. Documenting over a century of aquatic introductions in the United States. Pages 1–31 in R. Claudi and J.H. Leach, eds. Nonindigenous freshwater organisms: vectors, biology and impacts. CRC Press/ Lewis Publishers, Boca Raton, FL. 480 p.

Catling, P.M.; Spicer, K.W.; Lefkovitch, L.P. 1988. Effects of the floating Hydrocharis morsus ranae (Hydrocharitaceae) on some North American aquatic macrophytes. Nat. can. (Que.) 115:131–137.

Dale, H. 1982. An assessment of the potential of fanwort to produce nuisance growths if introduced into lakes of Ontario and Quebec. Unpublished report. Fisheries and Environment Canada, Ottawa, ON.

Environment Canada, Biodiversity Convention Office. 1995. Canadian Biodiversity Strategy: Canada's response to the Convention on Biological Diversity. Hull, Quebec. 93 p.

Hellquist, C.B.; Crow, G.E. 1984. Aquatic vascular plants of New England. Part 7. Cabombaceae, Nymphaceae, Nelumbonaceae, and Ceratophyllaceae. New Hampshire Agricultural Experiment Station, University of New Hampshire, Durham, NH. Stn. Bull. 527.

Holm, L.G.; Weldon, L.W.; Blackburn, R.D. 1969. Aquatic weeds. Science 166:699–709.

Les, D.H.; Mehrhoff, L.J. 1999. Introduction of nonindigenous aquatic vascular plants in southern New England: a historical perspective. Biol. Invasions 1:281–300.

Madsen, J.D. 1994. Invasions and declines of submersed macrophytes in Lake George and other Adirondack lakes. Lake Reservoir Manag. 10(1):19–23.

McFarland, D.G.; Poovey, A.G.; Madsen, J.D. 1998. Evaluation of the potential of selected nonindigenous aquatic plant species to colonize Minnesota water resources. Minnesota Department of Natural Resources, St. Paul, MN.

Mills, E.L.; Leach, J.H.; Carlton, J.T.; Secor, C.L. 1993. Exotic species in the Great Lakes: a history of biotic crises and anthropogenic introductions. J. Gt. Lakes Res. 19(1):1–54.

Oldham, M.J. 1999. Botany: 1999 botanical highlights. Ontario National Heritage Information Centre Newsletter [print and online] 5(2): 10–11. http://www.mnr.gov.on.ca/MNR/nhic/newslett.html

Reimer, D.N.; Ilnicki, R.D. 1968. Reproduction and overwintering of cabomba in New Jersey. Weed Sci. 16:101–102.

Rood, A. 1947. Cabomba. Ohio Conserv. Bull. (March): 29.

Sanders, D.R. 1979. The ecology of Cabomba caroliniana. Pages 133–146 in E.O. Gangstad, ed. Weed control methods for public health applications. CRC Press, Boca Raton, FL.

Sheldon, S.P. 1994. Invasions and declines of submersed macrophytes in New England, with particular reference to Vermont lakes and herbivorous invertebrates in New England. Lake Reservoir Manag. 10(1):13–17.

Tarver, D.; Sanders, D. 1977. Selected life cycle features of fanwort. J. Aquat. Plant Manag. 15:18–22.

[UNEP] United Nations Environment Programme. 1992. Convention on Biological Diversity [online]. http://www.biodiv.org/convention/articles.asp

White, D.J.; Haber, E.; Keddy, C. 1993. Invasive plants of natural habitats in Canada. Canadian Wildlife Service, Environment Canada. Ottawa, ON.

Intentional Introduction of Tench into Southern Quebec

Pierre Dumont, Nathalie Vachon, Jean Leclerc, and Aymeric Guibert

In October 1999, a commercial fisher reported that a new species of fish had been caught in a fyke net in the Île aux Noix area (Figure 1) of the Richelieu River in Quebec. The specimen was identified as a tench (*Tinca tinca* (L.)), a Cyprinidae of Eurasian origin (Figure 2). According to the information gathered during the investigation, the specimens found in the upper Richelieu come from a strain that is believed to have been directly imported in 1986 from a German fish-breeding facility for aquaculture purposes. The tench apparently escaped from a fish farm located a few kilometres from the main stream of the Richelieu River during one or more pond drainings.

This report describes an intentional introduction of a fish into the St. Lawrence River–Great Lakes basin, as defined by the National Code on Introductions and Transfers of Aquatic Organisms (Fisheries and Oceans 2002), that is, "the deliberate release, or holding, of live aquatic organisms in open-water or within a facility with flow-through circulation or effluent access to the open-water environment outside its present range." The objectives of the report follow:

- to describe the events leading up to and the circumstances that facilitated the introduction of tench in southern Quebec;
- to prepare an overview of the knowledge acquired on the biology of this species in Quebec since its discovery;
- to discuss the probable impact of this introduction on aquatic wildlife indigenous to southern Quebec and to the entire Great Lakes drainage basin.

Figure 1. The lower St. Lawrence River and Richelieu River watersheds.

Information Sources

Following the identification of the first specimen in the fall of 1999, the Société de la faune et des parcs du Québec (FAPAQ), which is responsible for wildlife management in Quebec, conducted an investigation of three commercial fishers working in the upper Richelieu to determine when the species first appeared in their fyke nets. Concurrently with the investigation, samples of specimens were regularly taken from their catch to take various measurements (length, body weight, gonad weight), make observations (sex, sexual maturity, anomalies), and collect samples (scales, operculi, stomach contents). The sampling was repeated in April 2000. A "research notice" was also mailed to the some 100 commercial bait fishers of southwestern Quebec. A review of the relevant scientific literature and contacts with European and North American researchers enabled us to refine our knowledge of this species. We held

Figure 2. Two tench caught in November 1999 in the Île aux Noix area of the Richelieu River. The female (*top*) is 345 mm and 710 g; the male (*bottom*) is 320 mm and 450 g. Photo by Nathalie Dubuc, FAPAQ.

exchanges with officers from the Saint-Jean-sur-Richelieu regional office of FAPAQ's Wildlife Protection Branch. We also contacted scientists from FAPAQ and from the Quebec Department of Agriculture, Fisheries and Food (MAPAQ) who had witnessed events or been made aware of facts that could be useful in tracing the source of the introduction. After the source was identified as a fish farm from the Saint-Alexandre region of southern Quebec, we conducted informal interviews of the owners by telephone and in person. In the summer of 2000, we gathered information on tench as part of two field operations. In June and September, we successively drained and applied rotenone to the nine rearing ponds likely to contain tench. In July, experimental seine, multimesh gill net, and fyke net fisheries were carried out in various parts of the Richelieu River and several of its tributaries to assess the extent of its spread, to gather additional data on its biology, and, more specifically, its habitats, and to confirm its reproduction in the natural environment.

History of Events

In the early 1980s, a farmer of European origin applied to the government for a permit to import mirror carp, a domestic variety of common carp (*Cyprinus carpio* L.) from Germany. Tench was never mentioned in the discussions. Carp was introduced into North America in the 1800s and is now considered naturalized in Quebec (Desrosiers 1995). The mirror variety was developed in Eurasia for pond rearing and is very rare in the natural environment. Its skin is almost scaleless, with only one or two rows of scales. At least two government bodies were contacted: MAPAQ and the Quebec Department of Recreation, Hunting and Fishing (MLCP), now called FAPAQ. Despite repeated requests, the response was always the same: the Quebec authorities could not issue such a permit because the Quebec Fishery Regulations restricted the rearing, holding in captivity, stocking, and live transport of fish to a very small number of species. Neither carp nor tench was on this list, which was established on the basis of the biogeographic zones of Quebec. In practice, importation in Canada is limited to species intended for aquarium hobbyists, with most (but not all) of the species in question being of tropical origin and relatively unlikely to become established locally, and to several species of the family Salmonidae. Importation of Salmonidae is subject to the federal Fish Health Protection Regulations (Canada), which are essentially designed to protect wild and farmed populations of Salmonidae from the risk of introduction of pathogens.

In 1983 or 1984, despite repeated notices prohibiting the rearing of this species in Quebec, small mirror carp were imported from Germany. The farmer transported them himself in a picnic cooler on a regular flight. The circumstances surrounding his clearance through Canadian customs are unknown.

In 1986, tench were imported from Germany. Thirty small specimens less than 6 cm long were transported in a picnic cooler. The contents of the cooler were declared at customs at Mirabel Airport. After making several telephone calls, the customs officers decided to allow him to clear customs. In such cases, the officers generally contact Agriculture Canada, which does not have jurisdiction over this type of import, and Fisheries and Oceans Canada, which cannot object to the import under the federal regulations unless the specimens in question belong to the family Salmonidae. The officers also sometimes contact the provincial authorities, but given the gray areas in the Quebec regulations regarding the importation of species for the aquarium hobby, it is not always possible to provide clear answers to the questions asked.

The farmer gradually built a network of 11 shallow ponds on his property, placed side by side and parallel to each other, for a total area of 6.5 ha. The ponds are located on a small plateau overlooking a vast plain under corn production, and are fed essentially by rainwater and groundwater. The tench were transferred to one or more of these ponds. According to the farmer, they reproduced but, unlike carp, they had slow growth and low survival rates. The results of marketing trials were also disappointing because Quebecers consume primarily Salmonidae and saltwater species.

The ponds have been drained on several occasions since 1986, two of which were documented. In 1990, the farmer took part in an experimental crayfish rearing program introduced by MAPAQ. Under the program, he was required to ensure that the ponds used in the program did not contain any fish and he therefore drained the ponds. Fish escaped into the network of small agricultural streams that crisscross the plain and flow into the Richelieu River and Missisquoi Bay in the Canadian portion of Lake Champlain. In mid-October 1991, several ponds were partially drained, this time to verify the effectiveness of the crayfish rearing trials. Observers from MAPAQ were present and reported that they captured thousands of carp (mirror and koi varieties), tench, and goldfish (*Carassius auratus* L.), another alien

Cyprinidae whose source of introduction into the ponds is unknown. They also observed hundreds of fish in the drainage ditches. Although they attempted to recover the fish, they did not inform the regional branch of the MLCP of the release. MLCP was, however, aware that tench had been present at the fish farm since the spring of 1991. In fact, for identification purposes, several specimens had been sent by conservation officers to a specialist from the Branch, who had recommended that the tench be restricted to the ponds. Legal action was launched under the Quebec Regulation Respecting Aquaculture and Fish-Breeding Areas, but was quickly dropped because the rearing of tench in this vast network of turbid ponds was at the time (erroneously) associated with the aquarium hobby, that is, the rearing of fish for ornamental purposes.

In October 1999, a commercial fisher from the upper Richelieu submitted the first specimen for identification. According to informal interviews of three commercial fishers from this area, tench appeared in their gear in about 1994. Since then, catches have been increasingly numerous. From a few specimens in the initial years, the number of tench caught rose to roughly 150 in the fall of 1999 and to 176 in the fall of 2000. They are somewhat higher in the fall, but the fishers also indicated spring catches. According to them, the fish were smaller in the spring than in the fall and the size range was smaller. To facilitate the examination of the fish, FAPAQ issued permits authorizing these fishers to keep and kill all specimens caught. However, requests to conduct marketing trials were rejected to eliminate the temptation to attempt to derive short-term gains from this introduction, which could encourage other introduction attempts.

In the summer of 2000, we poisoned all of the fish ponds. Our objective was twofold: to set an example and to reduce the risk of transfers of tench taken from these ponds, which are located along a road and whose existence is becoming more and more known, to other watersheds as fishing bait or ornamental fish.

Tench in the World

Tench is indigenous to Europe and Asia (Berg 1964). In Europe, the northern limit of its range corresponds to the northern tip of the Gulf of Bothnia (65.5°N) according to Bachasson (1995) and to its southern tip (61°N) according to Banarescu et al. (1971). In Asia, the northern limit is believed to be in Siberia at a latitude of 61° N (Bachasson 1995). Introduced into the United States

in 1877 from Germany, it has now been inventoried in 38 US states (Lee et al. 1980; Fuller et al. 1999). Until its recent discovery in Quebec, its presence in Canada had been reported only in southern British Columbia, where it appeared in about 1915 in a network of three small lakes after its introduction into an ornamental pond in Seattle (Scott and Crossman 1973; E. J. Crossman, Royal Ontario Museum, Toronto, ON, personal communication).

Adult tench generally measure 300–500 mm and weigh 1–4 kg. A record size of 700 mm (8 kg) was reported in a specimen from southeastern Europe. It has a lifespan of 20–30 years and reaches sexual maturity at 3–4 years (250–300 mm). In Europe, spawning occurs from May to July in shallow waters with lush vegetation and water temperatures of 19–20°C, and may be repeated in August. The diameter of the eggs in the ovaries varies over the course of the summer from 0.1 to 0.9 mm (O'Maoileidigh and Bracken 1989). Over two months and at roughly two-week intervals, the highly fecund female (up to 600 000 eggs/kg body weight) (Berg 1964; De Muus and Dahlström 1981) deposits her eggs in clusters on the vegetation or streambed. The eggs are greenish and sticky. Hatching occurs after three to six days of incubation (100–120 degree-days). On hatching, the larvae, which are 4–5 mm long, have attachment organs and remain passively attached to the vegetation for a few days. Resorption of the yolk sac is completed at 10 days and the fry begin to feed on zooplankton and algae. Annual recruitment may be highly variable; in England, warm summers appear to be important in producing strong year classes (Wright and Giles 1991). Young tench measure 40–80 mm in their first summer and 100–150 mm in their second summer. Growth is highly variable, even within the same environment (Weatherley 1959; O'Maoileidigh and Bracken 1989). In Europe, tench in rearing ponds average 120–412 mm at five years. In these rearing habitats, this large variability is believed to be associated with such factors as the abundance of food, sex-dependent growth potential, and repeated spawning over the summer, which leads to a significant disparity in the lengths reached at the end of the first year of life (Bachasson 1995).

Tench is ubiquitous but prefers habitats characterized by stagnant waters, abundant vegetation, and soft (muddy) substrates, such as lakes, marshes with clay bottoms, and silted up ponds. Its preferences may vary, however, with the seasons and, in the fall, it may occur in areas with sparse or no vegetation (Degiorgi 1994).

It also lives in slow-moving areas of rivers. It is highly tolerant of low oxygen levels (Weatherley 1959), and can colonize areas in which virtually no other species can survive. It may also occur in brackish waters (Weatherley 1959). Given its slow, fearful disposition, tench remains almost always at the bottom, stirring up the mud with its lips and barbels to feed on benthic organisms, such as insect larvae, crustaceans, mollusks, and worms, as well as plant debris (Weatherley 1959; O'Maoileidigh and Bracken 1989). Tench feeds primarily at night, in hot weather; in winter, it burrows into the silt and hibernates, not resurfacing until spring.

In Europe, tench is prized as a sport fish and is reared in ponds for food or as an ornamental species (Vostradovsky 1975; Bachasson 1995). It is edible and its meat is considered tender and flavourful. It is most popular as food in Germany and Italy, its meat being compared to that of rainbow trout (Oncorhynchus mykiss Walbaum). In North America, it is not very popular with either fishers or consumers.

Tench in Quebec

Some of the data collected to date on the biology of the tench in Quebec have already been presented in technical documents by Vachon and Dumont (2000) and Guibert (2000), the highlights of which follow. Other data are added, including a description of the specimens captured in the initial ponds when the ponds were poisoned in June and September 2000. Parasitological, bacteriological, and virological analyses of tench from the Richelieu River to verify whether certain pathogenic organisms may have been introduced with the first lot are being carried out by Andrée Gendron and David Marcogliese of the St. Lawrence Centre (Environment Canada, Montréal), Carl Uhland of the University of Montréal's faculty of veterinary medicine (Saint-Hyacinthe), and Carmencita Yason and Dave Groman of the University of Prince Edward Island. The results are not available yet.

At present, the distribution of tench appears to be limited to the introduction zone, that is, the first 20–30 km of the Richelieu River, and to Rivière du Sud, near its confluence with the Richelieu River. Commercial bait fishers and anglers have also reported tench elsewhere, at Saint-Jean-sur-Richelieu (20 km downstream), at Chambly (42 km downstream), and in Ewing Creek, a small tributary of Missisquoi Bay. However, their identification could not be confirmed by examination of the specimens. The increase in their

numbers in the fall catches of commercial fishers, from a few individuals in 1994 to close to 200 in 2000, shows that the tench population is growing, although it still appears to be small. In fact, tench accounts for only a small percentage of the fish caught in the fyke nets of commercial fishers. Similarly, in experimental surveys from the summer of 2000 in the upper Richelieu, only 8 of the 2 499 fish sampled with gill nets and fyke nets were tench. However, this seemingly low abundance must be interpreted cautiously. Tench are difficult to catch, have nocturnal habits, and live burrowed in the mud or sheltered in dense beds of floating or submerged vegetation (Weatherley 1959; Degiorgi 1994). We were able to observe the cryptic nature of this species when we poisoned the rearing ponds at Saint-Alexandre in June and September 2000. Hundreds of tench were captured in the ponds, rarely in the initial passes of the seine net, but rather after repeated passes on the bottom of the ponds that had been drained almost completely dry.

The aquatic environments in which tench were caught resemble the preferred habitats of tench as described in the scientific literature: large, shallow, grassy bays, near marshes and swampy forests (for example, Baie des Anglais or McGillivray Bay on the Richelieu River) or tributaries with very slow-moving currents bordered by dense grass beds (like Rivière du Sud). The water temperature in summer can be high (>25° C) and the concentration of dissolved oxygen very low.

Although tench appear to be relatively scarce in the upper Richelieu, they have adapted very well to their new environment, and likely much better than to the ponds at Saint-Alexandre. The specimens sampled in the natural environment between November 1999 and July 2000 are clearly larger and have a greater size range than those measured in the ponds (P<0.001; Mann-Whitney test) (Figure 3). They range from 169 to 519 mm (87 to 1 918 g) in the natural environment and from 42 to 265 mm (1 to 187 g) in the ponds. The same is true of relative condition, as measured using Fulton's condition factor, that is, the ratio of the weight of the specimen to the cubic value of its length (Ricker 1971). The values obtained in the Richelieu River are relatively high compared to those of tench in rearing facilities or in natural habitats in Eurasia (Table 1). The available data on small specimens suggest that, in fish of comparable size, condition factor values are higher in the natural environment than in the ponds at Saint-Alexandre (Table 1).

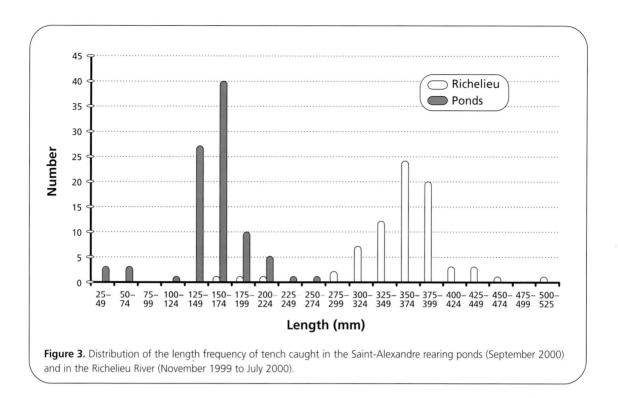

Figure 3. Distribution of the length frequency of tench caught in the Saint-Alexandre rearing ponds (September 2000) and in the Richelieu River (November 1999 to July 2000).

Table 1. Average and limit values (in parentheses) of Fulton's condition factor (K) for tench in different natural and rearing environments.

Location	Fulton's Condition Factor				Reference
	All specimens	< 265 mm	Females	Males	
Richelieu River	1.6 (1.32–1.9) (November to July)	1.74 (1.69–1.79) (April to July)			present study
Saint-Alexandre (rearing ponds)		1.18 (0.9–1.53) (September)			present study
Killarney Lake (Ireland)			1.6 (summer)	1.53–1.64 (summer)	O'Maoileidigh and Bracken 1989
France (rearing ponds)					Bachasson 1995
Dombes	0.94 (0.82–1.11)				
Brenne	1.18 (1.02–1.42)				
Léman	1.24 (1.03–1.42)				
Forez	1.33 (1.04–1.74)				
Sarthe	1.38 (1.02–1.79)				
Bourget	1.34				
Rhône-Alpes	2.54				
Lorraine	2.43–2.64				
Germany (rearing ponds)	1.33				Bachasson 1995
Poland (rearing ponds)	1.37				Bachasson 1995
Danube Delta			2.84	2.71	Moroz 1968

Reproduction in the Richelieu River was confirmed by the capture of six sexually mature specimens (317–398 mm long) during the first two weeks of July and of three two-year-old fish (in April and July), that were most likely born in the natural environment. The high fecundity of the species was also verified, with a female measuring 394 mm (986 g) bearing 221 750 eggs. The ovaries of this female contained eggs belonging to two size classes (0.3–0.5 mm and 0.7–1.0 mm), which suggests that, like the Eurasian populations, the breeding season of tench from the Richelieu River may be spread over several months. The stomach contents analysis of eight tench captured in July also confirms the opportunistic nature of this species: a large variety of animal prey was identified, including mollusks, crustaceans, and insect larvae.

Discussion

Released into the natural environment in the early 1990s, tench must now be considered naturalized in Quebec. Its population in the upper Richelieu is on the rise and it includes a wide range of sizes and young fish. Sexual maturity is reached in some individuals over 30 cm. The species appears to prosper in this sector of lentic waters, which provides vast areas of marshes and shoreline grass beds. It has a good condition factor and, in about 10 years, has reached high maximum sizes.

At present, the species' range appears to be limited and the expansion of its range appears to be relatively slow compared to several better known exotic species. For example, carp, which was introduced into North America in 1831, was first observed at the western tip of Lake Ontario in 1890, in the area of Toronto in 1901, and at the eastern tip of the lake in 1907. Since 1911, it has been considered a major nuisance in the upper reaches of the St. Lawrence River. The source of this invasion is believed to be the accidental release of specimens from rearing facilities into small tributaries in New York State (McCrimmon 1968). Another example is the zebra mussel (Dreissena polymorpha (Pallas)), which was introduced in 1986 through ships' ballast waters. In less than five years, it colonized a large part of the St. Lawrence–Great Lakes watershed and the Mississippi and Hudson river drainage basins (Griffiths et al. 1991). Round goby (Neogobius melanostomus (Pallas)), a small Eurasian fish, first appeared in the St. Clair River in 1990. Five years later, it was already present in at least four of the Great Lakes (Erie, Michigan, Superior, and Ontario) (Fuller et al. 1999). In 1997, catches were mentioned for the first time in the St. Lawrence River in the vicinity of Québec City (de Lafontaine and Costan, this publication, p.73).

The three intruders mentioned have caused and continue to cause major disruptions of North American aquatic ecosystems. However, the majority of the 157 species introduced into the St. Lawrence–Great Lakes system (see de Lafontaine and Costan, p.73 in this publication) have not experienced such spectacular spread or had such noticeable effects. We cannot predict what will happen in the case of tench. It is a long-lived, opportunistic, ubiquitous species with high fecundity and a high tolerance to low oxygen. Its discrete nature would make it relatively invulnerable to predation (Brönmark et al. 1995). Its Eurasian range in cold regions, such as Scandinavia and Siberia, demonstrates that it can adapt to local winter conditions. It therefore has the ability to expand its range in the Richelieu River, Lake Champlain, and the St. Lawrence River, environments in which its preferred habitats are plentiful. Its transfer to the Great Lakes is also possible, through the St. Lawrence River or Lake Champlain–Hudson River–Erie Canal system. It could even reach the brackish waters of the St. Lawrence estuary. Its spread will likely be slow (de Lafontaine and Costan, p.73 in this publication), but could be accelerated by human intervention, via the ballast waters of the many vessels that ply the waters between ports in Quebec and the Great Lakes, or more simply through the illegal use of this hardy, tolerant species as bait for fishing or as an ornamental species in decorative ponds, which are becoming increasingly popular. Given that the upper Richelieu is one of the primary sources of fish for commercial bait fishers in Quebec, the risks posed by the spread of this species into other watersheds are also far from negligible.

In most areas where tench was introduced, including the small drainage basin in southern British Columbia, little has been written about the impact of its presence (Fuller et al. 1999; Scott and Crossman 1973), likely because these concerns generated very little interest in the 19th century. However, in Maryland and Idaho, tench is extremely abundant and is considered a major nuisance (Fuller et al. 1999). Moyle (1976) believes that tench may compete for food resources with native Cyprinidae and sport species. Like carp, its burrowing habits cause resuspension of sediments, uprooting of vegetation, and increased turbidity and water temperatures.

The introduction of this new species may affect the aquatic communities of southern Quebec by competing with several native species, particularly those that use dense grass beds or marshes and that feed on invertebrates, such as yellow perch (*Perca flavescens* (Mitchill)), brown bullhead (*Ameiurus nebulosus* (Lesueur)), some sunfishes, and some insectivorous Cyprinidae. The spread of tench could also pose an additional threat to copper redhorse (*Moxostoma hubbsi* Legendre), a threatened species for which the lower half of the Richelieu River is the last habitat in the world in which it is known to breed (Mongeau et al. 1988). The diet of this Catostomidae consists almost exclusively of mollusks (Mongeau et al. 1992) and its only known spawning grounds are located in this river. Other redhorses at risk could also be affected, such as river redhorse (*M. carinatum* (Cope)), which has been considered a species at risk in Canada since 1983 (Parker 1988) and greater redhorse (*M. valenciennesi* Jordan), which could soon receive the same status (Campbell 1998). Recent studies in the Richelieu River reveal that at least in their first year of life, redhorses depend on shoreline grass beds (Vachon 1999).

Finally, the introduction of tench (and mirror carp) and their release into the natural environment may have resulted in the introduction of alien pathogens. The effects of such transfers, which can be observed in rearing facilities but are difficult to document in the natural environment unless they reach epidemic proportions, can sometimes be devastating for the indigenous fauna. For example, the importation of Japanese eel (*Anguilla japonica* Temminck and Schlegel) into Germany for rearing purposes was the source of the spread in a few years of *Anguillicola crassus* Kuwahara, Niimi and Itagaki, a parasite nematode of the swim bladder that now affects virtually all European eel (*Anguilla anguilla* (L.)) stocks and compromises their ability to complete the very long return migrations to their breeding grounds in the Sargasso Sea (Peters and Hartmann 1986). This parasite is also present in North America as a result of the importation of European eel for rearing purposes (Barse and Secor 1999).

Conclusion

The introduction of tench into southern Quebec and its subsequent spread in the Lake Champlain and St. Lawrence River network are the result of carelessness and indifference. The improbable occurred and should not have occurred. Apparently, thirty small specimens, imported in 1986, were enough to result in the establishment of a now naturalized local strain. The breeder responsible had been informed that all activity related to the transport of live fish and their rearing for food production purposes was authorized in Quebec only for a small group of fish species, which did not include carp or tench. At customs, a lack of communication between the various federal and provincial organizations involved and a regulatory gray area associated primarily, but not exclusively, with an overly broad definition of the "aquarium hobby" resulted in the entry of the species into Canada. Because of the uncertainty, no quarantine was imposed. In 1990 and 1991, at least, tench were released into the drainage system of the initial ponds without any precautions. In 1991, neither MAPAQ, which was content to limit its efforts to local damage control, nor MLCP, which equated the tench rearing operation in the vast network of turbid ponds with the aquarium hobby, took the necessary measures to attempt to avoid its introduction. It was not until 2000 that the initial ponds were poisoned, and it is likely not until April 2002, two and a half years into a lengthy provincial–federal approval process, that tench will probably be added to the list of species whose use as bait is prohibited in Quebec.

The problem has clearly caught the public's interest. After the first specimens were identified in the Richelieu River, we issued a brief news release informing the public of the risks of fish transfers and asking it to report any tench catches to us. Following this release, and for at least one month, we responded to over 25 requests for interviews from regional, national, and even international print and electronic media, which is unprecedented in the history of our Branch. In 1990, the Wildlife Ministers' Council of Canada adopted "A Wildlife Policy for Canada" (Wildlife Ministers' Council of Canada 1990). It states that the introduction of a species can be considered only if no uncontrollable adverse environmental impacts are anticipated. In signing the 1992 United Nations Convention on Biological Diversity, Canada undertook to develop national strategies, plans, and programs aimed at ensuring the conservation and sustainable use of biological diversity. Article 1.58 of the Canadian Biodiversity Strategy aims to "reduce to acceptable levels, or eliminate, adverse impacts of species introductions on aquatic biodiversity resulting from aquaculture projects, fisheries enhancement programs and interbasin transfers of water and organisms."

In practice, such objectives cannot be achieved without increased communication between the responsible government authorities; the elimination of regulatory gray areas; and harmonized, strengthened, and rigorously enforced regulations. The public must also be made aware of the risks to indigenous wildlife of certain behavior that may seem harmless, such as the release of bait fish or ornamental fish into the natural environment.

Acknowledgments

We wish to acknowledge the invaluable collaboration of three discerning commercial fishers of the upper Richelieu, G. Laramé, P. Gosselin, and R. Beaudin. Without them, the presence of tench in the Richelieu River would have gone undiscovered for some time longer. We would also like to thank E. Holm, E.J. Crossman, C.B. Renaud, J. Anderson, P. Elie, O. Schlumberger, J.F. Bergeron, Y. Mailhot, P.-Y. Collin, A. Deschênes, R. Rioux, F. Neeser, G. Neeser, E. Neeser, J.-P. Dorion, S. Gonthier, J. Dubé, and L. Lapierre for the information they provided on tench distribution and biology and the probable source of its introduction. We are grateful to C. Sirois, H. Massé, V. Boivin, A. Lincourt, M. Szapiel, A.-W. Van der Toorn, D. Bourbeau, D. Dolan, S. Dubois, F. Pelletier, P. Mathieu, P. Bérard, and Nathalie Dubuc, who participated in the field and laboratory work, to Y. de Lafontaine and E. Muckle-Jeffs, who prompted this report, and to P. Nantel and D. Rochon, who edited the original French manuscript.

References

Bachasson, B. 1995. Étude de quelques aspects de la morphologie, de la biologie et de la pisciculture de la tanche (*Tinca tinca* L.). Ph.D. thesis 114–95, Université Claude Bernard, Lyon 1, France.

Banarescu, P.; Blanc, M.; Gaudet, J.-L.; Hureau, J.C. 1971. Poissons des eaux continentales d'Europe. Catalogue multilingue. FAO, Fishing News (Books) Ltd., London.

Barse, A.M.; Secor, D.H. 1999. An exotic nematode parasite of the American eel. Fisheries (Bethesda) 24(2):6–10.

Berg, L.S. 1964. Freshwater fishes of the USSR and adjacent countries, 4th edition. Vol. II. Translated from Russian for the Smithsonian Institution and the National Science Foundation by Israel Program for Scientific Translations, Jerusalem, Israel.

Brönmark, C.; Paszkowski, C.A.; Tonn, W.M.; Hargeby, A. 1995. Predation as a determinant of size structure in populations of crucian carp (*Carassius carassius*) and tench (*Tinca tinca*). Ecol. Freshw. Fish 4:85–92.

Campbell, R.R. 1998. Rare endangered fishes and marine mammals of Canada: COSEWIC fish and marine mammal subcommittee status report: XII. Can. Field-Nat. 112:94–97.

Degiorgi, F. 1994. Étude de l'organisation spatiale de l'ichtyofaune lacustre — prospection multisaisonnière de 6 plans d'eau de l'est de la France à l'aide de filets verticaux. Ph.D. thesis 389, Université de Franche-Comté, France.

De Muus, B.J.; Dahlström, P. 1981. Guide des poissons d'eau douce et pêche. 3rd ed., Delachaux and Niestlé S.A., Neuchâtel, Switzerland. 224 p.

Desrosiers, A. 1995. Liste de la faune vertébrée du Québec. Government of Quebec, Department of Environment and Wildlife. Les Publications du Québec, Québec City, QC. 130 p.

Fisheries and Oceans Canada. 2002. National Code on Introductions and Transfers of Aquatic Organisms. Ottawa, ON.

Fuller, P.L.; Nico, L.G.; Williams, J.D. 1999. Nonindigenous fishes introduced into inland waters of the United States. Am. Fish. Soc. Spec. Publ. 27, Bethesda, MD. 613 p.

Griffiths, R.W.; Schloesser, D.W.; Leach, J.H.; Kovalak, W.P. 1991. Distribution and dispersal of the zebra mussel (*Dreissena polymorpha*) in the Great Lakes region. Can. J. Fish. Aquat. Sci. 48:1381–1388.

Guibert, A. 2000. La tanche (*Tinca tinca*) dans le Haut-Richelieu : État des connaissances et perspectives. Rapport de stage pour l'obtention d'une Maîtrise des sciences et techniques en ingénierie des milieux aquatiques et corridors fluviaux. [Report prepared for a university degree program.] University of Tours, Tours, France.

Lee, D.S.; Gilbert, C.R.; Hocutt, C.H.; Jenkins, R.E.; McAllister, D.E.; Stauffer, J.R. Jr. 1980. Atlas of North American freshwater fishes. Publ. 1980-12, North Carolina State Museum of Natural History, Raleigh, NC. 854 p.

McCrimmon, H.R. 1968. Carp in Canada. Fish. Res. Board Can. Bull. 165.

Mongeau, J.-R.; Dumont, P.; Cloutier, L. 1992. La biologie du suceur cuivré (*Moxostoma hubbsi*) comparée à celle de quatre autres espèces de *Moxostoma* (*M. anisurum*, *M. carinatum*, *M. macrolepidotum*, *M. valenciennesi*). Can. J. Zool. 70:1354–1363.

Mongeau, J.-R.; Dumont, P.; Cloutier, L.; Clément, A.M. 1988. Le statut du suceur cuivré au Canada. Can. Field-Nat. 102:132–139.

Moroz, V.N. 1968. Biology of the tench, *Tinca tinca* (L.), in the Kiliya Channel, Danube Delta. Probl. Ichthyol. 8:81–89.

Moyle, P.B. 1976. Inland fishes of California. University of California Press. Berkeley, CA. 405 p.

O'Maoileidigh, N.; Bracken, J.J. 1989. Biology of the tench, *Tinca tinca*, in an Irish lake. Aquac. Fish. Manag. 20:199–209.

Parker, B.J. 1988. Updated status of the river redhorse, *Moxostoma carinatum*, in Canada. Can. Field-Nat. 102:140–146.

Peters, G.; Hartmann, F. 1986. *Anguillicola*, a parasite nematode of the swimbladder spreading among populations in Europe. Dis. Aquat. Org. 1:229–230.

Ricker, W.E., ed. 1971. Methods of assessment of fish production in fresh waters. IBP Handbook No. 3, 2nd ed., Blackwell Scientific Publications, Oxford.

Scott, W.B.; Crossman, E.J. 1973. Freshwater fishes of Canada. Fish. Res. Board Can. Bull. 184. Ottawa, ON. 966 p.

Vachon, N. 1999. Écologie des juvéniles 0+ et 1+ de chevalier cuivré (*Moxostoma hubbsi*), une espèce menacée, comparée à celle des quatre autres espèces de *Moxostoma* (*M. anisurum, M. carinatum, M. macrolepidotum, M. valenciennesi*) dans le système de la rivière Richelieu.

M.Sc. thesis, Université du Québec à Montréal, Montréal, QC. 191 p.

Vachon, N.; Dumont, P. 2000. Caractérisation des premières mentions de captures de la tanche (*Tinca tinca*) dans le Haut-Richelieu (Québec). Société de la faune et des parcs du Québec, Direction de l'aménagement de la faune de la Montérégie, Longueuil, QC. Rapport technique [Technical Report]16–07.

Vostradovsky, J. 1975. Poissons d'eau douce. Atlas illustré. 2nd ed., Gründ, Paris.

Weatherley, A.H. 1959. Some features of the biology of the tench *Tinca tinca* (Linnaeus) in Tasmania. J. Anim. Ecol. 28:73–87.

Wildlife Ministers' Council of Canada. 1990. A wildlife policy for Canada. Canadian Wildlife Service, Ottawa, ON. 29 p.

Wright, R.M.; Giles, N. 1991. The population biology of tench, *Tinca tinca* (L.), in two gravel pit lakes. J. Fish Biol. 38:17–28.

Green Crab Introductions in North America: The Atlantic and Pacific Experiences

Glen S. Jamieson

The European green crab (*Carcinus maenas* (L.)) (Decapoda: Portunidae) is native to temperate waters of the Mediterranean Sea and the eastern Atlantic, from Mauritania to Norway. It was introduced, presumably accidentally, into several locations worldwide, including the western Atlantic sometime in the early 1800s, and the eastern Pacific near San Francisco, California, in the late 1980s. Several papers describe these North American introductions generally (Atlantic: Williams 1984; Pacific: Grosholz and Ruiz 1995, Grosholz 1996, Dumbauld and Kauffman 1998, Hunt et al. 1998, and Jamieson et al. 1998); however, no study to date has examined the oceanographic processes that have influenced range extension of this species. This information is relevant for several reasons.

First, because the green crab is new to these areas, its dispersal is relatively easy to document and correlate with oceanographic processes, such as the pattern of sea currents. Such an analysis would improve the evaluation of how these processes influence the dispersal of planktonic organisms that vertically migrate daily, that is, meroplanktonic species, including larvae from many alien and native species; this information would be difficult to obtain otherwise. The larvae of native species from different source sites are generally mixed, confusing the dispersal patterns from specific sources (Pulliam 1988; Roberts 1998). To preserve the metapopulation dynamics, it may be particularly important to identify significant source populations of native species to protect them. In this regard, an alien species model may present a unique opportunity to help identify potentially important sites.

Second, knowing the dispersal patterns of an alien species allows an assessment of its impact on the native ecosystem. Ideally, preinvasion monitoring can be conducted in areas where the green crab is not known to occur, but where it will likely occur as its distribution range expands. Then, once observed at a particular site, its impact on the population dynamics of native species can be assessed.

Third, alternative sites for the approved dumping of ballast water are presently being investigated using computer models that predict the dispersion of particles from a point source (M. Foreman, Fisheries and Oceans Canada, Sidney, British Columbia, personal communication). Knowing the dispersion pattern from an alien model species helps validate predictions. Ideally, potential discharge locations should be sink dispersal sites, that is, locations from which larvae are unlikely to disperse significantly (Pulliam 1988; Roberts 1998). Where an alien species may have a negative economic impact, warning of its incipient occurrence may encourage mitigation measures to be developed.

For these reasons, the general patterns of green crab range extensions that have occurred to date in the northern areas of both the western Atlantic and the eastern Pacific are here examined and compared in the context of regional North American oceanography. This chapter discusses why the rate of green crab range expansion on the Pacific coast has recently increased dramatically and how the species might affect the habitat and commercial bivalve fishery of the relatively sheltered waters of Washington and British Columbia.

Range Extension along the Atlantic Coast of North America

The green crab (Figure 1) was likely introduced into the western Atlantic in the New York area because its range in 1879 was reported by S.I. Smith as centering around Long Island and extending from Provincetown, Cape Cod, Massachusetts, to Great Egg Harbor, New

Figure 1. European green crab. Photo by R. Elner, Department of the Environment, Canadian Wildlife Service, Delta, BC.

Jersey (Berrick 1986). The first report of green crab in Canada was at St. Andrews, New Brunswick, in 1951, and by 1954 the species was considered abundant and a heavy predator of clams (MacPhail et al. 1955; Figure 2). It was first found off southern Nova Scotia in the mid-1950s (MacPhail et al. 1955), was present as far north as St. Margarets Bay by the 1970s (G. Jamieson, personal observation), had not yet reached Cape Breton by the late 1980s (R. Elner, Environment Canada, Delta, British Columbia, personal communication), but has been off Port Hawkesbury, Nova Scotia, since at least 1992 (J. Tremblay, Fisheries and Oceans Canada, Halifax, Nova Scotia, personal communication). By the late 1990s, it had reached Bras d'Or Lake (J. Tremblay, personal communication). Based on information from local eel net fishers, the species range started to expand into the southern Gulf of St. Lawrence in 1995. The species gradually progressed northward along the western coast of Cape Breton Island and was reported in Bay St. Lawrence at the northern tip of Cape Breton in 1998. Eel fishers in eastern Prince Edward Island started to capture green crab in 1998; in 1999, catches there

increased considerably (M. Moriyasu, Fisheries and Oceans Canada, Moncton, New Brunswick, personal communication).

This pattern indicates that it took about 40 years for the green crab to extend its range from Yarmouth to Port Hawkesbury, a linear distance of about 540 km, which is an average rate of dispersal of about 14 km per year. The green crab passed through the locks in the Canso Causeway, and once established in St. Georges Bay, Nova Scotia, on the other side of the causeway in the Gulf of St. Lawrence, its range has apparently expanded much more rapidly.

The general pattern of currents and water temperatures in the southern Gulf of St. Lawrence and along the outer coast of Nova Scotia show that near-shore currents off the outer coast of Nova Scotia flow southwest, from Cape Breton toward southern Nova Scotia, but wind events and eddies around headlands result in a complex pattern of currents (Loder et al. 1998). In the Gulf of St. Lawrence, the surface outflow from the St. Lawrence River, the Gaspé Current, sweeps around the Gaspé Peninsula, then goes south of the

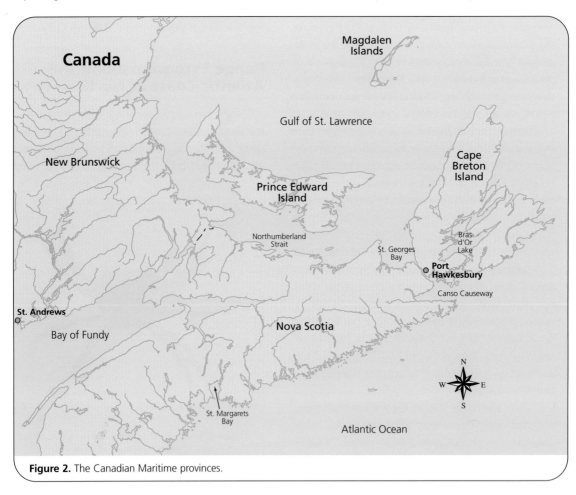

Figure 2. The Canadian Maritime provinces.

Magdalen shallows and hugs the northeast shore of Prince Edward Island and the western shore of Cape Breton (K. Drinkwater, Fisheries and Oceans Canada, Halifax, Nova Scotia, personal communication). The green crab has therefore tended to disperse against the prevailing currents on the outer coast of Nova Scotia, but probably along the currents in the southern Gulf of St. Lawrence. This likely explains the relatively rapid range expansion that is now occurring in the latter area where green crab recently dispersed over 200 km of shoreline in two to three years. These rates of dispersal also suggest that dispersal is likely natural and is not being accelerated by accidental or intentional transport by humans; otherwise, dispersal rates likely would have increased sharply. Periodic large-scale storms, such as hurricanes, during the summer and fall may potentially increase dispersal rate, but only if they occur when planktonic larvae are present.

Water temperatures are likely ideal for green crab during the summer: 10–16°C off outer Nova Scotia, and warmer in the shallow subtidal areas of the southern gulf. In the winter, water temperatures of 0–2°C are cold enough to prevent growth (Berril [1982] reported a cessation of growth in more southern Maine waters between mid-October and May), but are tolerable because the green crab is present. For most of the year, water temperatures are relatively cold and the probable result is that the green crab, on the outer coast of Nova Scotia at least, spawns only once a year. It may spawn more than once in some locations in the southern Gulf of St. Lawrence, where summer waters are warm enough for long enough, such as in shallow estuaries.

In Atlantic Canada, the green crab occurs from the intertidal to the subtidal zones, on rocky to sedimentary habitats, including sandy beaches, tidal flats, and salt marshes. Chapman et al. (this publication, page 133) speculate that in addition to decreasing bivalve densities, green crabs burrowing in surface sediments to escape desiccation and bird predation at low tide (Reise 1985) may affect roots and rhizomes of sea grasses or marsh grasses on tidal flats. This may change the marsh vegetation if green crabs attain high population densities in salt marshes in Atlantic Canada.

Range Extension along the Pacific Coast of North America

The green crab remained confined to San Francisco Bay from 1989/1990 to 1993, when it was found in Bodega Bay, about 100 km north (Cohen et al. 1995;

Grosholz and Ruiz 1995). It gradually extended its range northward in California at a rate of about 55 km per year to Humboldt Bay, inhabiting the small estuaries found along the outer coast. However, in 1997, adults were found in Coos Bay, Oregon, 300 km north of Humboldt Bay; in 1998, in Grays Harbor, Washington, 425 km farther north; and in 1999, in Barkley Sound, British Columbia, another 225 km north. In 2000, the green crab was found in both Clayoquot and Nootka Sounds, an additional 100 km north on the west coast of Vancouver Island (Figure 3). This represents a movement of about 1050 km in just two to three years.

The general pattern of currents off western North America north of San Francisco is considerably different than off the east coast (Thomson et al. 1989). It is characterized by a seasonal change in near-shore current flow direction, with a northward flowing David-son Current in the winter months and a southward flowing California Current in the summer (Figure 4). The periods when currents change direction are called the spring and fall transitions. These transitions are

Figure 3. West coast of North America from northern California to southern British Columbia.

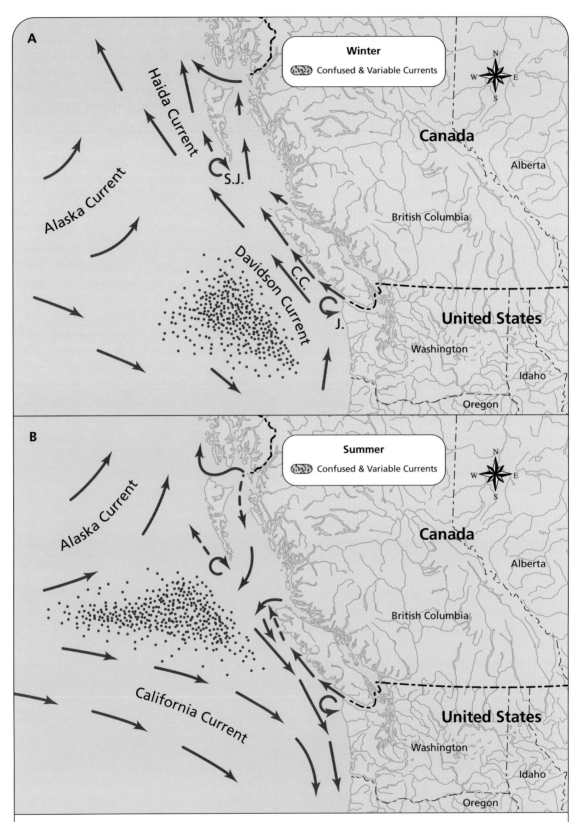

Figure 4. Regional surface circulation pattern for the northeast Pacific Ocean for (A) winter and (B) summer based on water property surveys and ship drift information. J., Juan de Fuca eddy; C.C., Vancouver Island coastal current; S.J., Cape St. James eddy (from Thomson et al. 1989).

not instantaneous: in 1998, for instance, the spring transition lasted from February 25 to about May 6. During these transitions, currents are irregular and no clear flow direction dominates. Off Vancouver Island, the outflow from the Strait of Juan de Fuca, driven by the Fraser River discharge, flows northward throughout the year as the Vancouver Island coastal current.

In contrast to the Maritimes, where no significant change in the current pattern has been documented between El Niño and non-El Niño years, there are strong differences on the Pacific coast off Oregon and British Columbia (McKinnell et al. 2001). In El Niño years, the spring transition may be delayed and may not maintain itself as rigorously as normal. El Niño also brings more northward transport, less upwelling and offshore movement in coastal areas, and water temperatures several degrees Celsius warmer off British Columbia (I. Perry, Fisheries and Oceans, Nanaimo, British Columbia, personal communication).

Near-shore water temperatures from northern California to British Columbia are generally comparable to that off the outer coast of Nova Scotia in the summer, that is, 12–16°C, but are warmer in the winter, typically 8–10°C. However, shallow water temperatures in estuaries, and particularly in the larger ones like Willapa Bay and Grays Harbor, Washington, may be much higher and stay warmer over a longer time period than in eastern Canada. A study noted that in the southern North Sea (Belgium), some green crab spawn more than once a year (d'Udekem d'Acoz 1994). Because the green crab growing season in some northeast Pacific estuaries is likely of similar duration to that in the southern North Sea, green crab probably spawn more than once each year in at least some populations in the northeast Pacific, creating a potentially longer time period for settlement compared with native crab species. Although currents can likely transport green crab larvae over considerable distances, there are presently no temporal data on the planktonic occurrence and spatial distribution of green crab off western North America. Studies indicate the species likely arrived on the southern outer coast of Washington via larval drift on ocean currents (Cook and Hanson 2000; Carr and Dumbauld 2000).

The scale of movements to Oregon and Washington suggests natural dispersal because the green crab seemed to be found in several estuaries almost simultaneously and in locations in the estuaries that argue against human transport (Hunt et al. 1998; Dumbauld and Kauffman 1998). In contrast, green crab dispersal

to British Columbia, which we suggest first occurred in 1998 (Jamieson et al. 2002), may have been aided by human activities. The scale of movement was limited because to date only low numbers of the species have been found in British Columbia. Also, to date most green crab have been found at the head of a bay near where "ballast water" obtained from an area inhabited by green crab was dumped. About 100 barge loads of rock were transported from Torquart Bay in Barkley Sound, British Columbia, between July and September 1998 to Wash-Away Beach in Willapa Bay, Washington. Five barges, each about 65 m by 20 m, were being operated simultaneously. Their bottom opened up hydraulically to drop the rock, and when closed, it scooped up seawater. However, although the barge may have been a mechanism that has recently conveyed some green crab to British Columbia, transport via currents, possibly storm generated, cannot be ruled out (Jamieson et al. 2002). The recent capture of a few green crab in 2001 and 2002 farther north than Barkley Sound along the west coast of Vancouver Island suggests that transport via currents has occurred, although the sources of transported larvae remain unknown.

Regarding the potential impact of green crab or any other potentially significant introduced predator of the intertidal zone, Washington State and British

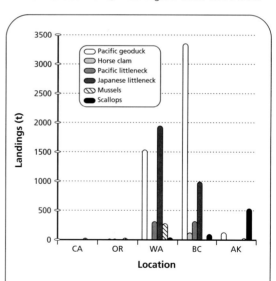

Figure 5. Bivalve landings (tonnes) by shellfish type and jurisdiction in the northeast Pacific in 1991. Pacific geoduck (*Panopea abrupta* (Conrad)); horse clam (*Tresus* spp.); Pacific littleneck (*Protothaca staminea* (Conrad)); Japanese littleneck (*Venerupis philippinarum* (A. Adams and Reeve)); mussels (*Mytilus* spp.); scallops (*Chlamys* spp.). CA, California; OR, Oregon; WA, Washington; BC, British Columbia; and AK, Alaska.

Columbia are the two areas in the eastern North Pacific that are likely to be most noticeably affected economically. These areas are where most intertidal bivalve fishing takes place in the region, both as wild clam harvest and through bivalve culture (Jamieson et al. 1998; Figure 5). These fisheries, which were worth over US$83 million in 1996, were developed in the absence of an intertidal predator capable of eating large numbers of moderately large clams. The population and ecosystem dynamics of any introduced species are often complex (for example, McDonald et al. 1998, 2000). Although green crab may or may not cause regional ecological and economic disturbances, the potential always exists for a significant intertidal predator species to do so, stressing the need to minimize the establishment of these alien species.

Comparisons between the Eastern and Western Range Extensions

The range extension of the green crab has differed dramatically between the east and west coast of North America and this may be related partly to differences in oceanographic regimes. However, proper interpretation of these patterns should rely on information on the duration, vertical distribution, and behavior of green crab larvae in the water column. This information is not available for North American waters, but it is for Europe (Queiroga 1996). Although green crab larvae are typically hatched in estuaries, their behavior with the tidal cycle ensures that most larvae are exported to the sea (Zeng and Naylor 1996). Green crab larval development includes four early larval stages termed zoea, and one relatively fast-swimming presettlement larval stage, the megalopa (Rice and Ingle 1975). Megalopae return to estuaries and settle as first crab instars four to nine weeks after hatching, depending on water temperature during development (Dawirs 1985; Mohamedeen and Hartnoll 1989; Nagaraj 1993). At 13.5°C and a seawater salinity of 35 parts per thousand, development takes about 56 days (Queiroga 1996).

In Maine, ovigerous females occur in the spring and early summer (Berril 1982). There is little published data on the occurrence of ovigerous females in Pacific waters. Yamada et al. (2000) note that sexual maturity in Oregon is reached within one year and that some females were ovigerous in November and December, but do not state that this is the main season of egg incubation. Carr and Dumbauld (2000) report ovigerous female green crab during the winter and spring months in Washington. In Europe, larvae can be found

in coastal waters during most of the year, but abundance peaks between April and July (Rees 1952; Lindley 1987). Two spawnings occur in Portugal estuaries, between February and April, and between June and July (Gonçalves 1991; Paula 1993; Queiroga 1995).

The spatial distribution of green crab larvae studied off Portugal shows that they are restricted to the inner and middle shelf, the later zoeae occur farthest offshore, mostly about 15–20 km from the coast, and all larvae occur within 45 km of the coast (Queiroga 1996). Megalopae showed evidence of moving onshore, which appeared to occur at a depth less than 30 m. All larvae were at 20–25 m depth during the day and about 30–45 m during twilight, with greater depth variability for the later larval stages.

Off the outer coast of Nova Scotia, the green crab has extended its range largely against the prevailing currents. The region is topographically complex, with many bays and rocky headlands, and although this may have facilitated larval establishment within bays, it may have hindered upstream movement from one bay to another. At an average rate of spread of about 14 km per year, range extension may have resulted largely from walking juveniles and adults. Once the crab had established in St. Georges Bay, Nova Scotia, in the Gulf of St. Lawrence, its range would have extended downstream off the north coast of Cape Breton. In the southern Northumberland Strait, where currents are mostly wind determined and fetch distances relatively short, dispersal observed to date could also have resulted from larval drift (Figure 2).

Off western North America, general current transport from northern California to Washington is northward before late February, irregular and largely wind driven typically between March and May, then southward during the summer (Thomson et al. 1989). Storms would create northward currents during the spring transition period, and because larvae would most likely be present at that time, the species likely extended its range mostly downstream. The rate of dispersal, which reached hundreds of kilometres a year, suggests that dispersal likely resulted from larvae drifting in currents, as hypothesized for the Dungeness crab (Cancer magister Dana) (McConnaughey et al. 1992). Studies suggest that larval transport was probably the main means of introduction of green crab to Oregon (Hunt et al. 1998) and Washington (Dumbauld and Kauffman 1998).

Accidental human transport may have been responsible for recent green crab introduction to British Columbia (Jamieson et al. 2002). However, because the species is now established in both Oregon and southern

Washington, its spread through natural dispersal would have likely occurred in the near future. Nevertheless, its more rapid spread along the Pacific coast resulting from human activities is preventable. The possibility of human activities being responsible for the recent transport of green crab to British Columbia should warn us that ongoing precautions to prevent the assisted spread of alien species are required.

Given the potential impact of the green crab on the British Columbia shellfish industry, increased monitoring and investigation of potential controls are justified. Information on how to identify green crab and to report any occurrences has been widely distributed regionally over the past few years. As a result, the public and fishers frequently submit information on potential sightings, and although important, such information is often spotty and will not actually describe the ecosystem changes that abundant green crab populations may cause. Baseline data from selected sites before green crab become established, and subsequent monitoring of the dynamics of likely impacted species, are needed if the full impact of green crab presence is to be assessed.

Acknowledgments

I thank Colin Levings for reviewing this manuscript and Renata Claudi for inviting it for inclusion in this publication. An anonymous reviewer and Elizabeth Muckle-Jeffs provided helpful review comments.

References

Berrick, S. 1986. Crabs of Cape Cod. Cape Cod Museum of Natural History, Brewster, MA. Cape Cod Mus. Nat. Hist. Ser. 3:76.

Berril, M. 1982. The life cycle of the green crab *Carcinus maenas* at the northern end of its range. J. Crustac. Biol. 2:31–39.

Carr, E.M.; Dumbauld, B.R. 2000. Status of the European green crab invasion in Washington coastal estuaries: Can expansion be prevented? [abstract]. J. Shellfish Res. 19:629–630.

Cohen, A.N.; Carlton, J.T.; Fountain, M.C. 1995. Introduction, dispersal and potential impacts of the green crab *Carcinus maenas* in San Francisco Bay, California. Mar. Biol. 122:225–237.

Cook, A.E.; Hanson, S. 2000. Progress implementing a plan to monitor for presence of the European green crab (*Carcinus maenas*) in Puget Sound, Washington [abstract]. J. Shellfish Res. 19:687–688.

Dawirs, R.R. 1985. Temperature and larval development of *Carcinus maenas* (Decapoda) in the laboratory: predictions of larval dynamics in the sea. Mar. Ecol. Prog. Ser. 24:297–302.

d'Udekem d'Acoz, C. 1994. Activités reproductrices saisonnières des différentes classes de tailles d'une population de crabes verts *Carcinus maenas* (Linnaeus 1758) dans le sud de la mer du Nord. Cah. Biol. Mar. 35:1–13.

Dumbauld, B.R.; Kauffman, B.E. 1998. The nascent invasion of green crab (*Carcinus maenas*) in Washington state coastal estuaries [abstract]. J. Shellfish Res. 17 (4).

Gonçalves, F. 1991. Zooplâe ecologia larvar de crustáceos decápodes no estuário do Rio Mondego. Ph.D. thesis, University of Coimbra, Coimbra, Portugal.

Grosholz, E.D. 1996. Contrasting rates of spread for introduced species in terrestrial and marine systems. Ecology 77:1680–1686.

Grosholz, E.D.; Ruiz, G.M. 1995. Spread and potential impact of the recently introduced European green crab, *Carcinus maenas*, in central California. Mar. Biol. 122:239–247.

Hunt, C.; Yamada, S.B.; Richmond, N. 1998. The arrival of the European green crab, *Carcinus maenas*, in Oregon estuaries [abstract]. J. Shellfish Res. 17 (4).

Jamieson, G.S.; Foreman, M.; Cherniawsky, J.; Levings, C. 2002. European green crab, *Carcinus maenas*, dispersal: the Pacific experience. Proceedings of the Lowell Wakefield Fisheries Symposium on Crabs in Cold Water Regions: Biology, Management, and Economics, 17–20 Jan., 2001, Anchorage, AK. In Press.

Jamieson, G.S.; Grosholz, E.D.; Armstrong, D.A.; Elner, R.W. 1998. Potential ecological implications from the introduction of the European green crab, *Carcinus maenas* (Linnaeus), to British Columbia, Canada, and Washington, USA. J. Nat. Hist. 32:1587–1598.

Lindley, J. A. 1987. Continuous plankton records: the geographical distribution and seasonal cycles of decapod crustacean larvae and pelagic post-larvae in the northeastern Atlantic Ocean and the North Sea. J. Mar. Biol. Assoc. UK 67:145–167.

Loder, J.W.; Petrie, B.; Gawarkiewicz, G. 1998. The coastal ocean off northeastern North America: a large-scale view. Pages 105–133 *in* A.R. Robinson and K.H. Brink, eds. The Sea, Vol. 11. John Wiley & Sons, New York, NY.

MacPhail, J.S.; Lord, E.I.; Dickie, L.M. 1955. The green crab—a new clam enemy. Atlantic Prog. Rep., Fish. Res. Board Can. 63:3–12.

McConnaughey, R.A.; Armstrong, D.A.; Hickey, B.M.; Gunderson, D.R. 1992. Juvenile Dungeness crab (*Cancer magister*) recruitment variability and oceanic transport during the pelagic larval phase. Can. J. Fish. Aquat. Sci. 49:2028–2044.

McDonald, P.S.; Jensen, G.C.; Armstrong, D.A. 1998. Green crabs and native predators: Possible limitations on the west coast invasion [abstract]. J. Shellfish Res. 17.

McDonald, P.S.; Jensen, G.C.; Armstrong, D.A. 2000. The potential impacts of *Carcinus maenas* introduction on juvenile Dungeness crab [abstract]. J. Shellfish Res. 19:632.

McKinnell, S.M.; Brodeur, R.D.; Hanawa, K.; Hallowed, A.B.; Polovina, J.J.; Zhang, C.-I. 2001. A conference on Pacific climate variability and marine ecosystem impacts, from the tropics to the Arctic. Prog. Oceanogr. 49(1–4):1–6.

Mohamedeen, H.; Hartnoll, R.G. 1989. Larval and post-larval growth of individually reared specimens of the common shore crab *Carcinus maenas* (L.). J. Exp. Mar. Biol. Ecol. 134:1–24.

Nagaraj, M. 1993. Combined effects of temperature and salinity on the zoeal development of the green crab, *Carcinus maenas* (Linnaeus, 1758) (Decapoda, Portunidae). Sci. March 57:1–8.

Paula, J. 1993. Ecologia da fase larvar e recrutamento de crustáceos decápodes no estuário do Rio Mira. Ph.D. thesis, University of Lisbon, Lisbon, Portugal.

Pulliam, H.R. 1988. Sources, sinks and population regulation. Am. Nat. 132:652–661.

Queiroga, H. 1995. Processos de dispersão e recrutamento das larvae do caranguejo *Carcinus maenas* (L.) na Ria de Aveiro. Ph.D. thesis, University of Aveiro, Aveiro, Portugal.

Queiroga, H. 1996. Distribution and drift of the crab *Carcinus maenas* (L.) (Decapoda, Portunidae) larvae over the continental shelf off northern Portugal in April 1991. J. Plankton Res. 18:1981–2000.

Rees, C.B. 1952. Continuous plankton records: the decapod larvae in the North Sea, 1947–49. Hull Bull. Mar. Ecol. 3:157–184.

Reise, K. 1985. Tidal flat ecology. Springer-Verlag, Berlin. 191 p.

Rice, A.L.; Ingle, R.W. 1975. The larval development of *Carcinus maenas* (L.) and *Carcinus mediterraneus* Czerniavsky (Crustacea, Brachyura, Portunidae) reared in the laboratory. Bull. Br. Mus. (Nat. Hist.) Zool. 28:101–119.

Roberts, C.M. 1998. Sources, sinks and the design of marine reserve networks. Fisheries (Bethesda) 23(7):16–19.

Thomson, R.E.; Hickey, B.M.; LeBlond, P.H. 1989. The Vancouver Island coastal current: fisheries barrier and conduit. Pages 265–296 *in* R.B.J. Beamish and G.A. McFarlane, eds. Effects of ocean variability on recruitment and an evaluation of parameters used in stock assessment models. Can. Spec. Publ. Fish. Aquat. Sci. 108.

Williams, A.B. 1984. Shrimps, lobsters, and crabs of the Atlantic Coast of the eastern United States, Maine to Florida. Smithsonian Institution Press, Washington, DC.

Yamada, S.B.; Hunt, C.; Kalin, A. 2000. Growth of the 1997/1998 year class of the European green crab, *Carcinus maenas*, in Oregon estuaries [abstract]. J. Shellfish Res. 19: 634–635.

Zeng, C.; Naylor, E. 1996. Endogenous tidal rhythms of vertical migration in field collected zoea-1 larvae of the shore crab *Carcinus maenas*: implications for ebb tide offshore dispersal. Mar. Ecol. Prog. Ser. 132:71–82.

Photo with chapter title: European green crab captured in south San Francisco Bay, CA. Photo by Thomas Niesen, San Francisco State University, San Francisco, CA.

Traits of Endangered and Invading Freshwater Mollusks in North America

Gerald L. Mackie

Of the 485 species of gastropods and 271 of bivalves that occur in the freshwaters of North America, 15 species of gastropods and 9 of bivalves are aliens and several species are at risk of extinction or extirpation, or are threatened, vulnerable, or of special concern. Data on the numbers and kinds of species at risk (SAR) are only now becoming available, but Williams et al. (1993) estimate that 70% of the bivalves alone are at some kind of risk.

Freshwater ecosystems change in morphological, physical, and chemical characteristics over time. For example, streams are constantly eroding new paths or becoming wider and shallower over time. The changes in stream morphometry are accompanied by corresponding changes in physical and chemical attributes. Eutrophication is a natural process but hundreds to thousands of years are required to change an oligotrophic lake into a eutrophic one under natural conditions. While the ecosystem changes slowly, organisms can adapt gradually. But if the rate of change is suddenly altered, only those organisms with life history traits that can accommodate the altered rate of change, or an unstable environment, will prevail.

Invasive species are not likely to become endangered or extinct. They are widely distributed and if pollution or intentional destruction by humans eradicates them in one part of the country, other populations will perpetuate the species. For example, of the fingernail clams, the arctic-alpine clam (*Pisidium conventus* Clessin) is more likely to become extinct than the ubiquitous pea clam (*Pisidium casertanum* (Poli)). The kinds of traits that would discriminate invasive from endangered mollusks have not been closely examined. Most of the alien species likely have traits and life histories that make them successful in a large variety of environments and in unstable environments as well. The opposite is probably true for SAR. Species that have life history traits adapted for a stable environment may eventually succumb in a rapidly changing environment. If humans alter the rate of change in habitat quality, eutrophic indicator species have less potential to become extinct than do oligotrophic indicator species.

Is there a specific rate, size, or quantity that separates a rare SAR from an omnipresent "weed"

species? Probably not, because the strengths and weaknesses of each species depend on the combinations, kinds, and magnitudes of stressors present. However, contrasting the life history and biological characteristics of these two extremes may help us to predict the potential for extinction or invasion of any given species. This chapter first discusses how its reproductive potential, life span and size, tolerances and requirements, and dispersal potential determine a species' potential to become abundant or decline in a changing environment. Then, an analysis of the distribution of traits among invasive species compared to threatened species identifies combinations of traits that help discriminate invasive species from SAR among mollusks of North America.

Reproductive Potential

For any given species, several aspects of its reproductive potential need to be considered: (1) its sexual state (for example, separate sex, hermaphrodite, or parthenogenetic); (2) its egg-laying habit (for example, oviparous, ovoviviparous, viviparous); (3) its fecundity (number of eggs produced); (4) its natality (number of eggs surviving); (5) its annual frequency of egg-laying habits (for example, univoltine, bivoltine, multivoltine); and (6) its lifetime frequency of egg-laying habits (for example, semelparity, iteroparity).

Hermaphroditism reduces the risk of a species being eliminated during periods when it is difficult to find a mate. Parthenogenesis would also allow a species to reproduce when mates are difficult to find. Apparently, a species is more likely to become endangered if dioecious than monoecious. Oviparity (egg-laying and young hatching from the egg) is more common than ovoviviparity (brooding of eggs and young, and birth of miniature adults) in freshwater animals, certainly within the Mollusca. Viviparity is absent in freshwater mollusks and in most freshwater invertebrates. Ovoviviparity seems to be more common in hermaphrodites than in dioecious species. Snails of the family Viviparidae are ovoviviparous (in spite of family name) and dioecious, but most species are also capable of parthenogenetic reproduction. Brooding is usually associated with few, small-sized young with a high survival rate (that is, high natality rate), while oviparity often results in enormous numbers of eggs; many eggs perish during development, but those that do survive mature and will probably become good competitors. For example, although the numbers are highly variable, ovoviviparous forms are about 10 times less fecund than oviparous forms (for example, 10:100).

Even though many ovoviviparous forms are parthenogenetic, reducing the risk of having to find a mate, the fecundities are still relatively low. Even ovipositing, oviparous forms have low natalities relative to planktonic, oviparous forms. Ovipositing, oviparous forms are about 1000 to 10 000 times less fecund than planktonic oviparous forms (for example, 100:100 000 to 100:1 000 000). Species that have planktonic larval stages have high biofouling potential for two reasons: (1) they usually produce large numbers of eggs, and (2) the developing (planktonic) larvae can enter a facility through the water intake by the millions, and then grow and reproduce to establish biofouling populations inside the facility.

Hermaphrodites also tend to have shorter life spans and higher frequencies of reproductive events per year (for example, bivoltinism, trivoltinism, or multivoltinism) but they have fewer reproductive events in their lifetime (that is, are semelparous) than do most dioecious species. For example, many species of sphaeriid clams reproduce twice per year (bivoltine) but live only one year (therefore are iteroparous); unionids reproduce once per year (univoltine) but live several years (also are iteroparous). Of the two families, unionids have a greater proportion of species that are endangered or at risk (about 72% according to Williams et al. [1993]), and are not represented by any invasive species in North America, compared with sphaeriids which have one species at risk and five (of 36) species introduced (Mackie 1999a, b, c).

Life Span and Body Size

The gene pools of species with a short life span probably change faster than for species with a long life span. If the rates of change in environmental quality and conditions increase, the genotypes and phenotypes selected will probably be from species with short life spans. Moreover, most species with short life spans become reproductively mature at an earlier age than species with long life spans. For example, some species of unionid clams (family Unionidae) live close to 100 years and do not begin reproducing until their 10th year of life. Most unionid species with life spans shorter than 10 years begin reproducing during or immediately after their first year of life and contribute to the gene pool at a rate 10 to 100 times faster than those living 100 years. Most gastropods and fingernail clams (family: Sphaeriidae) live less than one year, two to three years maximum, and begin producing gametes soon after birth.

Another correlate of life span is size; long-lived species are generally larger than short-lived species (within a taxon). Size affects not only a species' potential for dispersal, as discussed shortly, but also its reproductive potential; larger species generally produce more eggs than smaller species (within a taxon).

The Unionidae are the largest of the freshwater bivalves. They produce millions of larvae (glochidia) that must parasitize a fish or an amphibian to develop into juveniles. They mature slowly but live 10 to 100 years, depending on the species. However, the distribution of most unionids has been shrinking, not expanding. Of the two native families of bivalves, the Unionidae have 72% of the total number of species (about 300) listed either as extinct, endangered, threatened, or of special concern (Allan and Flecker 1993) and only 24% are currently stable (Williams et al. 1993). Only the Unionidae are not represented by alien species in North America.

The Sphaeriidae (fingernail clams) are the smallest of the freshwater bivalves, with some species growing only to about 1.5 mm in shell length. They are short-lived (one to two years), hermaphroditic, univoltine to bivoltine, semelparous to iteroparous, and ovoviviparous, brooding their larvae for two to five weeks. Most sphaeriids have low fecundities (5–50 young per parent) but high natalities and short development times (most are ready for birth in two to five weeks). Adults are sexually mature shortly after birth. Of the 36 species of Sphaeriidae, only 1 (*Pisidium ultramontanum* Prime) is potentially of special concern. They also have good dispersal potentials; five species were introduced to North America from Eurasia. However, none of the five introduced species has been documented as a nuisance. Indeed the species richness of sphaeriids appears to have been increased because of these aliens.

The Corbiculidae (Asian clam, *Corbicula fluminea* (Müller), Figure 1b) and Dreissenidae (quagga mussel, *Dreissena bugensis* Andrusov, and zebra mussel, *D. polymorpha* (Pallas)) (Figures 1g, h) are the most prolific of the four families of bivalves now present in North America. The corbiculids are short-lived (two to three years), monoecious to dioecious, univoltine to bivoltine

Figure 1. Mollusks introduced for food (a, *Cipangopaludina chinensis malleata*; b, *Corbicula fluminea*) and via ballast water exchange (c, *Bithynia tentaculata*; d, *Potamopyrgus antipodarum*; e, *Radix auricularia*; f,*Valvata piscinalis*; g, *Dreissena bugensis*; h, *D. polymorpha*; i, *Musculium lacustre*; j, *M. partumeium*; k, *Pisidium amnicum*; l, *P. henslowanum*; m, *P. moitessierianum,* provided by Dr. Igor Grigorovich, University of Windsor, Windsor, ON; n, *P. supinum*; o, *Sphaerium corneum*). *Musculium lacustre* and *M. partumeium* are endemic to North America but have Eurasian distribution and traits of invasive species.

(some populations have continuous breeding for three to four months), and are iteroparous. They brood up to 10 000 larvae for five to six weeks (some for two to three months) and then release them to a planktonic existence for three to five days. Apparently most of the larvae survive and settle. The juveniles grow quickly into moderately large (4–7 cm) adults, which attain relatively early sexual maturity. Of all the alien bivalves, only the Asian clam was intentionally introduced for its food value. Although only conjectural, the Asian clam has all the attributes of being capable of intercontinental (for example, Eurasia to North America), unintentional dispersal, as discussed later.

The Dreissenidae live only one to two years on average, are dioecious, univoltine to bivoltine, and iteroparous. Zebra and quagga mussels have extremely high fecundities (about 1 million eggs per female), the

eggs developing into planktonic larvae that have a short development time (two to four weeks). However, the larvae have a very low survival rate, less than 1% finding an appropriate substrate on which to settle. The adults have an early sexual maturity (about eight weeks or 5–8 mm in shell length) and grow to only 2–3 cm in shell length on average.

Tolerances and Requirements

The physiological and ecological tolerances and requirements describe the hardiness of a species. The hardier a species is, the greater its ability to adapt to quickly changing environments. Often morphological, behavioral, and/or physiological adaptations explain, at least partly, a molluskan species' success in a particular habitat. For example, often an invasive species will be better than a SAR at (1) avoiding desiccation or surviving prolonged periods of exposure; (2) exploiting either an infaunal existence in the soft sediments or an epifaunal existence on firm substrates; (3) tolerating high turbidities; (4) being eurythermous over its normal temperature range (for example, tropical eurytherms and temperate eurytherms); or (5) dealing with short periods of anoxia or low oxygen tensions. Zebra and quagga mussels are very tolerant, able to survive oxygen levels down to 2 mg/L, tolerate salinities up to eight parts per thousand, and grow best under mesotrophic to eutrophic conditions. They are also excellent competitors, known to have displaced entire unionid communities in some lakes (for example, Lake St. Clair and the western basin of Lake Erie [Mackie 1999b]). Asian clams are also extremely tolerant, even being used to clarify sewage, and are excellent competitors, known to displace both unionids and sphaeriids (McMahon 1999). There are distinct differences in the abilities of all mollusk species to tolerate anoxia but it is doubtful that any SAR can survive prolonged anoxic conditions. As a group, unionids are very sensitive to changing environmental conditions, habitat alteration being the most commonly cited cause of the high rates of species extinction. Some species of sphaeriids (for example, *Pisidium casertanum, Musculium lacustre* (Müller), and *M. partumeium* (Say)) are very tolerant of organic enrichment and have a global occurrence; others are very sensitive (for example, the oligotrophic indicators *P. conventus* and *Sphaerium nitidum* Westerlund) and are found globally only in cold, oligotrophic waters.

The physiological tolerances and requirements of an organism often determine the potential spread and continental limits of distribution of a species. For example, all freshwater mollusks require calcium for shell growth but some require higher levels than others and are restricted to hard waters. Of the 48 species of Unionidae (plus 2 species of Margaritiferidae) that occur in Canada, 22 are confined to hard water rivers of southern Ontario where 5 of the 8 Canadian SAR occur. However, more than calcium is limiting the distribution of unionids because other hard water areas in Canada have low unionid diversity.

Similarly, all species have thermal thresholds for growth and reproduction, and upper and lower thermal tolerance levels. Most cold stenotherms are also pollution sensitive species (for example, the sphaeriids *P. conventus* and *S. nitidum* and the unionid *Anodonta beringiana* Middendorff) and confined to northern latitudes and/or deep, cold oligotrophic lakes. Most

subpollution tolerant species are eurytherms and widely distributed (for example, the sphaeriids *M. lacustre* and *M. partumeium* [Figure 1]) and *P. casertanum* and the unionids *Lampsilis radiata radiata* (Gmelin), *Elliptio complanata* (Lightfoot), and *Pyganodon grandis* (Say)). All three sphaeriids are widely distributed throughout North America and Eurasia and all have invasive traits that make it possible (probable?) that those populations have been introduced from Eurasia, and are hybridizing with North American populations, or vice versa. Yet none of the unionids (including the three mentioned here) have been introduced to Eurasia, or from Eurasia to North America.

Dispersal Potential

Dispersal potential determines the range and numbers of populations that can be established by a species and is dictated largely by the factors previously discussed. For example, if the species does not have wide physiological and ecological tolerances and requirements, if it is too large to disperse, or if it does not have reproductive traits conducive to its dispersal, the species is destined to isolation (or will have a very small range) and extinction.

There are two basic types of dispersal mechanisms, **passive** and **active dispersal** (Table 1). Passive dispersal is hitchhiking a ride using abiotic (for example, water currents, wind, ships, boats, etc.) or biotic (for example, birds, insects, mammals) vectors. However, most of the active dispersal mechanisms are natural and include the swimming (for example, fish) or flying (for example, adult insects with aquatic larval stages) abilities of the species, and most of the passive dispersal mechanisms are anthropogenic. Dispersal by anthropogenic means can be intentional or unintentional. Intentional introductions are typical for mollusks valued as food and unintentional introductions are typical for mollusks in the aquarium trade. The dispersal ability of a species introduced intentionally by humans can often be ascertained by the rapid spread of the species throughout the continent, as in the case of the Asian clam in North America and other continents.

The dispersal mechanisms for SAR apply to alien species as well. However, alien species typically have an array of mechanisms and vectors. There are numerous mechanisms available to organisms for dispersal over short or long distances (Table 1); each mechanism has a potential for dispersal within a region (for example, by leapfrogging from lake to lake to eventually

Table 1. Dispersal mechanisms available to organisms for short-range (for example, regional = ⌂), mid-range (for example, intracontinental = ☎), or long-range (for example, intercontinental = ✈) transport.

Dispersal mechanisms	Potential
Natural mechanisms	
By insects, birds, or mammals	⌂ ☎
By fish or semiaquatic vertebrates	⌂
Currents	⌂ ☎
Waterspouts (planktonic stages only)	⌂
Wind	⌂ ☎
Unintentional anthropogenic mechanisms	
Interiors (for example, ballast tanks) or exteriors (for example, anchor holds) of ocean vessels	☎ ✈
Interiors (for example, fish wells) or exteriors (for example, hulls) of ships and crafts of rivers and lakes	⌂ ☎
Canals (irrigation and vessels)	⌂ ☎
Navigation and marker buoys and floats	⌂
Marina and boatyard equipment	⌂
Fisheries equipment (for example, cages, nets, bait buckets)	⌂
Amphibious and fire-fighting planes	⌂ ☎
Firetruck water	⌂
Commercial products (for example, logs, aesthetic and medicinal plants)	⌂ ☎ ✈
Aquarium releases	⌂ ☎ ✈
Recreational equipment (for example, floating docks)	⌂
Litter (for example, tires)	⌂
Scientific research	⌂ ☎ ✈
Intentional anthropogenic mechanisms	
Food	⌂ ☎ ✈
Sport	⌂ ☎ ✈

disperse throughout a province or state), a continent (for example, intracontinental, such as within North America or within Eurasia), or intercontinentally (for example, from Eurasia to North America). The list is based mainly on dispersal mechanisms used by zebra mussels (Carlton 1993) but it is not necessarily restricted to them.

Of the natural mechanisms, external transport (for example, feet and feathers) is generally a more effective dispersal mechanism than internal transport via the digestive tract. Sphaeriids can survive passage through the intestinal tract of waterfowl as extramarsupial larvae but internal transport probably is not prevalent (Mackie 1979). Large insects are able to disperse only small organisms, like *Pisidium* or young *Musculium*. Lake currents disperse only plankton or planktonic stages. River currents disperse organisms mainly downstream of their introduction. Waterspouts are probably of little dispersal value unless they are large and spill over into nearby and adjacent water bodies, and then only (mostly?) planktonic larvae (for example, veligers) can be dispersed this way.

The anthropogenic mechanisms are split between intentional (or deliberate) and unintentional (or accidental) releases because the former usually involves dispersal of large organisms for their food or sport value. Most alien fish species have both food and sport value, but mollusks such as the Chinese mysterysnail (*Cipangopaludina chinensis malleata* (Reeve)) and the Japanese mysterysnail (*C. japonica* (von Martens)) have no sport value and were introduced by Orientals purely for their food value as escargots. Mills et al. (1993) have attributed deliberate releases to 11 of 139 alien species in the Great Lakes, most of these being fish. Of the 144 species introduced into the Great Lakes (at least 5 more have been introduced since 1993), 81 have originated in Eurasia and were introduced by ballast water exchange, the main intercontinental release mechanism. About

32 species originated from somewhere in North America (for example, southern United States, Mississippi drainage, and Atlantic and Pacific sources). Mills et al. (1993) attribute aquarium releases to some species in the Great Lakes, claiming that many people released their pets without any intention of establishing self-sustaining populations.

Many of the most widely distributed species have selected a variety of dispersal mechanisms as part of the natural selection process. Others have evolved efficient dispersal stages. For example, the veliger larva can be considered an efficient dispersal stage of zebra mussels. Because humans seem to be continually altering aquatic habitats globally, the species most destined to extinction are those with poor dispersal mechanisms and/or very narrow ranges of physiological and ecological tolerances and requirements.

The size of a species is important because it partly determines the potential to spread great distances. Generally, small species disperse greater distances than large species (within a taxon). For example, fingernail clams (family Sphaeriidae) have a greater global distribution than freshwater pearly mussels (family Unionidae). There are apparently two reasons for this trend. First, big is more noticeable than small and the dispersal agent is more likely to unload a large hitchhiker sooner than a small one. Second, big also means heavy and a vector would have to spend more energy, and therefore risk its own life, to transport itself and its "baggage" (that is, large mollusks) great distances. Perhaps the only exception to the size rule is intentional introductions by humans. In this instance, large is an advantage if the introduction is for food (or sport). The mysterysnails *C. chinensis malleata* (Figure 1a) and *C. japonica* are large mollusks and, as stated earlier, were intentionally introduced for escargots.

Traits Representative of Invasive Species

This section examines attributes that would contribute to the decline and perhaps the disappearance of a species and compares it to those that have invaded North America, especially the Great Lakes. The analysis seeks the potential weaknesses of SAR and strengths of invasive species by ranking the different traits from those that theoretically would give a species a competitive edge to those that would contribute to its probable extinction (Table 2). Those with a competitive edge presumably would have good invasive potential.

The analysis confines the comparisons to alien aquatic species that have been introduced accidentally, that is, via ballast water exchange; they represent 46% (11 of 24) of the invasive species of mollusks (Mackie 1999b). It ignores those that have been introduced unintentionally through the aquarium trade (33% or 8 of 24 species) and intentionally for their value as food (21% or 5 of 24 species), because it is difficult to know whether most would have dispersed to North America without the help of humans.

The traits themselves are not ranked, for example, life span is not considered more important than parental care. Using these ranks, the ultimate mollusk "weed" species, which would grow almost everywhere under almost any conditions, would probably have nothing but [a] traits, indicative of potential invasiveness. The analysis clearly shows that the majority of them have [a] traits (Figure 2). Likewise, species like *M. lacustre* and *M. partumeium* that are ubiquitous and cosmopolitan in both Eurasia and North America (and have Pleistocene fossil records) also have numerous [a] traits. It is assumed that species with those invasive traits would eventually displace species with SAR traits,

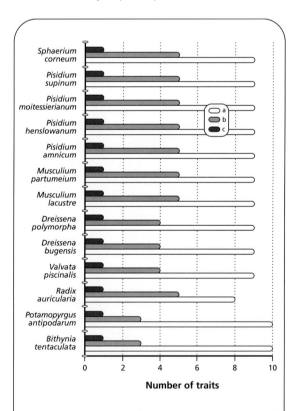

Figure 2. Number of [a], [b], and [c] traits for 13 species of freshwater mollusks accidentally introduced to North America (see Appendix).

Table 2. Ranking, [a] to [d], of life history traits, ecological tolerances and requirements, and dispersal potential that could lead to extinction of a species under rapidly changing aquatic (freshwater) conditions. The rankings are purely speculative but imply that species with [a] traits would be prevalent in invasive species and [c] and [d] traits would be prevalent in species at risk.

Life history and ecological traits	Ranking (from survivorship to extinction) (> indicates survives extinction longer than)
1. Life span	[a] short-lived (1–2 years) > [b] long-lived (>3 years)
2. Sex	[a] hermaphroditism > [b] separate sexes
3. No. of generations/year	[a] multivoltinism > [b] bivoltinism > [c] univoltinism
4. Lifetime no. of generations	[a] iteroparity > [b] semelparity
5. Parental care	[a] oviparity > [b] ovoviviparity > [c] viviparity > [d] parasitism
6. Fecundity	[a] high numbers (>1000) > [b] low numbers of eggs
7. Natality	[a] high survival (>50%) > [b] low survival rate of embryos
8. Development duration and rate	[a] short development time (weeks), fast rate > [b] long development time (months or years), slow rate
9. Age at sexual maturity	[a] early sexual maturation > [b] late sexual maturation
10. Adult size	[a] small (<1 cm) > [b] large
11. Ecological tolerances and requirements	[a] hardy and tolerant (for example, eutrophic indicators) > [b] moderately hardy and tolerant (for example, mesotrophic indicators) > [c] very sensitive, requiring pristine condition (for example, oligotrophic indicators)
12. Dispersal potential	[a] has evolved many dispersal mechanism(s), using a variety of natural and anthropogenic methods > [b] mostly unintentional anthropogenic methods > [c] has evolved few if any dispersal mechanisms; relies mostly on natural mechanisms or intentional introductions.

for example, [c] and/or [d] traits, unless humans intervened.

Different combinations of traits would lead to different probabilities of extinction. For example, theoretically, a species with only [a] traits would survive longer than a species with only [b] traits, which in turn would survive longer than a species with 1[b], 2[b], 3[c], 4[b], 5[d], 6[b], 7[b], 8[b], 9[b], 10[b], 11[c], and 12[b] traits. Support for the latter ranking can be seen in the four families of freshwater bivalves. Two families, Unionidae and Sphaeriidae, are native to North America and two others, Dreissenidae and Corbiculidae, are introduced. The Unionidae (pearly mussels) are long-lived (up to 100 years), dioecious, univoltine, and iteroparous. They produce parasitic larvae called glochidia that require a fish to complete development of most of its organ systems. Some unionids are very host-specific, requiring a specific fish (or an amphibian) species to parasitize. They have very high fecundities (about 1 to 2 million eggs are produced), but very low survival of young (< 0.0007%), because most glochidia do not find a

fish host and those that do may perish because the fish is preyed on. However, the glochidia have a relatively short (15–30 days as a parasite for most species) development time. Some adults attain sexual maturation after 1–5 years but many require up to 10 years to mature.

Of the gastropods, two subclasses (Pulmonata and Prosobranchia) are represented by freshwater species. Pulmonata is represented by five families, Acroloxidae (0), Ancylidae (0), Lymnaeidae (1), Physidae (3), and Planorbidae (1), and Prosobranchia by seven families, Bithyniidae (1), Hydrobiidae (1), Pleuroceridae (0), Pilidae (3), Thiaridae (2), Valvatidae (2), and Viviparidae (2). The numbers in parentheses indicate numbers of species introduced to North America (Mackie 1999 a, b, c). If we examine the traits of only those species that were introduced unintentionally (that is, through aquarium trade) or intentionably (that is, for food value), we are left with one lymnaeid (*Radix auricularia* (L.)), one bithyniid (*Bithynia tentaculata* (L.)), one hydrobiid (*Potamopyrgus antipodarum* (J.E. Gray)), and one valvatid

(*Valvata piscinalis* (Müller)) (Mackie 1999 a, b, c). Of these, two are hermaphrodites (*R. auricularia, V. piscinalis*) and the other two are dioecious. Otherwise, all four species are oviparous and mostly semelparous and univoltine, have short life spans, are small, and none have been reported as a nuisance species, except perhaps the mud bithynia (*B. tentaculata*) which has been reported to plug faucets of domestic supplies of freshwater (Mackie 1999b).

Of the bivalves, three families are endemic to North America (Margaritiferidae, Unionidae, Sphaeriidae) and two are introduced (Corbiculidae and Dreissenidae). Of the endemic families, only Sphaeriidae is represented by alien species (five). Only species within the introduced families have proven to be a nuisance, including the Asian clam which was imported for food (McMahon 1999).

Traits that dominate invasive mollusk species with no apparent impact:

- Short-lived.

- Capable of multivoltinism and iteroparity.

- Release few eggs or brood few young, but embryos have high survival rates.

- Develop quickly and adults mature sexually within a few weeks.

- Have moderately wide ecological and physiological tolerances.

- Use intercontinental dispersal mechanisms that apparently are more effective than intracontinental mechanisms.

Traits that dominate invasive mollusk species with nuisance attributes:

- Prolific, thousands to millions of eggs released once or more annually by dioecious species.

- Young are planktonic; survival rate apparently irrelevant.

- Have wide ecological and physiological tolerances (for example, eutrophic indicators are more liable to be nuisance species than oligotrophic indicators).

- Use a wide variety of mechanisms that provide for intercontinental and intracontinental dispersal (Table 1).

Traits Representative of Species at Risk

Most of the species that are registered as SAR in the United States and Canada belong to the family Unionidae (Turgeon et al. 1998). Only a few species have been officially listed as **endangered** or **threatened,** 8 in Canada (Mackie 2000b) and 86 (64 freshwater bivalves, 11 terrestrial gastropods, 11 freshwater gastropods) in the United States (Turgeon et al. 1998); traits of SAR are only now being examined.

When the list of traits in Table 2 is reviewed, the following appear to dominate SAR:

- Dioecious species predominate, but those capable of hermaphroditism are especially at risk.

- Species are univoltine and have either semelparous or iteroparous reproduction.

- Species may be oviparous or ovoviviparous but a parasitic life stage inhibits dispersal ability, and species that are host-specific are especially at risk.

- High fecundity is prevalent but mortality of young is dismally high.

- Species with very narrow ecological tolerances and requirements predominate, especially in southern Ontario.

Adaptive Capability and Invasiveness

Whether a species becomes rare or a nuisance depends partly on microevolutionary processes. Microevolution occurs constantly due to genetic drift, gene flow, mutations, nonrandom mating, and natural selection. Most human activities can affect one or more of those processes.

Genetic drift occurs mostly in small populations, but large populations can be reduced by a catastrophic event that may result in a bottleneck effect, or a new habitat may be colonized by a few individuals leading to a founder effect. Gene flow results from the gain or loss of alleles from a population by the movement of fertile individuals or gametes to another population. It tends to reduce genetic differences between populations. Today, air and sea travel have resulted in introductions of species from populations that were once geographically isolated but are now allowed to interbreed with North American populations. Mutations, or changes in an organism's DNA that create new alleles, are rare events for each gene. Over the short term, mutation does not have much effect on a single generation. However, over the long term, mutation is vital to evolution because it is the only force that generates new alleles. Nonrandom mating is selective mating that results in a departure from the Hardy-Weinberg equilibrium requirements. Finally, natural selection results from differential success in survival and reproduction, and is most likely to result in adaptive changes in a gene pool.

Some endangered species have low genetic variability (Campbell et al. 1997). As populations are reduced mostly through catastrophic events caused by humans (for example, habitat alteration), their gene pool diversity also declines. Species particularly at risk are those with homozygous recessive alleles that underwent natural selection for the environmental conditions that existed before the catastrophic event. Such populations have no way to alter the gene pool for the new habitat conditions, unless heterozygous individuals were introduced to the population. However, endangered species, by definition, are those with only a few populations still in existence. In most cases, the populations are in the same ecoregion and probably have similar gene pools. Endangered species also tend to display poor dispersal capabilities and are unlikely to migrate from one gene pool to another.

Alien species, however, are the "weeds" of their taxonomic group. Most populations have great genetic variability (Campbell et al. 1997), "weed species" perhaps because they tend to have a variety of dispersal mechanisms and can migrate to and alter several other gene pools and therefore adapt easily to a variety of environmental conditions. Although most (~64%) of the invasive mollusk species apparently had no detectable impacts on native populations of mollusks (or other organisms), the proportion of catastrophic introductions will increase if concerted efforts are not made to preserve existing habitats and restore others that have been lost. The genetic variability of "weed" and SAR within the Mollusca is not well known and is worthy of study.

Application: Averting a Potentially Damaging Invasion

A potentially damaging invasion of mollusks is expected in the near future. The freshwater mytilid *Limnoperna fortunei* (Figure 3) is native to China but has already found its way to South America (Darrigran and Ezcurra de Drago 2000; Mackie 2000c). Mytilids are true mussels, all of marine origin. The most common mytilid is the blue mussel (*Mytilus edulis* L.) a popular seafood delicacy. All mytilids produce byssal threads and, like the zebra mussel, attach to solid substrates. They also produce free-swimming veliger larvae that, like the zebra mussel, enter, settle on, and foul industrial and domestic pipelines.

The freshwater mytilid can tolerate salinities up to about 15 parts per thousand. It occurs naturally throughout China in creeks, rivers, and lakes. It is now in South America in the rivers de la Plata, Paraná, and Paraguay. The species first entered Río de la Plata, Argentina, in 1991, probably in ship's ballast water from either Korea or Hong Kong (Darrigran and Pastorino 1995). Although the freshwater mytilid and zebra and quagga mussels have some similarities, there are also many distinct differences (Table 3). There are also some major differences in the physical and chemical tolerances and requirements of freshwater mytilids and zebra and quagga mussels (Table 4). The most noticeable differences are in the buffer variables (pH, calcium level, alkalinity) and reproductive temperatures. The freshwater mytilid is a softwater species and the zebra and quagga mussels are hardwater species; the optimal temperatures for reproduction are above 15°C for the freshwater mytilid and near 6–8°C for quagga mussels and 10–12°C for zebra mussels. If any factor will limit the distribution of *Limnoperna* in North America, especially Canada, it will be the temperature needed for reproduction to occur (> 15°C).

The freshwater mytilid has all the traits of a nuisance and invasive species but will likely invade different kinds of habitats than the zebra and quagga mussels. It is normally dioecious but capable of switching to hermaphroditism. In subtropical freshwater habitats (for

Figure 3. A colony of *Limnoperna fortunei* from Argentina. Photo provided by Gustavo Darrigran, Científico Zoología Invertebrados, Argentina.

Table 3. Some visible differences between the freshwater mytilid and zebra and quagga mussels.

Feature	Freshwater mytilid	Zebra and quagga mussels
Shell byssal opening	Absent	Present
Shell nacre (mother-of-pearl) and color	Present (purple in posterior two-thirds, white in anterior third of shell)	Nacre absent, interior entirely whitish
Mantle fusion for siphons	Forms exhalant siphon only	Forms both inhalant and exhalant siphons
Siphon ornamentation	Tentacles absent on both siphons	Tentacles present on both siphons
Gill attachment to body	By ciliary fusion	By tissue fusion
Outer gill shape	Ends abruptly	Ends gradually

Table 4. Some major differences in water quality tolerances and requirements (given as ranges) of the freshwater mytilid and zebra and quagga mussels. Best growth and reproduction for both groups of bivalves occur at the upper end of the ranges given.

Water quality	Freshwater mytilid	Zebra and quagga mussels
pH	6.4–9.0	7.5–8.7
Reproductive temperature (°C)	>15	6–8 (quagga), 10–12 (zebra)
Conductivity (μS/cm); salinity (ppt)	32–57; 0–15	~75–>110; 0–8
Alkalinity (mg $CaCO_3$/L)	10–16	50–>122
Total hardness (mg $CaCO_3$/L)	8–17	50–>125
Calcium (mg Ca/L)	2.4–4.8	7.0–>35

example, Hong Kong), the species is dioecious and has one generation in its life span. But in neotropical habitats (for example, Argentina), hermaphroditism is present in up to 55% of the animals, and reproduction is continuous and marked by a major and a minor spawning event. The prolific nature of the species was demonstrated in Río de la Plata. In 1991, when it was first discovered, the maximum densities were 4–5/m²; by 1993, the maximum densities had risen to about 80 000/m², and in 1999, its maximum densities were 150 000/m² (Darrigran et al. 1999; Darrigran 2000).

The freshwater mytilid is having the same impact in China and South America as the zebra mussel has had in North America:

- Reduction of industrial pipe diameters and blockage of pipelines.

- Decreased water velocities caused by friction.

- Accumulations of empty shells on beaches and in wetwells of industries.

- Contamination of water pipelines by mass mortalities.

- Filter and condenser tube occlusions.

Conclusions

The comparisons of traits among introduced, invasive, and endangered species provide two important lessons. First, we need to beware of species that are relatively short-lived (two to four years), are prolific, releasing thousands to millions of eggs once or more annually into the water column, whose young and adults have wide ecological and physiological tolerances, and whose life stages are able to use a wide variety of mechanisms that provide for intercontinental and intracontinental dispersal. Those are potentially the most invasive and nuisance species. Second, we similarly need to be vigilant and protective of long-lived species that have one or more life stages that depend on the presence of other species, and have very narrow ecological and physiological tolerances and requirements and limited dispersal mechanisms. Those are potentially the species at most risk. Any process that both selects traits associated with invasiveness and rejects those associated with species at risk, and globalization is potentially one of them, is likely to result in a rapid decline in species diversity.

References

Allan, J.D.; Flecker, A.S. 1993. Biodiversity conservation in running waters. Identifying the major factors that threaten destruction of riverine species and ecosystems. BioScience 43:32–43.

Campbell, N.A.; Mitchell, L.G.; Reece, J.B. 1997. Biology: Concepts & connections, 2nd ed. The Benjamin/Cummings Publ. Co., New York, NY.

Carlton, J.T. 1993. Dispersal mechanisms of the zebra mussel (*Dreissena polymorpha*). Pages 667–697 *in* T.F. Nalepa and D.W. Schloesser, eds. Zebra mussels: biology, impact, and control. Lewis Publishers, Boca Raton, FL.

Darrigran, G. 2000. The reproductive cycle of the invasive bivalve *Limnoperna fortunei* (Dunker, 1857) (Mytilidae) from a neotropical temperate locality. Pages 219–221 *in* Proceedings of the 10th International Aquatic Nuisance Species and Zebra Mussel Conference, 13–17 February 2000, Toronto, ON. The Professional Edge, Pembroke, ON. 353 p.

Darrigran, G.; Ezcurra de Drago, I. 2000. Invasion of *Limnoperna fortunei* (Dunker, 1857) (Bivalvia: Mytilidae) in America. Nautilus 2: 69–74.

Darrigran, G.; Pastorino, G. 1995. The recent introduction of asiatic bivalve *Limnoperna fortunei* (Mytilidae) into South America. Veliger 38(2): 183–187

Darrigran, G.; Penchaszadeh, P; Damborenea, M.C. 1999. The life cycle of *Limnoperna fortunei* (Dunker,1857) (Bivalvia: Mytilidae) from a neotropical temperate locality. J. Shellfish Res. 18(2):361–365.

Grigorovich, I.A.; Korniushin, A.V.; MacIsaac H.J. 2000. Moitessier's pea clam *Pisidium moitessierianum* (Bivalvia: Sphaeriidae): A cryptogenic species in the Great Lakes. Hydrobiologia 435:153–165.

House of Commons of Canada, Bill C–33. 2000. An act respecting the protection of wildlife species at risk in Canada. First reading, 11 April 2000. Public Works and Government Services Canada–Publishing, Ottawa, ON.

Mackie, G.L. 1979. Dispersal mechanisms in Sphaeriidae (Mollusca: Bivalvia). Bull. Am. Malacol. Union Inc. 1979:17–21.

Mackie, G.L. 1999a. Chapter 9: Mollusc introductions through aquarium trade. Pages 135–150 *in* R. Claudi and J. Leach, eds. Nonindigenous freshwater organisms: vectors, biology and impacts. Lewis Publishers, Boca Raton, FL.

Mackie, G.L. 1999b. Chapter 15: Ballast water introductions of Mollusca. Pages 255–272 *in* R. Claudi and J. Leach, eds. Nonindigenous freshwater organisms: vectors, biology and impacts. Lewis Publishers, Boca Raton, FL.

Mackie, G.L. 1999c. Chapter 21: Introduction of molluscs through the import for live food. Pages 305–314 *in* R. Claudi and J. Leach, eds. Nonindigenous freshwater organisms: vectors, biology and impacts. Lewis Publishers, Boca Raton, FL.

Mackie, G.L. 2000a. Biology of freshwater corbiculacean clams of North America. Ohio State University Press, Columbus, OH. 1200 p. In Press.

Mackie, G.L. 2000b. Applied aquatic ecosystem concepts. Kendall/Hunt Publishing Company, Dubuque, IA.

Mackie, G.L. 2000c. A cottagers' guide to understanding their lake. Lithosphere Press, Guelph, ON. In Press.

McMahon, R. 1999. Invasive characteristics of the freshwater bivalve, *Corbicula fluminea*. Pages 315–346 *in* R. Claudi and J. Leach, eds. Nonindigenous freshwater organisms: vectors, biology and impacts. Lewis Publishers, Boca Raton, FL.

Mills, E.L.; Leach, J.H.; Carlton, J.T.; Secor, C.L. 1993. Exotic species in the Great Lakes: a history of biotic crises and anthropogenic introductions. J. Gt. Lakes Res. 19:1–54.

Stearns, S.C. 1976. Life-history tactics: a review of the ideas. Q. Rev. Biol. 51:3–47.

Turgeon, D.D.; Quinn, J.F., Jr.; Bogan, A.E.; Coan, E.V.; Hochberg, F.G.; Lyons, W.G.; Mikkelsen, P.M.; Neves, R.J.; Roper, C.F.E.; Rosenberg, G.; Roth, B.; Scheltema, A.; Thompson, F.G.; Vecchione, M.; Williams, J.D. 1998. Common and scientific names of aquatic invertebrates from the United States and Canada: Mollusks. 2nd ed. Am. Fish. Soc. Spec. Publ. 26. Bethesda, MD. 536 p.

Williams, J.D.; Warren, M.L. Jr.; Cummins, K.S.; Harris, J.L.; Neves, R.J. 1993. Conservation status of the freshwater mussels of the United States and Canada. Fisheries (Bethesda) 18(9):1–22.

Appendix

Apparent traits of 15 species of mollusks introduced as food (*Cipangopaludina chinensis malleata* and *Corbicula fluminea*) and via ballast water (rest of species listed except *Musculium lacustre* and *M. partumeium*) that are distributed throughout most of both Eurasia and North America.[1]

Species	Traits (see Table 2, column 1 for trait names for 1–12; species ecological impact is also given)												
	1	2	3	4	5	6	7	8	9	10	11	12	Impact
Cipangopaludina chinensis malleata, a	[b]	[b]	[c]	[a]	[b]	[b]	[a]	[b]	[b]?	[b]	[a]	[c]	0
Corbicula fluminea, b	[a]	[b]	[b-c]	[a]	[a]	[a]	[b]	[a]	[a]	[b]	[a]	[a]	-
Bithynia tentaculata, c	[a]	[b]	[a-c]	[a]	[a]	[b]	[a]	[a]	[a]	[a]	[a]	[a]	-?
Potamopyrgus antipodarum, d	[a]	[b]	[a-c]?	[a]?	[a]	[b]	[a]?	[a]?	[a]	[a]	[a]	[a]	-, 0?
Radix auricularia, e	[a]	[a]	[a-c]	[a]	[a]	[b]	[a]	[a]	[a]	[b]	[b]	[b]	0
Valvata piscinalis, f	[a]	[a]	[a-c]	[a]	[a]	[b]	[a]	[a]	[a]	[a]	[b]	[b]	0
Dreissena bugensis, g	[a]	[b]	[a-c]	[a]	[a]	[a]	[b]	[a]	[a]	[b]	[a]	[a]	–
Dreissena polymorpha, h	[a]	[b]	[a-c]	[a]	[a]	[a]	[b]	[a]	[a]	[b]	[a]	[a]	–
Musculium lacustre, i	[a]	[a]	[a-c]	[a-b]	[b]	[b]	[a]	[a]	[a]	[a]	[a]	[b]	0
Musculium partumeium, j	[a]	[a]	[a-c]	[a-b]	[b]	[b]	[a]	[a]	[a]	[a]	[a]	[b]	0
Pisidium amnicum, k	[a]	[a]	[a-c]	[a-b]	[b]	[b]	[a]	[a]	[a]	[a]	[a]	[b]	0
Pisidium henslowanum, l	[a]	[a]	[a-c]	[a-b]	[b]	[b]	[a]	[a]	[a]	[a]	[a]	[b]	0
Pisidium moitessierianum, m*	[a]	[a]	[a-c]?	[a-b]?	[b]	[b]	[a]	[a]	[a]	[a]	[a]	[b]	0
Pisidium supinum, n	[a]	[a]	[a-c]?	[a-b]?	[b]	[b]	[a]	[a]	[a]	[a]	[a]	[b]	0
Sphaerium corneum, o	[a]	[a]	[a-c]	[a-b]	[b]	[b]	[a]	[a]	[a]	[a]	[a]	[b]	0

[1] Impacts are either negative (–) or nil (0), as judged by the author. See Mackie (1999b, 2000a) and Grigorovich et al. (2000) for details of traits or references for those traits. Letters a–o in species column refer to Figure 1. "?" indicates uncertainty about the trait(s) due to lack of information.

*New species discovered in the Great Lakes by Grigorovich et al. (2000).

Part 4 How Do We Manage Alien Species?

Those who must deal with invasive alien species have four options: prevent the invasion; if this fails, eradicate the invaders; if this fails or is impractical, manage the established populations to slow their expansion or mitigate their impact; or ignoring the first three options, sit back and observe. In this part, each chapter discusses one or more of these options in various contexts and for different species.

Prevention is the most-favored option as it avoids the economic, social, and ecological costs possible with eradication or control. However, if the impacts of an alien species have not been researched and cannot be predicted, prevention becomes difficult.

The underlying message of many of the authors in this publication is that Canadians must learn from their experiences and from those of others to deal with the alien species problem. All over Canada, intentional and unintentional introductions of fishes have helped destabilize native fish populations. Many years of efforts at preventing the introduction of alien aquatic species in the Great Lakes have taught managers that prevention is not an easy task. Alien species are introduced by a variety of pathways and stopping them before they get in requires complex measures and strategies. Developing awareness at all levels is important and collaboration and communication among government agencies, the research community, industry, and nongovernmental agencies is essential. It avoids duplication, leverages funding, and provides for consistent messaging and program prioritization, thus saving time and money.

Plant quarantine has long been used for preventing the introduction of alien species harmful to agricultural crop plants and commercial forest trees. Targets of quarantine include insects, fungi, bacteria, nematodes, viruses, and weeds known to be harmful. Such species are controlled by the application of specific regulations aimed at preventing their spread by human means. In recent years, resources devoted to inspection, detection and identification, surveys, risk assessments, research, and treatments have not kept pace with the increasing risk of plant pest introductions from outside Canada. Only 1%–2% of incoming shipments into Canada are routinely inspected. Foreign-site surveys, early warning pest-prediction systems, enhanced monitoring of

high-risk commodities at Canadian ports, improved pest detection and testing methods, and enhanced plant quarantine pest surveys would all contribute to increasing the effectiveness of plant quarantine and similar prevention programs.

Four main methods are commonly used to control established populations of pests: mechanical, chemical, biological control, and ecosystem management. Each has produced various results, from failures to notable successes. Research will improve their effectiveness and provide data for making the best choice in a given situation. Key considerations in assessing control methods are comprehensive cost-benefit analyses, realistic appraisal of likelihood of success, and testing of probable nontarget impacts.

A problem peculiar to managing alien species is that the literature on new invasions and on techniques for dealing with them is often scattered and inaccessible. Enhanced use of linked databases should help solve this problem.

Finding efficient natural enemies of an alien species from its native range and releasing them in the invaded sites is called "classical biological control". A viable population of the enemy is expected to build up and, in doing so, stabilize the population of the invader. Classical biological control has been applied, for instance, against invasive alien weeds of rangeland and uncultivated areas where the use of herbicides had been considered too costly. Mass rearing and release of a native natural enemy of either a native or an alien species is called "inundative biological control". When applied to weeds, it can reduce and even sometimes replace herbicide applications.

In Canada, biological control of native and alien weeds using their natural enemies has been researched for over 50 years, and several successes have been achieved. A prerequisite for both classical and inundative biological control is a thorough investigation of problems and options. One of the criticisms of biological control is the lack of long-term monitoring of the introduced natural enemies. There are well-documented instances where the introduced consumer of a pest species has attacked nontarget native species, including rare ones. The challenge to proponents of classical biological control will be to persuade society that it can be used safely and that the ecological benefits of successful programs, such as those against alien plant pests of natural areas, justify the expenditures needed. Will funding agencies accept the 20-year program duration that would be necessary for post-release monitoring?

Controlling an already-established invasive species involves more than just the technical considerations. Purple loosestrife, a European plant, invades wetland areas, displacing up to 60% of native vegetation. An effective initiative to control purple loosestrife across Canada has shown that stimulating political awareness and, more importantly, political buy-in to the processes and programs are key parts of strategic planning. Other important elements are having well-documented evidence of an invasion, a capacity to communicate this knowledge to the public and politicians, and support from interests that could be negatively affected by planned remedial actions. The toughest part of the purple loosestrife initiative is proving to be the delivery of solutions, partly because of the expense and partly because the initial enthusiasm may be waning.

Intentional Introductions of Alien Species of Fish: Have We Learned from Our Mistakes?

Dennis Wright

The human race is one of the few species on this planet with the ability to manipulate its environment to suit its own perceived needs, and we have a long history of tinkering with nature. As we have colonized the Earth, we have transported plants and animals from one ecosystem to another to provide food, sport, and ornamentation. However, in many cases we have given little or no consideration to the ecological integrity of the recipient ecosystem. Because of various characteristics inherent to fish, to engineering, and to basic human nature, many fish species have moved or been moved to new environments. When we have deliberately moved fish or altered waterways, our intentions may have been good, and we may have reaped temporary socioeconomic benefits, but what long-term costs have our actions imposed on native fish communities and their environments?

The invasion of ecosystems by alien species is one of the most important issues in natural resources management today. This situation was evinced in a 1995 report by the US National Research Council entitled *Understanding Marine Biodiversity: A Research Agenda for the Nation* (National Research Council 1995), which recognized the introduction of alien species and the degradation of marine biodiversity as one of the five most critical environmental issues facing the United States at that time. Conservative estimates put the economic losses due to invasive or alien fish species in the United States at more than US$1 billion annually and total environmental losses from all introductions of alien biota at more than US$138 billion per year (Pimentel et al. 2000).

The problem is not new, and although many invading species arrive uninvited, as stowaways and hitchhikers, many others have become established in new environments as a result of our own actions. The common carp (*Cyprinus carpio* L.) was probably one of the first fish species transferred deliberately beyond its native range: originally found in the Danube River drainage basin, it is believed to have been moved by the Romans beginning about the first century AD (Balon 1995). During the late medieval period, monastic orders spread carp throughout Europe, and Arctic char (*Salvelinus alpinus* (L.)) was introduced into many of the high alpine lakes in Scandinavia and the Austrian

Tyrol (Pechlaner 1984). In North America, introductions and transfers began soon after the arrival of the first European settlers. DeKay (1842) reported that goldfish (*Carassius auratus* (L.)) were brought to North America in the early part of the 17th century. Citing that work, Courtenay et al. (1984) reported that the first recorded goldfish releases in the United States occurred during the late 1600s. They suggested that these earliest introductions resulted from intentional releases by settlers wanting to add to the North American fish fauna. Even today, introductions of alien fish species continue at an alarming rate. For example, European ruffe (*Gymnocephalus cernuus* (L.)), round goby (*Neogobius melanostomus* (Pallas)), and tubenose goby (*Proterorhinus marmoratus* (Pallas)) have recently been introduced to the Great Lakes.

Such transfers have not been entirely benign, and we have learned from long and sometimes bitter experience that the introduction of alien species into any aquatic ecosystem cannot be accomplished without serious adverse effects on native species and their habitats. Too often, our measures to solve immediate or local problems have had negative long-range or broad-scale consequences. Moyle et al. (1986) referred to this as the "Frankenstein effect", in reference to Mary Shelley's famous novel of 1818. Shelley's novel spoke directly to popular fears about the dangers—and the consequences—of overstepping nature's boundaries. Dr. Frankenstein, in his attempt to create a "new and improved" human being, discovered, to his mortal distress, that he had brought danger and destruction to the lives of those he loved and that he had created more problems than he had solved.

Like Dr. Frankenstein, we have tried to improve upon local fisheries without considering the effects on native fish communities. We have been slow to heed the words of Dr. Henry Regier (1968), one of Canada's most eminent fisheries scientists, who, in his paraphrase of President John F. Kennedy's inaugural address, warned us that "we choose exotics on the basis of what they can do for us and not primarily on what they can do for the nonhuman system."

Yet, despite all of the experience and warnings available to us, we continue to introduce new species to ecosystems. Have we learned anything at all from the history of introductions, or, by not heeding the experiences of others, are we bound to repeat some of their mistakes? This paper looks at examples of intentional introductions and their negative effects on native aquatic communities, examines some of the management attitudes that have guided our thinking in the past, and outlines a course of action for the future.

Decline of Native Fishes and Concurrent Rise of Alien Fishes

When the Great Lakes emerged from beneath the last great continental ice sheets, which retreated about 15 000 years ago, they were populated with some 160 species of fish arriving from glacial refugia in the Mississippi River and Atlantic regions (Mandrak and Crossman 1992; Tanner 2000). A rich and stable aquatic community soon became established. Salmonids constituted the largest component of the fish populations in these lakes (Thwaites 1896; Trautman 1957). In Lake Ontario, planktivorous coregonids constituted the greatest biomass, and the Atlantic salmon (*Salmo salar* L.) was the most important and abundant piscivore. In the upper deep-water lakes, the lake trout (*Salvelinus namaycush* (Walbaum)) filled this role. Yellow perch (*Perca flavescens* (Mitchill)), sauger (*Stizostedion canadense* (Smith)), walleye (*S. vitreum vitreum* (Mitchill)), and blue pike (*S. vitreum glaucum* Hubbs[1]) were particularly abundant in Lake Erie (Smith 1995). On the basis of paleoecological studies, researchers estimate that, collectively, some 19 different species accounted for the greatest numbers and biomass of fishes and represented the main components of a highly productive and stable fish community (Smith 1995).

After the War of 1812, a tide of European settlers arrived in the Great Lakes drainage basin. The cutting of forests and the development of agricultural land proceeded at a furious rate, such that, by the 1890s, the drainage basin of Lake Ontario in western New York State was almost entirely deforested (Rafter 1897;

Warwick 1978). Similar changes occurred within the Canadian portion of the drainage basin. Concurrent with the deforestation, many wetlands were drained and the watersheds industrialized. The discharge of mill and manufacturing wastes into the streams powering the mills resulted in heavy pollution of nearly all streams throughout the drainage basin by the mid-1800s (Stone and Stewart Publishing 1866; Smith 1892). Low flows, elevated stream temperatures, dams, and pollution reduced the amount of habitat available to stream-spawning species, which in turn resulted in their decline.

Coincident with the development of the land, unrestricted and wasteful fisheries developed along the shores of the lakes. For example, lake whitefish (*Coregonus clupeaformis* (Mitchill)) was processed for use as fertilizer (Adams 1912), and lake herring or cisco (*C. artedi* Lesueur) and lake sturgeon (*Acipenser fulvescens* Rafinesque) were simply "destroyed as nuisances" (Koelz 1926).

Excessive exploitation coupled with habitat degradation had a major negative influence on fish stocks. By the mid-1800s, catches of all species in Lake Ontario, perhaps the most productive of the deep-water Great Lakes, were greatly reduced. By 1900, Atlantic salmon had been extirpated from Lake Ontario (Huntsman 1944). Smith and Snell (1891) concluded that "fishing as a livelihood along the shores of the great lake [Lake Ontario]…is rapidly decaying…once lively towns became dead and musty nets rotted on drying wheels."

When fishing pressure was reduced, the stocks did not recover, which indicated that factors other than fishing might have been involved in the declines. In response to this problem in the Great Lakes and other areas, President Ulysses S. Grant created the US Fish Commission in 1871, charging this agency with the responsibility to study "the decrease of the food fishes of the seacoasts and the lakes of the United States and to suggest remedial measures."

In 1871, the artificial propagation of trout and other fishes was in its infancy but had already captured the imagination of a growing number of fisheries scientists intent on improving the stocks of available sport and food fish. The introduction of vast numbers of native and alien species of fish to new waters appeared to be an easy way to increase fishing opportunities for everyone. The next three-decade period was clearly the age of introductions as fishery managers tried many species in a wide variety of waters. Rainbow trout (*Oncorhynchus mykiss* (Walbaum)) were brought from California to

---

[1] Blue pike is considered by some taxonomists to be a subspecies of walleye. This fish, which inhabited only Lake Erie and Lake Ontario, is now considered rare and in fact is probably extinct. There is considerable debate about its taxonomic classification, and DNA analysis of some recently collected specimens suspected to be blue pike is under way. However, no reliable reference specimen exists from which to obtain DNA for comparison. The typical compounds used to preserve specimens (such as formalin and alcohol) destroy DNA, so museum specimens are unsuitable for this purpose.

the east coast and the Great Lakes beginning in 1874 (McCrimmon 1971). The US Fish Commission began introducing common carp from Germany in 1877, and for the next two decades the agency stocked and distributed carp as food fish throughout much of the United States. Canada followed this trend, and between 1881 and 1893 the Fisheries Branch of Canada's Department of Marine and Fisheries and the Ontario Game and Fish Commission introduced carp into Ontario as a "means of furnishing in the future, a cheap article of food" (Crossman 1968). Enthusiasm for the program developed quickly, and carp were introduced into every imaginable stream or body of water. They quickly spread and increased in abundance, causing significant damage to and loss of habitat in near-shore vegetated areas. Before long, public acceptance waned, and criticism by fishery professionals and the public at large grew, such that within 19 years of the first introduction of carp the Ontario Department of Fish and Game reported "it is conceded that the promiscuous introduction of carp on this continent has been attended with nothing but evil results" (Crossman 1968). To this day, the introduction of this now largely unwanted species stands as a monument to inadequate study before the introduction of an alien animal species.

J.D. Whish, a lay participant at the 1906 meeting of the American Fisheries Society, made the following observations and comments, which hold as true today as they did in the early years of the last century (Whish 1906):

> It all comes, in my judgement, from trying to get something foreign in place of something which is native born, believing that because a thing comes from Europe it is just a little better than anything that grows in America…I have been somewhat of a fisherman ever since I was a little farmer boy with ragged trousers and could get a pin and a piece of string; and I remember when eminent scientific gentlemen threw up their hands and cheered at the discovery of the great carp. I have sat in societies and heard gentlemen of eminence confess– I say also, confess very carefully–that the introduction of carp was a fish cultural tragedy.

Brown trout (*Salmo trutta* L.) were introduced from Germany and Scotland by both the Canada Department of Marine and Fisheries and the US Fish Commission beginning in the 1880s (McCrimmon and Marshall 1968) in an attempt to find a replacement for Atlantic salmon. This introduction was very successful in terms of its intended purpose, and self-sustaining populations were established in habitats that had been degraded by the incursion of "civilization". However, this too was not without its impacts on native species.

New York State sharply reduced the extent of its brown trout propagation program in 1906 because of serious competition with native brook trout (*Salvelinus fontinalis* (Mitchill)) (Bean 1906), an action to which Whish (1906) responded as follows:

> I am hearing the successors of these scientific gentlemen confessing very cautiously that the introduction of the noble brown trout is the same thing…
>
> But here is your carp question: Would it not have been better if they had found out where these fish were suited to go before they put them in the waters of the country? And would not the same thing have been better with relation to the brown trout?
>
> Of what worth is your scientific man if he cannot give proper advice when great questions of this kind arise? For is it a great question to introduce into the waters of the state, or of a nation, a fish about whose habits you know nothing except as they occur on the other side of the ocean; and however they may have been on the other side they certainly are different when they get here; and I think that in the future, if somebody offers a species of fish that is great and good in another country, it would be the part of wisdom—to try it out in a secluded spot, well fenced in, before giving it to the nation at large to the destruction of the better fishes.

Transfer of Native Fishes outside Their Natural Ranges

Perhaps we did learn something about the introduction of alien species from the problems of the 1800s, and, in an effort to avoid a recurrence of the "common carp mistake", introductions from the 1890s to the 1950s consisted mainly of the transfer of species native to North America to areas outside their natural ranges. The belief that such transfers would be without negative consequences might have resulted from a common misconception that although exotic species from distant lands will cause problems for native biota, the transfer of native species to nearby ecosystems is safe (Dextrase and Coscarelli 1999). Many of the introductions of this period had little chance of success because environmental, physiological, and ecological factors that limited survival were not adequately considered. Many species were released into environments that were completely unsuitable for self-sustaining populations.

Although some of the transfers were highly successful in terms of their intended purposes, such as the introduction of rainbow trout to areas east of the Rocky Mountains in 1874 and the introduction of striped bass (*Morone saxatilis* (Walbaum)) to the Pacific Ocean near Martinez, California, in 1879, others have been, to say the least, ecologically disastrous.

In 1912, as part of a program to introduce Atlantic salmon to the upper Great Lakes, the Michigan Department of Conservation stocked eggs from an anadromous Atlantic coast stock of rainbow smelt (*Osmerus mordax* (Mitchill)) (Figure 1) into Crystal Lake, a tributary to Lake Michigan, to provide a forage species for the salmon (Van Oosten 1937). Although none of the desired species, Atlantic salmon, survived that

Figure 1. Rainbow smelt. Photo © John G. Shedd Aquarium, Chicago, IL.

introduction, the rainbow smelt did. The smelt migrated downstream to Lake Michigan and there established a self-sustaining population that spread rapidly throughout the Great Lakes (Figure 2). The introduction of rainbow smelt to the Great Lakes is considered to have been a major factor in the decline, and probable extinction, of several species of ciscoes or tullibees with extremely limited distribution that had evolved to take advantage of the local environment (Loftus and Hulsman 1986; Evans and Loftus 1987). These species represented important food for lake trout and were also caught, smoked, and sold as "chubs", which were regarded as a delicacy. Canada and the United States have been unsuccessful in restoring naturally reproducing populations of lake trout in the Great Lakes, apparently because of low concentrations of thiamine in the eggs, a direct result of a diet consisting almost entirely of rainbow smelt and alewife (*Alosa pseudoharengus* (Wilson)), which contain high concentrations of the

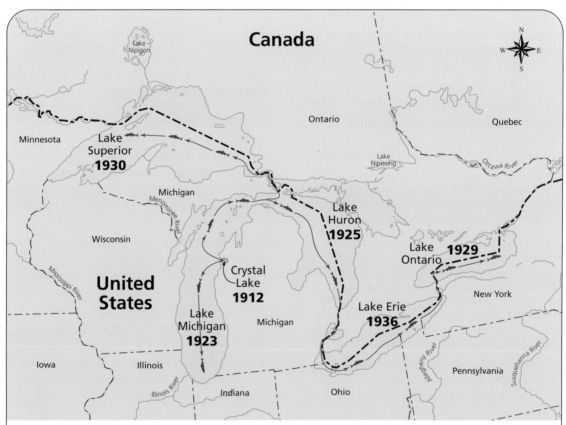

Figure 2. Dates of first observations of rainbow smelt in the Great Lakes. Arrows show the postulated migration of the fish from Crystal Lake throughout the Great Lakes system. It is suspected that smelt reached Lake Erie sometime between 1925, when they were detected in Lake Huron, and 1929, when they were first detected in Lake Ontario, but that they were not detected because the population was kept low by the large number of predator species in Lake Erie. Once a few of the smelt reached Lake Ontario, where the predators were absent, the population in that lake increased rapidly, such that the species was detected in Lake Ontario before it was detected in Lake Erie.

thiamine-destroying enzyme thiaminase (Fitzsimons et al. 1995; Fitzsimons and Brown 1998; Ji et al. 1998). Rainbow smelt may also have contributed to the extirpation from Lake Erie and Lake Ontario of the blue pike, a presumed native subspecies of walleye that was unique to those lakes (Christie 1974; Becker 1983; Todd 1986) (see also footnote 1).

We are told that the study of history teaches us about our past, about mistakes that have been made and their consequences, and that such study will ensure that the same mistakes are not repeated. But apparently we did not learn from the experience of the introduction of rainbow smelt into the Great Lakes. The impoundment of the Missouri River behind Garrison Dam in North Dakota in the 1950s resulted in the formation of Lake Sakakawea, a very large, deep lake in an area not known for extensive recreational fishing opportunities. As the reservoir filled, state fishery managers stocked the lake with chinook salmon (*Oncorhynchus tshawytscha* (Walbaum)) and coho salmon (*O. kisutch* (Walbaum)), as well as lake trout and brown trout. Some 7500 gravid female rainbow smelt were introduced into Lake Sakakawea from Lake Superior in April 1971 to establish a forage base for the salmonids (Mayden et al. 1987). The salmonids must be continually replaced with fish spawned and reared in hatcheries, to satisfy the demands of the "put–grow–take" recreational fishery that has developed. The smelt, on the other hand, flourished and quickly established a large, self-sustaining population. By 1974, smelt had moved downstream to Lake Oahe, South Dakota, the next downstream impoundment, and by 1978 had become the most common fish species in the lake (Figure 3). After becoming established in Lake Oahe, the smelt spread rapidly down the Missouri River and into the next three reservoirs. Rainbow smelt are now present in low numbers in these reservoirs but are not as well established as in the upstream reservoirs, apparently because of inferior habitat (Mayden et al. 1987). This species has also been recorded from a number of locations further downstream in the main-stem portions of the Missouri and Mississippi rivers and was collected from as far south as Louisiana in 1979 (Suttkus and Connor 1979). In 1979 rainbow smelt were collected in the Missouri River upstream of Lake Sakakawea as far as the tailrace of the Fort Peck Dam, Montana, and

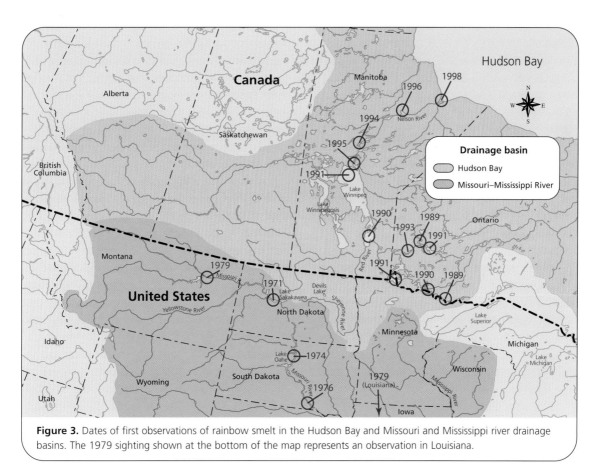

Figure 3. Dates of first observations of rainbow smelt in the Hudson Bay and Missouri and Mississippi river drainage basins. The 1979 sighting shown at the bottom of the map represents an observation in Louisiana.

in the Yellowstone River in Montana (Gould 1981). Most of the Mississippi River occurrences and all of the Missouri River occurrences are presumed to have resulted from that one Lake Sakakawea introduction (Mayden et al. 1987).

Dispersion of Alien Fishes through River Diversions

The introduction of alien biota is the cornerstone of opposition by the governments of Canada and Manitoba to two water diversion projects in North Dakota, the Garrison Diversion and the Devils Lake Emergency Outlet. The Garrison Diversion project is a multipurpose water resource project to divert Missouri River water into the central and eastern areas of the state within the Hudson Bay drainage basin, to provide water for irrigation and for municipal and industrial uses. Devils Lake is a closed or noncontributing basin situated within the Hudson Bay drainage basin. Its level has risen more than 8.5 m since 1993 because of excessive precipitation and drainage of wetland storage areas within the drainage basin. In the process, the lake has more than doubled in volume and has tripled in surface area, from 16 000 to 48 000 ha. The resulting flooding has caused approximately Can$450 million in damages, including the loss of over 300 dwellings and thousands of hectares of agricultural land, the relocation or rebuilding of roads and infrastructure, and the building of a 15-m-high dike to protect the city of Devils Lake. The construction of an artificial outlet from Devils Lake to the Sheyenne River, a tributary to the Red River, has been proposed as a way to mitigate the flooding. However, the construction of the Garrison Diversion and the Devils Lake outlet would create new pathways whereby both known and unknown alien species could enter Canadian waters, in particular the Lake Winnipeg system.

One of the major species of concern with respect to biota transfer through the Garrison Diversion has been rainbow smelt. Although not a drop of water has been transferred by either of the projects described above, the concerns about interbasin transfer of alien fish are justified, as Lake Winnipeg already has a population of rainbow smelt (Campbell et al. 1991; Franzin et al. 1994).

Where this population originated is unknown, but the fish could have reached Lake Winnipeg by one or more of several possible routes. Rainbow smelt have been introduced by a variety of methods into several lakes in the upper portion of the Winnipeg River system in northwestern Ontario and to the Rainy River in northern Minnesota: by anglers attempting to introduce a forage species for walleye and lake trout, through the careless disposal of surplus bait, and by the inadvertent release of fertilized eggs during the processing of rainbow smelt captured during spawning runs in other bodies of water (Evans and Loftus 1987; Remnant 1991; Wain 1993). Rainbow smelt became established and soon moved downstream in both systems but were not found in the Winnipeg River below Lake of the Woods before they were captured in the south basin of Lake Winnipeg in 1990 (Figure 3). There is also an anecdotal report of a single rainbow smelt being caught from the Red River below the St. Andrews Dam in 1975, which raises the possibility that the Lake Winnipeg rainbow smelt came from a separate introduction directly into the Red River. Since 1990, rainbow smelt have moved out of Lake Winnipeg and down the Nelson River. By 1996, they had moved at least 525 km downstream of the outlet from Lake Winnipeg, and in 1998 they were captured in the Nelson River estuary on Hudson Bay (Remnant et al. 1997; Bretecher and MacDonell 1998).

It is too early to estimate the magnitude of the impact of rainbow smelt on the Can$15 million commercial fishery in Lake Winnipeg. Nonetheless, the smelt are expected to cause declines in populations of several coregonid species and other small fish such as emerald shiner (*Notropis atherinoides* Rafinesque) and spottail shiner (*N. hudsonius* (Clinton)) and may have some other detrimental impacts. Because rainbow smelt have a high fat content, predators that feed on them usually grow more rapidly and get fatter than they would feeding on native forage fish. However, feeding on rainbow smelt has decreased the quality of walleye and lake trout consumed by people. The flesh of smelt-feeding walleye develops a soft, greasy, bland quality, and the flesh of lake trout that feed on smelt acquires a strong cucumber-like odor, which is not removed by cooking. There are additional problems, because rainbow smelt are fish predators that feed on the young of larger fish such as walleye, northern pike (*Esox lucius* L.), whitefish, and ciscoes. Adult rainbow smelt also compete with young stages of the larger species, which can reduce the number of larger fish that survive long enough to begin feeding on smelt. In addition, because rainbow smelt are piscivorous, they add another step in the food chain for the predators that feed on them. This has caused increases in the concentration of pollutants such as mercury in the predatory fish that feed on rainbow smelt. At this time, we can only guess what other negative impacts rainbow smelt might have in Lake Winnipeg, so detailed studies will be necessary.

The rainbow smelt is but one of a number of Missouri River species of concern to Canada and Manitoba. Although rainbow smelt has already arrived in the Lake Winnipeg system, there are several other species that could make use of the pathway offered by the Garrison Diversion. Therefore, because of the risks involved, both Canada and Manitoba adhere to the "precautionary principle" (Cameron and Abouchar 1991) and oppose any scheme that would divert water to bodies of water in the Hudson Bay drainage basin.

Transjurisdictional Dispersion

Manitoba has been the unwilling recipient of another alien species introduced by North Dakota. The North Dakota Game and Fish Department introduced white bass (*Morone chrysops* (Rafinesque)) as a sport fish into the newly created Lake Ashtabula (behind the Baldhill Dam on the Sheyenne River) in 1953 (Cross et al. 1986). The white bass, like rainbow smelt, has no respect for political boundaries and moved from Lake Ashtabula and the Sheyenne River to the Red River and downstream to Lake Winnipeg, where the first specimen was collected in 1963 (Scott and Crossman 1973). It has spread throughout the south basin of Lake Winnipeg and is now taken regularly in the commercial fishery (Hanke and Stewart 1994). The impact of this introduction on the community of native fishes has yet to be completely determined. However, it appears that the introduced species is in competition with several of the native species. Additionally, white bass is considered a nuisance by the commercial fishery because there is a limited market for it and removing it from nets takes up valuable time.

North Dakota embarked on a program to introduce zander (*Stizostedion lucioperca* (L.)), a Eurasian cousin or congener of walleye, into Lake Sakakawea in 1987 (Anderson 1992). At the time, this reservoir had some of the finest walleye fishing in North America, although walleye numbers were in decline because of several factors. Low water levels, a result of several years of drought, may have decreased the amount of available spawning habitat. Fluctuating water temperatures during spawning and recruitment periods may have also resulted in unsuccessful recruitment. However, instead of augmenting the walleye population by stocking or by reducing water releases during spawning

time, the state presented the case that zander was more suited to the prevailing conditions than was the native walleye. The argument was also presented that zander grow to a much larger size than the native walleye and that 10-kg fish would be readily available to anglers. However, although zander do spawn later than walleye and thus may be less susceptible to the vagaries of spring weather in these climes, and although they are more tolerant than walleye of degraded, highly eutrophied systems, they do not reach the size (at northern latitudes) promised by their proponents. Despite objections from surrounding jurisdictions that might become the unwilling recipients of zander, the state imported zander eggs from Holland in 1987 (Wright 1992). The US Fish and Wildlife Service ordered that these be destroyed when it was learned that they might be carrying a pike fry rhabdovirus, which was not present in North America. A second attempt was made in 1989 with eggs obtained from a certified disease-free facility in Finland, and the resulting fry were introduced into Spiritwood Lake, a small lake with no outlet near Jamestown, North Dakota. A combination of drought, high water temperatures, and the native fish community, as well as a hungry population of mud puppies (*Necturus maculosus* Rafinesque), appears to have caused the failure of this attempt. This outcome was indeed fortunate, because the next year, high water levels linked this "closed lake" with the James River, a tributary to the Missouri River. The North Dakota Game and Fish Department has since discarded the philosophy of fishery management by introductions and transfers of alien species and is now an ardent supporter of a thorough risk analysis of the possible negative impact of any new species considered for introduction to state waters. However, in June 2000, a strange-looking fish was recovered from Spiritwood Lake by the North Dakota Game and Fish Department. Tissue samples of the unknown fish, as well as samples of walleye and sauger from Spiritwood Lake and zander from the same Finnish stock that was used in the 1989 introduction, were subjected to mitochondrial DNA analysis. The results of this analysis confirmed that the unknown specimen was a zander and had the same genetic composition as the Finnish samples. The age of the fish captured in Spiritwood Lake was 2+ years, which indicates that the fish was not from the original 1989 introduction but was the result of natural reproduction of fish introduced at that time. Spiritwood Lake has recently been connected to the James River because of high water conditions, which have persisted for at least three years. There is concern that zander may have escaped from the lake where they were introduced and may now be resident in the James River or may have moved downstream to the main stem of the Missouri River. The consequences of this introduction are as yet unknown and are under study by the North Dakota Game and Fish Department.

Canadians cannot sit back and look smugly at the folly of other jurisdictions with regard to intentional introductions and transfers of alien species of fish. Table 1 summarizes known intentional (and unintentional) introductions of freshwater fish in Canada. For example, brook trout were introduced to lakes in

Table 1. Known introductions of freshwater fish in Canada.

Family and species name	Common name	NF	NS	PE	NB	QC	ON	MB	SK	AB	BC	NT	YT
Petromyzontidae	Lampreys												
Petromyzon marinus L.	Sea lamprey						UB						
Lepisosteidae	Gars												
Lepisosteus platyrhincus DeKay	Florida gar						IB						
Hiodontidae	Mooneyes												
Hiodon alosoides (Rafinesque)	Goldeye										IA		
Anguillidae	Freshwater eels												
Anguilla rostrata (Lesueur)	American eel						UB		IA	UB			
Clupeidae	Herrings												
Alosa pseudoharengus (Wilson)	Alewife					UB	UB						
Alosa sapidissima (Wilson)	American shad						IA				IA		
Dorosoma cepedianum (Lesueur)	Gizzard shad						UB						
Cyprinidae	Carps and minnows												
Carassius auratus (L.)	Goldfish		IB		IB		IB? UB?	IB UA	IB	IB	IB		
Couesius plumbeus (Agassiz)	Lake chub										IA		
Ctenopharyngodon idella (Valenciennes)	Grass carp						UB UA?			IA			
Cyprinus carpio L.	Common carp			IA	UB?		IA UB?	IA	UB?		IA UB?		
Notemigonus crysoleucas (Mitchill)	Golden shiner			IA									
Notropis hudsonius (Clinton)	Spottail shiner								IA		IA		
Notropis sp.	Unidentified shiner								IA				
Platygobio gracilis (Richardson)	Flathead chub										IA		
Richardsonius balteatus (Richardson)	Redside shiner										IA		
Scardinius erythrophthalmus (L.)	Rudd						UB						
Tinca tinca (L.)	Tench										IA		
Catostomidae	Suckers												
Catostomus catostomus (Forster)	Longnose sucker										IA		
Catostomus commersoni (Lacepède)	White sucker									IA	IA		
Ictiobus cyprinellus (Valenciennes)	Bigmouth buffalo								IA				
Characidae	Characins												
Colossoma sp.	Unidentified pacu						IB						
Colossoma cf. Bidens	Pacu species						IB						

(Continued)

Note: IA = intentional: authorized introduction, including transfer to another watershed within the same province; IB = intentional: release by a fish hobbyist; UA = unintentional: unintentional release, including escape from a fish culture facility, or unauthorized release; UB = unintentional: invasion as a result of human actions (e.g., building of canals), including invasion after intentional release elsewhere (e.g., United States); UC = unintentional: arrival in ballast water or by some other method.

Table 1. (Continued)

Family and species name	Common name	NF	NS	PE	NB	QC	ON	MB	SK	AB	BC	NT	YT
Province or territory													

Family and species name	Common name	NF	NS	PE	NB	QC	ON	MB	SK	AB	BC	NT	YT
Ictaluridae	Bullhead catfishes												
Ameiurus melas (Rafinesque)	Black bullhead							UB			UB		
Ameiurus nebulosus (Lesueur)	Brown bullhead							UB			UB IA		
Ictalurus punctatus (Rafinesque)	Channel catfish							UB			IA?		
Noturus flavus Rafinesque	Stonecat							UB					
Loricariidae	Suckermouth catfishes												
Panaque nigrolineatus (Peters)	Royal panaque						IB						
Esocidae	Pikes												
Esox americanus americanus Gmelin	Redfin pickerel					UB							
Esox lucius L.	Northern pike								IA		IA		
Esox masquinongy Mitchill	Muskellunge				UB	IA		IA					
Esox niger Lesueur	Chain pickerel		IA		UB IA?	UB?							
Umbridae	Mudminnows												
Dallia pectoralis Bean	Alaska blackfish						IA						
Osmeridae	Smelts												
Osmerus mordax (Mitchill)	Rainbow smelt	IA			IA	UB	UA UB	UB	IA				
Salmonidae	Salmon, trouts, and whitefishes												
Coregonus artedi Lesueur	Lake herring or cisco								IA	IA			
Coregonus clupeaformis (Mitchill)	Lake whitefish	IA				IA		IA	IA	IA	IA		
Coregonus laveratus (L.)	Powan					IA?							
Hucho hucho (L.)	Huchen or Danube salmon					IA							
Oncorhynchus aquabonita (Jordan)	Golden trout								IA	IA			
Oncorhynchus clarki (Richardson)	Cutthroat trout					UA	IA?	IA	IA	IA		IA	
Oncorhynchus clarki lewisi (Girard)	Westslope cutthroat trout					IA	IA	IA	IA				
Oncorhynchus gorbuscha (Walbaum)	Pink salmon	IA	UB		UB	UB	UA IA						
Oncorhynchus keta (Walbaum)	Chum salmon						IA?				IA		
Oncorhynchus kisutch (Walbaum)	Coho salmon		UB		UB		IA		IA	IA			IA
Oncorhynchus masou (Brevoort)	Cherry salmon						IA						
Oncorhynchus mykiss (Walbaum)	Rainbow trout or steelhead	IA UA	IA	IA	IA UA	IA UB	IA UB	IA	IA UA	IA	IA	IA	IA UA
Oncorhynchus mykiss (Palomino)	Rainbow trout, Palomino strain						UB						
Oncorhynchus mykiss (Skamania)	Rainbow trout, Skamania strain						IA UB						
Oncorhynchus mykiss (Tagworker)	Rainbow trout, Tagworker strain						IA	IA					
Oncorhynchus nerka (Walbaum)	Sockeye salmon or kokanee					IA	IA	IA	IA	IA	IA		
Oncorhynchus tshawytscha (Walbaum)	Chinook salmon or king salmon			UB	IA UB	UB	IA UB				IA		
Salmo salar L.	Atlantic salmon	IA	IA	IA	IA	IA	IA UB	IA?	IA	IA	IA UA		
Salmo trutta L.	Brown trout	IA	IA			IA UB	IA	IA	IA	IA	IA		
Salmo trutta microstigma	Brown trout					IA							
Salvelinus alpinus (L.)	Arctic char	IA	IA	IA	IA		IA UA	IA	IA	IA	IA	IA	

(Continued)

Table 1. *(Continued)*

Family and species name	Common name						Province or territory						
		NF	NS	PE	NB	QC	ON	MB	SK	AB	BC	NT	YT
Salvelinus fontinalis (Mitchill)	Brook trout		IA	IA	IA		IA	IA	IA	IA	IA	IA	
Salvelinus malma (Walbaum)	Dolly Varden									IA	IA		
Salvelinus namaycush (Walbaum)	Lake trout						IA		IA	IA			
Oncorhynchus clarki lewisi × *O. mykiss*	Cutbow trout hybrid						IA		IA	IA			
O. mykiss × *H. hucho*						IA							
Salmo salar × *S. trutta*	Sambrown	IA											
Salmo trutta × *Salvelinus fontinalis*	Tiger trout					IA				IA	IA?		
S. fontinalis × *S. alpinus*										IA			
S. fontinalis × *S. malma* or *S. confluentus*						IA	IA	IA	IA	IA	IA	IA	
S. fontinalis × *S. namaycush*	Splake									IA	IA	IA	
(*S. fontinalis* × *S. namaycush*) × *S. namaycush*							IA						
S. namaycush × *S. malma* or *S. confluentus*										IA	IA?		
Thymallus arcticus (Pallas)	Arctic grayling					IA	IA	IA	IA		IA		
Percopsidae	Trout-perches												
Percopsis omiscomaycus (Walbaum)	Trout-perch										IA		
Gadidae	Cods												
Lota lota (L.)	Burbot, ling, or maria										IA		
Poeciliidae	Livebearers												
Gambusia affinis (Baird & Girard)	Western mosquitofish						IA	IA		IA	IA?		
Poecilia latipinna (Lesueur)	Sailfin Molly									IB			
Poecilia reticulata Peters	Guppy									IB			
Xiphophorus helleri Heckel	Green swordtail									IB	IA?		
Gasterosteidae	Sticklebacks												
Apeltes quadracus (Mitchill)	Fourspine stickleback					UC?							
Culaea inconstans (Kirtland)	Brook or fivespine stickleback										IA		
Gasterosteus aculeatus L.	Threespine stickleback					UC?				UA	IA		UA
Cottidae	Sculpins												
Cottus rhotheus (Smith)	Torrent sculpin									UA?			
Moronidae (also Percichthyidae)	Temperate basses												
Morone americana (Gmelin)	White perch						UB						
Morone chrysops (Rafinesque)	White bass						UB	UB					
Centrarchidae	Sunfishes												
Ambloplites rupestris (Rafinesque)	Rock bass						UB						
Lepomis gibbosus (L.)	Pumpkinseed					IA					UB / IA		
Lepomis macrochirus Rafinesque	Bluegill							IA / UA	IA				
Micropterus dolomieu Lacepède	Smallmouth bass		IA			IA / UB	IA	IA	IA	IA	IA	IA / UB	
Micropterus salmoides (Lacepède)	Largemouth bass						IA	IA	IA	IA	UB		
Pomoxis annularis Rafinesque	White crappie							UB	IA				
Pomoxis nigromaculatus (Lesueur)	Black crappie						UB / IA	IA	IA		UB / IA?		
Percidae	Perches												
Etheostoma spp.	Darters									IA			
Gymnocephalus cernuus (L.)	Ruffe						UC						

(Continued)

Table 1. (Concluded)

Family and species name	Common name	NF	NS	PE	NB	QC	ON	MB	SK	AB	BC	NT	YT
Perca flavescens (Mitchill)	Yellow perch								IA	IA	UB IA	IA	
Stizostedion vitreum (Mitchill)	Walleye						IA		IA	IA	IA UB	IA	
Cichlidae	Cichlids												
Astronotus ocellatus (Agassiz)	Oscar						IB						
Cichlasoma managuense (Günther)	Aztec cichlid or jaguar guapote						IB						
Cichlasoma nigrofasciatum (Günther)	Convict cichlid									IB			
Hemichromis letourneauxi (Sauvage)	Jewel cichlid									IB			
Pterophyllum scalare (Lichtenstein)	Freshwater angelfish									IB?			
Gobiidae	Gobies												
Neogobius melanostomus (Pallas)	Round goby						UC						
Proterorhinus marmoratus (Pallas)	Tubenose goby						UC						
Belontiidae	Gouramies												
Betta splendens Regan	Siamese fighting fish									IB			
Trichogaster trichopterus (Pallas)	Threespot gourami									IB			
Pleuronectidae	Righteye flounders												
Platichthys flesus (L.)	European flounder						UC						

Adapted, with the permission of the publisher, from Crossman (1991).

Banff National Park, Alberta, as early as 1900 (Banff National Park 1910; Schindler and Pacas 1996) to provide additional recreational opportunities for visiting anglers. Rainbow trout were introduced in 1919, with splake (*Salvelinus fontinalis* × *S. namaycush*), a brook trout–lake trout hybrid, added in the 1950s. The introduction of these alien species made for better fishing in the short term but eventually led to the degradation of the native ecosystem. The alien species outcompeted the native bull trout (*S. confluentus* (Suckley)) and the westslope cutthroat trout (*Oncorhynchus clarki lewisi* (Girard)), and food sources such as planktonic invertebrates began disappearing. Stocking in Banff was halted in 1988, but native populations have not recovered. Park officials plan to restore the native bull trout population in Moraine Lake as one of the park's first fish restoration projects, under a 1994 federal policy that encourages repopulating native species of wildlife and plants and removing alien species. The project has outraged many in the general public, who consider such a venture a waste of time and money, and has drawn sharp criticism from recreational anglers, as it would be at least four years before alien species were eliminated and bull trout reintroduced and even longer before recreational fishing could resume.

Effects of Alien Species on Aquatic Food Webs

When alien species are introduced to an established aquatic ecosystem, the effects may be more complex than simple displacement of native species. Even if such displacement does not occur, the food web may be altered dramatically. The following examples, the alewife and an introduced invertebrate fish food organism, the opossum shrimp (*Mysis relicta* Lovén), illustrate the potential problems.

Habitat destruction in the Great Lakes drainage basin and overfishing of fish stocks created a very unstable ecosystem in the mid-1800s. It was about this time that the alewife invaded Lake Ontario through the Erie Canal (Smith 1970, 1995). Although this was not a deliberate introduction, the creation of the Erie Canal and the linking of the Mohawk and Hudson rivers (which drain to the Atlantic Ocean) with the Oneida and Oswego rivers (which enter Lake Ontario) and Lake

Ontario created a pathway for the transfer of this alien species. The alewife was not a successful invader until the decline of predators such as lake trout and Atlantic salmon in the 1860s. However, within two decades of the first observation of alewife in the main body of the lake, in 1873, the population had increased rapidly, such that it had become "the most abundant fish occurring in Lake Ontario" (Smith 1892). Modifications to the Welland Canal and declines in the population of large predator species such as lake trout and walleye allowed alewife to reach the upper lakes and establish large populations there. The species was first reported in Lake Erie in 1931, in Lake Huron in 1933, in Lake Michigan in 1949, and in Lake Superior in 1954 (Scott and Crossman 1973). By 1966, alewives made up 95%, by weight, of the fish in Lake Michigan and Lake Huron (Smith 1970). During the period of increase and dominance of alewives in the Great Lakes, a similar sequence of changes to the fisheries was observed:

- a decline in shallow-water planktivores (e.g., lake herring and emerald shiner) accompanied by a short-term increase in minor piscivores (e.g., smallmouth bass [*Micropterus dolomieu* Lacepède], largemouth bass [*M. salmoides* (Lacepède)], northern pike, walleye, and yellow perch) in the first decade after establishment;

- a decline in minor piscivores in the second decade after establishment, as alewives became increasingly abundant; and

- a decline in deep-water planktivores (e.g., several species of deep-water lake herring or ciscoes [*Coregonus* spp.]) in the third decade after establishment (Smith 1970, 1995).

In some instances, alewives were so abundant that they clogged municipal and industrial water intakes. In addition, massive die-offs of alewives in shallow water, due to rapidly rising or fluctuating water temperatures during the spring and summer months, fouled recreational beaches and harbors. Commercial exploitation of alewives for use as fertilizer and animal feeds was attempted in the early 1960s and 1970s, but these efforts failed because of the high cost of production, low market value, and unacceptable levels of contaminants in the alewives' flesh (Emery 1985).

Aquatic food webs can also be affected by the introduction of organisms other than fish. The opossum shrimp is an important component of the diet of several fish species. The role of this invertebrate in the food web prompted biologists to introduce it as a means of enhancing rainbow trout production in oligotrophic (nutrient-poor) lakes in British Columbia, where food was perceived as a limiting factor (Lazenby et al. 1986). Although the expected growth response of rainbow trout was not as great as expected, the growth rate and size of planktivorous kokanee (*Oncorhynchus nerka* (Walbaum)) increased dramatically. These results have been used as the rationale for widespread introduction of opossum shrimp in western North America (Northcote 1970). However, behavioral aspects of the biology of the mysids that were not recognized in the initial studies, such as their diurnal vertical migration in thermally stratified lakes, produced undesirable results: in these lakes, the mysids were unavailable to daylight-feeding kokanee and competed with them for the same zooplankton food resources. The kokanee declined in both size and numbers and virtually disappeared from some lakes (Martinez and Bergersen 1989; Spencer et al. 1991). In some places, the effects have reverberated throughout the food web and have resulted in the displacement of migrating bald eagles (*Haliaeetus leucocephalus* (L.)) and grizzly bears (*Ursus arctos* L.) and may have contributed to an increase in the mortality rate of bald eagles (Spencer et al. 1991; Li and Moyle 1993). Unfortunately, by the time these problems were recognized, it was impossible to eliminate the introduced species.

Restoration of the Great Lakes

By the 1960s, the Great Lakes were an ecological disaster. Commercial fishermen were for the most part "on the beach", with little left to fish, and the sport fishery had virtually disappeared. Although the total weight of the harvest equaled previous levels, it was made up almost exclusively of two species that had low public acceptance, rainbow smelt and alewife. Resource managers were faced with two alternatives: try to rehabilitate the lakes and reestablish a high-value fishery or accept the deteriorated conditions and the fishery that these had produced. Accepting a fishery based on rainbow smelt and alewife would clearly have been a surrendering of environmental stewardship. Canada and the United States embarked on an ambitious program to clean up the Great Lakes and restore a high-value fishery. These goals were to be accomplished through programs to control nutrient inputs and reverse the trend toward eutrophication, through restoration of habitats both within the lakes and in the watersheds, through control of sea lamprey (*Petromyzon marinus* L.), and through restoration of populations of large piscivores. However, even though some of these programs were successful, it proved impossible to restore the endemic fish populations. It is here that a divergence of philosophy occurred. Some jurisdictions opted for a sustainable, long-term solution and used only native species (specifically, lake trout) to redevelop the resource as a commercial fishery. Others decided that, although restoration of lake trout was desirable, rapid development of a recreational fishery was the best allocation of the resources (Tanner 2000); these jurisdictions introduced coho and chinook salmon, beginning in 1964. The fish grew well and consumed huge quantities of alewives and rainbow smelt, and an outstanding and very popular sport fishery quickly developed.

The economic benefits of this massive stocking program have been substantial in some areas, although the lack of coordination between management agencies and the fact that fish do not respect political boundaries have compromised the management plans of some jurisdictions (Christie 1968). In 1996, direct expenditures for recreational fisheries in the Great Lakes exceeded US$1.4 billion, but economists have estimated the total economic activity generated by these fisheries at several billion dollars annually (Tanner 2000). The revitalized recreational fishery has also increased environmental awareness and support for environmental protection and restoration in the Great Lakes (Dextrase and Coscarelli 1999). However, although the introduction of alien salmonids has created a sport-fishing boom, the inability of these fish to establish largely self-sustaining populations has placed a tremendous burden upon management agencies to develop and operate culture facilities to sustain the demand (Jones et al. 1993). Regier (1968) warned that to justify these expenses might require that the whole fishery be realigned and aimed specifically at these introduced species. What might initially have been conceived as the addition of a top predator to an existing system became a policy of changing the system and managing it for the benefit of the introduced terminal predator.

The recent collapse of the Lake Michigan chinook salmon fishery and reductions in catches of this species in Lake Ontario, brought about by sharp declines in the alewife prey base and invasion and establishment of yet another alien species, the zebra mussel (*Dreissena polymorpha* (Pallas)), has brought these warnings to fruition. Lake managers now find themselves having to respond to the sport fishing fraternity and their concern for the decrease in the production of salmon. One

solution that has been proposed is the relaxing of nutrient controls that were established in the 1970s to arrest the cultural eutrophication of the Great Lakes (Stockner et al. 2000). This measure, it has been postulated, would stimulate the production of phytoplankton and zooplankton and thus compensate for the production removed by zebra mussels, so that more food would be available to alewives and rainbow smelt and thus to the production of salmon. More practical, however, would be a reduction in the numbers of salmonids introduced annually by the various management agencies to ensure an adequate supply of the introduced forage upon which both introduced and native piscivorous sport fishes depend. This option does not sit well with the angling community.

To use introductions to correct imbalances created by past mistakes frequently compounds the problem, such that we end up playing out a version of the children's song "I know an old woman who swallowed a fly." Are we well intentioned but ill advised, or has the introduction of alien species become, as Courtenay and Robins (1989) asked, a common form of mismanagement or an admission of no management?

Risk Assessment and Legal Measures

Canada and the United States have recently taken major strides in looking at the issue of the deliberate introduction or transfer of alien species. Both the Canadian and US procedures encompass risk assessment and risk analysis protocols by which to evaluate and either approve or reject proposals for the introduction or transfer of aquatic organisms. Fisheries and Oceans Canada and the provincial and territorial fisheries management agencies have developed a National Code on Introductions and Transfers of Aquatic Organisms (Fisheries and Oceans Canada 2002). The purpose of this code is to establish the scientific criteria for the intentional introduction or transfer of live aquatic organisms. The criteria are designed to minimize the undesirable impacts of these activities. The federal and provincial governments intend to work cooperatively to apply this code to their respective regulations and policies dealing with intentional introductions and transfers. A code of practice on genetically modified aquatic organisms, which is now under development, will encompass a similar risk assessment procedure. These activities represent a start to addressing the issue, but additional initiatives are required to eliminate some of the other pathways by which alien species may be introduced to our waters, including the live food-fish trade, the aquarium industry, the live-bait trade, and the ballast waters of ships engaged in international trade.

In the United States, the *Nonindigenous Aquatic Nuisance Prevention and Control Act* of 1990 and the *National Invasive Species Act* of 1996 have been enacted and, although primarily designed to arrest the accidental introduction of alien species in ballast water, are being used as the legislative mandate to control intentional introductions as well. These important directives and statutes were bolstered in February 1999 by an executive order from the US president that directs all federal agencies to prevent and control introductions of invasive species in a cost-effective and environmentally sound manner.

It is anticipated that these initiatives will assist Canada in minimizing the negative impacts of introductions and transfers, as part of its responsibility to protect aquatic resources. It is also hoped that they will permit environmentally sound enhancement of the fisheries resource and development of aquaculture. However, if the outcome or impact is uncertain, the "precautionary approach" (FAO 1995, 1996) will be adopted, and priority will be given to conserving the productive capacity of the native resource.

In the past, it was common to view the introduction and transfer of alien species as a "quick fix" to many fish management problems. Despite good intentions, these introductions and transfers involved many mistakes, mistakes that have proven difficult, if not impossible, to remediate. In fact, many of the fishery management problems that we now face stem from the creation of inherently unstable fish communities through uncoordinated, poorly considered, intentional (or unintentional) introductions and transfers or through the destruction or alteration of habitat.

We are now learning that solving such problems cannot be achieved immediately but can only come through a coordinated approach among and between the various levels of government and other stakeholders. At the same time, our understanding of ecological systems is developing in ways that should help to ensure that more responsible management is the central focus of fish introductions and transfers.

As we move toward a global economy, with its increasing demand for foreign products, greater mobility, and easier accessibility to distant locations, former methods of dealing with alien species are no longer adequate. The problem is not limited to Canada or to North America but affects all parts of the world. Scientists, academics, governments, and industry leaders now recognize alien species as one of the most serious environmental threats of the 21st century (Mooney and Hobbs 2000). Only through the development of a comprehensive and coordinated effort can we hope to minimize the introduction of alien species. Our greatest asset in meeting this challenge will be an informed and involved public. Let us hope that we can learn from the past so that we will not repeat our mistakes.

References

Adams, J. 1912. Ten thousand miles through Canada. Methuen and Co., Ltd., London. 310 p.

Anderson, R.O. 1992. A case for zander: fish of the future? Pages 22–32 in D. Csanda, ed. In-Fisherman walleye guide 1992. In-Fisherman Publications, Brainerd, MN.

Balon, E.K. 1995. Origin and domestication of the carp, *Cyprinus carpio*: from Roman gourmets to the swimming flowers. Aquaculture 129:3–48.

Banff National Park. 1910. Report on the meetings of the Alberta and Saskatchewan Fisheries Commission. 25th sitting, 17 October 1910. National Park files, Banff, AB. 9 p.

Bean, T.A. 1906. *In* Discussion period of the thirty-fifth annual meeting of the American Fisheries Society. Trans. Am. Fish. Soc. 35:137.

Becker, G.C. 1983. Fishes of Wisconsin. University of Wisconsin Press, Madison, WI. 1052 p.

Bretecher, T.L.; MacDonell, D.S. 1998. A fisheries investigation of the Lower Nelson River 1997. Unpublished manuscript. North/South Consultants Inc., Winnipeg, MB. 11 p.

Cameron, J.; Abouchar, J. 1991. The precautionary principle: a fundamental principle of law and policy for the protection of the global environment. Boston Coll. Int. Comp. Law Rev. 14:1–27.

Campbell, K.B.; Derksen, A.J.; Remnant, R.A.; Stewart, K.W. 1991. First specimens of the rainbow smelt, *Osmerus mordax*, from Lake Winnipeg, Manitoba. Can. Field-Nat. 105(4):568–570.

Christie, W.J. 1968. The potential of exotic fishes in the Great Lakes. Pages 73–91 in K.H. Loftus, ed. A symposium on introductions of exotic species. Ontario Department of Lands and Forests, Research Branch, Toronto, ON. Res. Rep. No. 82.

Christie, W.J. 1974. Changes in the fish species composition of the Great Lakes. J. Fish. Res. Board Can. 31:827–854.

Courtenay, W.R., Jr.; Hensley, D.A.; Taylor, J.N.; McCann, J.A. 1984. Distribution of exotic fishes in the continental United States. Pages 41–77 in W.R. Courtenay, Jr., and J.R. Stauffer, Jr., eds. Distribution, biology and management of exotic fishes. Johns Hopkins University Press, Baltimore, MD.

Courtenay, W.R.; Robins, C.R. 1989. Fish introductions: good management, mismanagement or no management? CRC Crit. Rev. Aquat. Sci. 1(1):159–172.

Cross, F.B.; Mayden, R.L.; Stewart, J.D. 1986. Fishes in the western Mississippi drainage. Pages 363–412 in C.H. Hocutt and E.O. Wiley, eds. The zoogeography of North American freshwater fishes. John Wiley and Sons, New York, NY.

Crossman, E.J. 1968. Changes in the Canadian fish fauna. Pages 1–20 in K.H. Loftus, ed. A symposium on introductions of exotic species. Ontario Department of Lands and Forests, Research Branch, Toronto, ON. Res. Rep. No. 82.

Crossman, E.J. 1991. Introduced freshwater fishes: a review of the North American perspective with emphasis on Canada. Can. J. Fish. Aquat. Sci. 48(Suppl. 1):46–57.

DeKay, J.E. 1842. Zoology of New York, or the New York fauna. Part IV. Fishes. W. and A. White and J. Visscher, Albany, NY.

Dextrase, A.J.; Coscarelli, M.A. 1999. Intentional introductions of nonindigenous freshwater organisms in North America. Pages 61–98 in R. Claudi and J.H. Leach, eds. Nonindigenous freshwater organisms: vectors, biology, and impacts. Lewis Publishers, Boca Raton, FL.

Emery, L. 1985. Review of fish species introduced into the Great Lakes, 1819–1974. Great Lakes Fishery Commission, Ann Arbor, MI. Tech. Rep. No. 45. 31 p.

Evans, D.O.; Loftus, D.H. 1987. Colonization of inland lakes in the Great Lakes region by rainbow smelt, *Osmerus mordax*: their freshwater niche and effects on indigenous fishes. Can. J. Fish. Aquat. Sci. 44(Suppl. 2):249–266.

[FAO] Food and Agriculture Organization. 1995. Precautionary approach to capture fisheries and species introductions. Elaborated by the Technical Consultation on the Precautionary Approach to Capture Fisheries (Including Species Introductions), Lysekil, Sweden, 6–13 June 1995. FAO, Rome. FAO Technical Guidelines for Responsible Fisheries No. 2. 54 p.

[FAO] Food and Agriculture Organization. 1996. Precautionary approach to fisheries. Part 2: scientific papers. Prepared for the Technical Consultation on the Precautionary Approach to Capture Fisheries (Including Species Introductions), Lysekil, Sweden, 6–13 June 1995. FAO, Rome. FAO Fish. Tech. Pap. No. 350, Pt. 2. 210 p.

Fisheries and Oceans Canada. 2002. National Code on Introductions and Transfers of Aquatic Organisms. Ottawa, ON.

Fitzsimons, J.D.; Brown, S. 1998. Reduced egg thiamine levels in inland and Great Lakes lake trout and their relationship with diet. Pages 160–171 in G.J. McDonald, J.D. Fitzsimons, and D.C. Honeyfield, eds. Early life stage mortality syndrome in fishes of the Great Lakes and Baltic Sea. American Fisheries Society Symposium, Vol. 21. American Fisheries Society, Bethesda, MD.

Fitzsimons, J.D.; Brown, S.; Niimi, A.J. 1995. Pages 86–87 in Proceedings of the 38th Conference of the International Association for Great Lakes Research. International Association for Great Lakes Research, Ann Arbor, MI.

Franzin, W.G.; Barton, B.A.; Remnant, R.A.; Wain, D.B.; Pagel, S.J. 1994. Range extension, present and potential distribution and possible effects of rainbow smelt in Hudson Bay drainage waters of northwestern Ontario, Manitoba and Minnesota. N. Am. J. Fish. Manage. 14:65–76.

Gould, W.R. 1981. First records of the rainbow smelt (Osmeridae), sicklefin chub (Cyprinidae) and white bass (Percichthyidae) from Montana. Proc. Mont. Acad. Sci. 40:9–10.

Hanke, G.F.; Stewart, K.W. 1994. Evidence for northward dispersion of fishes in Lake Winnipeg. Pages 133–149 in Proceedings of the North Dakota Water Quality Symposium, Fargo, ND, 30–31 March 1994. Water Resources Research Institute, Fargo, ND.

Huntsman, A.G. 1944. Why did Lake Ontario salmon disappear? Trans. R. Soc. Can. Ser. 3, 38(Sect. 5):83–102.

Ji, Y.Q.; Warthesen, J.J.; Adelman, I.R. 1998. Thiamine nutrition, synthesis, and retention in relation to lake trout reproduction in the Great Lakes. Pages 62–72 in G. McDonald, J.D. Fitzsimons, and D.C. Honeyfield, eds. Early life stage mortality syndromes in fishes of the Great Lakes and Baltic Sea. American Fisheries Society Symposium, Vol. 21. American Fisheries Society, Bethesda, MD.

Jones, M.L.; Koonce, J.F.; O'Gorman, R. 1993. Sustainability of hatchery-dependent salmonine fisheries in Lake Ontario: the conflict between predator demand and prey supply. Trans. Am. Fish. Soc. 122:1002–1018.

Koelz, W. 1926. Fishing industry of the Great Lakes. Pages 553–617 in Report of the United States Commission of Fish and Fisheries for fiscal year 1925. Washington, DC.

Lazenby, D.C.; Northcote, T.G.; Fürst, M. 1986. Theory, practice and effects of *Mysis relicta* introductions into North American and Scandinavian lakes. Can. J. Fish. Aquat. Sci. 43:1277–1284.

Li, H.W.; Moyle, P.B. 1993. Management of introduced fishes. Pages 287–308 *in* C.C. Kohler and W.A. Hubert, eds. Inland fisheries management in North America. American Fisheries Society, Bethesda, MD.

Loftus, D.H.; Hulsman, P.F. 1986. Predation on larval lake whitefish (*Coregonus clupeaformis*) and lake herring (*C. artedi*) by rainbow smelt (*Osmerus mordax*). Can. J. Fish. Aquat. Sci. 43:812–818.

Mandrak, N.E.; Crossman, E.J. 1992. Postglacial dispersal of freshwater fishes into Ontario. Can. J. Zool. 70:2247–2259.

Martinez, P.J.; Bergersen, E.P. 1989. Proposed biological management of *Mysis relicta* in Colorado lakes and reservoirs. N. Am. J. Fish. Manage. 9:1–11.

Mayden, R.L.; Cross, F.B.; Gorman, O.T. 1987. Distributional history of the rainbow smelt, *Osmerus mordax* (Salmoniformes:Osmeridae) in the Mississippi River basin. Copeia 1987:1051–1054.

McCrimmon, H.R. 1971. World distribution of rainbow trout (*Salmo gairdneri*). J. Fish. Res. Board Can. 28(5):663–704.

McCrimmon, H.R.; Marshall, T.L. 1968. World distribution of brown trout, *Salmo trutta*. J. Fish. Res. Board Can. 25(12):2527–2548.

Mooney, H.A.; Hobbs, R.J., eds. 2000. Invasive species in a changing world. Island Press, Washington, DC. 457 p.

Moyle, P.B.; Li, H.W.; Barton, B.A. 1986. The Frankenstein effect: impact of introduced fishes on native fishes in North America. Pages 415–426 *in* R.H. Stroud, ed. Fish culture in fisheries management. American Fisheries Society, Bethesda, MD.

National Research Council, Committee on Biological Diversity in Marine Systems. 1995. Understanding marine biodiversity: a research agenda for the nation. National Academy Press, Washington, DC.

Northcote, T.G. 1970. Advances in management of fish in natural lakes of western North America. Pages 129–139 *in* N.G. Benson, ed. A century of fisheries in North America. Am. Fish. Soc. Spec. Publ. 7.

Pechlaner, R. 1984. Historical evidence for the introduction of Arctic charr into high-mountain lakes of the Alps by man. Pages 549–577 *in* L. Johnson and B.L. Burns, eds. Biology of the Arctic charr, Proceedings of the International Symposium on Arctic Charr, Winnipeg, MB, May 1981. University of Manitoba Press, Winnipeg, MB.

Pimentel, D.; Lach, L.; Zuniga, R.; Morrison, D. 2000. Environmental and economic costs of nonindigenous species in the United States. BioScience 50:53–65.

Rafter, G.W. 1897. Stream flow in relation to forests. Pages 501–521 *in* Second annual report of the commissioner of fisheries and game. State of New York.

Regier, H.A. 1968. The potential misuse of exotic species as introductions. Pages 92–111 *in* K.H. Loftus, ed. A symposium on introductions of exotic species. Ontario Department of Lands and Forests, Research Branch, Toronto, ON. Res. Rep. No. 82.

Remnant, R.A. 1991. An assessment of the potential impact of rainbow smelt on the fishery resources of Lake Winnipeg. M.Sc. thesis, University of Manitoba, Winnipeg, MB. 170 p.

Remnant, R.A.; Graveline, P.G.; Bretecher, R.L. 1997. Range extension of the rainbow smelt, *Osmerus mordax*, in the Hudson Bay drainage of Manitoba. Can. Field-Nat. 111(4):660–662.

Schindler, D.W.; Pacas, C. 1996. Cumulative effects of human activity on aquatic ecosystems in the Bow Valley of Banff National Park. Pages 5-1–5-59 *in* J. Green, C. Pacas, L. Cornwell, and S. Bayley, eds. Ecological outlooks project. A cumulative effects assessment and futures outlook of the Banff Bow Valley. Prepared for the Banff Bow Valley Study. Department of Canadian Heritage, Ottawa, ON.

Scott, W.B.; Crossman, E.J. 1973. Freshwater fishes of Canada. Fish. Res. Board Can. Bull. 184. 966 p.

Smith, H.M. 1892. Report on the fisheries of Lake Ontario. Bull. U.S. Fish Comm. 10(for 1890):177–215.

Smith, H.M.; Snell, M.M. 1891. Review of the fisheries of the Great Lakes in 1855. Report of the Commissioner for 1887. Part 15. United States Commission of Fish and Fisheries, Washington, DC.

Smith, S.H. 1970. Species interactions of the alewife in the Great Lakes. Trans. Am. Fish. Soc. 99(4):754–765.

Smith, S.H. 1995. Early changes in the fish community of Lake Ontario. Great Lakes Fishery Commission, Ann Arbor, MI. Tech. Rep. No. 60. 38 p.

Spencer, C.N.; McLelland, B.R.; Stanford, J.A. 1991. Shrimp stocking, salmon collapse, and eagle displacement: cascading interactions in the food web of a large aquatic ecosystem. BioScience 41:14–21.

Stockner, J.; Rydin, G.; Hyenstrand, P. 2000. Cultural oligotrophication: causes and consequences for fisheries resources. Fisheries 25(5):7–14.

Stone and Stewart Publishing. 1866. New topographic atlas of Thompkins County, New York. Philadelphia, PA. 57 p.

Suttkus, R.D.; Connor, J.V. 1979. The rainbow smelt, *Osmerus mordax*, in the lower Mississippi River near St. Francisville, Louisiana. Am. Midl. Nat. 104:394.

Tanner, H. 2000. Tragedy to triumph: establishment of the Michigan Great Lakes salmonid fishery. Fisheries 25(7S):S12–S14. Suppl.: Celebrating 50 years of the sport fishery restoration program.

Thwaites, R.G., ed. 1896. The Jesuit relations and allied documents. Travels and exploitations of the Jesuit missionaries in New France, 1610–1791. Burrows Brothers Co., Cleveland, OH. 73 vols.

Todd, T.N. 1986. Artificial propagation of coregonines in the management of the Laurentian Great Lakes. Arch. Hydrobiol. Beih. Ergeb. Limnol. 22:31–50.

Trautman, M.B. 1957. The fishes of Ohio. Ohio State University Press, Columbus, OH. 683 p.

Van Oosten, J. 1937. The dispersal of smelt, *Osmerus mordax* (Mitchill), in the Great Lakes region. Trans. Am. Fish. Soc. 66:160–170.

Wain, D.B. 1993. The effects of introduced rainbow smelt (*Osmerus mordax*) on the indigenous pelagic fish community of an oligotrophic lake. M.Sc. thesis, University of Manitoba, Winnipeg, MB. 131 p.

Warwick, W.F. 1978. Man and the Bay of Quinte, Lake Ontario: 2800 years of cultural influence, with special reference to the Chironomidae (Diptera), sedimentation and eutrophication. Ph.D. thesis, University of Manitoba, Winnipeg, MB. 290 p.

Whish, J.D. 1906. *In* Discussion period of the thirty-fifth annual meeting of the American Fisheries Society. Trans. Am. Fish. Soc. 35:137–139.

Wright, D. 1992. Zander hot line. Am. Fish. Soc. Introd. Fish Sect. Newsl. 11(3):2.

Photo with chapter title: Rainbow smelt. Courtesy of the Department of Fisheries and Oceans Photo Library, Winnipeg, MN.

Preventing the Introduction and Spread of Alien Aquatic Species in the Great Lakes

Alan Dextrase

The St. Lawrence River–Great Lakes system is one of the largest freshwater systems in the world (Figure 1). The Great Lakes span a distance of 1200 km and cover a surface area of 244 000 km^2 (Fuller et al. 1995). They account for 18% of the planet's supply of fresh surface water, which is surpassed in volume only by the polar ice caps (only 1% of the Great Lakes' freshwater supply is renewable). The waters of the Great Lakes flow eastward into the Atlantic Ocean through the St. Lawrence River. The ecosystems contained within the Great Lakes drainage basin are richly diverse and include 100 taxa and 31 ecological community types that are considered globally significant by the Nature Conservancy (Rankin and Crispin 1994). The Great Lakes basin has also been important to the history and development of the United States and Canada. Significant industrial and agricultural development has occurred within the basin: 45% of Canada's industrial capacity and 25% of Canada's agricultural capacity. More than 33 million people live within the Great Lakes basin (Fuller et al. 1995), with about 9 million residing in Canada. Great Lakes water resources provide billions of dollars of economic value and thousands of jobs to the region. For example, the Great Lakes sport and commercial fishing industry contributes US$4.5 billion annually and supports 81 000 jobs in the region (GLPANS 1998).

Aquatic ecosystems within the Great Lakes basin have changed constantly over time. Changes to the

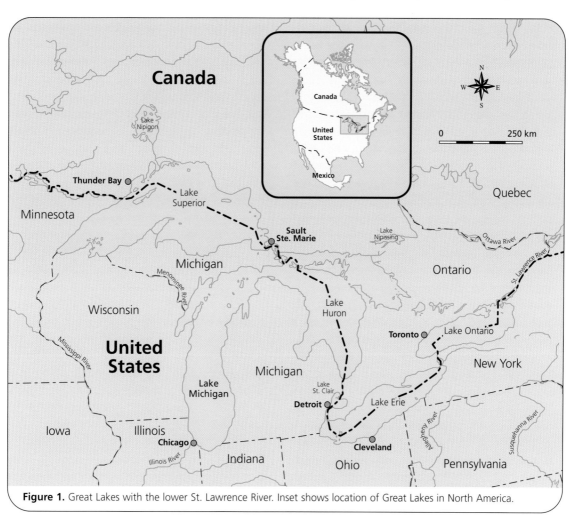

Figure 1. Great Lakes with the lower St. Lawrence River. Inset shows location of Great Lakes in North America.

flora and fauna of the basin have been dramatically accelerated over the last two centuries, driven by extensive human settlement and development. The physical and chemical make-up of the lakes has been altered due to human activities such as industrial and agricultural development, resource extraction, and urbanization. Many aquatic resources have also been selectively exploited to the point that populations of some species, and in some instances entire fish communities, have been severely degraded (Smith 1972). Although habitat and exploitation stresses are reversible to some extent if checked, the introduction of alien species has resulted in permanent additions to the flora and fauna. Alien species currently play an important and often dominant role in many Great Lakes ecosystems. Ecosystem and related management problems associated with alien species continue to grow as established species spread within the basin and new species are introduced.

The earliest known introduction of an alien species into the Great Lakes was the invasion of the sea lamprey (*Petromyzon marinus* L.) into Lake Ontario in the 1830s. The rate of alien species invasions has increased steadily over the last 150 years. The Great Lakes have been particularly vulnerable to invasion by alien species for several reasons. First, there is a large human population living within the basin. Consequently the habitats and ecological communities have been disturbed by human activities. Disturbed ecosystems are generally more vulnerable to the invasion and establishment of alien species than healthy ones (Pimm and Hyman 1987; Baltz and Moyle 1993). Second, there are several large ports on the Great Lakes that participate in a significant amount of global trade, thereby providing opportunities for frequent pathways of entry into the basin. Much of this trade has been with European countries that have a similar temperate climate to that of the Great Lakes region. More than half of the alien species in the Great Lakes have originated from Eurasia (Mills et al. 1993). Third, establishment of numerous alien species in the basin has likely facilitated the invasion of additional alien species—a phenomenon known as "invasional meltdown" (Simberloff and Von Holle 1999). Finally, the resources of the Great Lakes are managed by two countries (Canada and the United States) and, within these countries, by one province and eight states. Interjurisdictional complexities created by this arrangement have likely facilitated alien species invasions. A consistent and coordinated approach to policy and regulatory initiatives is required to manage alien species on an ecosystem basis.

At least 160 alien species have become established in the Great Lakes basin over the last 200 years (A. Ricciardi, Dalhousie University, Halifax, NS, personal communication). Undoubtedly many more species have been introduced, but have failed to establish populations. Several species that are native to the basin have also extended their ranges within the Great Lakes. Although most of the alien species found their way accidentally through various pathways, at least 11 were intentionally introduced (Mills et al. 1993). The rate of introduction has increased in the last few decades. Currently, it is estimated that one new alien aquatic species is introduced into the Great Lakes each year (Bright 1998).

About 10% of the alien species in the Great Lakes are known to have had significant effects, although the impacts of most have not been studied or pre-date investigations (Mills et al. 1993). Significant ecological impacts have been associated with species such as the zebra mussel (*Dreissena polymorpha* (Pallas)), which have fundamentally changed ecosystems in areas where they have become abundant (Nalepa et al. 1999). Alien species have also had significant economic impacts: they have caused losses to recreational and commercial fisheries (for example, sea lamprey); required costly control measures (for example, zebra mussel); and created sport fisheries (for example, Pacific salmon, *Oncorhynchus* spp.; rainbow trout, *O. mykiss* (Walbaum); and brown trout, *Salmo trutta* L.). Ricciardi and Rasmussen (1999) predict that alien aquatic species will in part contribute to the extinction of native freshwater species in North America at a rate of 4% per decade over the next century. Freshwater organisms are expected to go extinct five times faster than terrestrial organisms and three times faster than coastal marine mammals.

The large numbers of alien species in the Great Lakes and their associated ecological and economic impacts have led to substantial efforts to control alien species and prevent new introductions. These efforts have been accelerated over the last decade as the recent introduction of well-known invaders such as the zebra mussel, ruffe (*Gymnocephalus cernuus* (L.)) and round goby (*Neogobius melanostomus* (Pallas)) and the spread of purple loosestrife (*Lythrum salicaria* L.) have raised the profile of alien species issues within the Great Lakes basin.

This chapter provides an overview of efforts that have been made to combat alien species in the Great Lakes region and identifies where additional work is required. It is not intended to provide an exhaustive overview of species introductions within the Great

Lakes and their impacts (see Mills et al. 1993; Ricciardi and MacIsaac 2000), but rather to examine alien species control and prevention efforts, including ones on eradication, cooperation, and public awareness, in the basin.

Eradication of Alien Species

Eradication is the ultimate and preferred form of alien species control because it removes the problem. Although some eradication efforts have been successful in instances where alien species are confined to small areas (for example, the elimination of alien vertebrates from oceanic islands), there have been no successful eradications of alien aquatic species in the Great Lakes basin. Even though eradication has been called for in a number of instances, such as in the case of zebra mussel and ruffe, the open nature of the system in the Great Lakes basin often allows alien species to become established and widespread before they are recognized as a problem. Public opinion has also thwarted efforts to control the potential range expansion of alien species when pesticide control treatments were proposed (for example, ruffe in the Wisconsin and Michigan waters of Lake Superior). This may have discouraged other potential eradication activities. Once alien species become well established, the probability of successfully eliminating them from large, open aquatic systems such as the Great Lakes is low.

Trying to eradicate well-established, widespread alien species is like "trying to unscramble an egg" (Harty 1993). Therefore, "introductions, like extinctions, are forever" (Marsden 1993). This is not meant to imply that eradication programs should not be considered when a new alien species is introduced, but such attempts will likely be successful only if the species is confined to a small area, such as an isolated lake. Effective early detection and response programs are required to act in a timely fashion. Such responses are often not coordinated because of the lack of emergency response planning and because there are a host of environmental, organizational, societal, and political issues that must be managed (see MacDonald, this publication, p.161).

Control Programs

Control programs are generally species-specific efforts to mitigate the impacts of an alien species after it is introduced and well established. Several alien species control programs have been implemented in the Great Lakes at both the local and basin-wide levels. These programs do not attempt to eliminate the alien species from the ecosystem, but aim to lower their numbers at specific locations to lessen their harmful impacts. Control programs are motivated by a desire to restore native plant and animal communities (for example, the biological control of purple loosestrife) and commercial, recreational, and other societal benefits that are derived from them. There are three options for implementing control programs. Physical or mechanical control involves physically removing the alien species by hand or with some sort of mechanical harvesting gear such as nets. Chemical control involves the use of chemical pesticides to reduce the abundance of alien species. Biological control involves the introduction of predators or pathogens of the alien species (usually from its native range) and aims to reduce the target alien species population to a level that allows recolonization and recovery of native plants and animals.

Control programs are generally very costly and can have unwanted ecological side effects as nontarget organisms are often impacted. This is particularly true when the application of pesticides may involve human health issues (Marsden 1993). When mechanical and chemical control programs are implemented, the economic and ecological costs are recurring and cumulative. Successful biological control is particularly attractive, because biological control agents reproduce and there are no ongoing expenditures to maintain the desired level of control (see Corrigan, this publication, p. 279). However, a thorough advance screening is required to ensure that the biological control agent will not impact nontarget native species of flora and fauna. Most successful biological control programs have been directed toward alien plants and insect pests in agricultural settings (for example, control of erect prickly-pear, *Opuntia stricta* (Haw.) Haw., in Australia with the Argentine cactus moth, *Cactoblastis cactorum* (Bergroth); control of St. John's-wort, *Hypericum perforatum* L., in California with leaf beetles, *Chrysolina* spp.). There have also been many cases where biological control agents have become pests themselves (Howarth 1991). Examples of Great Lakes alien species targeted by the different types of control programs are provided below.

Physical or Mechanical Control Programs

Eurasian water-milfoil (*Myriophyllum spicatum* L.) has been the target of several mechanical control programs on inland lakes within the Great Lakes region, where it often interferes with boating, swimming, and other recreation. Mechanical harvesters have been used to provide short-term relief from this plant by keeping clogged waterways open to watercraft and swimmers, but its ability to reproduce asexually by fragmentation means there is a need for ongoing removal programs. Attempts to remove common carp (*Cyprinus carpio* L.) from the Great Lakes and to keep them out by using physical barriers are ongoing as part of several wetland rehabilitation projects (Hagen 1996). The costs and effectiveness of these programs vary, but efforts to exclude common carp from large areas tend to be labor-intensive and expensive. Great Lakes natural resource management agencies recognize the impacts of common carp, but most choose not to control them because they are so widespread.

Chemical Control Programs

The best-known control effort on the Great Lakes is the sea lamprey control program that was initiated in 1958 (GLFC 1985). The program involves the regular treatment (every three or four years) of about 300 Great Lakes tributaries with the lampricide TFM (3-trifluoromethyl-4-nitrophenol). TFM is applied to kill sea lamprey ammocoetes (larvae), which reside in streams for four to seven years before transforming into predators and entering the lakes. The program has been successful in reducing the abundance of adult sea lampreys by 90% and has allowed populations of lake trout (*Salvelinus namaycush* (Walbaum)) and other top predators to rebound. Although TFM is relatively selective for sea lamprey over other fishes, it does cause mortality in other species of native lampreys (*Ichthyomyzon* spp. and *Lampetra appendix* (DeKay)), and in some invertebrate species such as mayflies (Ephemeroptera). The sea lamprey control program costs about US$15 million per year for ongoing treatments. The Great Lakes Fishery Commission (GLFC) administers the program and is using integrated pest management to reduce the reliance on pesticides for sea lamprey control (GLFC 1992). Alternative control techniques, such as the release of sterile males, electric weirs, and velocity barriers on spawning streams, are also being used.

Herbicide applications to control nuisance aquatic plant growths have largely targeted Eurasian water-milfoil. In Canada, most of these applications are directed towards small-scale local control to allow for recreational activities (for example, swimming and boating) at specific sites, but in the United States large-scale, organized control programs have been conducted.

These programs require ongoing, expensive treatments and do not eliminate Eurasian water-milfoil.

The zebra mussel became abundant in the Great Lakes in the late 1980s and quickly clogged water intake pipes of municipal and industrial water users, affecting delivery capabilities and causing safety hazards in fire water systems (Claudi and Mackie 1994). There was an immediate need to develop control programs. Chlorine has been the chemical of choice for controlling zebra mussels in water intake pipes, as it is relatively inexpensive and effective. Despite extensive research into nonchemical means of control, chlorine is still widely used. From 1989 to 1994, zebra mussel control has cost more than US$100 million in North America (Hushak et al. 1995). Average-sized municipalities can spend about US$365 000 for zebra mussel control and monitoring, while nuclear power plants can spend up to US$2 million annually. In the United States, zebra mussel control and damages are estimated to cost US$100 million annually (Pimentel et al. 2000). Zebra mussel control programs have been limited to these industrial applications and there are no known methods for controlling this species in open waters.

Biological Control Programs

Biocontrol agents show promise as effective tools to combat the invasion of purple loosestrife in the United States and Canada. Several species of European beetles were approved for release in North America in 1992 as part of a biological control program to mitigate the harmful impacts of purple loosestrife on wetland ecosystems. Beetles released at thousands of sites across North America have successfully overwintered and established at most locations. Encouraging results are now being seen with respect to control by the beetles at many Canadian and US locations (J. Corrigan, personal communication; Skinner 1999; Lindgren, this publication, p. 259). Releases are expected to substantially reduce purple loosestrife abundance throughout most of its North American range over the next 15–20 years. Research is currently ongoing regarding the potential use of native weevils for the control of Eurasian water-milfoil (Sheldon 1997; Newman et al. 1999; Solarz and Newman 2001). Attempts to control the abundance of ruffe in the St. Louis River, which flows into the western end of Lake Superior, by enhancing the abundance of native predators, such as walleye (*Stizostedion vitreum* (Mitchill)) and northern pike (*Esox lucius* L.), through stocking and reduced bag limits have not been successful (Mayo et al. 1998).

Containment of Alien Species

While control programs attempt to mitigate the harmful impacts of alien species, containment aims to limit the geographic extent of impacts. Great Lakes management agencies generally try to prevent or slow the spread of alien species within the basin and prevent their introduction into new watersheds through public awareness campaigns and specific policies and legislation directed toward certain resource sectors (for example, recreational anglers, aquaculture industry). One of the main objectives of the Ruffe Control Program was to contain ruffe in western Lake Superior through a multifaceted program that included public awareness, legislation, ballast water guidelines, and biological control (Busiahn 1996). In 1995, ruffe were discovered in Thunder Bay on Lake Huron, at Alpena, Michigan, but it is not clear whether or not they invaded Lake Huron before the control program and ballast water guidelines were initiated. There has been no significant range expansion in the subsequent five-year period, and ruffe have not been found in any inland waters.

Prevention of Alien Species Introductions

Given the difficulty and costs associated with eradication and control programs in large open systems, preventing introductions is really the "best medicine". A proactive approach that prevents introductions of alien species can potentially save millions of dollars in impacts and control costs, eliminate harmful ecological side effects from control programs, and avoid the ecosystem problems and management uncertainty that are created when alien species become established. Alien species invasions have continued at an increasing rate because existing legislation and policies, and current levels of awareness, knowledge, and resources are inadequate to prevent new introductions from occurring (US Congress 1993). Preventing introductions is often very complicated. However, several significant steps have been made to help prevent new introductions in the Great Lakes basin, particularly in the last decade.

Alien species are introduced to the Great Lakes by a variety of pathways or vectors. The relative risks associated with these pathways are not static as they can be affected by changes in technology, modes of transportation, and market forces. Prevention efforts must focus on these pathways to be successful. Although many of these pathways are higher risk than others, it is important that all pathways be considered, as the introduction of a single alien organism from a low risk pathway may have significant ecosystem effects. A discussion of prevention efforts for these pathways in the Great Lakes basin is provided below.

Intentional Introductions

Fish-stocking programs have traditionally played a large role in fisheries management on the Great Lakes. Ten alien fish species have been intentionally introduced (Mills et al. 1993). Most of these are salmonids, which were introduced to create sportfishing opportunities. Significant sport fisheries and substantial economic benefits have been derived from these introductions. However, there are outstanding ecological concerns related to some of these introductions, and the costs of maintaining fisheries based largely on artificial propagation are high. Although there has been no new alien species introduced intentionally in the last 35 years, intensive stocking programs for many of the alien salmonids that have become naturalized in the lakes continue. Fish stocking has also played an important role in the rehabilitation efforts for native species such as lake trout and Atlantic salmon (*Salmo salar* L.).

Approving authority for stocking is at the state level in the United States and at the provincial level in Canada. Formal procedures for consultation between jurisdictions with respect to intentional introductions were introduced in 1992 by Great Lakes management agencies through the GLFC's Council of Lake Committees (GLFC 1992). A model fish disease program to prevent the introduction of alien fish diseases has also been developed for the Great Lakes basin (Hnath 1993). These processes have prevented the introduction of several alien fish species and of two serious fish diseases: viral infectious hematopoietic necrosis and viral hemorrhagic septicemia (Dochoda 1991). The United States and Canada have also recently developed generic risk assessment protocols used to evaluate risks associated with proposed introductions (RAMC 1996; ITTG 2000). The intentional introduction of biological control organisms is governed by federal approvals in the United States and Canada after the biological control agents have been properly screened.

Unauthorized intentional introductions continue to be a problem within the basin. In Ontario, unauthorized intentional introductions of bass (*Micropterus* spp.) and black crappie (*Pomoxis nigromaculatus* (Lesueur)) have been made into numerous water bodies, presumably to create and enhance fishing opportunities (Krishka et al. 1996). Although enforcement is generally ineffective at preventing these introductions, increasing the awareness of the possible consequences may help to deter such actions.

Ballast Water

Transport of alien organisms in ballast water is a global environmental problem (Carlton and Geller 1993) that has attracted the attention of the International Maritime Organization (IMO) and the International Council for the Exploration of the Sea (ICES). More than 30 alien species have been introduced to the Great Lakes through ballast water, including such well-known species as the zebra mussel, spiny water flea (*Bythotrephes cederstroemi* Schodler), ruffe, and round goby (see Wiley and Claudi, this publication, p. 233). As such, ballast water has been one of the most important pathways for alien species invasions in the Great Lakes since the St. Lawrence Seaway was enlarged in 1959 (Mills et al. 1993). Ballast water has also been a pathway for the movement of alien organisms within the Great Lakes.

In 1989, Canada introduced voluntary guidelines requesting ships to exchange fresh water ballast with salt water before entering the St. Lawrence Seaway. This would theoretically displace and perhaps kill freshwater organisms within the ballast holds and reduce the risk of new introductions. The United States introduced parallel voluntary guidelines in 1990. In 1993, the United States introduced legislation making mid-ocean ballast water exchange mandatory for all vessels operating outside the 200-nautical-mile Exclusive Economic Zone entering the Great Lakes, regardless of whether their destination port was Canadian or American. Binders, brochures, and videotapes to help encourage compliance and cooperation with the shipping industry have accompanied these guidelines and legislation.

Despite the current ballast water exchange regulations and a high rate of compliance, the risk of new introductions is still significant. Most vessels (about 80%) entering the Great Lakes carry no ballast on board (NOBOB); that is, they are fully loaded with cargo. They are therefore not subject to the legislation (Wiley and Claudi 1999). However, the sediments and residual water in the ballast tanks of NOBOB vessels often contain viable organisms that can be introduced into the Great Lakes. The recent findings of individual Chinese mitten crabs (*Eriocheir sinensis* H. Milne Edwards) and European flounders (*Platichthys flesus* (L.)) in the Great Lakes, along with the establishment of several new alien species—

fish hook water flea (*Cercopagis pengoi* (Ostroumov)), New Zealand mud snail (*Potamopyrgus antipodarum* J.E. Gray), and an alien amphipod (*Echinogammarus ischnus* (Stebbing))—suggest that the current regime of legislation and voluntary guidelines is inadequate to protect the Great Lakes against future ballast water invasions. Lack of legislation to effectively address all issues related to the introduction of alien species through ballast water has led to the recent introduction of bills to regulate ballast water in the state of Michigan and the province of Ontario. Although a consistent, binational legislative and policy approach is needed to effectively manage ballast water in the Great Lakes, these bills have served to raise awareness of the importance of expediently addressing the issue.

Most agree that to kill alien organisms ballast water needs to be treated either while onboard or after it has been pumped into an onshore treatment facility. Potential treatment measures include physical methods (for example, filtration, ultraviolet light, and heat) and chemical treatments. Although scientists and shipping industry representatives have developed and ranked lists of possible treatment technologies, there have been few tests of their practicality or effectiveness (see Wiley and Claudi, this publication, p. 233). These experiments are very expensive and have yet to demonstrate effective, commercially practical applications (Wiley and Claudi 1999). Many more research projects and millions of dollars will likely be required before practical treatment technologies are available. Significant global interest should help to find a solution to this problem. The ballast water problem is a good example of an alien species issue that is difficult to resolve. Despite substantial cooperative efforts, the Great Lakes and much of the world's coastlines remain vulnerable to alien species invasions through this pathway.

Recreational Boating

Boaters, anglers, and other recreational water users represent a high risk pathway for the spread of aquatic alien species. Many aquatic species such as the zebra mussel can survive for several days to weeks on boat hulls after removal from the water. In addition to direct attachment to boat hulls, live alien species may be transported in live wells, and alien plant species (and attached organisms) can be transported when they become entangled on propellers and boat trailers. When these boats are moved to a new body of water, alien species can easily be introduced. Recreational boaters are an important secondary invasion pathway for alien species that were originally introduced to the region through other pathways (for example, ballast water). The Great Lakes Panel on Aquatic Nuisance Species has developed standardized messages to boaters and other recreational water users. The effectiveness of these public awareness efforts can be difficult to assess, but a recent survey demonstrated that boaters in areas with aggressive alien-species public-awareness campaigns were more likely to change their behavior to prevent the spread of alien species than were boaters in areas with less active campaigns (Gunderson 1994). The spread of alien species to water bodies where overland transport of boats is required has been much slower than to interconnected water bodies (Krishka et al. 1996).

Efforts to stop the spread of alien species are voluntary in most jurisdictions on the Great Lakes. In Minnesota, however, legislation prohibits the overland transport of boats with aquatic invasive species attached to them (MDNR 1995). Intensive efforts to prevent zebra mussels from colonizing the Saint Croix River (Minnesota and Wisconsin in the Mississippi basin) and harming native unionid mussels included legislation, public outreach, boat inspections, access management, research, and monitoring. For nearly a decade, these efforts successfully protected the river by slowing the zebra mussel invasion upstream. In 2000, the lower Saint Croix below Hudson, Wisconsin, became infested (Karns 2000). Although preventing the spread of alien species by boaters and other recreational water users through public awareness programs is not absolutely effective, these efforts do substantially reduce risks. Vigilance in this area should be maintained to help slow the spread of alien species and prevent the infestation of new watersheds.

Canals

The Great Lakes system of canals, locks, and dams used for shipping and recreational boating provide artificial connections between watersheds or make existing connections navigable. Canals provide a constant two-way route for invasions, particularly for vagile species such as fish. At least 12 species have invaded the Great Lakes in part through these canal systems (Fago 1993; Mills et al. 1993), and several others have invaded new watersheds from the Great Lakes. For example, after being introduced to the Great Lakes, zebra mussels gained access to the Mississippi River drainage basin through the Chicago Shipping Canal at the south end of Lake Michigan (O'Neill and Dextrase 1994). Short of converting canals to terrestrial habitats, it is difficult

to address these invasion routes. At least one effort is being planned to prevent the spread of alien aquatic species along contiguous waterways. An electrical barrier is currently being installed as a demonstration project in the Chicago Shipping Canal to attempt to prevent the dispersal of alien species between Lake Michigan and the Mississippi River. This barrier will consist of two electrode installations 1.6 km apart that will be installed in the floor and walls of the canal channel. When operational, the electrodes will produce an electric field in the water that repels fish.

Horticulture

Escape of cultivated plants has been the major pathway for the establishment of alien vascular plants in the Great Lakes basin. Although many of these species persist only in disturbed areas, several have caused ecosystem problems (for example, purple loosestrife; European frog-bit, *Hydrocharis morsus-ranae* L.; glossy buckthorn, *Rhamnus frangula* L. = *Frangula alnus* Mill.). Some jurisdictions prohibit the possession and sale of plants that are deemed to be noxious weeds, but most horticultural plants are largely unregulated and there is a large amount of trade through garden centers. This trade has been assisted through the Internet, which now offers consumers the ability to order a myriad of horticultural varieties online. When problems have been identified, cooperation by the horticultural industry has generally been good, with some species being voluntary removed from sale (for example, purple loosestrife). However, there are many lower profile species that have caused or have the potential to cause ecosystem problems (for example, flowering-rush, *Butomus umbellatus* L.). Increased public awareness efforts and discussions with the horticultural and landscaping industry are required in this area.

Live Bait Use

Use of live bait has long been recognized as a potential pathway for the introduction of alien species. Several alien species of fish and one mollusk are suspected of having been introduced to the Great Lakes basin through this practice (Mills et al. 1993), and many native species have undoubtedly extended their ranges within the basin the same way (Litvak and Mandrak 1993). Use of live bait also has the potential to spread alien species to inland waters, particularly species such as the zebra mussel with microscopic life stages that may be present in water used for holding bait fish (Goodchild 1999). Despite the associated risks, regulations with respect to live bait in the Great Lakes are relatively liberal. A large industry (for example, estimated at US$250 million per year in six midwestern states [Meronek et al. 1995]) has developed around the harvest and sale of live bait. Limited restrictions on the collection and use of live bait have been put in place in specific areas to prevent introductions (for example, the ban of live bait harvest in Lake Superior waters with ruffe infestations), but widespread use is generally allowed. Although most jurisdictions prohibit the import and release of live bait, studies in Ontario have indicated that almost 50% of anglers released their unused bait into the waters in which they were fishing at the end of their fishing trips (Litvak and Mandrak 1993; A. Dextrase, Ontario Ministry of Natural Resources, and B. MacKay, Ontario Federation of Anglers and Hunters, Peterborough, ON, unpublished data).

Increased public awareness efforts, in collaboration with the bait industry and retail shops, are required to reduce the risk of alien species introductions associated with the use of live bait. Resource management agencies need to work with the bait industry to establish guidelines (for example, best management practices) to reduce the risk of spreading alien species through the harvest and sale of bait. Although some efforts have been made in these areas, it may also be necessary to further restrict the transport, use, and harvest of live bait within the basin.

Aquaculture

Escape of fish and the transfer of diseases associated with aquaculture operations have long been of concern in the Great Lakes region. Although no alien fish species have become established in the Great Lakes from aquaculture activities, individual specimens of the grass carp (*Ctenopharyngodon idella* (Valenciennes)), bighead carp (*Hypophthalmichthys nobilis* (Richardson)), and striped bass (*Morone saxatilis* (Walbaum)) collected in recent years from the lower Great Lakes may have originated from aquaculture operations in the United States. Risk of escape is relatively higher from cage culture operations and outdoor ponds than enclosed recirculating systems. Two alien fish pathogens are thought to have been introduced with fish imported for culture purposes: furunculosis and whirling disease (Mills et al. 1993). Management of aquaculture within the basin has been subject to different approaches in different jurisdictions, and agricultural and resource management agencies are often involved. Concerns about the incidental spread of alien species, such as the zebra mussel, when distributing live aquaculture products have led to the development of awareness programs and guidelines for aquaculture operators.

The aquaculture industry is currently in a growth period with a trend towards diversification of species and products. In Ontario, this has resulted in an expanded list of species eligible for culture, but individual facilities are subject to ecological risk analyses to determine which species may be safely raised in particular locations. Cooperation is required between all agencies and the aquaculture industry in the development of a responsible approach to aquaculture in the Great Lakes.

Although no aquatic genetically modified organisms or GMOs have been introduced intentionally or accidentally into the Great Lakes basin, there is significant concern surrounding their use, as well as a growing interest in their possible benefits for aquaculture. In Canada, a federal policy on the use of genetically modified aquatic organisms is currently under development. The policy will address permitted uses and containment measures. Use of genetically modified organisms in Canada is broadly regulated by the *Canadian Environmental Protection Act*. In the United States, the development and release of genetically modified organisms are regulated under a coordinated federal framework; however, the transport and release of genetically modified fish are not specifically addressed by the framework (US Congress 1993). Release of genetically modified fish is controlled by states and provinces (in the same way that the release of other alien species are controlled), but there are no laws that specifically relate to their release. Proactive legislation and policies related to the use and release of genetically modified organisms are required to keep pace with developments in this area.

Live Food Fish

The importation of live fish for sale in markets and restaurants has been identified as a potential source of fish introductions in Canada. Several alien species, such as tilapias (*Tilapia* spp.), blue tilapias (*Oreochromis* spp.), and Asian carps (grass carp; silver carp, *Hypophthalmichthys molitrix* (Valenciennes); and bighead carp), are imported live in large numbers from aquaculture facilities in the southern United States for sale in large cities within the basin. This is a growing industry in Canada. Concerns center around the possibility of people buying and liberating live fish, or for the transport trucks shipping the fish to release them accidentally or intentionally into some waterway. An additional concern is that people will use this mechanism to acquire live fish that may be prohibited from import for other purposes. The disposal of shipping water and packing materials also has the potential to result in the introduction of plants, invertebrates, and fish pathogens. There are several examples of marine plants and invertebrates that have been introduced to North American coastlines as by-products of the trade (Olsen and Linen 1998). The import and sale of live fish for food is largely unregulated in much of Canada.

Aquarium Trade

Escape of aquarium fish from breeding facilities and from aquarium releases has been a large problem in the southern United States. At least 27 alien fish species associated with the aquarium trade have been introduced to the United States (US Congress 1993). Most species in the aquarium trade are tropical and pose little ecological threat to the temperate waters of the Great Lakes. However, as many as 12 alien species may have been introduced into the Great Lakes in part through this pathway (Mills et al. 1993), and several temperate species are sold in the aquarium trade. In addition to the species that have become established, each year there are records of species such as piranha (*Pygocentrus* spp.), pacu (*Colossoma* spp.), oscar (*Astronotus ocellatus* (Agassiz)), and red-eared slider (*Trachemys scripta elegans* (Wied-Neuwied), a turtle) from the Great Lakes basin, indicating that the practice of releasing aquarium pets is ongoing and common.

Aquarium releases normally occur when pets outgrow their tanks or are no longer wanted. Owners then release them into a nearby pond or river as an "act of kindness". The likelihood of invertebrates and plants becoming established through this practice is probably greater than it is for fishes. Some plant and invertebrate species can establish populations with a minimal number of founding individuals. The recent introduction of the alien aquatic plant, fanwort (*Cabomba caroliniana* A. Gray) in an Ontario lake, was most likely the result of an aquarium introduction (MacDonald, this publication, p. 161). An additional risk in this area is the growing popularity of outdoor ornamental ponds, which is accompanied by the trade in new species of aquatic plants as well as fish and amphibians.

Importation of aquarium and/or pond organisms is largely unregulated in the United States and Canada. Direct release into the environment is illegal in most jurisdictions, but there is little control over the fate of these organisms once they are in the hands of the hobbyist. Awareness efforts directed to the hobbyist and retail sector in the Great Lakes basin have been wanting, but several partners in Ontario have recently initiated outreach efforts. A Fish Rescue Program has been established, which consists of a network of contacts that will help to find homes for unwanted aquarium pets. Hobbyists can access the network through a toll-free hotline. Fact sheets and flyers are also being developed to get the message out through pet stores.

Alien Species Used in Research

To understand the impacts of alien species on ecosystems, it is often necessary to conduct experiments with live organisms in the laboratory. This presents the possibility of unintentional introduction and dispersal of alien species. A generic protocol has been established for research projects conducted under the 1990 *Nonindigenous Aquatic Nuisance Prevention and Control Act*[1] in the United States, which establishes a process and provides decision criteria for evaluating the risks associated with individual projects (ANSTF 1994). A specific containment protocol has also been developed for zebra mussel research projects under this act (ANSTF 1993). Projects funded by public agencies are required to follow these protocols. The application of such protocols to a broader range of alien species research projects should probably be considered in the United States and Canada.

Public Awareness Efforts

Public awareness is essential in preventing new introductions and slowing the spread of established alien species. It is also the foundation on which to create and maintain support for control programs and other initiatives. Significant resources in the Great Lakes have been directed towards increasing public awareness of alien species, the threats that they pose, and precautions and measures that can be taken to prevent their spread. A survey of Great Lakes management agencies conducted in 1996 revealed that four agencies spent between US$50 000 and US$200 000 per year on awareness programs (A. Dextrase, unpublished data). Messages to the public have been delivered in the form of numerous brochures, fact sheets, news releases, billboards, advertising (radio, television, and newspaper), public service announcements, and World Wide Web home pages that have reached millions of people.

---

1 Amended and reauthorized in 1996 as the *National Invasive Species Act*.

The Great Lakes Sea Grant Network[2] in the United States has been particularly effective with outreach, education, and communication activities. Under this network each Great Lakes state has a program that is, in part, dedicated to addressing alien invasive species research and outreach issues. The Ontario Federation of Anglers and Hunters and the Ontario Ministry of Natural Resources have successfully established an Invading Species Awareness Program in the province. The program includes a toll-free Invading Species Hotline (which the public can call to get information and report sightings), a volunteer monitoring program, a demonstration boat wash program, and several outreach materials and activities. This program contacts more than 100 000 people in Ontario each year. Awareness efforts have also reached the classroom, with the creation of alien species curriculum materials and youth education traveling trunk resources designed for use by educators. The plethora of public awareness materials from numerous management agencies prompted the Great Lakes Panel on Aquatic Nuisance Species to develop an Information/Education Strategy to coordinate alien species awareness efforts in the Great Lakes basin. An inventory and description of available public awareness/education materials is maintained by the panel and is available online (http://www.glc.org/ans/ans-ie/ httoc.html).

Recent boater surveys in the United States and Ontario have demonstrated that effective awareness programs can reduce the risk of spreading alien species (Gunderson 1994; A. Dextrase and B. MacKay, unpublished data). Survey respondents in Ontario identified the media (newspapers, television, and magazines) as their most important source of information on alien species (A. Dextrase and B. MacKay, unpublished data). The increased popularity of the Internet has made this a valuable tool for delivering alien species outreach messages and information to the public. However, the Internet is also facilitating trade in live plants and animals that can be shipped around the world in a matter of days, simply by clicking a mouse.

Awareness programs for the general public and specific resource user groups are fundamental to alien species control and prevention efforts; however, politicians and decision makers must also be made aware of alien species issues so that they can support alien

species programs. A brochure recently produced by the Great Lakes Panel was specifically designed to increase the awareness levels of politicians and senior government officials as well as the media.

Partnerships and Cooperation

Cooperative efforts between resource management agencies, the research community, nongovernmental organizations, industry, and the general public have been extremely important in alien species prevention and control efforts in the Great Lakes region. Collaborative efforts have allowed agencies to prioritize issues, leverage funding, avoid duplication of effort, and save limited resources. Many existing programs and success stories would not have been possible without this cooperation.

Some of these partnerships have been institutionalized. For example, the Great Lakes Fishery Commission was established in 1955 with Canadian and US representatives in response to the sea lamprey invasion, but has evolved into an interjurisdictional body that develops consensus on Great Lakes fisheries management and research objectives, including alien species issues (Dochoda 1991). The Great Lakes Panel on Aquatic Nuisance Species was formed in 1991 under the US *Nonindigenous Aquatic Nuisance Prevention and Control Act* to provide a forum for the coordination of policy issues and control, management, awareness, and research activities related to alien species within the Great Lakes region. The panel has representatives from Canadian and US government agencies, tribal agencies, the US Great Lakes Sea Grant Network, universities, industry, and nongovernment organizations. This organization has worked collectively to develop several policy positions, model legislation, and a model plan of aquatic alien species management for use by Great Lakes jurisdictions and beyond. The panel also recently developed a Great Lakes Action Plan for the Prevention and Control of Nonindigenous Aquatic Nuisance Species that has been endorsed by provincial premiers and state governors with Great Lakes jurisdictions.

Other less formalized partnerships have been equally effective. Cooperative efforts between government agencies, the research community, and industry have been important to the development of ballast water programs and zebra mussel control methods. Nongovernmental organizations, such as angler and hunter groups and cottage associations, have become involved with disseminating information and monitoring

---

2 Sea Grant is a partnership between US universities and the National Oceanic and Atmospheric Administration formed in 1966; it focuses on coastal, ocean, and Great Lakes research and education.

for alien species. Several organizations have also collaborated on, or sponsored production of, recent public awareness products. These collaborative efforts have resulted in the production of awareness products with consistent messages across several jurisdictions. The shipping, aquaculture, bait, nursery, and aquarium industries are to varying degrees assisting in awareness efforts.

Partnerships and cooperation will continue to play an important role in managing alien species issues on the Great Lakes. The complex nature of many alien species problems often necessitates the involvement of diverse interests, and by pooling resources a collective approach will prove more effective.

Summary

Although there are areas where additional efforts are required to help prevent and control alien species introductions in the Great Lakes basin, significant progress has been made on several fronts. The following points summarize experiences with the management of alien species issues in the Great Lakes basin and are probably applicable to the management of alien species in other large aquatic systems.

Large human populations, significant global trade, and aquatic ecosystems that have been severely disturbed by human actions are a recipe for alien species invasions. The establishment of alien species may facilitate additional invasions. Management efforts directed at maintaining healthy ecosystems and rehabilitating degraded systems may decrease the risk of invasions by some alien species and reduce the impact of alien species that become established.

Eradication of alien species from large open aquatic systems is virtually impossible once they have become established. Efforts to control alien species are usually expensive, can have undesirable effects on non-target organisms, and must be repeatedly applied to be effective. Preventing introductions before they occur is therefore the "best medicine". Successful prevention efforts can avoid the ecosystem impacts and management uncertainty often associated with alien species and eliminate the need for costly control programs.

Preventing the introduction of alien species is difficult to accomplish. Alien species are introduced by a variety of pathways that often require complex solutions. Developing awareness at all levels is extremely important to the success of alien species prevention and control programs. Partnerships and cooperation

between government agencies, the research community, industry, and nongovernmental agencies are essential in addressing alien species issues. Collaboration provides for consistent messaging and for program prioritization, avoids duplication, leverages funding, and saves money.

References

[ANSTF] Aquatic Nuisance Species Task Force. 1993. Zebra mussel-specific containment protocols. Washington, DC. 45 p + app.

[ANSTF] Aquatic Nuisance Species Task Force. 1994. Protocol for evaluating research proposals concerning nonindigenous aquatic species. Washington, DC. 20 p.

Baltz, D.M.; Moyle, P.B. 1993. Invasion resistance to introduced species by a native assemblage of California stream fishes. Ecol. Appl. 3:246–255.

Bright, C. 1998. Life out of bounds: bioinvasion in a borderless world. W.W. Norton and Company, New York, NY. 286 p.

Busiahn, T.R. 1996. Ruffe control program. Submitted to the Aquatic Nuisance Species Task Force by the Ruffe Control Committee, 21 Oct. 1996. Unpublished report. Available from the Ashland Fishery Resources Office, US Fish and Wildlife Service, Ashland, WI 54806.

Carlton, J.T.; Geller, J.B. 1993. Ecological roulette: the global transport of nonindigenous marine organisms. Science 261:78–82.

Claudi, R.; Mackie, G.L. 1994. Practical manual for zebra mussel monitoring and control. CRC Press, Boca Raton, FL. 227 p.

Dochoda, M.R. 1991. Meeting the challenge of exotics in the Great Lakes: the role of an international commission. Can. J. Fish. Aquat. Sci. 48 (Suppl. 1):171–176.

Fago, D. 1993. Skipjack herring, *Alosa chrysochloris*, expanding its range into the Great Lakes. Can. Field-Nat. 107:352–353.

Fuller, K; Shear, H.; Wittig, J. Eds. 1995. The Great Lakes: an environmental atlas and resource book. 3rd ed. Government of Canada, Toronto, ON/ United States Environmental Protection Agency, Chicago, IL. 46 p.

[GLFC] Great Lakes Fishery Commission. 1985. TFM (3-trifluoromethyl-4-nitrophenol) vs. the sea lamprey: a generation later. Great Lakes Fish. Com. Spec. Pub. 85–6. 17 p.

[GLFC] Great Lakes Fishery Commission. 1992. Strategic vision of the Great Lakes Fishery Commission for the decade of the 1990s. Ann Arbor, MI. 40 p.

[GLPANS] Great Lakes Panel on Aquatic Nuisance Species. 1998. Biological invasions: how aquatic nuisance species are entering North American waters, the harm they cause and what can be done to solve the problem. Ann Arbor, MI. 8 p.

Goodchild, C.D. 1999. Ecological impacts of introductions associated with the use of live bait. Pages 181–202 in R. Claudi and J.H. Leach, eds. Nonindigenous freshwater organisms: vectors, biology, and impacts. CRC Press, Boca Raton, FL.

Gunderson, J. 1994. Exotic species and freshwater boating survey: results and technical report. Minnesota Sea Grant, Duluth, MN. 61 p.

Hagen, A. 1996. Carp control techniques for aquatic plant management. Great Lakes Cleanup Fund Fact Sheet. Environment Canada, Burlington, ON. 10 p.

Harty, F.M. 1993. How Illinois kicked the exotic habit. Pages 195–210 in N.N. McKnight, ed. Biological pollution: the control and impact of invasive exotic species. Indiana Academy of Science, Indianapolis, IN.

Hnath, J.G., ed. 1993. Great Lakes fish disease control policy and model program. Great Lakes Fish. Comm. Spec. Pub. 93–1:1–38.

Howarth, F.G. 1991. Environmental impacts of classical biological control. Annu. Rev. Entomol. 36:485–509.

Hushak, L.; Deng, Y.; Bielen, M. 1995. Water user expenditures on zebra mussel monitoring and control. Ohio Sea Grant, Columbus, OH. 2 p.

[ITTG] Introductions and Transfers Task Group. 2000. National code on introductions and transfers of aquatic organisms. Draft policy. Unpublished report. Available from Aquaculture and Oceans Science Branch, Fisheries and Oceans Canada, Ottawa, ON K1A 0E4. 52 p.

Karns, B. 2000. Zebra mussel response plan: final report, 22 December 2000. Saint Croix National Scenic River, National Parks Service, Saint Croix Falls, WI. 11 p.

Krishka, B.A.; Cholmondeley, R.F.; Dextrase, A.J.; Colby, P.J. 1996. Impacts of introductions and removals in Ontario percid communities. Percid Community Synthesis, Introductions and Removals Working Group, Ontario Ministry of Natural Resources, Peterborough, ON. 111 p.

Litvak, M.K.; Mandrak, N.E. 1993. Ecology of freshwater baitfish use in Canada and the United States. Fisheries 18(12):6–13.

Marsden, J.E. 1993. Responding to aquatic pest species: control or management? Fisheries 18(1):4–5.

Mayo, K.R.; Selgeby, J.H.; McDonald, M.E. 1998. A bioenergetics modeling evaluation of top-down control of ruffe in the St. Louis River, western Lake Superior. J. Great Lakes Res. 24:329–342.

[MDNR] Minnesota Department of Natural Resources. 1995. Ecologically harmful exotic aquatic plant and wild animal species in Minnesota: annual report 1995. St. Paul, MN. 98 p.

Meronek, T.G.; Copes, F.A.; Coble, D.W. 1995. A summary of bait regulations in the north central United States. Fisheries 20(11):16–23.

Mills, E.L.; Leach, J.H.; Carlton, J.T.; Secor, C.L. 1993. Exotic species in the Great Lakes: a history of biotic crises and anthropogenic introductions. J. Great Lakes Res. 19:1–54.

Nalepa, T.F.; Fahnenstiel, G.L.; Johengen, T.H. 1999. Impacts of the zebra mussel (Dreissena polymorpha) on water quality: a case study in Saginaw Bay, Lake Huron. Pages 255–271 in R. Claudi and J.H. Leach, eds. Nonindigenous freshwater organisms: vectors, biology, and impacts. CRC Press, Boca Raton, FL.

Newman, R.M.; Ragsdale, D.W.; Biesboer, D.D. 1999. Factors influencing the control of Eurasian watermilfoil with native or naturalised insects. Completion Report to the Minnesota Department of Natural Resources, Ecological Services. St. Paul, MN. 55 p.

Olsen, A.; Linen, E. 1998. Exotic species and the live aquatics industry. Pages 155–161 in B. Paust and J.B. Peters, eds. Marketing and shipping live aquatic products. Proceedings of a conference, 13–15 October 1996, Seattle, WA. Northeast Regional Agricultural Engineering Service, Ithaca, NY.

O'Neill, C.R., Jr; Dextrase, A.J. 1994. The introduction and spread of the zebra mussel in North America. Pages 433–446 in Proceedings of the 4th International Zebra Mussel Conference. Wisconsin Sea Grant Institute, Madison, WI.

Pimentel, D; Lach, L.; Zuniga, R.; Morrison, D. 2000. Environmental and economic costs of nonindigenous species in the United States. BioScience 50:53–65.

Pimm, S.L.; Hyman, J.B. 1987. Ecological stability in the context of multispecies fisheries. Can. J. Fish. Aquat. Sci. 44(Suppl. 2):84–94.

[RAMC] Risk Assessment and Management Committee. 1996. Generic nonindigenous aquatic organisms risk analysis review process. Risk Assessment and Management Committee, Aquatic Nuisance Species Task Force, Washington, DC. 33 p.

Rankin, D.; Crispin, S. 1994. The conservation of biological diversity in the Great Lakes ecosystem: issues and opportunities. The Nature Conservancy Great Lakes Program, Chicago, IL. 118 p.

Ricciardi, A.; MacIsaac, H. 2000. Recent mass invasion of the North American Great Lakes by Ponto-Caspian species. Trends Ecol. Evol. 15:62–65.

Ricciardi, A.; Rasmussen, J. B. 1999. Extinction rates of North American freshwater fauna. Conserv. Biol. 13:1220–1222.

Sheldon, S.P. 1997. Investigations on the potential use of an aquatic weevil to control Eurasian watermilfoil. Lake Reservoir Manag. 13:79–88.

Simberloff, D.; Von Holle, B. 1999. Positive interactions of nonindigenous species: invasional meltdown? Biol. Invasions 1:21–32.

Skinner, L. 1999. Biological control of purple loosestrife in North America [abstract]. Page 93 in Proceedings of the 9th International Zebra Mussel and Aquatic Nuisance Species Conference, 26–30 April 1999, Duluth, MN. The Professional Edge, Pembroke, ON.

Smith, S.H. 1972. The future of salmonid communities in the Laurentian Great Lakes. J. Fish. Res. Board Can. 19:951–957.

Solarz, S.L.; Newman, R.M. 2001. Variation in host-plant preference and performance by the milfoil weevil, *Euhrychiopsis lecontei* Dietz, exposed to native and exotic watermilfoils Oecologia 126:66–75.

US Congress, Office of Technology Assessment. 1993. Harmful non-indigenous species in the United States. OTA-F-565. Government Printing Office, Washington, DC. 391 p.

Wiley, C.J.; Claudi, R. 1999. The role of ships as a vector for nonindigenous freshwater organisms, with focus on Great Lakes. Pages 203–214 in R. Claudi and J.H. Leach, eds. Nonindigenous freshwater organisms: vectors, biology, and impacts. CRC Press, Boca Raton, FL.

Photo with chapter title: Sea lamprey on a lake trout. Photo courtesy Great Lakes Fishery Commission, Ann Arbor, MI.

Alien Species Transported in Ships' Ballast Water: From Known Impact to Regulations

Christopher J. Wiley and Renata Claudi

For centuries, ships have been the number one agent of international commerce, and they continue in this role to this day. Ships, as well as the cargo they carry, have been identified as one of the primary pathways by which alien species reach new ecosystems worldwide. Alien species have been transported on hulls, clinging to anchor chains, in cargo areas, with ships' crews and passengers, and in ballast. Of all the possible ways by which ships may help transfer alien species, ballast, and specifically ballast water, has attracted the most attention.

Ships are equipped with ballast tanks that can be filled with water to reduce their buoyancy and increase stability when needed. The water pumped into ballast tanks can contain large numbers of living organisms, which are then transported by the ship to another destination, sometimes on another continent. Ballast water is discharged from the tanks when ships are being loaded with cargo. This also means discharging the living organisms. The impact this has will depend on the origin of the organisms and the location of the point of discharge. Carlton et al. (1995) estimate that over 3000 species a day are transported to harbors and ports of the world in the ballast tanks of the current deep-sea fleet. The volume of ballast water discharged is enormous. Between June and September 1999, the inner Vancouver Harbour received about 4.9 million tonnes of ballast water (Vancouver Port Authority, unpublished data). Undoubtedly there were many alien species present in this volume of water.

In the early days of shipping, when solid ballast was used, a number of terrestrial plants, insects, and snails were introduced into port cities everywhere (Mills et al. 1993). According to G.G.E. Scudder (University of British Columbia, personal communication) many ground-dwelling bugs, such as the seed bugs, were introduced in solid ballast on both the east and west coasts of Canada.

In the 1840s, solid ballast began to be replaced by water. In 1882, the first ship built with an iron hull and carrying water for ballast was put in service on the Great Lakes (Wiley and Claudi 1999). With the ever-increasing size and number of ships, ballast water soon became one of the main transfer mechanisms for alien aquatic species both to coastal cities and on the Great Lakes.

Further, ships and recreational boats aid in the dispersal of alien aquatic species once they arrive on the North American continent. In many cases, live organisms, ranging from zebra mussels to alien water plants, have been found on the hulls of recreational boats, barges, and commercial ships moving among the different water bodies of the eastern seaboard.

This chapter summarizes the contribution of ballast water discharge as a means of alien species introduction and describes the control measures Canada has adopted to address this problem. It then identifies the need for future measures to further decrease the risks of alien species introduction.

Impact of Ballast Water Discharge on Canadian Aquatic Ecosystems

Canada is vulnerable to alien invasions mediated by ships on the Pacific and Atlantic coasts, in the Arctic, and in the Great Lakes, which are accessible through the St. Lawrence Seaway. However, it is in the Great Lakes region that ballast water has received the most attention as a means of introducing alien aquatic species. There were numerous warnings about the possible human-assisted dispersal of mollusks into new areas, including the ballast water pathway (Kew 1893; Johnson 1921; Sinclair 1964). By the 1980s, the large number of ballast water introductions to the Great Lakes had caused sufficient concern to warrant a study. Howarth (1981) was commissioned to produce a report by Environment Canada's Environmental Protection Branch on this issue.

Until the 1986 invasion of zebra mussel (*Dreissena polymorpha* (Pallas)), there was no general understanding that alien aquatic invasive species could be not only a huge environmental problem but also an economic headache. Once introduced, the zebra mussels quickly expanded their range. This expansion was assisted by the hulls of commercial and recreational boats and by the more than 50 million tonnes of ballast water transported annually by the domestic Great Lakes fleet. Zebra mussels are now present throughout the eastern seaboard, to the mouth of the Mississippi River at the Gulf of Mexico.

The zebra mussel is not the only invader of the Great Lakes. At least 163 species have been introduced into the Great Lakes–St. Lawrence River basin during the past two centuries (de Lafontaine and Costan, this publication, p. 73), many of them unintentionally. Although there is some dispute about the actual number that could be attributed to ballast water, the best estimate is that about a third of the unintentional introductions are the result of ballast water discharge.

The presence and rate of introduction of alien aquatic species into the Great Lakes are comparatively well known, based on extensive scientific research and relatively intensive monitoring efforts (Mills et al. 1993; Locke et al.1993; Leach 1995; de Lafontaine and Costan, this publication, p. 73). Much less is known about the state of alien aquatic invasions on the two Canadian coastlines or in the Canadian Arctic.

In the United States, Hines et al. (2000) discussed a three-year investigation to evaluate the risk of biological invasion by alien species transported to Alaska in the ballast water of oil tankers. The study found that tanker ballast water contains abundant and diverse planktonic communities. Experiments on temperature and salinity tolerance conducted on plankton collected from tanker ballast water indicated a high rate of survival of common ballast-water organisms at temperatures and salinities found in Port Valdez, Prince William Sound (Alaska). In addition, sediment samples from tanker ballast tanks contained an array of taxa including polychaete worms, adult crabs and other crustacea, mollusks, and fish. During the field survey portion of this study, the number of alien invertebrate species found was low compared with the number in source ports on the west coast. No equivalent study has been done in the Canadian Arctic.

Locke (2000) considers ballast water an even greater problem in Atlantic Canada than in the Great Lakes. According to Smith and Kerr (1992), shipping in Atlantic Canada involves larger vessels that are capable of carrying more ballast than those entering the Great Lakes. Also, more vessels arrive in ballast. Different shipping patterns (trans-Atlantic, intracoastal, and others) are followed, and generally vessels have a shorter travel time (since they do not have to negotiate the St. Lawrence Seaway). In addition, the salinity of ballast water from mid-ocean exchange tends to be the same as that found in the receiving marine port. This greatly reduces the likelihood of killing organisms that were not flushed out of the tank during the exchange.

Locke (2000) considers coastal waters possibly more susceptible to invasion. There is some evidence that the brackish-water portions of estuaries may be more open to invasion (20%–28% of species in brackish waters of northern Europe are invaders) than either marine or freshwater environments (where only 3%–5% of species are invaders) (Leppäkoski 1991). Disturbed environments, such as those found in many harbors and near aquaculture sites, may be more amenable to invasion. Aquaculture and commercial fisheries are susceptible to the effects of phytotoxins resulting from algal blooms (for example, paralytic shellfish poisoning and fish kills).

In a study of ballast water entering the Great Lakes, Locke et al. (1991) found many ships carrying saltwater ballast from a variety of locations. Subba Rao et al. (1994) analyzed these data with a view to assessing their risk to Atlantic Canadian waters. The results were not encouraging.

In total, 94 phytoplankton taxa (mostly diatoms and dinoflagellates) were identified in the samples. Some of the preserved specimens were in good condition, contained chloroplasts, and were probably alive when sampled. It was possible to establish cultures from unpreserved samples. At least 25 potentially bloom-forming, red tide or toxic algal species were identified. Thirteen taxa were new to Atlantic Canada, including 3 species of diatoms and 10 dinoflagellate species (Subba Rao et al. 1994).

Chapman et al. (this publication, p. 133) document five species of seaweed that have invaded Atlantic Canada. This represents only 1.5 % of the algal flora. By comparison, 4%–5% of seaweed species in the Mediterranean region and 2%–3% in Atlantic Europe and in Australasia are introduced (Ribera and Boudouresque 1995). Of the few species that have invaded Atlantic Canada, all but oyster thief (Colpomenia peregrina (Sauv.) Hamel) have become abundant, resulting in large changes in community structure.

Another invader of concern is green crab (Carcinus maenas (L.)), a European species. This crab has invaded many parts of the world, where its appetite for commercially valuable clams and crabs has threatened important fisheries. Within Atlantic Canada, green crab was first observed in the early 1950s (Grosholz and Ruiz 1996), after it had been present in New England for more than 100 years (Glude 1955). Although not well documented, green crab has recently entered the Gulf of St. Lawrence through the Canso Strait (between the Nova Scotia mainland and Cape Breton Island) and is expanding its range much more rapidly than it did along the outer coast of Nova Scotia (Jamieson 2000).

On the west coast of North America, aquatic invasions have been most intensively studied in the San Francisco Bay and Delta region (often known as the San Francisco Bay estuary), where the establishment of more than 200 alien species has been documented, including plants, protists, and invertebrate and vertebrate animals (Cohen and Carlton 1995). Another 100–200 species should be considered cryptogenic—species that, based on current knowledge, could be either native or alien (Carlton 1996).

A 1998 study, involving the sampling of ballast water from ships arriving in Vancouver Harbour from northeast Asia and other northeast Pacific ports, showed that the ballast water contained up to about 13 000 invertebrates per tonne (Levings et al. 1998).

Alien species have been reported in virtually all harbors and bays along the Pacific coast (Carlton 1979). Once established in one bay, organisms may readily invade another either through natural range expansion or assisted by coastal shipping. For example, green crab, first reported in 1989–90 from San Francisco Bay, was found in estuaries from Elkhorn Slough to Humboldt Bay by 1995, reached southern Oregon in 1997, and was found in Barkley Sound, British Columbia, in 1999 (Jamieson 2000). On the Pacific coast there is concern that the green crab could affect oyster farms and clam fisheries by preying on young oysters and clams and adult clams, and that it may compete with or eat young Dungeness crab (*Cancer magister* Dana), which uses bays and estuaries as nursery areas (Grosholz and Ruiz 1996). Based on its distribution in other parts of the world, and observations of adult mortality and breeding limitations, it appears that the expansion of green crab will ultimately be limited in the north by winter surface temperatures averaging about 1°C to 0°C, and in the south by average summer temperatures of about 22°C. These physiological limits correspond to a potential range from north of the Aleutians in Alaska down to central Baja California (Cohen and Carlton 1995; Cohen et al. 1995). Green crab thus poses a threat to British Columbia shell fisheries, which annually produce in excess of 53 000 tonnes of oysters and 7000 tonnes of clams (Japanese littleneck, *Venerupis philippinarum* (A. Adams and Reeve)) (Levings et al., this publication, p. 111).

In 1992 Smith and Kerr wrote "…the threat to Canada's coastal regions is immediate and pressing." To date (2001) the situation has not changed.

Regulation of Ballast Water Discharge in Canada and the United States

Following the introduction of ruffe (*Gymnocephalus cernuus* (L.)) and zebra mussel, the International Joint Commission (IJC) and the Great Lakes Fishery Commission (GLFC) called on the governments of the United States and Canada to deal with the issue of ballast water, in a series of letters and meetings during 1988. This culminated in their joint report "Exotic Species in the Shipping Industry; The Great Lakes–St. Lawrence Ecosystem at Risk", published in 1990 (IJC and GLFC 1990).

In May 1989, reacting with a speed not normally associated with government agencies, the Canadian Coast Guard promulgated the Voluntary Guidelines for the Control of Ballast Water Discharges from Ships Proceeding to the St. Lawrence River and Great Lakes (Transport Canada 1989).

Consistent with the Canadian government's requirement of transparency in process, the Guidelines were put into place after extensive but timely consultation with many stakeholders, including the US Coast Guard, Environment Canada, Fisheries and Oceans Canada, the Great Lakes Fishery Commission, and the domestic and international shipping industry. It is also important to note that the promulgation of the Guidelines was not a regulatory action in the more traditional sense.

At that time there was no legal authority in the *Canada Shipping Act* to bring in regulations. There were few scientific data to justify regulation and there were no technological alternatives identified to the ballast water exchange. The Guidelines were not totally without regulatory or statutory teeth, however. While it was expected, thanks to early and ongoing consultation with the industry, that the shipping community as a whole would likely comply with the Guidelines, there was an added incentive in the use of the existing regulatory powers of vessel traffic regulators. A $50 000 fine was included should vessels falsely declare compliance with the requested procedures.

The Guidelines were modified a number of times but remained in place until superceded by the Canadian Ballast Water Management Guidelines in 2000 (discussed later). In March 1997, the Port of Vancouver put in voluntary guidelines, followed by a mandatory regime under the *Canada Ports Corporation Act*. However, the regime did not include ships from the west coast of North America, north of Cape Mendocino

Ballast Water Treatment

Present guidelines recognize ballast water exchange in mid-ocean as the most widely accepted approach to minimize the risk of introducing new species to freshwater environments. The intent of the guidelines was to get ships in ballast to flush out the freshwater taken onboard in foreign ports, and replace it with high-salinity water, thereby flushing out most of the freshwater organisms present and exposing any remaining biota to water of high salinity. As most freshwater species do not survive in salinity above 8 g/L salinity, about 35 g/L was considered to provide an effective means of control for any freshwater organisms that may be present (Wiley and Claudi 1999). However most ships are designed to take on and discharge ballast in port, under sheltered conditions, not while sailing in the middle of the ocean. The feasibility of developing shore-side facilities for ballast water discharge is currently being investigated.

Although mid-ocean ballast water exchange procedures are a big step toward minimizing introductions of alien organisms to freshwater, opportunities still do exist. The majority of ships entering the Great Lakes have no ballast on board (NOBOB), but they can still have unpumpable water and sediment in the ballast tanks. Studies have indicated that viable organisms can be contained in this residue (Transport Canada 1996). Should these ships take on freshwater in the Great Lakes, it would mix with the residue that could be released in another part of the Great Lakes. There is currently no regulatory control for ships that declare NOBOB.

NOBOBs could also contribute to interbasin transfer of species that are present in one of the Great Lakes but not yet in another. A good example is that of ruffe (mentioned previously), thought to have been introduced at the twin ports of Duluth–Superior on western Lake Superior through ballast water discharge. Ruffe present a significant threat to the commercial Great Lakes fishery. To minimize the

Figure 1. The *Federal Yukon* is typical of the newer generation of ocean-going ships of the maximum allowable dimensions to navigate the St. Lawrence Seaway. Operated by Fednav Limited of Montréal, this vessel is fitted with copper ion and sodium hypochlorite dosing systems, on an experimental basis, to test the concept of using biocides as a shipboard treatment option for ballast water of ships entering the Great Lakes. Photo by Jeff Cameron—www.wellandcanal.ca.

risk of interbasin transfer of ruffe, commercial ship operators have implemented a voluntary ballast water management regime in ruffe-infested ports. During the period May to July, when small ruffe could be drawn into ships' ballast tanks, ships will exchange ballast water in the middle of Lake Superior as a means of preventing further expansion of ruffe distribution by ballast water.

There are other options for treating ballast water onboard ships that are currently being researched and tested (see the appendix and Figure 1). Physical measures include filtration, ultraviolet sterilization, acoustics, various forms of heat treatment, and the redesign of ballast water tanks for more effective exchange. Chemical treatment options that have been utilized for alien species mitigation in industrial facilities are also being considered for ballast water treatment. These include chlorine, hydrogen peroxide, organic acids, sodium metabisulphite and gluteraldehyde. However, none of these treatment options have been proven to be effective or economical for shipboard application.

in California, nor cruise ships and vessels carrying less than 1000 tonnes of ballast.

The United States has been a partner with Canada in cooperative efforts to protect the shared ecosystem of the Great Lakes from invasions via ballast water and in parallel efforts, in close consultation with Canada, in making ballast water a global issue. In 1993, the

United States issued mandatory regulations, modeled closely on the Canadian Voluntary Guidelines discussed previously, requiring exchange or other measures to protect the Great Lakes. The United States also promulgated national voluntary guidelines and is considering national mandatory regulations. However, the US legal regimes, while important in creating the first mandatory ballast water regime in the Great Lakes, are far less than fully effective. The details of current US laws, defects in those laws, critical issues, controversies, and notes on other cooperative efforts with US federal and state authorities around the Great Lakes are described in Reeves (2000).

Global Ballast Water Management

At the 26th meeting of the Marine Environmental Protection Committee (MEPC) of the International Maritime Organization (IMO) in 1988, the issue of global ballast water management was presented as a subject worth examining by Canada, the United States, and Australia. Their efforts bore fruit in 1991 with the adoption by MEPC of International Voluntary Guidelines, based on the Canadian experience "for preventing the introduction of unwanted aquatic organisms and pathogens from ships' ballast water and sediment discharges."

This initiative was further supported two years later when the IMO as a whole adopted Resolution A774(18) (IMO 1993), which recognized that

> …the discharge of ballast water and sediment has led to unplanned and unwanted introductions of harmful aquatic organisms, disease bacteria and viruses that are known to have caused injury to public health and property and to the environment.

The IMO in its resolution also noted that

> …uncontrolled discharge of ballast water containing harmful aquatic organisms not only remains a major international problem but one which is expected to worsen.

More recently, in November 1997, noting the objectives of the 1992 Convention on Biological Diversity (a United Nations initiative), the IMO adopted resolution A.868(20) containing guidelines for the control and management of ships' ballast water to minimize the transfer of harmful aquatic organisms and pathogens. Further, the IMO assembly requested that governments take urgent action in applying these guidelines as the basis for any measures they might adopt to minimize the risk of introduction of such harmful aquatic organisms. They further suggested that the MEPC work toward a legally binding Annex of MARPOL 73/78[1] on ballast water management.[2]

The 1992 Convention on Biological Diversity (UNEP 1992), which specifically addressed the issue of alien invasive species in Article 8(h), stated that

> …each Contracting Party shall, as far as possible and appropriate, prevent the introduction of, control or eradicate those alien species which threaten ecosystems, habitats or species.

At the fifth Conference of the Parties to the Convention, held in Nairobi in May 2000, a progress report (UNEP 2000) was given on the implementation of a program of work on the biological diversity of inland water systems, as well as marine and coastal ecosystems. Specifically, element 5.2 of the program of work aimed to identify

> …gaps in existing or proposed legal instruments, guidelines and procedures to counteract the introduction of, and the adverse effects exerted by, alien species (and genotypes) which threaten ecosystems, habitats or species…

A second portion of this element stated the aim of

> …collecting information on national and international actions to address these problems with a view to prepare for the development of a scientifically based strategy for dealing with the prevention, control and eradication of alien invasive species which threaten marine and coastal ecosystems, habitats and species.

Future of Ballast Water Control in Canada

The legal instruments and the proposed global strategy for addressing the problem of alien invasive species will now be examined with respect to Canada's ballast water program.

Recently, House of Commons Bill C-15 amended the *Canada Shipping Act* to allow for a ballast water management program.[3] Given Royal Assent on 11 June 1998 and Governor-in-Council authority on 31 October 1998, the act now provides Canada with statutory authority to bring in regulations involving ballast water management.

The regulatory process started almost immediately. A working group on ballast water was established on 4 November 1998 under the Standing Committee on the Environment, a committee of Canada's Marine

---

[1] Annex III to the Protocol of 17 February 1978 relating to the International Convention for the Prevention of Pollution from Ships of 2 November 1973 (MARPOL 73/78), as amended on 30 October 1992. MARPOL is an acronym for "marine pollution".

[2] See http://www.epa.gov/owow/OCPD/marpol.html for more information on this international treaty regulating disposal of wastes generated by normal operation of vessels.

[3] See http://laws.justice.gc.ca/en/index/44833_7503.html for more information on the act and http://laws.justice.gc.ca/en/1998/16/3276.html for details of its amendment.

Advisory Council (CMAC). The CMAC is a long-standing body with representation from federal departments, the transportation industry, labor associations, recreational boaters, environmental groups, and other interested marine stakeholders.

The fruits of their labors are ultimately intended to provide a scientifically based regulatory environment that will, to the greatest extent possible, prevent future introductions of aquatic alien species from the ballast water of ships. Given the great dependency of Canada's economy on international trade, the final regime is hoped to have a minimal impact on trade, yet be safe for both the mariner and the environment, and effective and enforceable in all regions of the country. Further, the final regime needs to be consistent not only with future international regulatory requirements but also with those of the United States. Indeed, the Great Lakes Water Quality Agreement of 1978 (as amended by protocol in 1987) specifically requires that Canada and the United States have compatible regulations.

As a first step, taking advantage of the considerable knowledge and data obtained from 10 years of experience with the Voluntary Guidelines for the Great Lakes and St. Lawrence Seaway, the working group developed guidelines that extend the ballast water regime to all areas of the country, not only the Great Lakes–St Lawrence, but the eastern, western, and arctic coasts. To that end, and consistent with the government management model that provides for national focus but regional implementation, regional working groups on ballast water were formed to reflect the differences in trade, shipping patterns, types of ships, geography, and oceanography that characterize Canada. The regional implementation is also consistent with the reality that ecosystems are not politically defined by either provincial or national boundaries.

In format, each regional annex to the regulations sets out the role of the regulators and industry in protecting the environment from ballast water discharges, including agencies to be contacted regionally, what actions are required by all parties, and the implications if these actions are not taken. The scientific community has ensured that the proposed actions are based on sound science and make ecological sense. A communications strategy ensures that everyone affected will know the regional requirements. US Coast Guard membership on the national and regional working groups ensured compatibility with the intentions of the United States, and an understanding of the balancing act between protecting the environment and maintaining a vibrant trade.

For example, support for the location of alternative exchange zones has come from scientific studies, either completed or underway in both jurisdictions, that examine ballast discharge in relation to geography, oceanography, and current. Both Canadian and US jurisdictions have also compiled significant databases of the types of organisms found in ballast water coming into their respective regions.

In contrast to data from the Great Lakes–St. Lawrence waters, scientific data supporting the proposed regime for the east coast and the Arctic are relatively scarce.

The guidelines are intended to be an iterative document, being revised appropriately as scientific data warrant and eventually resulting in a regulatory format. This should be timed to coincide with the promulgation of international regulations. One of the unresolved issues at this point is how to deal with vessels that report NOBOB. In most cases, these vessels have a layer at the bottom of the ballast water tanks that cannot be pumped out, and a study has found that these water remnants contain live organisms (Transport Canada 1996). When ballast is taken on board, this layer can act as a source of undesirable organisms within the ballast water tank and during the subsequent discharge. Scientists are currently working to find an acceptable means of dealing with NOBOB vessels.

In September 2000, after consultation with numerous stakeholders across the country, the Canadian Ballast Water Management Guidelines (Transport Canada 2000) were put in place nationwide. The next step is expected to be a mandatory regulatory regime for the Great Lakes based on the 2000 Guidelines and eventually a mandatory regulatory regime for all Canadian waters based on international requirements being developed by the IMO.

References

Carlton, J.T. 1979. History, biogeography, and ecology of the introduced marine and estuarine invertebrates of the Pacific coast of North America. Ph.D. thesis, University of California, Davis, CA. 904 p.

Carlton, J.T. 1996. Biological invasions and cryptogenic species. Ecology 77:1653–1655.

Carlton, J.T.; Reid, D.M.; van Leeuwen, H. 1995. The role of shipping in the introduction of nonindigenous aquatic organisms to the coastal waters of the United States (other than the Great Lakes) and an analysis of control options. US Coast Guard and US Department of Transportation,

National Sea Grant College Program/Connecticut Sea Grant. USGC Rep. No. CG–D–11–95. Natl. Tech. Inf. Serv. (NTIS) Rep. AD–A294809, Washington, DC.

Cohen, A.N.; Carlton, J.T. 1995. Nonindigenous aquatic species in a United States estuary: a case study of the biological invasions of the San Francisco Bay and Delta. National Technical Information Service, Springfield, VA.

Cohen, A.N.; Carlton, J.T.; Fountain, M.C. 1995. Introduction, dispersal and potential impacts of the green crab *Carcinus maenas* in San Francisco Bay, California. Mar. Biol. 122(2):225–237.

Glude, J.B. 1955. The effects of temperature and predators on the abundance of the softshell clam, *Mya arenaria*, in New England. Trans. Am. Fish. Soc. 84:13–26.

Grosholz, E.D.; Ruiz, G. M. 1996. Predicting the impact of introduced marine species: lessons from the multiple invasions of the European green crab *Carcinus maenas*. Biol. Conserv. 78:59–66.

Hines, A.H.; Ruiz, G.M.; Chapman, J.; Hansen, G.I.; Carlton, J.T.; Foster, N.; Feder, H.M. 2000. Biological invasions of cold-water coastal ecosystems: ballast-mediated introductions in Port Valdez/Prince William Sound, Alaska [online]. Final Project Report 15 March 2000. Regional Citizens' Advisory Council of Prince William Sound, Valdez, AK. 12 p. http://www.pwsrcac.org

Howarth, R.S. 1981. Presence and implication of foreign organisms in ship ballast waters discharged into the Great Lakes. Vol. 1(1–97) and Vol. 2. Report to Environmental Protection Service, Environment Canada, Ottawa.

[IJC/GLFC] International Joint Commission; Great Lakes Fishery Commission. 1990. Exotic species and the shipping industry: The Great Lakes–St. Lawrence ecosystem at risk. Special report to the governments of the United States and Canada. 74 p.

[IMO] International Maritime Organization. 1993. Guidelines for preventing the introduction of unwanted aquatic organisms and pathogens from ships' ballast water and sediment discharges: Resolution A774(18). IMO Doc. A18/Res 774, IMO, London, UK.

[IMO] International Maritime Organization. 1997. Guidelines for the control and management of ships' ballast water to minimize the transfer of harmful aquatic organisms and pathogens: Resolution A868(20). [Online] http://globallast.imo.org/resolution.htm

Jamieson, G.S. 2000. European green crab, *Carcinus maenas*, introductions in North America: differences between the Atlantic and Pacific experiences. Pages 307–316 *in* Proceedings of the 10th International Aquatic Nuisance Species and Zebra Mussel Conference, 13–17 February 2000, Toronto, ON. The Professional Edge, Pembroke, ON. 353 p.

Johnson, C.W. 1921. *Crepidula fornicata* in the British Isles. Nautilus 35:62–64.

Kew, H.W. 1893. The dispersal of shells: an enquiry into the means of dispersal possessed by fresh-water and land mollusca. Kegan Paul, Trench, Trench Trubner and Co., London, UK.

Leach, J.H. 1995. Non-indigenous species in the Great Lakes: were colonization and damage to ecosystem health predictable? J. Aquat. Ecosyst. Health 4:117–128.

Leppäkoski, E.J. 1991. Introduced species–resource or threat in brackish-water seas? Examples from the Baltic and the Black Sea. Mar. Pollut. Bull. 23: 219–223.

Levings, C.D.; Piercey, G.E.; Galbraith, M.; Jamieson, G.S. 1998. Analyses of invertebrate fauna in ballast water collected in ships arriving at British Columbia ports, especially those from the western North Pacific. Pages 111–124 *in* Proceedings of the 8th International Zebra Mussel and Aquatic Nuisance Species Conference, 15-19 March 1998, Sacramento, CA. The Professional Edge, Pembroke, ON. 346 p.

Locke, A. 2000. Marine bioinvasions via ballast water: what can we learn from the Great Lakes experience? Pages 297–303 *in* Proceedings of the 10th International Aquatic Nuisance Species and Zebra Mussel Conference, 13–17 February 2000, Toronto, ON. The Professional Edge, Pembroke, ON. 353 p.

Locke, A.; Reid, D.M.; Sprules, W.G.; Carlton, J.T.; van Leeuwen, H.C. 1991. Effectiveness of mid-ocean exchange in controlling freshwater and coastal zooplankton in ballast water. Can. Tech. Rep. Fish. Aquat. Sci. 1822.

Locke, A.; Reid, D.M.; van Leeuwen, H.C.; Sprules, W.G.; Carlton, J.T. 1993. Ballast water exchange as a means of controlling dispersal of freshwater organisms by ships. Can. J. Fish. Aquat. Sci. 50: 2086–2093.

Mills, E.L.; Leach, J.H.; Carlton, J.T.; Secor, C.L. 1993. Exotic species in the Great Lakes: a history of biotic crises and anthropogenic introductions. J. Great Lakes Res. 19:1–54.

Reeves, E. 2000. Exotic politics: an analysis of the law and politics of exotic invasions of the Great Lakes. Toledo J. Great Lakes' Law Sci. Policy 2(2):125–206.

Ribera, M.A.; Boudouresque, C.-F. 1995. Introduced marine plants, with special reference to macroalgae: mechanisms and impact. Prog. Phycol. Res. 11: 217–268.

Sinclair, R.M. 1964. Clam pests in Tennessee water supplies. J. Am. Water Works Assoc. 56: 592–599.

Smith, T.E.; Kerr, S.R. 1992. Introductions of species transported in ships' ballast waters: the risk to Canada's marine resources. Can. Tech. Rep. Fish. Aquat. Sci. 1867: 16 p.

Subba Rao, D.V.; Sprules, W.G.; Locke, A.; Carlton, J.T. 1994. Exotic phytoplankton from ships' ballast waters: risk of potential spread to mariculture sites on Canada's east coast. Can. Data Rep. Fish. Aquat. Sci. 937:51.

Transport Canada. 1989. Voluntary guidelines for the control of ballast water discharges from ships proceeding to the St. Lawrence River and Great Lakes. Marine Safety Directorate, Ottawa, On.

Transport Canada. 1996. Examination of aquatic nuisance species introductions to the Great Lakes through commercial shipping ballast water and assessment of control options. Phase I and Phase II final report. ASI Project E9225/E9285. Transport Canada, Ottawa, ON.

Transport Canada 2000. Guidelines for the control of ballast water discharge from ships in waters under Canadian jurisdiction [Online]. Marine Safety Directorate, Ottawa, ON. http://www.tc.gc.ca/MarineSafety/Tp/Tp13617/Tp13617e.htm

[UNEP] United Nations Environment Programme. 1992. Convention on Biological Diversity. [Online] http://www.biodiv.org/convention/articles.asp

[UNEP] United Nations Environment Programme. 2000. Convention on Biological Diversity. Conference of the Parties to the Convention on Biological Diversity, fifth meeting, 15-26 May 2000, Nairobi. [Online] http://www.biodiv.org/doc/meetings/cop/cop-05/information/cop-05-inf-09-en.pdf

Wiley, C.J.; Claudi, R. 1999. The role of ships as vector of introduction for nonindigenous freshwater organisms, with focus on the Great Lakes. Pages 203–213 in R. Claudi and J.H. Leach, eds. Non-indigenous freshwater organisms; vectors, biology and impacts. Lewis Publishers, Boca Raton, FL.

Appendix

Options to help minimize the risk of transferring alien ballast-borne organisms to new ecosystems.

Approach	Comments
Exchanging ballast water in deep ocean water (≥ 2000 m deep), where organisms are few and unlikely to survive transfer to coastal or freshwater environments.	Seen as most effective practical method of minimizing the risk of transfer of unwanted species. Ship safety aspects may inhibit operations.
Taking on clean ballast by following precautionary measures, e.g. avoidance of shallow water, dredging operations, and areas of known outbreak of disease or plankton bloom.	May be little choice over where ballasting can take place.
Certifying through laboratory analysis that ballast water is free of aquatic organisms or pathogens considered harmful by the receiving state.	Not seen as an effective method of minimizing risk.
Not releasing ballast water.	Not an option for many ships, such as bulk carriers and tankers.
Relying on differences of temperature and salinity between ballast water intake and discharge areas; aquatic organisms are unlikely to survive significant changes in these conditions.	More research is needed and it depends on locations.
Keeping water in ballast tanks for more than 100 days; most organisms cannot survive the absence of light and the higher iron content of ballast water for long periods.	Tankers and bulk carriers may not have the option of maintaining ballast water for 3 months.
Disposing of sediment, which contains many aquatic organisms; this involves routinely cleaning all sources of sediment retention, e.g. anchor cables.	All ships are not yet designed to minimize sediment retention.

(Continued)

Appendix *(Concluded)*

Approach	Comments
Discharging ballast water into reception facilities.	May provide adequate means of control, but is dependent on these facilities being provided.
Filtering water as it is being pumped into ballast tanks to remove large particles, e.g. small seaweeds.	Residues would be released in the area of ballasting. Capital costs to develop the infrastructure necessary to filter out microorganisms would be high.
Irradiating ballast water with ultraviolet.	Effect varies with type of organism, with some highly resistant to UV radiation. It could be effective in combination with filtration. No toxic side effects and no adverse effects on pipework, pumps, or coatings.
Heating ballast water; temperatures above 40°C for 8 minutes can be lethal to all waterborne organisms; e.g., heating temperatures of 36–38°C for 2–6 hours has been shown to kill zebra mussels.	Potentially attractive solution. Dependent on availability of heat to treat ballast water during voyage; thermal stresses also need to be addressed.

Based on Resolution A.868(20)—Ballast water guidelines/Disinfection of ballast water:
A review of potential options (IMO 1997).

Plant Quarantine: Preventing the Introduction and Spread of Alien Species Harmful to Plants

Marcel Dawson

Invasive alien species have been reported to cause serious damage to agriculture, forestry, and the environment in many countries, including Canada. International actions to reduce the spread and damage of all invasive species are currently being undertaken under the 1992 Convention on Biological Diversity to which Canada is a party. Plant quarantine pests are invasive alien pests that are capable of causing economic damage to agricultural crops or forest trees. These pests, which are classified as either absent or of restricted distribution in Canada, are controlled by the application of specific regulations aimed at preventing their artificial spread by human means (FAO 1999). Included in the classification are insects, fungi, bacteria, nematodes, viruses, and weeds; to date, weeds have not been subjected to quarantine actions.

Impact of Plant Quarantine Pests on Canada's Land Base Resources

Each year Canada's agricultural and forest land base produces $86 billion worth of plant products (forestry, $71 billion; agriculture, $15 billion), which sustain industries providing about 762 000 jobs. In past years, numerous plant quarantine pests have entered and become established in Canada with devastating effects on agricultural crops (Appendix 1) and forest trees (Appendix 2). Damage resulting from past introductions of harmful invasive plant pests is currently estimated to be $7.3 billion annually (Table 1). Examples of the impacts of quarantine plant pests are presented here according to the activities or amenities affected: agriculture, forestry, the environment, and trade.

Agriculture

A large number of pests of agricultural crops have been introduced in the past 100 years causing catastrophic damage to a wide range of cultivated species. Noteworthy examples include the golden nematode (*Globodera rostochiensis* (Wollenweber) Behrens), oriental fruit moth (*Grapholita molesta* (Busck)), dwarf bunt (*Tilletia controversa* Kühn), and soybean cyst nematode (*Heterodera glycines* Ichinohe). Golden nematode is a major pest of potatoes in cool-temperate regions; it attacks the roots of the potato plants, causing the foliage to yellow, wilt, and die. The oriental fruit moth

Table 1. Estimated losses[a] in agriculture and forestry due to alien species harmful to plants.

Category of alien species	Resource	Total crop produced (billions $)	Losses due to alien species (billions $) Damage by alien species	Control or treatment costs	Total	% Value of the crop impacted[b]
Weeds	Crops	15.0	1.3	0.30	1.60	8.6
	Pastures	1.0	0.1	0.50	0.60	9.0
Insects	Crops	15.0	0.8	0.05	0.85	5.2
	Forests	71.1	1.9	ND	1.90	2.7
Plant pathogens	Crops	15.0	1.1	0.05	1.15	7.8
	Forests	71.1	1.2	ND	1.20	2.7
Total			**6.4**	**0.90**	**7.30**	

[a] Canadian losses were calculated based on US estimates by Pimentel et al. (1999) and by substituting Canadian values for plant resources.

[b] Calculated by dividing the value of crop production loss from damage by alien species by the value of the total crop produced, multiplied by 100%.

ND = no data.

is an important pest of peaches, apricots, and nectarines; it feeds on the new shoots and fruits. Dwarf bunt is a fungus that infects grains of wheat and some grasses. The soybean cyst nematode attacks the roots of soybeans; stunting and discoloration of the foliage occur. Damage from these pests results in lower yields and economic loss.

In 2000, the plum pox virus or sharka (*Potyvirus: Potyviridae*), capable of causing serious damage to stone fruits (plums, peaches, nectarines, and almonds), was detected in Canada for the first time and is currently the subject of quarantine actions by the Canadian Food Inspection Agency (CFIA). Quarantine actions against the plum pox virus include the establishment of a quarantine zone in infested areas of Ontario and Nova Scotia, with domestic movement restrictions applied on the virus-susceptible trees of the *Prunus* genus. Also in 2000, potato wart, a serious disease of potatoes caused by the fungus *Synchytrium endobioticum* (Schilb.) Perc., was found for the first time on Prince Edward Island, a major potato-producing province (Watler 2000). This has resulted in trade restrictions by the United States and demands from growers for compensation due to market losses.

Forestry

North American forests are particularly vulnerable to invasions of insects and diseases from the temperate regions of Asia, Europe, and South America. These alien species often have few natural enemies in their new habitat (see Hendrickson, this publication, p. 59). Recent invaders include the pine shoot beetle (*Tomicus piniperda* (L.)) and the brown spruce longhorn beetle (*Tetropium fuscum* (Fabricius)). The pine shoot beetle was first detected in Ontario in 1993 and has since spread throughout southern portions of Ontario and of Quebec. The brown spruce longhorn beetle was introduced to the city of Halifax, Nova Scotia, in the early 1990s, but only identified as the cause of spruce mortality in 2000. It is currently the subject of the following quarantine actions by the CFIA: establishment of a quarantine zone in the infested areas in Halifax; removal of infested trees within the zone; and restrictions on movement of host trees and logs as well as infested wood out of the zone.

The Environment

Designation as a plant quarantine pest only applies to invasive species capable of damaging agricultural crops or forests. Although some species under quarantine also harm or displace native plant species,

the plant protection program does not focus on environmental impacts. In the absence of quarantine restrictions, a number of weeds have been introduced into Canada that negatively affect the environment, for example, purple loosestrife (*Lythrum salicaria* L.), European frog-bit (*Hydrocharis morsus-ranae* L.), Scotch broom (*Cytisus scoparius* (L.) Link), and gorse (*Ulex europaeus* L.). Purple loosestrife threatens natural wetland ecosystems, especially in Quebec, Ontario, and Manitoba; European frog-bit clogs lakes and rivers in eastern Canada; and Scotch broom and gorse hinder the regeneration of commercial tree species such as Douglas-fir (*Pseudotsuga menziesii* (Mirb.) Franco var. *menziesii*) and encroach on stands of the endangered Garry oak (*Quercus garryana* Dougl.) in British Columbia. For more information on these plants, see Haber, this publication (p. 43).

The broad environmental issues and initiatives resulting from invasive alien species are currently the subject of international deliberations under the Convention of Biological Diversity. Initiatives against plant quarantine pests of agricultural crops and forestry are a subset of, and in turn support, the larger international environmental thrusts aimed at preventing the spread of invasive alien pests.

Export Trade

The introduction and spread of plant quarantine pests can cause the loss of export markets and may increase the costs of exporting Canadian plants and plant products. Canada currently exports $50 billion worth of agricultural and forest products annually to more than 180 countries. Approximately $23.6 billion worth of plant products require inspection, testing, and certification by the CFIA to ensure they are free from plant pests designated by importing countries as invasive and harmful. These activities are undertaken by the CFIA under the authority of the *Plant Protection Act*, in accordance with the 1952 United Nations International Plant Protection Convention (IPPC) and the 1994 Agreement on the Application of Sanitary and Phytosanitary Measures (SPS) of the World Trade Organization (WTO).

When new harmful invasive plant pests are introduced into Canada, importing countries may seek to protect their agriculture and forest resources, export trade, and environment by imposing restrictions on imports of plants or plant products from Canada. These restrictions could range from prohibitions to expensive testing and certification programs. Since Canada is a major exporter of agriculture and forest products, it is always vulnerable to export trade restrictions resulting from the introduction of new harmful invasive plant pests.

In its 1999 report *Safeguarding American Plant Resources* (USDA 1999), the National Plant Board of the United States expressed concerns about the numerous documented harmful pest introductions from Canada and recommended that import restrictions against Canada be strengthened. Since Canada exports approximately 80% of its agricultural and forest products to the United States, there are potentially serious trade implications for Canada in the future unless steps are taken to address US concerns.

Canada's Plant Protection Programs

In Canada, federal plant quarantine legislation dates back to over 100 years ago with the establishment of the *San Jose Scale Act* in 1898. This was followed by more comprehensive legislation and inspection systems in the 1900s. The present *Plant Protection Act* was adopted in 1990. Plant protection activities are administered under the authority of the federal *Plant Protection Act* by the CFIA, consistent with Canada's international obligations under the IPPC and WTO/SPS.

There are three plant protection programs in Canada, each dealing specifically with either import, domestic, or export trade. Their objectives are to reduce the risks of introduction of plant quarantine pests into Canada; eradicate newly introduced plant quarantine pests when feasible; control the spread of introduced plant quarantine pests within Canada; and facilitate the export of Canadian plants and plant products by certifying that they meet the plant quarantine import requirements of the importing countries. Scientific support for the program is provided by two federal departments: Natural Resources Canada and Agriculture and Agri-Food Canada. The Department of Foreign Affairs and International Trade also provides support to the CFIA in negotiating trade agreements with foreign countries to facilitate the export of plant material from Canada. Provincial governments support educational activities for farmers and the general public, which are necessary for effective enforcement of quarantine regulations.

Import Program

The aims of the Plant Protection Import Program are as follows: identify possible pathways for pest introductions into Canada; identify potentially harmful invasive plant pests through risk assessments; develop early warning, detection, and inspection systems to reduce the risk of entry into Canada; monitor imported plant products for compliance with Canadian import requirements, through inspection and testing of plant products; and refuse entry or safely dispose of pest-infested plant material. Currently $8 billion worth of agricultural and forest products are imported into Canada annually; these are monitored for the presence of harmful invasive plant pests by the CFIA in close conjunction with Canada Customs and Revenue.

Four factors are complicating the development and enforcement of import restrictions: the potential number (hundreds) of harmful invasive plant pests; their diversity (insects, fungi, bacteria, nematodes, viruses); the large number of potential pathways for entry into Canada (land, air, and sea); and limited detection methods and scientific expertise. At present, there are 227 regulated plant quarantine insects, fungi, bacteria, nematodes, and viruses for which various commodities are subjected to import restrictions. The list is based on pest risk assessments carried out by the Pest Risk Assessment Unit of the CFIA; these determine which pests could become established in Canada and cause losses to agricultural crops and forestry. The number of plant quarantine pests is increasing steadily as pest risk assessments identify new candidates.

Domestic Program

The aim of the Plant Protection Domestic Program is to eradicate or repress newly introduced plant quarantine pests that have become established in a limited area of the country. Currently Canada regulates 87 plant quarantine pests domestically. Delimitation surveys are conducted to determine the range of a pest. Regulated areas are then established based upon the distribution and the mobility of the pest. Monitoring the movement of potentially infested (regulated) commodities domestically, where borders do not exist, requires the development of awareness programs in partnership with the provinces and industry. In addition, all citizens must cooperate to ensure that regulated plant materials are subjected to appropriate inspection or testing by the CFIA before moving them from a regulated area. The CFIA conducts pest detection surveys to identify new pest introductions. It is also responsible for publishing various regulations, policy directives, and pest fact sheets on existing or new domestic movement requirements and for communicating this information to affected industries and to the public.

Export Program

The Plant Protection Export Program manages activities related to the inspection and certification of Canadian plants and plant products for export markets and the negotiation of certification entry requirements for these products with foreign countries. In addition, Canadian plant health officials participate in the development of regional (North American Plant Protection Organization) and international (International Plant Protection Convention) plant health standards. They also provide technical expertise in resolution of WTO/SPS trade disputes involving plant quarantine pests. At present, agricultural and forest products valued at $23.6 billion are certified under the program for export to more than 180 countries.

Global Trade, New Technologies, and Increased Incidences of Alien Pests

In recent years, the rate of interception of harmful alien plant pests has increased significantly. Since January 1999, more than 50 plant quarantine pests from 26 countries have been intercepted at Canadian ports of entry (Lam 1999), indicating a need for urgent preventive action. In 2000, four new plant quarantine pests were found in Canada: brown spruce longhorn beetle, affecting spruce (*Picea* spp.); plum pox virus, affecting the fruits of *Prunus* spp.; chrysanthemum white rust (caused by the fungus *Puccinia horiana* P. Henn.), affecting chrysanthemums; and the pepino mosaic virus (*Potexvirus*), affecting tomatoes. The CFIA is currently active in eradicating these newly introduced pests. It has identified a number of high-risk pests and developed import restrictions to reduce the risks of their entry into Canada. In addition, enhanced monitoring and survey programs are in place to detect and eradicate these pests should they be found at ports of entry or at inland locations.

High-risk pests of agricultural crops (Watler 2000) include the following:

- black stem rust of wheat (*Puccinia graminis* Pers.:Pers.)
- chrysanthemum white rust (*Puccinia horiana* P. Henn.)
- crown rust of oats (*Puccinia coronata* Corda)
- golden nematode (*Globodera rostochiensis* (Wollenweber) Behrens)
- grapevine corky bark virus (*Closterovirus*)
- karnal bunt of wheat (*Tilletia indica* (Mitra) Mundkur)

- khapra beetle (*Trogoderma granarium* Everts)
- little cherry virus (*Closterovirus*)
- plum pox virus (*Potyvirus: Potyviridae*)
- potato wart (*Synchytrium endobioticum* (Schilb.) Perc.)
- soybean cyst nematode (*Heterodera glycines* Ichinohe)

High-risk pests for forest trees (Krcmar-Nozic et al. 2000; Watler 2000) include the following:

- Asian long-horned beetle (*Anoplophora glabripennis* (Motchulsky))
- bacterial canker of poplar (*Xanthomonas populi* (Ridé) Ridé & Ridé)
- brown spruce longhorn beetle (*Tetropium fuscum* (Fabricius))
- gypsy moth, Asian race (*Lymantria dispar* (L.))
- Japanese cedar longhorned beetle (*Callidiellum rufipenne* (Motchulsky))
- nun moth or black arches moth (*Lymantria monacha* (L.))
- oak wilt (*Ceratocystis fagacearum* (Bretz) Hunt)
- Siberian silk moth (*Dendrolimus superans* (Butler))
- Sirex woodwasp (*Sirex noctilio* Fabricius)
- sudden oak death (*Phytophthora* spp.)

The increased number of foreign pests detected at Canadian ports results from an increased volume of import trade from a larger number of high-risk countries, modernization in transportation, and enhanced wood-packing inspection efforts since 1998. Between 1995 and 1999, imports of plant products into Canada went from $11.7 billion to $15.3 billion annually—a 30% increase. During the same period, the number of countries exporting plant products to Canada grew from 161 to 186—a 15% increase. The number of countries located in high-risk pest regions with temperate areas comparable to Canada, such as Asia and the Pacific Rim, has increased significantly. Imported goods are now shipped more rapidly and usually in containers that are opened at inland destinations, close to agricultural fields and to forests. These containers often use pest-infested wood-packing material of low quality to support various cargoes, such as steel cables, machinery, and granite.

Despite the increasing risk of introducing harmful invasive plant pests into Canada in recent years, resources devoted to inspection, detection and identification, surveys, risk assessments, research, and treatments have not kept pace. For example, import trade using high-risk shipping containers is so large (more than one million shipments imported from off the continent in 1999) that Canada can manage to inspect only 1%–2% of incoming shipments. This is inadequate to detect and evaluate new harmful invasive plant pests by this pathway. At present, there is a shortage of scientific taxonomic experts in Canada to detect and identify potentially harmful pests and to conduct research relating to their regulation and control.

In the future, priority should be given to proactive activities that emphasize pest exclusion from Canada. Some examples include foreign site surveys, pest prediction systems for early warning, enhanced monitoring of high-risk commodities at Canadian ports of entry, improved pest detection and testing methods, and enhanced plant quarantine pest surveys.

Post-entry activities, such as eradication and control, are costly and less effective than pre-entry activities that are aimed at preventing pest entry. However, these activities can be made more efficient by developing pest-specific emergency action plans in advance of a pest introduction. In addition, the creation of a Canadian funding mechanism for eradication of new pests would allow for rapid response, immediately after introduction, which would increase the chances of successful eradication actions and further reduce the costs of these activities.

References

Allen, E.A. 1998. Exotic insect interceptions from wooden dunnage and packing material. Natural Resources Canada, Canadian Forest Service, Pacific Forestry Centre, Victoria, BC.

Allen, E.A.; Humble, L.M.; Humphreys, N.; Duncan, R.W.; Bell, J.D.; Gill, B. 1999. Do imports of granite blocks and wire rope pose a risk to Canada's forests? Natural Resources Canada, Canadian Forest Service, Pacific Forestry Centre, Victoria, BC/Canadian Food Inspection Agency, Ottawa, ON. Poster.

[CFIA] Canadian Food Inspection Agency. 1996–1999. Plant pest surveillance annual reports [online]. Ottawa, ON. http://www.inspection.gc.ca/english/ppc/science/pps/situe.shtml

[CFIA] Canadian Food Inspection Agency. 1998. Summary of plant quarantine pest and disease situations in Canada [online]. Ottawa, ON. http://www.inspection.gc.ca/english/ppc/science/pps/sit98e.shtml

[CFIA] Canadian Food Inspection Agency. 1999. Plant Health Risk Assessment Unit [Web site]. Ottawa, ON. http://www.inspection.gc.ca/english/ppc/science/phra/phra_e.shtml

[FAO] Food and Agricultural Organization of the United Nations. 1999. Glossary of phytosanitary terms. Secretariat of the International Plant Protection Convention, Rome. International Standards for Phytosanitary Measures Publ. No. 5.

Hall, J.P.; Moody, B. 1994. Forest depletions caused by insects and diseases in Canada 1982–1987. Forest insect and disease survey. Natural Resources Canada, Canadian Forest Service. Ottawa, ON. Information Report ST-X-8.

Hewitt, C.G. 1912. The control of insects in Canada. Department of Agriculture, Division of Entomology, Ottawa, ON. Bulletin No. 4.

Hubbes, M. 1999. The American elm and Dutch elm disease. For. Chron. 75(2):265–273.

Kahn, R.P. 1989. Plant protection and quarantine. Vol. I, Biological concepts. CRC Press, Boca Raton, FL.

Kim, K.C. 1983. How to detect and combat exotic pests. Pages 262–319 in C.L. Wilson and C.L. Graham, eds. Exotic plant pests and North American agriculture. Academic Press, New York, NY.

Krcmar-Nozic, E; Wilson, B.; Arthur, L. 2000. The potential impacts of exotic forest pests in North America: a synthesis of research [print and online]. Natural Resources Canada, Canadian Forest Service, Pacific Forestry Centre, Victoria, BC. Information Report BC-X-387. http://bookstore.cfs.nrcan.gc.ca/default.htm

Lam, A. 1999. Evaluation of pest interceptions from imported non-manufactured wood packing materials. Canadian Food Inspection Agency, Ottawa, ON.

Mulligan, G.A. Editor. 1979. The biology of Canadian weeds. Contributions 1–32. Agriculture Canada Publication 1693. Ottawa, ON. 380 p.

Mulligan, G.A. Editor. 1984. The biology of Canadian weeds. Contributions 33–61. Agriculture Canada Publication 1765. Ottawa, ON. 415 p.

Pimentel, D.; Lach, L.; Zuniga, R.; Morrison, D. 1999. Environmental and economic costs associated with non-indigenous species in the United States [online]. College of Agriculture and Life Sciences, Cornell University. http://www.news.cornell.edu/releases/Jan99/species_costs.html

Sailer, R.I. 1983. History of insect introductions. Pages 15–38 in C.L. Wilson and C.L. Graham, eds. Exotic plant pests and North American agriculture. Academic Press, New York, NY.

[USDA] United States Department of Agriculture. 1999. Safeguarding American plant resources: a stakeholder review of the APHIS-PPQ safeguarding system [online]. USDA, Animal and Plant Health Inspection Service, Plant Protection and Quarantine. http://www.aphis.usda.gov/ppq/safeguarding

Watler, D. 2000. Some exotic organisms which have become invasive agricultural pests. Unpublished report. Available from Plant Health Risk Assessment, Canadian Food Inspection Agency, Ottawa, ON K1A 0Y9.

Williamson, M.; Fitter, A. 1996. The varying success of invaders. Ecology 77:1661–66.

Wilson, C.L. and C.L. Graham, eds. 1983. Exotic plant pests and North American agriculture. Academic Press, New York, NY.

Photo with chapter title: Asian long-horned beetle. Photo by Kenneth R. Law, USDA, APHIS, Plant Protection and Quarantine, Newburgh, NY.

Appendix 1

Significant agricultural pests established in Canada, in chronological order of introduction.

Pest	Year introduced	Primary hosts[a]
Wild oats (*Avena fatua* L.)	1622	Field crops (weed)
Quack grass (*Elytrigia repens* (L.) Desv. ex B.D. Jacks)	1663	Field crops (weed)
Hessian fly (*Mayetiola destructor* (Say))	1816	Wheat and other cereals
Broad-leaved plantain (*Plantago major* L.)	1821	Field crops (weed)
Flixweed (*Descurainia sophia* (L.) Webb ex Prantl)	1821	Cultivated fields (weed)
Yellow foxtail (*Setaria pumila* (Poir.) Roem. & Schult.)	1821	Grains and forage crops (weed)
Wheat midge (*Sitodiplosis mosellana* (Gehin))	1828	Wheat and other cereals
Wild mustard (*Sinapis arvensis* L.)	1829	Cereal crops (weed)
Common barberry (*Berberis vulgaris* L.)	1830(?)	Alternate host for stem rust of wheat
Potato late blight (*Phytophthora infestans* (Mont.) de Barry)	1830(?)	Potatoes
Stinkweed (*Thlaspi arvense* L.)	1860	Field crops (weed)
Cinch bug (*Blissus leucopterus leucopterus* (Say))	1866	Wheat and other cereals, grasses
Colorado potato beetle (*Leptinotarsa decemlineata* (Say))	1870	Potato
Wild buckwheat (*Polygonum convolvulus* L.)	1873	Field crops (weed)
White cockle (*Silene pratensis* (Raf.) Godr. & Gren.)	1875	Field crops (weed)
Narrow-leaved hawk's beard (*Crepis tectorum* L.)	1877	Perennial forage crops (weed)
Heart-podded hoary cress (*Cardaria draba* (L.) Desv. subsp. *draba*)	1878	Field crops (weed)
Wild carrot (*Daucus carota* L.)	1879(?)	Pasture (weed)
Field bindweed (*Convolvulus arvensis* L.)	1879	Field crops (weed)
Mediterranean flour moth (*Ephestia kuhniella* (Zeller))	1889	Cereal flour
Clover root borer (*Hylastinus obscurus* (Marsh.))	1891	Clover
Spotted knapweed (*Centaurea maculosa* Lam.)	1893	Pasture (weed)

(Continued)

Appendix 1 *(Concluded)*

Pest	Year introduced	Primary hosts[a]
Apple fruit moth (*Argyresthia conjugella* Zeller)	1896	Apple
San Jose scale (*Quadraspidiotus perniciosus* (Comstock))	1898	Apple
Pea aphid (*Acyrthosiphon pisum* (Harris))	1899	Alfalfa, clover, pea
Potato wart (*Synchytrium endobioticum* (Schilb.) Perc.)	1909	Potatoes
European corn borer (*Ostrinia nubilalis* (Hubner))	1920	Maize
Oriental fruit moth (*Grapholita molesta* (Busck))	1925	Fruit trees and ornamentals
Bacterial ring rot (*Clavibacter michiganensis* subsp. *sepedonicus* (Spieckerman & Kotthoff) Davis et al.)	1930(?)	Potatoes
Pear trellis rust (*Gymnosporangium fuscum* Hedw.)	1932	Pears and junipers
Little cherry virus (*Closterovirus*)	1933	Cherries
Diffuse knapweed (*Centaurea diffusa* Lam.)	1936	Pasture (weed)
Japanese beetle (*Popillia japonica* Newman)	1940	Many hosts
Potato rot nematode (*Ditylenchus destructor* Thorne)	1945	Potatoes
Dwarf bunt (*Tilletia controversa* Kühn)	1952	Wheat
Wheat bulb fly (*Delia coarctata* (Fallén))	1954	Wheat and other cereals
European chafer (*Rhizotrogus majalis* (Razoumowshy))	1959	Grasses
Johnson grass (*Sorghum halepense* (L.) Pers.)	1959	Field crops (weed)
Golden nematode (*Globodera rostochiensis* (Wollenweber) Brehrens)	1962	Potatoes
Alfalfa snout beetle (*Otiorhynchus ligustici* (L.))	1967	Alfalfa
Cereal leaf beetle (*Oulema melanopus* (L.))	1967	Cereals, grasses
Pea seed-borne mosaic virus (*Potyvirus: Potyviridae*)	1968	Peas
Anthracnose of field bean (*Colletotrichum lindemuthianum* (Sacc. & Magn.) Bri. & Cav.)	1976	Field beans
Pale cyst nematode (*Globodera pallida* (Stone) Behrens)	1977	Potatoes
Verticillium wilt of alfalfa (*Verticillium albo-atrum* Reinke & Berth.)	1977	Alfalfa
Blue mold of tobacco (*Peronospora tabacina* D.B. Adam)	1979	Tobacco
Head smut of corn (*Sphacelotheca reiliana* (Kühn) G.P. Clinton)	1979	Maize
Brown garden snail (*Helix aspersa* Müller)	1979	Many hosts
Apple ermine moth (*Yponomeuta malinellus* Zeller)	1981	Apple
Strawberry anthracnose (*Colletotrichum acutatum* J.H. Simmonds)	1981	Strawberries
Tobacco rattle virus, potato corky ring spot virus (*Tobravirus*)	1981(?)	Potatoes
Soybean cyst nematode (*Heterodera glycines* Ichinohe)	1987	Soybeans
Cherry bark tortrix (*Enarmonia formosana* (Scopoli))	1989	Fruit trees
Arabis mosaic virus (*Nepovirus: Comoviridae*)	1990(?)	Grapevines
Cherry ermine moth (*Yponomeuta padellus* L.)	1993	Cherry
Plum pox virus (*Potyvirus: Potyviridae*)	2000(?)	Stone fruit

[a] The term "host" is used broadly here; agricultural crops and pasture are not primary hosts for the weeds listed as pests. Weeds do not feed directly on crops, but compete with them, thereby reducing crop yield. Weeds may also serve as hosts to diseases or provide protection to injurious organisms of crop plants.

Sources: CFIA 1996–1999, 1998, 1999; Hewitt 1912; Kim 1983; Mulligan 1979, 1984; Sailor 1983; Watler 2000; Williamson 1996; Wilson and Graham 1983.

Appendix 2

Significant forest pests established in Canada, in chronological order of introduction

Pest	Year introduced	Primary hosts
Larch sawfly (*Pristiphora erichsonii* (Htg.))	1882	Larches
Beech bark disease (*Nectria coccinea* var. *faginata* (Pers.: Fr.)) and beech scale (*Cryptococcus fagisuga* Lind.)	1890	American beech
Dothichiza canker (*Cryptodiaporthe populea* (Sacc.) Butin = *Discosporium populeum* (Sacc.) B. Sutton)	pre-1900	Poplars
Browntail moth (*Euproctis chrysorrhoea* (L.))	1902	All deciduous species
Chestnut blight (*Cryphonectria parasitica* (Murr.) Barr)	post-1904	American chestnut
Poplar sawfly (*Trichiocampus viminalis* Fall.)	1904	Trembling aspen, largetooth aspen, balsam poplar
Larch casebearer (*Coleophora laricella* (Hbn.))	1905	Larches
Late birch leaf edgeminer (*Heterarthus nemoratus* (Fall.))	1905	Birches
Balsam woolly adelgid (*Adelges piceae* (Ratz.))	1908	Balsam fir, grand fir, subalpine fir, amabilis fir
White pine blister rust (*Cronartium ribicola* J.C. Fisch)	1917	Eastern white pine, whitebark pine, western white pine
Winter moth (*Operophtera brumata* (L.))	1920s	Oaks, maples, willows
Satin moth (*Leucoma salicis* (L.))	1920	Poplars
European spruce sawfly (*Gilpinia hercyniae* (Htg.))	1922	Spruces
Gypsy moth, European race (*Lymantria dispar* (L.))	1924	Oaks, birches, larches, willows, basswood, Manitoba maple
Willow scab (*Venturia saliciperda* Nüesch)	ca. 1925	Willows
European pine shoot moth (*Rhyacionia buoliana* (Denis & Schiff.))	1925	Red pine, jack pine, Scots pine
Mountain ash sawfly (*Pristiphora geniculata* (Htg.))	1926	Mountain ash
Birch leafminer (*Fenusa pusilla* (Lep.))	1929	Birches
Introduced pine sawfly (*Diprion similis* (Htg.))	1931	Pines
Birch casebearer (*Coleophora serratella* (L.))	1933	Poplars
European pine sawfly (*Neodiprion sertifer* (Geoff.))	1939	Red pine, Scots pine
Dutch elm disease (*Ophiostoma ulmi* (Buisman) Nannf.)	1944	Elms
Elm leaf beetle (*Pyrrhalta luteola* (Müll.))	1945	Elms
Smaller European elm bark beetle (*Scolytus multistriatus* (Marsh.))	1946	Elms
Ambermarked birch leafminer (*Profenusa thomsoni* (Konow))	1948	Birches
Apple ermine moth (*Yponomeuta malinellus* Zeller)	1957	Apple
Pine false webworm (*Acantholyda erythrocephala* (L.))	1961	Pines
European pine needle midge (*Contarinia baeri* (Prell))	1964	Red pine, Scots pine
Early birch leaf edgeminer (*Messa nana* (Klug))	1967	Birches
Scleroderris canker, European race (*Gremmeniella abietina* (Lagerb.) Morelet)	1978	Pines
European larch canker (*Lachnellula willkommii* (R. Hartig) Dennis)	1980	Larches
Pear thrips (*Taeniothrips inconsequens* (Uzel))	1989	Sugar maple, red maple

(Continued)

Appendix 2 *(Concluded)*

Pest	Year introduced	Primary hosts
Brown spruce longhorn beetle (*Tetropium fuscum* (Fabricius))	1990	Pines, spruces, true firs
Butternut canker (*Sirococcus clavignenti-juglandacearum* Nair, Kostichka & Kuntz)	1991	Butternut
Pine shoot beetle (*Tomicus piniperda* (L.))	1993	Pines, spruces

Sources: Allen 1998; Allen et al. 1999; CFIA 1996–1999, 1998, 1999; Hall and Moody 1994; Hubbes 1999; Krcmar-Nozic et al. 2000; Lam 1999; Watler 2000.

Stimulating Political Awareness of Invasive Alien Species: Lessons Learned from Canada's Purple Loosestrife Initiatives

Gerry Lee

In June 1999, the Subsidiary Body on Scientific, Technical and Technological Advice (SBSTTA) of the Conference of the Parties to the Convention on Biological Diversity discussed and adopted an action plan to develop "guiding principles for the prevention of impacts of alien species…" This latest initiative highlighted the continuing concerns of the global community regarding the ecological, social, and economic consequences of unwanted alien organisms and demonstrated the growing acceptance of global cooperation as the key to future solutions. Yet while nations were setting the stage for future cooperation and effort, the reality of whether nations were adequately equipped to carry forward the various initiatives was being openly discussed among many of the delegates. Third World countries were concerned about their lack of resources and capacity to respond. Island nations were feeling particularly hard-pressed because of the havoc alien species were already exerting on their lives and livelihoods. Large land-based countries like Canada and the United States were equally concerned because of the magnitude of the land base that was, or could be, affected by harmful alien species. Collectively, the global community worried as it mustered the courage to take a step into new territory.

Frequently the first step in the prevention of introductions is establishing an awareness of the problem at a number of different levels. I will illustrate this process using the lessons learned during a decade-long national program to control and manage the purple loosestrife (*Lythrum salicaria* L.) problem in Canada. Many of the lessons are generic to the management of environmental issues and have application to the problems of alien organisms in general.

Background

Various observers and writers began sounding the alarm on purple loosestrife during the 1980s with articles on background meeting discussions related to purple loosestrife and wetlands. Apart from momentary flurries of concern and discussion, little, if any, action resulted. In general, the Canadian public seemed disin-

terested in the subject, in part because of a lack of a clear understanding of the potential consequences to particular ecosystems and individual species. Canadian resource agencies themselves had not yet become aware of the magnitude of the issue and therefore could not inform the public.

The publication of a major review of loosestrife by the US Fish and Wildlife Service, *Spread, Impact and Control of Purple Loosestrife, Lythrum salicaria, in North American Wetlands* (Thompson et al. 1987), produced a significant wake-up call that started a ripple, that became a wave, and then a storm of activity on this invasive alien species. Thanks to the efforts of these authors, awareness was raised of the breadth of the invasion in the United States, the suspected presence of the plant in Canadian wetlands, the various attributes of the plant itself, and the magnitude of the impact the plant was likely to have on ecosystems. Based on this information, the Canadian Wildlife Service (CWS), Environment Canada, initiated an informal sounding across Canada to discover whether loosestrife was present and whether it was causing problems.

During the winter of 1990–91, reports trickled in from wildlife and other agencies that, for the first time, provided Canada with a national snapshot of the range and impacts of purple loosestrife. All 10 provinces confirmed its presence. It was found in saltwater as well as freshwater marshes, and a majority thought that it was, or was going to be, causing significant problems. Within one week of being asked by the CWS to support a national campaign against this alien species, all jurisdictions had agreed.

Simultaneously, Ducks Unlimited Canada (a nongovernmental conservation agency dedicated to wetland conservation) was gearing up to do battle with this plant on its project lands. Working with the CWS, Ducks Unlimited Canada pulled together an ad hoc national steering committee of concerned partners in 1991 that included nongovernmental and industry groups. With limited funds provided by these partners, this consortium agreed (sometimes grudgingly) to the language for a brochure and began the process of sensitizing the Canadian public to the perils this plant represented to natural habitats. The 1991 brochure, *Beautiful Killer,* drew the immediate attention of supporters and nonsupporters alike. The newspaper-style headlines dramatizing the impact of this plant on wetlands left many uneasy and uncomfortable. But with the wisdom of hindsight, it is now possible to say "it worked!" Phones began to ring, interviews were sought and given, school and community projects started, a database on purple loosestrife location and density was created, and the search for solutions was blessed (if not always funded). The response of the public to that first year of the campaign could best be characterized as "we hear you, we are generally with you, what can we do to help?"

Equally important, the first year of activity brought about close collaboration among a number of agencies and individuals interested in solving the problem. Loosestrife was no longer "somebody else's issue"; it had become "everybody's issue".

In 1992, another brochure was produced, the National Workshop on Purple Loosestrife Management in Canada (Rubec and Lee 1992) took place, and the United States and Canada cooperated on finalizing research on and seeking approvals for the use of three European biological control insects. Agriculture Canada, Canada's approving authority for alien biological control agents, joined in to provide the proper safeguards and scientific expertise to the biological control process. Working through a long-standing Canada–US committee, Agriculture Canada expanded the testing to include additional Canadian plants, closely related to purple loosestrife, before approvals for use could be considered. While tedious to some, that testing protocol was essential to the credibility of subsequent approvals for release in Canada and strongly influenced the National Workshop's recommendation that biological controls be the preferred control option. Also in 1992, the honey industry, the Canadian Nursery Trades Association, and many horticultural outlets were given all the available information and asked to participate in the control efforts. Community group actions (digouts, flower head cutting), research on hybridization with cultivars, school and university projects, herbicide trials, and of course, many more media interactions took place. A benchmark review (White et al. 1993) of alien species in natural habitats of Canada was initiated and published the following year, through a collaborative effort between the Canadian Museum of Nature and the CWS. That report would go on to become a "best seller" for Environment Canada. There

have been three printings, and it is currently available on the Internet (http://www.cws-scf.ec.gc.ca/habitat/inv/index_e.html).

To a large degree, 1993 was a repeat of the previous year but for an increasing focus on the production and release of biological control insects and the formation of provincial committees to deal with province-specific initiatives and the distribution of brochures. A toll-free number, sponsored by the Canadian Wildlife Federation, was added to the brochures to facilitate easier, no-cost reporting by the public; this approach was also adopted by the Ontario Federation of Anglers and Hunters in their Project Purple campaign. Of interest was the emergence of a small dissenting faction of gardeners, incited by a newspaper gardening columnist and a radio gardening show commentator. Casting the loosestrife campaign as an anti-gardening, pro-hunting, and pro-fishing initiative, they urged gardeners to ignore the claims of the campaign supporters and to continue planting loosestrife (both wild stock and cultivars). This opposition proved to be very useful in the campaign, as it gave the media a continuing reason to stay tuned to the issue.

In 1994, the campaign took a new turn, one that surprised most of the ad hoc national steering committee. In addition to the campaign's growing support from all quarters, a Manitoba horticultural outlet, convinced by research results that proved *Lythrum* cultivars produced viable seed when crossed with wild stock, took the proactive step of running a *Lythrum* trade-in program. Widely publicized within and outside Manitoba, this private sector initiative not only benefitted the business itself but also helped to convince others in the horticulture trade and gardening activity that reasonable alternatives to beautiful but environmentally unacceptable purple loosestrife were available. The City of Winnipeg provided further assistance by making a vacant greenhouse available to members of the Manitoba Purple Loosestrife Project, who then set about rearing biological control insects on the traded-in plants. A detailed description is given by Lindgren in this publication (p. 259).

A national television documentary, produced by the Canadian Broadcasting Corporation's *The Nature of Things*, was also aired during prime time in 1994 and proved to be the most watched program of the series for that year. Covering a range of invasive alien plants and animals, it has since been replayed a number of times, helping to keep the issue of unwanted alien species in the fore. Later the same year, the Global

Television Network in Canada filmed and aired a piece that moved from loosestrife to European frogbit (*Hydrocharis morsus-ranae* L.), another wetland invader that had escaped from a demonstration pond in Ottawa during the 1930s and was now infesting many of the wetlands of eastern Ontario. Representatives of Global Television asked the ad hoc steering committee, as had several other media outlets, to be kept apprised of other species that might become newsworthy in the future, confirming the willingness of the media to play a role when there is a good story.

In 1995, a breakthrough was made in the control of purple loosestrife when insects released as potential biological control agents succeeded in reducing the stands of purple loosestrife in the Toronto area. In fact, most of the sites where the University of Guelph had released the insects across southern and southeastern Ontario showed evidence of overwintering success of the insects, with visual damage on loosestrife at several locations. The media was again on the alert, wanting to know whether the insect predators would stay on loosestrife or attack something else once the loosestrife was gone. Although the media and the public generally supported the use of biological controls, they still had some lingering uneasiness about interfering with nature (despite expert opinion). This reaction was encouraging because it clearly illustrated the lay public's awareness of ill-conceived biological control attempts that had gone wrong in the past.

From 1996 onward, the purple loosestrife problem became part of broader national and international initiatives dealing with invasive alien species. In March 1996, Environment Canada convened a national think-tank workshop to explore the growing problems and concerns regarding harmful alien species. The United Nation's Norway Conference on Alien Species (summer 1996) was followed up by a World Conservation Congress Workshop in Montréal (October 1996); a third (November 1996) and a fourth meeting (May 1998) of the Conference of the Parties to the Convention on Biological Diversity; and the SBSTTA meeting (June 1999) mentioned earlier. Throughout this period, work on monitoring the impact of biological controls at the various release sites quietly continued. Although the purple loosestrife problem is far from being resolved, the campaign to engender public and political support has subsided. This results partly from a lack of willingness to assign significant resources to the problem and partly from the difficulty of maintaining a high profile for the issue while the released insects go through the laborious process of becoming established and controlling the loosestrife.

Many release sites now exhibit successfully reproducing insect populations and levels of control of loosestrife; however, the abundance of loosestrife, coupled with relatively slow-spreading insect populations and marginal funding for trapping and relocation of wild biological control insects, has yet to yield the range and extent of control desired.

Lessons Learned

The experience derived from attempting to control purple loosestrife is a good basis for building strategies to combat invasive alien species globally. Fundamental to the loosestrife initiative was stimulating political awareness and, more importantly, political buy-in to the processes and programs needed to resolve the problem. The following observations on Canada's purple loosestrife initiative may contribute to the development of a support base for the prevention and control of alien organisms generally and prove useful as elements of any strategic planning for problem solving.

Presenting Scientific Evidence

The evidence of a problem with an alien species must be presented in a way that people can understand. In the case of purple loosestrife, its striking, long-lasting blooms proved useful as the public did not have to be guided to the growing sites. Most wet ditches, riverbanks, and adjacent wetlands were ablaze with the purple flower heads over a two- to three-month period each summer. The task was to link the extensive presence of this species with the absence of other things, to convince the public that behind the beauty was a beast. Although most of the lay public understood the biomass productivity limitations of a site, the few who were challenging the campaign demanded specific measurements of loss or impact. To counter this, a strategy on an invasive alien species should anticipate opposition, analyze the perspective or ulterior motive of that opposition, and prepare honest, factual responses in advance. No one can have all the answers. Respondents should be prepared to admit to a lack of information or data, and if appropriate, give assurance that an answer will be forthcoming. Incomplete evidence is not an excuse for inaction, as the Preamble to the Convention on Biological Diversity clearly articulates. It also notes that where there is a threat of significant reduction or loss of biological diversity, lack of full scientific certainty should not be used as a reason for postponing measures to minimize such a threat.

Building Support

Some interests may be affected by the remedial actions for an invasive alien species; it is important to seek out these factions and understand their concerns. For example, some beekeepers saw purple loosestrife as an important honey producer. The horticultural industry had been marketing loosestrife and related cultivars for several decades, aided and abetted by cultivar research efforts of Agriculture Canada, and purple loosestrife had become an accepted garden ornamental. Representatives from these groups were thus included in the 1992 National Workshop on Purple Loosestrife Management in Canada (Rubec and Lee 1992) and played a key role in sensitizing others to the economic benefits and drawbacks that could occur from a national anti-loosestrife campaign. The nonconfrontational, nonlegislative approach that followed this workshop reflected those sensitivities and made supporters and participants out of potential dissenters.

Support was also built by including representatives from biological control and herbicide companies in the National Workshop. Potentially these participants could be either partners in the solution-delivery process or, as environmental interests saw them, problem creators. The frank and open discussion that ensued among all parties, however, created an atmosphere of respect. Eventually, all agreed that the biological control approach was the most acceptable and most effective. The herbicide controls, although not endorsed because they were not substantive, were also not ruled out for future consideration.

Environment Canada's March 1996 alien species think-tank also included Transport Canada representatives involved with the ballast water control program. Ballast water discharge is a common vector for the entry and spread of alien species. Discussions of issues concerning various alien species helped to provide these individuals with a renewed sense of purpose in their efforts to deal with ships' ballast. The Transport Canada representatives, in turn, were able to sensitize proponents for change to ballast rules to the specific difficulties in effecting such change, for example, the impact changes could have on ship safety and ship registration. The issue of ballast water is discussed in detail in Wiley and Claudi's article in this publication (p. 233). However, input into international protocols on ballast discharge by parties other than the shipping industry will be necessary for a more expedient completion and implementation of changes to these protocols.

Public involvement and concern can help to accelerate action. Crusaders in an alien species campaign can learn from the public debates on the issue of genetically modified organisms (GMOs). GMOs quickly went from being a non-issue to having an international protocol established on their production and use. This debate was driven by citizens' groups and professionals in the field skeptical of responses on the long-term consequences of GMOs on human and ecological health, once again illustrating the power of the interested public.

Harmful alien species can directly impact ecological and economic health, as was the case of infestations of the brown spruce longhorn beetle (*Tetropium fuscum* (F.)) of spruce trees in Nova Scotia. Public lobbying regarding the source and entry pathways for the beetles could do much to raise awareness and support for detection and prevention actions.

Communicating to the Public and the Media

Before the purple loosestrife campaign began, it would have been difficult to find many Canadians who knew what purple loosestrife was, let alone its environmental effects. Through brochures, posters, and media interviews, public awareness blossomed, making the task of moving into the solution-delivery stage much easier.

As mentioned earlier, the wording of the original brochures initially caused some concerns. Scientists were trying to write catchy paragraphs for a lay public, alongside professional nonscientist writers trying to capture the highlights of the science. Both points of view were required and middle ground was eventually struck. Subsequent brochures and information pamphlets went much more smoothly. Of importance, however, was the response to the first brochure. The title *Beautiful Killer* and some of the provocative statements made in the brochure proved to be the needed catalyst to start the program. The text conjured images of the "death" of wetlands due to purple loosestrife and described this as "colorful silence". The experience with this brochure supports an aggressive strategy in initial communications on an invasive species. The first document should be hard-hitting, factual, and dramatic yet hopeful; it should then be followed by increasingly positive and constructive messages and brochures.

The media (print and broadcast) played a major role in conveying the message about purple loosestrife.

Release of *Beautiful Killer* soon led to media requests for more details on the extent and nature of the problem, and what the ad hoc national steering committee was planning to do about it. Subsequently, members of the media began to explore the pros and cons of possible solutions and, on occasion, posed questions raised by those objecting to the campaign. In response to these questions, as well as to those beginning to come to the Canadian Wildlife Service via questions in the House of Parliament, a series of questions and answers (Q&A's) was prepared, which all agencies began using in media responses. The Q&A's provided a consistent flow of information to the public and a means of checking the accuracy of the information. Occasionally the media were given the Q&A's in advance of an interview, helping to stimulate more meaningful interviews. The media can thus be a useful ally in the war against invasive aliens. They must be treated fairly (for example, given all available information including the issues raised by detractors), made aware of significant events and issues, and given some possible news "angles". Surprisingly, perhaps, in an age of confrontation, cooperative partnerships can be forged and a good story on an important issue gets out.

Delivering Solutions

Perhaps the toughest part of a remedial program is the delivery of solutions, partly because it can often be the most expensive aspect of the program and partly because the initial enthusiasm of issue awareness and strategic planning may be wearing off. Maintaining interest for up to four to five years, or more, is difficult. In addition, the delivery of the solution may involve a new set of partners, or a major new role for a previously less active partner. Although involving others is inevitable (and probably necessary), maintaining connections with the original partners is advantageous from the perspective of credibility, resources, and initial focus. To date this has worked well for the purple loosestrife campaign in Canada.

Most of the parties originally involved in the loosestrife initiative are still active; however, the roles of many of them have evolved. For example, university-driven research on the rearing and release techniques of biological control insects has given way to the collection and transport of successful wild populations. Monitoring and assessment of release continues, again mainly driven by university and nongovernmental organizations. Federal, provincial, and territorial governments are broadening their alien species initiatives in response

to obligations under the Convention on Biological Diversity, but continue to refer back to relationships and partnerships from the loosestrife initiative as a basis for dialogue and cooperation.

Finding the Hook for Political Support

In retrospect, perhaps the most important component of the loosestrife campaign was finding the right "hook" on which to hang the issue. The nationwide concern for wetland loss and the threat of further losses from purple loosestrife proved to be a key ingredient in obtaining the support of the public and the politicians.

Issues of invasive alien species can be linked to concerns for biodiversity conservation and protection of endangered species, which are readily understood and already established. Public and political support can be garnered through such issues, if properly presented. For example, a preliminary analysis of the 1998 COSEWIC list of endangered, threatened, and vulnerable species suggested that about 25% of Canada's endangered, 31% of its threatened, and 16% of its vulnerable species are in some way at risk because of alien species. (COSEWIC, the Committee on the Status of Endangered Wildlife in Canada, comprises federal, provincial, and territorial experts, supported by the Canadian Wildlife Service; it assesses the status of species and, as required, implements recovery programs.) The public is sensitive to species in peril, and the Canadian government is currently establishing endangered species legislation. A concerted effort to build remedial programs on alien species into the recovery plans for affected native species under this legislation should therefore be fruitful.

A process that assesses and grades the impact of harmful alien species could lead to priority-setting initiatives and remedial planning. Sound scientific assessments and remedial plans to deal with these unwanted aliens would have to be part of an action program that could be endorsed politically and publicly.

Conclusions

The kinds of partnerships, struggles, and opportunities that arose from dealing with purple loosestrife have generic applications to national and global initiatives on other invasive alien species. The 1996 World Conservation Congress workshop and the United Nation's Norway Conference (previously mentioned) have shown that all nations face similar issues and could benefit from shared experiences and information. Canada has the opportunity to make some progress on the issue through a well-planned and coordinated effort. Building public and political awareness of the problems alien species represent is the necessary first step towards prevention and mitigation.

References

Rubec, C.D.A.; Lee, G.O., editors. 1992. Draft Proceedings of a National Workshop on Purple Loosestrife Management in Canada, 3–5 March, 1992. Canadian Wildlife Service, Environment Canada/North American Wetlands Conservation Council (Canada), Ottawa, ON. Unpublished report. 195 p.

Sandlund, O.T.; Schei, P.J.; Viken, A. 1996. Proceedings of the Norway/UN Conference on Alien Species. Trondheim, Norway. Directorate for Nature Management, Trondheim, Norway. 233 p.

Thompson, D.Q.; Stuckey, R.L.; Thompson, E.B. 1987. Spread, impact and control of purple loosestrife, *Lythrum salicaria*, in North American wetlands. US Fish and Wildlife Service, Department of the Interior, Washington, DC. 55 p.

White, D.J.; Haber, E.; Keddy, C. 1993. Invasive plants of natural habitats in Canada. Canadian Wildlife Service, Environment Canada/Canadian Museum of Nature/North American Wetlands Conservation Council (Canada), Ottawa, ON. 121 p.

Photo with chapter title: Purple loosetrife. Photo by G. Bowles and C. Medina.

Manitoba Purple Loosestrife Project: Partnerships and Initiatives in the Control of an Invasive Alien Species

Cory J. Lindgren

As the trend towards globalized economies continues, the introduction rate of alien species into Canada, which includes alien plant species, is not likely to decline. "In the last 200 years as intercontinental travel has increased we have effectively broken down barriers to plant dispersal that have driven evolution since the breakup of Pangaea, the original supercontinent." (Reichard and Hamilton 1997). The landscaping trade has been, and continues to be, instrumental in the proliferation of alien plant species, including purple loosestrife (*Lythrum salicaria* L.). For example, of the 235 woody plants that have been introduced to North America and naturalized, 85% have been introduced through the landscape trade and the remainder through agriculture and forestry activities (Reichard 1994). The majority of these alien plant introductions have been environmentally benign. However, several, including purple loosestrife, have resulted in the loss of our native flora and fauna, changing the integrity of our ecosystems. The ultimate result of alien invaders of natural habitats is the loss of native biodiversity (Catling 1997).

Introductions of alien species can have significant environmental and economic consequences. Wilcove et al. (1996) reported that 46% of threatened and endangered species in the United States are at risk because of alien species. Similarly Stein and Flack (1996) estimated that alien species have contributed to the decline of 42% of threatened or endangered species in the United States and have caused an estimated $97 billion in direct economic loss. Purple loosestrife is an economic and environmental concern to wildlife managers, conservation biologists, weed supervisors, weed inspectors, horticulturalists, anglers, hunters, farmers, naturalists, and so on. It has impacted riparian and wetland habitats, agricultural areas, roadside ditches and rights-of-way, farm dugouts, railway lines, and pipelines.

Partnerships and cooperation among agencies to achieve shared objectives is not a novel approach towards the management of natural areas. With the current trend being to manage natural areas from a larger ecosystem vision, the formation of partnerships between agencies and across political boundaries is becoming more common. The Manitoba Purple Loose-strife Project (MPLP) is one example of how partnerships have been used to address an alien species issue. In this paper, I discuss these collaborative partnerships and highlight some of the initiatives taken in the management of purple loosestrife in Manitoba.

Formation of the Manitoba Purple Loosestrife Project

Purple loosestrife is a Eurasian perennial plant that was accidentally introduced into North America in the early 1800s (Thompson et al. 1987). It was first reported in Manitoba in1896 (Scoggan 1957, p. 619) and has since been described as an invasive alien, a noxious weed, a wetland invader, a beautiful killer, as well as a popular garden perennial. However, there is little doubt that purple loosestrife is an invasive species that has disrupted the ecology of natural habitats across North America by displacing native vegetation (Figure 1),

Figure 1. Seeds from garden plantings of purple loosestrife in Winnipeg, MB, flowed downstream along the Red River to the Netley-Libau Marsh (shown here in 1999), located on the Lake Winnipeg shoreline. The extensive loosestrife infestation changed the native plant community. No biological control agents have been released on this population of loosestrife.

and in many cases, forming dense monocultures. Wildlife that depended upon the displaced native vegetation for food, shelter, and breeding areas is forced to leave habitats invaded by purple loosestrife. Mal et al. (1992) concluded that where purple loosestrife populations are on the increase, wildlife species are in decline. In the absence of its natural predators, purple loosestrife has spread into every major river system and watershed in southern Manitoba and has been found as far north as The Pas.

Purple loosestrife has presented a unique challenge to those individuals and groups concerned with its invasion into Manitoba. Initial efforts to control this plant began not in the field, but in the backyard, where educational campaigns and public outreach programs were focused. These initiatives would not have been successful without the forging of partnerships. Groups with diverse agendas were drawn together by a common objective—to address the significant habitat losses resulting from the invasion of purple loosestrife in Manitoba.

In the early 1990s, no one agency was capable of addressing the invasion of purple loosestrife into Manitoba and, furthermore, no one agency was in any position to fund an invasive species control program. Collaboration was necessary. As a result, a number of agencies formed a multipartnered working group comprising local community groups, provincial and federal agencies, and nonprofit groups to address the loss of habitat attributed to the invasion of purple loosestrife in Manitoba. The group was initiated in 1992 after several individuals from Manitoba attended meetings held in Ottawa addressing concerns over purple loosestrife in Canada (the March 1992 National Workshop on Purple Loosestrife Management). The multipartnered Manitoba Purple Loosestrife Project became a reality as a nonprofit coalition between Agriculture and Agri-Food Canada; the City of Winnipeg; the Canadian Wildlife Service, Environment Canada; Ducks Unlimited Canada; Manitoba Conservation; the Manitoba Naturalists Society; the Manitoba Weed Supervisors Association; and the Delta Waterfowl Foundation.[1] Partnerships provided opportunities to pool agency resources; this has been critically important because the project has never had long-term sustained funding. The list of stakeholder groups, or partners, within the MPLP reflects the

many environmental disciplines with interest in the management of an alien species.

The project partners formulated a mission statement with the following objectives to direct project activities:

- increase community awareness through education;

- lead habitat restoration and purple loosestrife removal campaigns;

- develop a purple loosestrife distributional database through mapping and monitoring the spread of purple loosestrife in Manitoba; and

- deliver a sustainable classical biological control program.

These objectives have guided the MPLP since 1992.

Since the formation of the MPLP, partnerships have been forged and initiatives taken. These are discussed in the following sections and a summary can be found in Table 1. Some initiatives are discussed following the section on partnerships.

MPLP Partnerships

Nongovernmental Organizations

The diverse nature of the project collaborators has provided the MPLP with opportunities to deliver an invasive species program across numerous levels. Partnerships with grassroots community groups or nongovernmental organizations have been most productive. Groups such as the Manitoba Weed Supervisors Association (MWSA) and the Manitoba Naturalists Society (MNS) have been instrumental in delivering the program into local communities and to local landowners. The MWSA has served as the eyes and ears of the initiative— 35 municipalities in Manitoba support weed supervisors who annually identify purple loosestrife populations in their district and report the data to the MPLP. Partnerships with the various weed districts of the MWSA have been important in communicating project objectives and in delivering educational materials into the individual communities within each weed district. The MWSA has also been active in rearing and releasing biological control agents as well as monitoring their performance post-release.

Ducks Unlimited Canada has also been instrumental in the delivery of project objectives. It has provided office space, support, and significant in-kind and financial contributions to the project. The organization has led efforts to produce varied educational material and

---

[1] Agriculture and Agri-Food Canada was formerly known as Agriculture Canada and Manitoba Conservation as the Manitoba Department of Natural Resources and Manitoba Environment.

Table 1. Chronology of major Manitoba Purple Loosestrife Project (MPLP) initiatives and partnerships.

Year	Initiatives	Partners
1992	Formation of MPLP	Agriculture and Agri-Food Canada; City of Winnipeg; Canadian Wildlife Service; Delta Waterfowl Foundation; Ducks Unlimited Canada; Manitoba Conservation (Wildlife, Environment); Manitoba Naturalists Society; Manitoba Weed Supervisors Association; Manitoba Agriculture
	Funding for importation of biocontrol agents into Canada	Province of Ontario; Ducks Unlimited Canada
	Release of *Hylobius transversovittatus*	Agriculture and Agri-Food Canada (Lethbridge)
1994	Support from garden/seed center received	T&T Seeds Catalogue
	Purple Loosestrife in Western Canada brochure produced	Canadian Nursery Trades Association— 8 partners
	Winnipeg Purple Loosestrife Swap Program	City of Winnipeg; Urban Green Team Program; Ducks Unlimited Canada
1995	Set-up of the Saskatchewan Purple Loosestrife Project assisted	Saskatchewan Purple Loosestrife Group; Ducks Unlimited Canada
	MPLP becomes Canadian contact for biological control of purple loosestrife	Expert Committee on Weeds
	Biocontrol mass rearing in Manitoba	City of Winnipeg; Manitoba Weed Supervisors Association
	Manitoba survey finds no retail sales of *Lythrum*	MPLP
	Public service announcements and educational video	Red River College
1996	Purple loosestrife Web site	Ducks Unlimited Canada
	Provincial purple loosestrife swap program	Manitoba Weed Supervisors Association
	Manitoba's *Noxious Weeds Act* revised to include all *Lythrum* spp.	Manitoba Agriculture
	European collection of *Nanophyes* spp.	Cornell University; Minnesota Department of Natural Resources
	Research into integrated vegetation management	University of Manitoba; Institute for Waterfowl and Wetlands Research
1997	*What You Should Know...* brochure	US agencies; Ontario Federation of Anglers and Hunters
1999	Aquatic nuisance species surveys in Manitoba initiated	Fish Futures Inc.; Manitoba Conservation
2000	Summary chapter for a publication on the Canadian biological control effort, 1992–99	University of Guelph; Agriculture and Agri-Food Canada; Natural Resources Canada

assisted with the construction, and is the host of, the MPLP purple loosestrife information center (www.ducks.ca/purple/).

Provincial and Federal Governments

The roles of the provincially based agencies have allowed for overall program coordination and delivery across Manitoba. Since purple loosestrife can be found through most of southern Manitoba, project partners felt it was important that an individual from Manitoba Conservation function as the chair of the MPLP. Manitoba Conservation has also contributed financial support.

The Canadian Wildlife Service (CWS) provided the initial seed money that allowed for the formation of the MPLP in 1992. Individuals from the CWS (see paper by Lee, p. 253 in this publication) developed the initial partnerships with US cooperators that allowed for the introduction of biological control agents into Canada. The CWS enabled the delivery of an invasive species program on a larger regional basis, which has fostered greater awareness of invasive plants across Canada. For example, funds were made available by the CWS to reprint and distribute the educational brochure *Purple Loosestrife in Western Canada*.

North American Neighbors

Efforts to manage purple loosestrife in Manitoba have benefitted from partnerships forged internationally. Managing invasive species cannot be achieved by maintaining only a local or even a provincial perspective. Invasive species cross boundaries. Manitoba must be kept aware of what programs are being delivered by its neighbors: Saskatchewan, Ontario, North Dakota, and Minnesota. The MPLP has partnered with these Manitoba neighbors in various initiatives. Biological control initiatives involving the Minnesota Department of Natural Resources are discussed in another section in this paper.

Local Media

The media has unknowingly been an invisible partner in the MPLP. Media stories reach a large number of people in a short time and are usually cost effective. Tangley (1997) pointed out that to be successful in science and conservation, communication is critical. All efforts to control invasive alien species should involve a partnership with the media. Initially it was not difficult to enlist the media as invasive purple loosestrife was considered newsworthy. The challenge has been maintaining and cultivating media interest. This has

been achieved by providing new opportunities in which the media can participate.

One such opportunity involves dig-out campaigns. Most efforts to control purple loosestrife through these campaigns provide little, if any, sustained control. A single mature purple loosestrife plant can generate as many as 2.7 million seeds annually (Thompson et al. 1987); hence, the resulting seed bank is immense. However, a dig-out or removal campaign can attract grassroots involvement, foster awareness, and capture media attention. In Manitoba, there are numerous youth groups that want to be partners in environmental projects and can provide a day or half-day of volunteer labor. Inviting the media to cover a community-based purple loosestrife removal campaign presents opportunities to cultivate awareness of the loosestrife issue. In almost all cases, the MPLP has been successful in attracting the local media to cover local purple loosestrife dig-outs, which have received front page coverage on numerous occasions.

The Community

Community education is the foundation upon which any environmental or conservation program striving for success should be built. In addressing concerns and management of invasive species, one must strive to foster broad public and private awareness. The model program to control any invasive species cannot be delivered effectively without community buy-in, and even more importantly, a sense of community ownership. The importance of communicating the environmental consequences of an invasive species, as well as what can be done and how the public can become a partner, cannot be over stressed.

The task of the MPLP was to present community groups with accurate scientific data showing that all varieties of *Lythrum* were contributing to habitat loss. This demanding task was made even more so in the early 1990s when a local nursery worker announced in the popular media that garden cultivars were indeed safe for use. It was also difficult, and in some cases has been impossible, to convince gardeners who had cultivated purple loosestrife for over 20 years that they should destroy it. It became evident that to manage purple loosestrife in Manitoba, bridges needed to be built with horticulturists and gardeners. As a result, they were invited to become a partner in the production of the 1994 brochure *Purple Loosestrife in Western Canada*, which targeted gardeners. The intention of the brochure was to increase awareness and provide gardeners with environmentally safe alternatives to the *Lythrum* cultivars. This educational product, coupled with the purple loosestrife exchange program (discussed in a subsequent section), has resulted in the elimination of *Lythrum* from numerous gardens across Manitoba.

A number of educational initiatives have been delivered by the MPLP to increase awareness of the negative environmental impacts associated with the spread of purple loosestrife in Manitoba. With each educational product have come new partnerships. Products include brochures, posters, public service announcements, educational videos, interpretative signage, and a Web site dedicated to purple loosestrife. Project partners such as the MWSA, MNS, Manitoba Agriculture, Ducks Unlimited Canada, and the City of Winnipeg have provided opportunities to foster community awareness through annual meetings, magazines, and newsletters.

Public Outreach: The Swap Program

In a proactive effort to educate and encourage gardeners to destroy their purple loosestrife, a purple loosestrife exchange (or swap) program was developed in Manitoba in 1994. At the time, purple loosestrife was a popular plant in gardens across Manitoba; homes on every city block within Winnipeg displayed it. The MPLP's strategy was to enlist the support of gardeners through a program that would provide an environmentally safe perennial replacement (*Liatris* spp.) for loosestrife, at no cost to the gardener.

The MPLP created the Project Purple Green Team to provide a free removal service for senior citizens and residents otherwise unable to dig out their purple loosestrife. It was staffed through the province's Urban Green Team Program. The City of Winnipeg made available greenhouse space as an in-kind project contribution from which to run the swap program.

The success of the exchange program depended upon a high level of media coverage. Each first of June news releases were sent to Manitoba newspapers and television stations. In 1997, after an article on the swap program was published in the *Winnipeg Free Press*, about 50 people per day for the next few days dropped off their purple loosestrife and another 75 phone calls were received within 24 hours of the article's publication.

In 1994, a surprise partner came forth. T&T Seeds, a large horticultural operation based in Winnipeg, placed a full-page color advertisement in their catalog describing the dangers of purple loosestrife and provided gardeners with suggested environmentally safe replacement plants (see page 41, 1994 T&T Seeds catalog). T&T Seeds also provided the MPLP with environmentally safe perennials for the swap program at below cost. It is through the proactive initiatives of T&T Seeds and the City of Winnipeg that purple loosestrife in residential gardens is being destroyed.

Cultivar Confusion: When Is an Invasive Species a Garden Flower?

Considerable confusion existed within the gardening community and the commercial horticultural industry surrounding the sterility of *Lythrum* cultivars. The greatest challenge to the control of purple loosestrife was, and still is in many parts of Canada, its horticultural sale. Numerous cultivars of purple loosestrife have been developed for use in residential landscaping and gardens (Harp and Collicut 1983; Anderson and Ascher 1993; Ottenbreit and Staniforth 1994). Agriculture and Agri-Food Canada introduced Morden Pink as a garden cultivar in 1937, followed by Morden Gleam in 1953 and Morden Rose in 1954 (Harp and Collicutt 1983). These garden cultivars were advertised by Agriculture and Agri-Food Canada as ideal perennials for the home garden, excellent choices for perennial or mixed borders, and winter hardy. In the late 1980s and early 1990s, garden centers in Manitoba estimated that in some years their annual revenues from the sale of *Lythrum* cultivars alone approached $10 000. These cultivars were sold as sterile plants and therefore could not produce seed or contribute to the naturalization of purple loosestrife. At the time, it was believed that these cultivars could not contribute to the spread of purple loosestrife.

Purple loosestrife has been listed in Manitoba's *Noxious Weeds Act* since the early 1980s. However, the act did not give any associated scientific name. The questions arose: Are the garden varieties of purple loosestrife, *L. virgatum*, considered noxious weeds? Is the designation restricted to the naturalized *L. salicaria*? Is the entire *Lythrum* family considered a noxious weed? Subsequent research showed that all *Lythrum* garden cultivars produce viable pollen and seed and can spread (Anderson and Ascher 1993; Lindgren and Clay 1993; Ottenbreit and Staniforth 1994). Armed with these scientific data, the MPLP approached Manitoba Agriculture to suggest the listing for purple loosestrife be revised to eliminate any cultivar confusion. The Government of Manitoba revised the *Noxious Weeds Act* in March 1996 to include purple loosestrife (*Lythrum* spp.) and all its cultivars. In Manitoba, individuals can be fined for selling or planting loosestrife. Legally defining all varieties of purple loosestrife as noxious weeds was the biggest step towards implementing an effective purple loosestrife control program, second only to community education. No invasive species can effectively be controlled or managed unless it is recognized as deleterious by the public and legally identified as such.

The City of Winnipeg[2] and the rural municipalities of Morris and Montcalm undertook their own proactive measures to control purple loosestrife. In 1993, the City of Winnipeg adopted a policy to remove all purple loosestrife and domestic cultivars planted in parks maintained by the city. In 1996, the Morris–Montcalm Weed District designated purple loosestrife (*Lythrum* spp.) as a local noxious weed. These actions have further allowed weed supervisors and weed inspectors to approach residents with purple loosestrife in their gardens and request removal.

Biological Weed Control Program

Biological control programs against weeds have historically been targeted at agricultural weeds. Because purple loosestrife is a weed of aquatic habitats, new audiences are being introduced to biological weed control (Blossey et al. 1996). In 1992, the MPLP launched an aggressive media campaign. The primary message was that purple loosestrife was an alien invasive species responsible for habitat losses. This was followed by a notice that the MPLP intended to release another alien species to control purple loosestrife. Members of the general public expressed concern that to control one alien plant species (purple loosestrife) yet more alien species (biological control insects) were being released— in somewhat the same way as the old woman in the famous American folk poem sent a spider after a fly she swallowed, then a bird after the spider, and so on. The public realized that the introduction of an alien species was not without consequences.

Why use an alien species to control another alien species? Past attempts to control purple loosestrife by cutting, burning, mowing, or water manipulation (cultural and mechanical control methods) had not pro-

vided any sustained control. In addition, no herbicides are registered for the control of purple loosestrife near or over open water in Canada. Even if that had not been the case, the MPLP was not comfortable with the use of herbicides near sensitive aquatic habitats. As well, no native insects were capable of limiting purple loosestrife populations (Diehl et al. 1997). Since no effective management strategies existed for purple loosestrife, Agriculture and Agri-Food Canada recommended that biological weed control agents be released against purple loosestrife in Canada (De Clerck-Floate 1992). The classical biological control of alien weeds is the deliberate use of herbivorous insects to reduce the population density of an alien target weed below its economic injury level (Gassmann and Schroeder 1995; see also Harris and Shamoun in this publication, p. 291). Biological control currently represents a potential long-term management strategy for purple loosestrife (Malecki et al. 1993; Blossey et al. 1994; Hight et al. 1995).

The release of biological control agents in Manitoba involved collaboration between the MPLP and the associated government and public bodies. In the summer of 1992, approval was received from the Canadian government for the release of biological control agents against purple loosestrife (Hight et al. 1995). The MPLP also requested and received a letter of support for a biological weed control program against purple loosestrife from the Manitoba Minister of Agriculture. Because no formal provincial processes were identified for releasing biological control agents in Manitoba, the MPLP initiated two proactive steps. First, an application for a pesticide use permit was adapted for use in the biological weed control program. Through this permit process, agent releases were approved through Manitoba Conservation. Second, through notices in local newspapers before actual agent releases, the general public was provided with opportunities to comment on the releases of these agents. The Manitoba biological control program proceeded in October 1992, with releases of the root-boring weevil *Hylobius transversovittatus* (Goeze) near Spruce Woods Provincial Park, followed by initial releases of the leaf-eating beetle *Galerucella calmariensis* (L.) in June of 1993. The MPLP currently mass-rears biological control agents for release into Manitoba habitats.

Establishing a biological weed control program within the capital region of Winnipeg has presented challenges that have required forming further partnerships between the MPLP and the City of Winnipeg's Insect Control Branch and Weed Control Branch.

---

[2] The City of Winnipeg has been a lead partner of the MPLP since its inception. Its involvement is discussed throughout this paper in lieu of a separate section identifying its role. The City of Winnipeg has provided both in-kind and financial support.

Winnipeg has its fair share of mosquitoes and the City of Winnipeg has an aggressive mosquito control program. The Insect Control Branch uses granules of the insecticide Dursban[3] to control mosquito larvae and fogs with malathion to control adult mosquitoes. In areas where the MPLP has released biological control agents, the Insect Control Branch agreed not to fog with malathion. It does use Dursban in these areas as the biological control agents do not have an aquatic life stage and therefore will not be affected by the insecticide. The Weed Control Branch has also been cooperative concerning the biological control agents and refrains from herbicide applications where these insects have been released. The cooperation and partnerships with the City of Winnipeg have been vital to establishing and sustaining a biological control program in the capital region of Winnipeg.

Partnerships between Canadian provinces have allowed for continued monitoring of the performance of the biological control program and sharing of beetles across Canada. When biological control agents are released, individual agencies across Canada forward release records to the MPLP so that a central Canadian database is available. Between 1992 and 1999, close to one million agents have been released across Canada, with provinces reporting various levels of success (Lindgren et al. 2001). Initial results indicate that the biological control effort is providing measurable levels of control. Data from an ongoing long-term monitoring project in Manitoba have indicated that close to 100% control (Figure 2) has been achieved in many areas (Lindgren 2000).

The Minnesota Department of Natural Resources Purple Loosestrife Program (Luke Skinner, Coordinator) and Cornell University's Department of Natural Resources (Bernd Blossey, Director) have also been instrumental in the development of a biological control program against purple loosestrife in Manitoba. The Minnesota Purple Loosestrife Program, established in 1987, was the first project of its kind in the United States (Skinner et al. 1994) and has served as a model for the MPLP. The objectives of the MPLP are similar to those of the Minnesota Purple Loosestrife Program. Both of the above agencies have provided the MPLP with biological control agents and shared their experience on rear-

Figure 2. The biological control agent *Galerucella calmariensis* was released on this population of purple loosestrife in the Netley-Libau Marsh, Manitoba, in 1994 (*upper*). By 1998, nearly 100% control of the loosestrife was achieved and has been maintained through 2000 (*lower*).

ing, releasing, and monitoring the performance of the insects. In 1996, the MPLP also partnered with these agencies to collect biological control agents, the weevils *Nanophyes marmoratus* Goeze and *N. brevis* Boheman[4], from Europe.

Partnerships between agencies, between provinces, and between countries will ultimately allow for further support of the biological weed control program against purple loosestrife and provide a basis for actions to combat other invasive species in the future. According to Blossey et al. (1996), one of the major accomplishments of the biological weed control program against purple loosestrife in North America has been in keeping the numerous agencies actively involved and informed.

Is Purple Loosestrife Under Control?

At present, the MPLP cannot announce that purple loosestrife is under control in Manitoba. If the biological control agents continue to perform as effectively as they have since their release in 1992, measurable

---

[3] Dursban is a trademark of Dow AgroSciences LLC. Dow AgroSciences Canada Inc. is a licensed user.

[4] *Nanophyes brevis* was not released in Canada.

levels of control across many naturalized areas in Canada are predicted. Unfortunately, a number of provincial programs for biological control have been discontinued due to a lack of long-term funding, and such funding sources are a requisite for combating invasive species. Since its formation the MPLP has funded project initiatives through short-term partnerships (Table 2). In most cases, three to five years of funding is not sufficient to establish a biological weed control program for an invasive plant species—planning must be done for 10–20-year programs.

The MPLP must also continue to partner with the horticultural industry towards the elimination of all *Lythrum* cultivars from residential gardens as they represent a seed and pollen source. While some provinces have been successful in eliminating the sale of *Lythrum*, it is still available in other provinces. The battle against invasive species cannot progress if one province institutes a management program while another province liberally retails the same invasive species. Nationwide, and preferably continent-wide, management programs are required to avoid such situations.

Table 2. Manitoba Purple Loosestrife Project funding sources, 1992–2000.

Category	Funding sources
Private	Murphy Foundation
	Canada Trust Friends of the Environment
	Shell Environmental Fund
	Manitoba Hydro
	Ducks Unlimited Canada
	City of Winnipeg
	North American Waterfowl Management Plan
	Fish Futures Inc.
Provincial	Sustainable Development Innovations Fund
	Special Conservation Fund
	Fisheries Enhancement Initiative
	Urban Green Team Program
	Manitoba Conservation
	Manitoba Liquor Control Commission
Federal	EcoAction 2000
	Action 21
	Canadian Wildlife Service, Environment Canada
	Canada-Manitoba Agreement on Agricultural Sustainability

Partnerships, task forces, working groups, and so on are usually forged when an invasive species has already reached a crisis level. The management of purple loosestrife across Canada has been no exception. Effective purple loosestrife control across Canada requires a national effort involving partnerships within and between provinces, and between the various levels of the federal and provincial governments. A Canadian strategy for the prevention of invasive plant species is also needed. Initial steps may include the development of federal legislation to be used to coordinate weed control programs among provinces. For example, although purple loosestrife and all its cultivated varieties have noxious weed status in Manitoba, Alberta, and Prince Edward Island, during the summer of 2000 purple loosestrife was included in the landscaping around the provincial government buildings in Québec City. Partnerships can provide the infrastructure from which alien invasive species can be managed and perhaps the introduction of new species can be prevented.

References

Anderson, N.O.; Ascher, P.D. 1993. Male and female fertility of loosestrife (*Lythrum*) cultivars. J. Am. Soc. Hortic. Sci. 118:851–858.

Blossey, B.; Malecki, R.A.; Schroeder, D.; Skinner, L. 1996. A biological weed control programme using insects against purple loosestrife, *Lythrum salicaria*, in North America. Pages 351–355 *in* V.C. Moran and J.H. Hoffmann, eds. Proceedings of the IX International Symposium on Biological Control of Weeds, 19–26 January 1996, Stellenbosch, South Africa. University of Cape Town.

Blossey, B.; Schroeder, D.; Hight, S.D.; Malecki, R. 1994. Host specificity and environmental impact of two leaf beetles (*Galerucella calmariensis* and *G. pusilla*) for biological control of purple loosestrife (*Lythrum salicaria*). Weed Sci. 42:134–140.

Catling, P.M. 1997. The problem of invading alien trees and shrubs: some observations in Ontario and a Canadian Checklist. Can. Field-Nat. 111:338–342.

De Clerck-Floate, R. 1992. The desirability of using biocontrol against purple loosestrife in Canada. Agriculture Canada, Lethbridge, AB. 27 p.

Diehl, J.K.; Holliday, N.J.; Lindgren, C.J.; Roughley, R.E. 1997. Insects associated with purple loosestrife, *Lythrum salicaria* L., in southern Manitoba. Can. Entomol. 129:937–948.

Gassmann, A.; Schroeder, D. 1995. The search for effective biological control agents in Europe: history and lessons from leafy spurge (*Euphorbia esula* L.) and cypress spurge (*Euphorbia cyparissias* L.). Biol. Control 5:466–477.

Harp, H.F; Collicutt, L.M. 1983. *Lythrums* for home gardens. Morden Research Station, Morden, MB. Agriculture Canada Publ. 1285E.

Hight, S.D.; Blossey, B.; Laing, J.; De Clerck-Floate, R. 1995. Establishment of insect biological control agents from Europe against *Lythrum salicaria* in North America. Environ. Entomol. 44:965–977.

Lindgren, C.J. 2000. Performance of a biological control agent, *Galerucella calmariensis* (Coleoptera: Chrysomelidae) on purple loosestrife *Lythrum salicaria* L. in southern Manitoba. Pages 367–382 *in* N.R. Spencer, ed. Proceedings of the X International Symposium on Biological Control of Weeds, 4–10 July 1999, Bozeman, MT.

Lindgren, C.J.; Clay, R.T. 1993. Fertility of Morden Pink *Lythrum virgatum* L. transplanted into wild stands of *L. salicaria* L. in Manitoba. Hort. Sci. 28:954.

Lindgren, C.J.; Corrigan, J.; De Clerk-Floate, R. 2001. *Lythrum salicaria* L. (Lythraceae). *In* P.G. Mason and J.T. Huber, eds. Biological control programmes in Canada, 1981–2000. CABI Publishing, Wallingford, Oxon, UK.

Mal, T.K.; Lovett-Doust, J.; Lovett-Doust, L.; Mulligan, G.A. 1992. The biology of Canadian weeds. 100. *Lythrum salicaria*. Can. J. Plant Sci. 72:1305–1330.

Malecki, R.A.; Blossey, B.; Hight, S.D.; Schroeder, D.; Kok, L.T.; Coulson, J.R. 1993. Biological control of purple loosestrife; a case for using insects as control agents, after rigorous screening and for integrating release strategies with research. BioScience 43:680–686.

Ottenbreit, K.; Staniforth, R.J. 1994. Crossability of naturalized and cultivated *Lythrum* taxa. Can. J. Bot. 72:337–341.

Reichard, S.E. 1994. Assessing the potential of invasiveness in woody plants introduced in North America. University of Washington, Seattle, WA.

Reichard, S.H.; Hamilton, C.W. 1997. Predicting invasions of woody plants introduced into North America. Conserv. Biol.11:193–203.

Scoggan, H.J. 1957. Flora of Manitoba. Natl. Mus. Can. Bull. 140.

Skinner, L.C.; Rendall, W.J.; Fuge, E. 1994. Minnesota's purple loosestrife program: history, findings and management recommendations. Minn. Dep. Nat. Resour. Spec. Publ. 145. 29 p.

Stein, B.A.; S. Flack, editors. 1996. America's least wanted: alien species invasions of U.S. ecosystems. The Nature Conservancy, Arlington, VA. 31 p.

Tangley, L. 1997. The importance of communicating with the public. *In* G. Meffe and C. Ronald Carrol, eds. Principles of conservation biology. 2nd ed. Sinauer Associates, Inc. Sunderland, MA.

Thompson, D.Q.; Stuckey, R.L.; Thompson, E.B. 1987. Spread, impact and control of purple loosestrife (*Lythrum salicaria*) in North American wetlands. US Fish Wildl. Serv. Fish Wild. Res. 2. 55 p.

Wilcove, D.S.; Bean, M.J.; Bonnie, R.; McMillan, M. 1996. Rebuilding the ark: toward a more effective endangered species act for private land. Environmental Defense Fund, Washington, DC.

Managing Established Populations of Alien Species

Daniel Simberloff

If an alien species has breached whatever barriers were supposed to keep it out, three options exist: do nothing, try to eradicate it (that is, remove every single individual), or attempt to maintain it at an acceptable level. For want of knowledge about the invasion or of funding to do something about it, the do-nothing option is undoubtedly the one most frequently employed. Seldom is the choice based on a systematic, deliberate judgment that the invasion is unlikely to generate a major impact or that there is no conceivable way to control it. Further, eradication is often discounted as a possibility at the outset, without thorough review of the likelihood of success. However, all three options deserve careful consideration.

Doing Nothing

The do-nothing option may seem appropriate for the following reasons. Only a minority of alien species have substantial ecological or economic impacts. Williamson and Brown (1986) and Williamson (1996) suggest that about 10% of established alien species will become pests—the "tens rule". *Pest* is an arbitrary word; one person's pest may be another person's valued resource. Perhaps the best-known example of this quandary is Paterson's curse (*Echium plantagineum* L.), a notorious weed in Australia. It is hated by the livestock industry there, but much favored by apiarists for its nectar and pollen production and is thus also known as Salvation Jane (Cullen and Delfosse 1985; Delfosse 1985). Nevertheless, by several definitions of what constitutes a pest, the tens rule has held up fairly well. When researchers have examined many different species, they usually find that between 5% and 20% have had substantial impacts (Williamson 2000; Lockwood et al. 2001). The tens rule, however, does not identify which invaders will cause substantial problems and thus is not very useful to a manager confronted with a specific new invader. In invasion biology, it has proven difficult to predict which species will become invasive and to what degree (for example, Hobbs and Humphries 1995). Poor quantification, including determining the costs and benefits of various possible

management strategies, adds to this difficulty (Thomas and Willis 1998; Louda 2000).

Further, a fraction of all introduced species, including some classified as major pests, will probably recede in importance (Simberloff, this publication, p. 29). This spontaneous collapse or at least retrenchment is little studied as a general phenomenon, although some striking cases are well documented, for example, elodea, or Canadian waterweed (*Elodea canadensis* Michx.) in England (Arber 1920; Elton 1958; Simpson 1984), Germany (Scherer-Lorenzen et al. 2000), and Sweden (Andersson and Willén 1999). On the other hand, the phenomenon of a time lag in population explosions is fairly well known (for example, Crooks and Soulé 1996). In many instances, introduced species have persisted innocuously at low levels, often geographically restricted, for decades before quickly expanding to become major pests. Cutleaf teasel (*Dipsacus laciniatus* L.), for example, was present in North America in the 19th century and probably in the 18th century, but without pest status and with a rather restricted distribution in the United States (Solecki 1993) and Canada (Werner 1975). It has spread rapidly in the northeastern and midwestern United States in the last 10–30 years, perhaps because of highway construction, and is now a major pest in natural areas (Solecki 1993). The causes of both lags and spontaneous declines are often mysterious, and the frequency of both phenomena is not known, but time lags are more commonly reported (Simberloff, this publication, p. 29). Therefore, the existence of these processes does not argue for the do-nothing option.

Another argument made in support of the do-nothing approach is that few species introduced outside their native ranges have invaded large areas of natural habitats. Many newly established species are therefore not likely to expand their populations rapidly. Venus flytrap (*Dionaea muscipula* Ellis) is a species of conservation concern because of restrictive habitat requirements and a declining range in its native state, North Carolina (Culotta 1994). It has survived as small, introduced populations in north Florida for years and shows no tendency to become invasive (Simberloff et al. 1997). To attempt to eradicate this invasion now would probably not be an efficient use of limited funds. South

American water hyacinth (*Eichhornia crassipes* (Mart.) Solms-Laub.), one of the most widespread and damaging of all aquatic weeds (Cronk and Fuller 1995), has frequently been shipped from Florida to Canada as an ornamental (Brown 1997). In Canada, water hyacinth is no threat because it is doomed to die each winter, although there is some concern that Canadian mail-order businesses will ship the plant to warmer regions. From a purely Canadian standpoint, a reasonable response to a patch of water hyacinth in Canada is to do nothing. (However, as a member of the international community, Canada might feel compelled to participate in area-wide prevention of water hyacinth movement.) Unfortunately, many species will not be so easy to assess.

Thus, arguments about when to employ the do-nothing option for an established alien species are currently similar to those about which planned introductions should be permitted and which should be forbidden (for example, National Research Council 2000): we are usually not yet able to make sound predictions.

Eradication

Eradication of an established alien species is often argued to be impractical at best and a waste of resources with potential devastating side effects at worst (for example, Dahlsten 1986). Part of the antipathy toward this approach derives from a few well-publicized, costly failures (cf. Myers et al. 1998, 2000), such as the attempt in the United States to eradicate the red imported fire ant (*Solenopsis invicta* Buren = *S. wagneri* Santschi). This was an expensive disaster that was inherently impractical and that inflicted so much collateral damage on nontarget species (Davidson and Stone 1989) that it was termed the "Vietnam of entomology" by biologist E.O. Wilson (Brody 1975). Less dramatically, in the Okanagan Valley, British Columbia, the goal of an attempt by Agriculture Canada and the British Columbia Fruit Growers Association to eradicate the codling moth (*Cydia pomonella* (L.)) with insecticides and the release of sterile males was changed to maintenance management, in spite of a noteworthy reduction in densities, because of how slow and expensive the process had become (Myers et al. 2000).

An examination of successes and failures (Myers et al. 2000; Simberloff 2002) suggests eradication is often a plausible goal, but failed attempts can be costly in terms of ecology, the economy, and public confidence.

The methods used in an eradication program may be the same as those in a maintenance management one. In such a case, even a failed eradication attempt can be beneficial (Simberloff 1997) if the pest population has been lowered and the ecological and economic costs are not disproportionate to the level of control achieved. However, if maintenance management and eradication employ different means, a failed eradication attempt can cause great harm (Dahlsten 1986). For example, a chemical pesticide used to eradicate a target species may fail to eliminate the species and instead damage populations of its natural enemy or competitor— thus exacerbating the existing problem. On the other hand, a failed maintenance management program for the same pest (for example, hand-pulling a particular noxious weed species) might at worst have no effect.

Certain criteria relating to feasibility, cost-benefit ratios, and nontarget impacts should be met before eradication is implemented:

- **Resources should be sufficient to see an eradication program through to completion and commensurate with expected benefits.** For widely established pests, successful eradication could cost millions of dollars. The remarkable eradication of the African mosquito (*Anopheles gambiae* Giles), a malaria vector, from a large area in northeastern Brazil (Soper and Wilson 1943; Davis and Garcia 1989), was well funded by the Brazilian government and the Rockefeller Foundation.

- **The authority for carrying out an eradication program should be clear and sufficiently powerful to allow an individual, agency, or interagency program to undertake all necessary activities.** Eradication programs often cross several jurisdictions (for example, provinces, municipalities, private landholdings), and stakeholders within these jurisdictions view the costs and benefits of an eradication attempt differently (for example, members of the public may object to aerial chemical sprays that the agriculture industry see as crucial). Eradication requires cooperation from all stakeholders, or it runs the risk of being subverted (Perkins 1989; Simberloff 2002). The failed codling moth eradication in British Columbia lacked this feature (Myers et al. 2000).

- **The biology of the target organism must be sufficiently researched to form a scientific basis for predicting the success of eradication.** For example, the successful eradication of the giant African snail (*Achatina fulica* (Férussac)) from parts of Florida (Mead 1979) and Queensland, Australia (Colman 1978), was possible only because this snail does not self-fertilize. Similarly, plants with a persistent seed bank in the soil are more difficult to eradicate.

- **Often there must be a reasonable prospect that reinvasion will not reestablish a population that had been eradicated.** A number of vertebrate populations have been successfully eliminated from islands (Simberloff 2002), with reinvasion either very slow or absent to date. Isolation makes islands particularly tempting eradication sites. One such case is the eradication of the Norway rat (*Rattus norvegicus* (Berkenhout)) from Langara Island in the Queen Charlotte Islands, British Columbia (Myers et al. 2000). On the other hand, even if codling moths were eliminated from the Okanagan Valley, they would be bound to reinvade quickly from other apple-growing areas.

- **If the stakes are high enough, resources are sufficient, and the method is effective, eradication may be appropriate, even if occasional reinvasion is likely.** There have been 20 programs to eradicate the gypsy moth (Asian race, *Lymantria dispar* (L)) in British Columbia (Myers et al. 2000), yet the species continues to invade. The largest project, in 1992, entailed spraying 19 000 ha with a microbial insecticide at a cost of about Can$6.5 million (Nealis, this publication, p. 151). The efforts to eradicate gypsy moth can be justified for the following reasons: each time, there is good evidence that the moth was eradicated; the moth is a poor disperser; the method (a microbial insecticide, *Bacillus thuringiensis*, strain *Btk*) has relatively benign nontarget impacts if used locally; and the potential ecological and economic damage from a regionally established population in British Columbia and the US Pacific Northwest is staggering.

- **Eradication should not lead to a worse problem.** For example, even if reinvasion does not occur, will the eradicated species simply be replaced by another harmful alien species? Or will some totally new problem arise? On Santa Cruz Island, California, removal of large introduced grazers led to a massive increase of alien weeds, particularly sweet fennel (*Foeniculum vulgare* P. Mill.) (Dash and Gliessman 1994).

Maintenance Management

If eradication fails or is not an option and a decision has been made to intervene, then the strategy may be to maintain populations of pest species at levels low enough to be acceptable. Several approaches exist for maintenance management: mechanical control, chemical control, biological control, and ecosystem management (Simberloff et al. 1997; Simberloff 2000). These approaches are not mutually exclusive and none is infallible. However, each has proven useful in certain circumstances and thus each has a place in the arsenal that can be deployed against invasive species.

The term "integrated pest management" (IPM) is frequently used, particularly in agriculture, in reference to maintenance management. The term IPM means different things to different people (Cate and Hinckle 1994; US Congress 1995; Ehler and Bottrell 2000; Lockwood 2000). Originally (in the late 1950s and 1960s), IPM connoted a greatly reduced use of chemical pesticides (including a threshold pest density below which chemicals would not be used at all); it relied on managing the environment to enhance existing populations of the pest's natural enemies (cultural control), with occasional releases of alien natural enemies (classical biological control) or of additional individuals to augment populations of native or alien natural enemies (inundative releases). Nowadays, some see IPM as the use of all these methods and more; others, primarily as chemical control with a threshold pest density required for spraying (rather than a routine spraying schedule independent of pest density). Because of confusion in the use of the term, I will only discuss the key component technologies of IPM.

Mechanical Control

Mechanical control involves a variety of techniques, from hand-picking plants or animals to the use of complex machinery. Mechanical removal of plants and animals can be remarkably effective, but it is labor-intensive. Volunteer labor has frequently been used in pest control, particularly by conservation organizations, such as the Nature Conservancy (for example, Randall et al. 1997). In Florida, a volunteer-driven program, the Pepper Busters, has been crucial to attempts to control the state's worst invasive plant, the Brazilian peppertree (*Schinus terebinthifolius* Raddi) (Zarillo 1999). More recently, the large convict labor pool in the United States is being tapped for assistance in maintenance management of some species. In Kentucky, the State Nature Preserves Commission has successfully used volunteers convicted of driving under the influence of alcohol to manage musk thistle (*Carduus nutans* L., also commonly known as nodding plumeless thistle) in certain areas

(J. Bender, Kentucky State Nature Preserves Commission, Frankfort, KY, personal communication). Florida inmates are a crucial component of successful efforts to reduce the area occupied by the Australian paperbark tree (*Melaleuca quinquenervia* (Cav.) S.T. Blake) (Campbell and Carter 1999).Paid labor also becomes an option for removal of an alien species that society feels is worth the expense. In South Africa, the Working for Water Programme is a massive public works project that has played a key role in battling damaging alien plants, and mechanical control by teams of employees is a major component (McQueen et al. 2000; van Wilgen et al. 2000).

The efforts of large numbers of individuals in volunteer programs and public works, such as Working for Water, sensitize the public and engage them in the battle against alien invasive species. In Victoria, British Columbia, the Garry Oak Meadow Invasive Plant Removal Project centers around "broom bashes" to remove Scotch broom (*Cytisus scoparius* (L.) Link); so many private citizens participate that a monthly listing is required in the local environmental newsletter (Econews 1998). The campaign generates substantial local publicity (for example, Curtis 1996) about Scotch broom and alien plants in general. Perhaps most importantly, it attracts many young people, such as elementary school students and Girl Guides (V.G. Nealis, Canadian Forest Service, Victoria, BC, personal communication), and educates them about alien species.

Chemical Control

Chemicals (herbicides, rodenticides, insecticides, etc., including microbial pesticides such as *Btk*) are sometimes effective in maintenance management, although they are often controversial. Some early-generation pesticides had substantial nontarget impacts, including human health effects; the disastrous fire ant eradication campaign (using chlorinated hydrocarbons), mentioned previously, is an example. Well-publicized accounts of problems with the use of pesticides, beginning with Rachel Carson's *Silent Spring* (1962), have left a widespread legacy of chemophobia (Williams 1997).

Although many modern pesticides have fewer nontarget impacts, there are other disadvantages (Simberloff 2000). Many pesticides are expensive, particularly if used on a continuing basis over large natural areas. Species evolve resistance to pesticides so that greater quantities have to be used, increasing their expense; eventually a chemical becomes ineffective against its target. Nevertheless, pesticides, alone or

with mechanical control, are often useful. For example, water hyacinth has been drastically reduced and maintained at acceptable levels in Florida primarily by use of the herbicide 2,4-D combined with some mechanical removal (Schardt 1997). On the other hand, some impacts of chemicals or their breakdown products on nontarget species may be subtle or complex as well as harmful. Biological magnification, which eventuated in the decline of raptor populations as DDT concentrations induced thin eggshells (Stiling 1996), is one well-known example.

Biological Control

Classical biological control involves the introduction of an alien pest's natural enemy (usually a predator, herbivore, parasite, or disease) to maintain the pest species at acceptable levels (Greathead 1995). Its goal is not explicitly to eradicate (Center et al. 1997), but rather to establish a homeostatic ongoing relationship between pest and enemy—an increase in the pest population beyond some low density triggers an automatic increase in the natural enemy population that redresses the pest increase.

Classical biological control has sometimes been very effective, particularly in agriculture and silviculture. In Canada, for instance, musk thistle is well controlled by the alien seed-head weevil *Rhinocyllus conicus* Froel. (Harris 1984). In Africa, South American cassava (*Manihot esculenta* Crantz) was devastated by a South American mealybug *Phenacoccus manihoti* (Matile-Ferrero) that arrived in the early 1970s. This problem was well controlled by an imported South American wasp parasitoid *Epidinocarsis lopezi* (De Santis) (Odour 1996; Bellotti et al. 1999). Examples such as these have led many to see biological control as a "green" alternative to chemical control. Indeed, some tout it as the only answer to invasive alien species. McFadyen (1998, p. 369) argues that "biocontrol offers the only safe, economical, and environmentally sustainable solution" to alien weeds. When biological control works as planned, it has two obvious advantages over chemical control: control activities need only be conducted in a limited part of the range of the target species (the biocontrol agent can disperse on its own), and the control will work in perpetuity without need of repeated treatment. However, classical biological control is no panacea, for five main reasons:

- **Biological control usually does not work.** Although successes are numerous, most species introduced for classical biological control do not provide substantial control of the target pest. In fact, many alien enemy species survive and establish populations, but typically only one-third of these actually act to control their intended targets (Williamson 1996).

- **Biological control sometimes has nontarget impacts.** Although touted as environmentally friendly (for example, Odour 1996; McFadyen 1998), biological control projects have inimically affected nontarget species, including some of conservation concern (Simberloff and Stiling 1996). For example, the seed-head weevil *Rhinocyllus conicus* brought in to control musk thistle in Canada (mentioned previously) dispersed on its own and was also widely distributed in the United States and Canada by government agencies and private citizens. This weevil now threatens several native thistle species in the genus *Cirsium*, including one species listed in the US *Endangered Species Act* (Louda et al. 1997; US Department of the Interior 1997). One of the great conservation tragedies, the extinction of several species of native land snails from Pacific islands, resulted from a predatory biological control agent, the rosy wolfsnail (*Euglandina rosea* (Férussac)). The introduction of the wolfsnail was a failed attempt to control the giant African snail (*Achatina fulica* (Férussac)), populations of which eventually declined on their own even on islands without the introduced predator (Civeyrel and Simberloff 1996). Similarly, the introduction of the small Indian mongoose (*Herpestes javanicus* (E. Geoffroy Saint-Hilaire)) to many island groups around the world for rat control has led to numerous global extinctions of nontarget vertebrate prey species (Honegger 1981; Cheke 1987; Funasaki et al. 1988).

What is at issue now is whether modern biological control procedures can overcome the problem of nontarget impacts. There is substantial debate on this matter (for example, Hokkanen and Lynch 1995; Follett and Duan 2000). Although many authors argue against the use of species that are not highly adapted to affect only the target species (for example, Center et al. 1997; Cowie 2001), this view is not universally held. The A&T State University Cooperative Extension (North Carolina State University 2000), for example, advocates the use of the generalized herbivore grass carp (*Ctenopharyngodon idella* (Valenciennes)) to control alien aquatic weeds in North Carolina.

- **Biological control agents can spread to areas in which they are not wanted.** All living organisms have means of dispersing, and, once dispersed, can establish new populations. For example, a South American cactus moth (*Cactoblastis cactorum* (Bergroth)), introduced to the island of Nevis to control prickly-pear (*Opuntia* spp.), has spread throughout much of the West Indies and into the eastern United States, where it has attacked a narrowly restricted native species (Simberloff 1992). It now threatens to spread westward to the US Southwest and Mexico, where it could become a substantial conservation and agricultural problem (Stiling and Simberloff 2000).

- **Cost-benefit analyses (for example, Frank 1998) are flawed.** Analysis of any proposed control method, including biological control, should be as comprehensive as possible (Simberloff and Stiling 1998; Louda 2000). However, assessing conservation costs and benefits, such as those attached to the existence or loss of a rare, noncommercial species, is far more difficult than tallying agricultural costs and benefits in economic terms (Simberloff 1992).

- **Biological control introductions are usually irreversible.** Except in the case of nonreproducing organisms (for example, triploid grass carp, but see Fuller et al. 1999), once an introduced species is established, eradication is generally not an option (Greathead 1995; Simberloff and Stiling 1996). Thus, a mistake (for example, a nontarget impact) cannot be easily redressed. With chemical control, one can simply stop using the chemical (though a chemical or its breakdown products may persist).

In addition to classical biological control, a number of other approaches are lumped under the rubric of biological control (US Congress 1995). For example, in inundative or augmentative release, natural enemies are collected or reared for release to augment existing populations of either native or introduced natural enemies (US Congress 1995). For some of these approaches (for example, inundative release or release of sterile insects), there is a substantial literature on various uses; for others, there is much less. Classical biological control is used far more often than any of these other biological technologies.

Ecosystem Management

Management of an entire ecosystem can sometimes create conditions more favorable to native than to alien species. This was, in essence, the underlying philosophy of cultural control (Stiling 1985), an ancient agricultural approach and a key component of early

IPM in agricultural systems. Ecosystem management as a means of managing introduced species simply extends cultural control beyond the agricultural domain. For example, in longleaf pine (*Pinus palustris* P. Mill.) forests of the southeastern United States, the maintenance of a natural fire regime may have impeded the invasion of alien plants and animals (Simberloff 2001). Louda (2000) argues that good pasture management, especially prevention of overgrazing, keeps musk thistle from becoming an economically important weed; it loses out in competition with grasses (Austin et al. 1985; Hamrick and Lee 1987; Popay and Medd 1990).

"Ecosystem management" has become a mantra in many resource management circles. However, it has been primarily a catch-phrase rather than a specific set of management techniques, and it has rarely been rigorously tested (Simberloff 1998). Because it is the newest of the four approaches to maintenance management, ecosystem management is most in need of enhanced research.

Discussion

Common themes in the approaches outlined above are as follows: a single best way to manage all invasions does not exist; substantial debate on some subjects (for example, cost-benefit analyses, eradication, chemical and biological control) is taking place; and management options must be carefully assessed for impacts on target and nontarget species. Much research is needed on these approaches. Further, invasion biologists have grappled for decades with the fundamental question — why do some invasions fail and others have staggering impacts? Perhaps the reason why this question remains unanswered is the present focus of research in invasion biology. It tends to be in the realm of applied rather than pure science, targeted at a few pests once they have become problems. Pure research on the biology of invasions generally could help guide the management of specific invasions and their pathways and determine whether a species is ever going to become a pest.

Research on the management of biological invasions is frequently published in gray literature (open-source material not usually available through normal channels or systems of publication), if reported at all; some research is spread by word-of-mouth (Simberloff 1999). The tradition of publishing research in certain key journals is especially weak in the areas of eradication and mechanical control; and although, a mature, large literature exists for chemical and biological control,

sharing knowledge is also problematic in these areas. As a result, some control methods or techniques, even ones that have failed, are reinvented, while reports of novel successes or illuminating attempts are often slow in reaching pest managers.

Management of alien species is also hampered by a lack of comprehensive studies on all possible options for dealing with an invasion (Louda et al. 1998; Thomas and Willis 1998; Louda 2000). To address this problem, responsible agencies must have broadly knowledgeable staff and engage all stakeholders in management decisions. Invasive species too often become the responsibility of individuals whose expertise is either limited or tangential to the problem, and/or of persons heavily committed to one management technique. Adequate staffing and a decision-making mechanism will entail new costs, but a problem of the magnitude of invasive alien species demands this commitment. Underlying any effective approach to this problem will be good scientific research, and the current investment by most nations is far from commensurate with the problem. The basic biology of many devastating invaders is barely understood and demands enhanced scientific effort.

In the age of information technology, credible Web sites with extensive linkages could greatly increase the speed with which pest managers learn about the advent of new invasions, the threats they may pose, and new advances in technologies that might be deployed against them (Ricciardi et al. 2000). Such Web sites are now evolving rapidly, for example, those of the US Invasive Species Council (http://www.invasivespecies.gov/), the Hawaiian Ecosystems at Risk Project (http://www.hear.org), and the US Sea Grant (http://www.sgnis.org). A persistent challenge in the maintenance of Web sites is the need to update and verify the accuracy of data and information. On existing Web sites, validating species identifications is sometimes difficult, although generally less problematic than determining the accuracy of management methods and assessing claims of their efficacy. While rigorously peer-reviewed scientific literature is most reliable, it is often slow to appear and needs interpretation for nonscientists. Qualified, critical Web site managers could play a key role by vetting, interpreting, summarizing, and assessing published and unpublished reports.

Effective invasive species management requires an efficient monitoring and rapid-response mechanism (Simberloff 1999; Weiss 1999). As the area of an invasion increases, so does eradication expense; it is best to eradicate early (for example, Simberloff 1997; Weiss 1999;

Myers et al. 2000). An example of the benefits of acting very quickly is the eradication of the Caribbean black-striped mussel (perhaps *Mytilopsis sallei* (Recluz)) in Australia (Myers et al. 2000). This relative of the zebra mussel (*Dreissena polymorpha* (Pallas)) was discovered in 1999 in Cullen Bay, Darwin Harbor, within six months of its arrival and before it had spread farther in Australia. Within nine days, the bay had been quarantined and treated with 160 tonnes of bleach and 54 tonnes of copper sulfate. All living organisms were believed killed, and the mussel population was eradicated. One can speculate on the savings in North America had zebra mussel been discovered soon after invasion and eradicated. Even when eradication is not feasible, locating an introduced species and initiating maintenance management early can maintain the invader at a low level in perpetuity, and often in a geographically restricted region. The same species, once well established over a large region, can engender an ongoing major expense (cf. Schardt 1997). Monitoring is not free, but its benefits transcend the detection of invaders (for example, the status of threatened species or ecosystems of conservation concern can be ascertained). The maintenance of a rapid-response mechanism is perhaps less a function of hiring new personnel as of having the legal and administrative means to mobilize existing resources and to act quickly. This is illustrated by the effective campaign in Chicago and New York to control the Asian long-horned beetle (*Anoplophora glabripennis* (Mots.)) (Van Driesche and Van Driesche 2000).

Finally, even with all the shortcomings listed above for eradication methods and various maintenance management procedures, there are many success stories. It is important not to be too pessimistic about the prospect of managing existing invasions, although acknowledging that it is much more efficient to keep them out. Imagine how effective pest management would be if invasive alien species received the political and budgetary attention commensurate with the global threat that they pose.

Acknowledgments

I thank Renata Claudi, Ole Hendrickson, and Vince Nealis for constructive comments on a draft of this paper.

References

Andersson, B.; Willén, E. 1999. Lakes. Acta Phytogeog. Suec. 84:149–168.

Arber, A. 1920. Water plants. A study of aquatic angiosperms. Cambridge University Press, Cambridge, UK. Reprint 1963. J. Cramer, Lehre. Reprint 1972. Codicote, Herts, Wheldon & Wesley.

Austin, M.P.; Groves, R.H.; Fresco, L.M.F.; Kaye, P.E. 1985. Relative growth of six thistle species along a nutrient gradient with multispecies competition. J. Ecol. 73:667–684.

Bellotti, A.C.; Smith, L.; Lapointe, S.L. 1999. Recent advances in cassava pest management. Annu. Rev. Entomol. 44:343–370.

Brody, J.E. 1975. Agriculture department to abandon campaign against the fire ant. New York Times, 20 April 1975, p. 46

Brown, T.C. 1997. The state's role. Pages 339–356 in D. Simberloff, D.C. Schmitz, and T.C. Brown, eds. Strangers in paradise. Impact and management of nonindigenous species in Florida. Island Press, Washington, DC.

Campbell, C.; Carter, F.D. 1999. The Florida department of corrections involvement in exotic pest plant control. Pages 147–149 in D.T. Jones and B.W. Gamble, eds. Florida's garden of good and evil. Florida Exotic Pest Plant Council, West Palm Beach, FL.

Carson, R. 1962. Silent spring. Houghton Mifflin, Boston, MA.

Cate, J.R.; Hinckle, M.K. 1994. Integrated pest management: the path of a paradigm. National Audubon Society, New York, NY.

Center, T.D.; Frank, J.H.; Dray, F.A. Jr. 1997. Biological control. Pages 245–263 in D. Simberloff, D.C. Schmitz, and T.C. Brown, eds. Strangers in paradise. Impact and management of nonindigenous species in Florida. Island Press, Washington, DC.

Cheke, A.S. 1987. An ecological history of the Mascarene Islands, with particular reference to extinctions and introductions of land vertebrates. Pages 5–89 in A.W. Diamond, ed. Studies of Mascarene Island birds. Cambridge University Press, Cambridge, UK.

Civeyrel, L.; Simberloff, D. 1996. A tale of two snails: is the cure worse than the disease? Biodivers. Conserv. 5:1231–1252.

Colman, P.H. 1978. An invading giant. Wildl. Aust. 15(2):46–47.

Cowie, R.H. 2001. Can snails ever be effective and safe biocontrol agents? Int. J. Pest Manage. 47(1):23–40.

Cronk, Q.C.B.; Fuller, J.L. 1995. Plant invaders. Chapman and Hall, London, UK.

Crooks, J.; Soulé, M.E. 1996. Lag times in population explosions of invasive species: causes and implications. Pages 39–46 in O.T. Sandlund, P.J. Schei, A. Viken, eds. Proceedings,

Norway/UN Conference on Alien Species. Directorate for Nature Management and Norwegian Institute for Nature Research, Trondheim, Norway.

Cullen, J.M.; Delfosse, E.S. 1985. *Echium plantagineum*: Catalyst for conflict and change in Australia. Pages 249–292 *in* E.S. Delfosse, ed. Proceedings of the VI International Symposium on Biological Control of Weeds. Agriculture Canada, Vancouver, BC.

Culotta, E. 1994. Vanishing fly-traps. Audubon 96(2):16–18.

Curtis, M. 1996. Community groups make a clean sweep to eliminate broom. Victoria Times-Colonist (Victoria, BC), 1 November 1996, p. A4.

Dahlsten, D.L. 1986. Control of invaders. Pages 275–302 *in* H.A. Mooney and J.A. Drake, eds. Ecology of biological invasions of North America and Hawaii. Springer-Verlag, New York, NY.

Dash, B.A.; Gliessman, S.R. 1994. Nonnative species eradication and native species enhancement: fennel on Santa Cruz Island. Pages 505–512 *in* W.L. Halvorson and G.J. Maender, eds. The Fourth California Islands Symposium: Update on the Status of Resources. Santa Barbara Museum of Natural History, Santa Barbara, CA.

Davidson, N.A.; Stone, N.D. 1989. Imported fire ants. Pages 196–217 *in* D.L. Dahlsten and R. Garcia, eds. Eradication of exotic pests. Yale University Press, New Haven, CT.

Davis, J.R.; Garcia, R. 1989. Malaria mosquito in Brazil. Pages 274–283 *in* D.L. Dahlsten and R. Garcia, eds. Eradication of exotic pests. Yale University Press, New Haven, CT.

Delfosse, E.S. 1985. *Echium plantagineum* in Australia: effects of a major conflict of interest. Pages 293–299 *in* E.S. Delfosse, ed. Proceedings of the VI International Symposium on Biological Control of Weeds. Agriculture Canada, Vancouver, BC.

Econews 1998. City wide broom bash. Newsletter 77 (Nov. 1998) [online]. http://www.earthfuture.com/econews/back_issues/98-11.htm

Ehler, L.E.; Bottrell, D.G. 2000. The illusion of integrated pest management. Issues Sci.Technol. 16(3):61–64.

Elton, C.S. 1958. The ecology of invasions by animals and plants. Methuen Publishing, London, UK. Reprint 2000, University of Chicago Press, Chicago, IL.

Follett, P.A.; Duan, J.J., eds. 2000. Nontarget effects of biological control. Kluwer Academic Publishers, Boston, MA.

Frank, J.H. 1998. How risky is biological control? Comment. Ecology 79:1829–1834.

Fuller, P.L.; Nico, L.G.; Williams, J.D. 1999. Nonindigenous fishes introduced into inland waters of the United States. American Fisheries Society, Bethesda, MD.

Funasaki, G.Y.; Lai, P.Y.; Nakahara, L.M.; Beardsley, J.W.; Ota, A.K. 1988. A review of biological control introductions in Hawaii: 1890 to 1985. Proc. Hawaii. Entomol. Soc. 28:105–160.

Greathead, D.J. 1995. Benefits and risks of classical biological control. Pages 53–63 *in* H.M.T. Hokkanen and J.M. Lynch, eds. Biological control. Benefits and risks. Cambridge University Press, Cambridge, UK.

Hamrick, J.L.; Lee, J.M. 1987. Effect of soil surface topography and litter cover on the germination, survival, and growth of musk thistle (*Carduus nutans*). Am. J. Bot. 74:451–457.

Harris, P. 1984. *Carduus nutans* L., nodding thistle, and *C. acanthoides* L., plumeless thistle (Compositae). Pages 115–126 *in* J.S. Kelleher and M.A. Hulme, eds. Biological control programmes against insects and weeds in Canada 1969–1980. Commonwealth Agricultural Bureaux, Farnham Royal, UK.

Hobbs, R.J.; Humphries, S.E. 1995. An integrated approach to the ecology and management of plant invasions. Conserv. Biol. 9:761–770.

Hokkanen, H.M.T.; Lynch, J.M., eds. 1995. Biological control. Benefits and risks. Cambridge University Press, Cambridge, UK.

Honegger, R.E. 1981. List of amphibians and reptiles either known or thought to have become extinct since 1600. Biol. Conserv. 19:141–158.

Lockwood, J.A. 2000. Nontarget effects of biological control: what are we trying to miss? Pages 15–30 *in* P.A. Follett and J.J. Duan, eds. Nontarget effects of biological control. Kluwer Academic Publishers, Boston, MA.

Lockwood, J.; Simberloff, D.; McKinney, M.; Von Holle, B. 2001. How many, and which, plants will invade natural areas? Biol. Invasions 3:1–8.

Louda, S.M. 2000. Negative ecological effects of the musk thistle biological control agent, *Rhinocyllus conicus*. Pages 215–243 *in* P.A. Follett and J.J. Duan, eds. Nontarget effects of biological control. Kluwer Academic Publishers, Boston, MA.

Louda, S.M.; Kendall, D.; Connor, J.; Simberloff, D. 1997. Ecological effects of an insect introduced for the biological control of weeds. Science 277:1088–1090.

Louda, S.M.; Simberloff, D.; Boettner, G.; Connor, J; Kendall, D.; Arnett, A. 1998. Insights from data on the nontarget effects of the flowerhead weevil. Biocontrol News and Information 19(3):70N–72N.

McFadyen, R.E.C.1998. Biological control of weeds. Annu. Rev. Entomol. 43:369–393.

McQueen, C.; Noemdoe, S.; Jezile, N. 2000. The Working for Water Programme. Pages 51–54 in G. Preston, G. Brown, and E. van Wyk, eds. Best management practices for preventing and controlling invasive alien species. Symposium proceedings. Working for Water Programme, Cape Town, SA.

Mead, A.R. 1979. Ecological malacology: with particular reference to Achatina fulica. Vol. 2b of V. Fretter; J. Fretter; J. Peake, eds. Pulmonates. Academic Press, London, UK.

Myers, J.H.; Savoie, A.; van Randen, E. 1998. Eradication and pest management. Annu. Rev. Entomol. 43:471–491.

Myers, J.H.; Simberloff, D.; Kuris, A.M.; Carey, J.R. 2000. Eradication revisited—dealing with exotic species. Trends Ecol. Evol.15:316–320.

National Research Council. 2000. Incorporating science, economics, and sociology in developing sanitary and phytosanitary standards in international trade. National Academy Press, Washington, DC.

North Carolina State University, A&T State University Cooperative Extension. 2000. Using grass carp for aquatic weed management in North Carolina [online]. http://www.ces.ncsu.edu/nreos/wild/aquatics/weed/grasscarp

Odour, G. 1996. Biological pest control and invasives. Pages 116–122 in O.T. Sandlund, P.J. Schei, and A. Viken, eds. Proceedings of the Norway/UN Conference on Alien Species. Directorate for Nature Management and Norwegian Institute for Nature Research, Trondheim, Norway.

Perkins, J.H. 1989. Eradication: Scientific and social questions. Pages 16–40 in D.L. Dahlsten and R. Garcia, eds. Eradication of exotic pests. Yale University Press, New Haven, CT.

Popay, A.I.; Medd, R.W. 1990. The biology of Australian weeds 21. Carduus nutans L. Plant Prot. Quart. 5:3–13.

Randall, J.M.; Lewis R.R. III; Jensen, D.B. 1997. Ecological restoration. Pages 205–219 in D. Simberloff, D.C. Schmitz, and T.C. Brown, eds. Strangers in paradise. Impact and management of nonindigenous species in Florida. Island Press, Washington, DC.

Ricciardi, A.; Steiner, W.W.M; Mack, R.N.; Simberloff, D. 2000. Toward a global information system for invasive species. BioScience 50:239–244.

Schardt, J.D. 1997. Maintenance control. Pages 229–243 in D. Simberloff, D.C. Schmitz, and T.C. Brown, eds. Strangers in paradise. Impact and management of nonindigenous species in Florida. Island Press, Washington, DC.

Scherer-Lorenzen, M.; Elend, A.; Nöllert, S.; Schulze, E-D. 2000. Plant invasions in Germany: general aspects and impacts of nitrogen deposition. Pages 351–368 in H.A. Mooney and R.J. Hobbs, eds. Invasive species in a changing world. Island Press, Washington, DC.

Simberloff, D. 1992. Conservation of pristine habitats and unintended effects of biological control. Pages 103–114 in W.C. Kauffman and J.E. Nechols, eds. Selection criteria and biological consequences of importing natural enemies. Entomological Society of America, Baltimore, MD.

Simberloff, D. 1997. Eradication. Pages 221–228 in D. Simberloff, D.C. Schmitz, and T.C. Brown, eds. Strangers in paradise. Impact and management of nonindigenous species in Florida. Island Press, Washington, DC.

Simberloff, D. 1998. Flagships, umbrellas, and keystones: is single-species management passé in the landscape era? Biol. Conserv. 83: 247–57.

Simberloff, D. 1999. Needs and opportunities. Pages 38–41 in R.L. Ridgway, W.P. Gregg, R.E. Stinner, and A.G. Brown, eds. Invasive species databases. Proceedings of a workshop. US Departments of the Interior, Agriculture, and Commerce/C.V. Riley Memorial Foundation, Silver Spring, MD.

Simberloff, D. 2000. Nonindigenous species: a global threat to biodiversity and stability. Pages 325–334 in P. Raven and T. Williams, eds. Nature and human society: the quest for a sustainable world. National Academy Press, Washington, DC.

Simberloff, D. 2001. Biological invasions—How are they affecting us, and what can we do about them? West. N. Am. Nat. 61:308–315.

Simberloff, D. 2002. Why not eradication? In A.B. Damania, ed. Managing for healthy ecosystems. Proceedings of the International Congress on Ecosystem Health. Congress Secretariat, Davis, CA.

Simberloff, D.; Schmitz, D.C.; Brown, T.C. 1997. Why we should care and what we should do. Pages 359–367 in D. Simberloff, D.C. Schmitz, and T.C. Brown, eds. Strangers in paradise. Impact and management of nonindigenous species in Florida. Island Press, Washington, DC.

Simberloff, D.; Stiling, P.D. 1996. How risky is biological control? Ecology 77:1965–1974.

Simberloff, D.; Stiling, P.D. 1998. How risky is biological control? Reply. Ecology 79:1834–1836.

Simpson, D.A. 1984. A short history of the introduction and spread of Elodea Michx in the British Isles. Watsonia 15:1–9.

Solecki, M.K. 1993. Cut-leaved and common teasel (*Dipsacus laciniatus* L. and *D. sylvestris* Huds.): profile of two invasive aliens. Pages 85–92 *in* B.N. McKnight, ed. Biological pollution. The control and impact of invasive exotic species. Indiana Academy of Science, Indianapolis, IN.

Soper, F.L.; Wilson, D.B. 1943. *Anopheles gambiae* in Brazil, 1930 to 1940. The Rockefeller Foundation, New York, NY.

Stiling, P.D. 1985. An introduction to insect pests and their control. Macmillan Publishers, London, UK.

Stiling, P.D. 1996. Ecology. Theory and applications. 2nd ed. Upper Saddle River, Prentice-Hall, Englewood Cliffs, NJ.

Stiling, P.D.; Simberloff, D. 2000. The frequency and strength of nontarget effects of invertebrate biological control agents of plant pests and weeds. Pages 31–43 *in* P.A. Follett and J.J. Duan, eds. Nontarget effects of biological control. Kluwer Academic Publishers, Boston, MA.

Thomas, M.B.; Willis, A.J. 1998. Biological control—risky but necessary? Trends Ecol. Evol. 13:325–329.

US Congress, Office of Technology Assessment. 1995. Biologically based technologies for pest control. US Government Printing Office, Washington, DC.

US Department of the Interior, Fish and Wildlife Service. 1997. Endangered and threatened wildlife and plants; determination of endangered status for two tidal marsh plants— *Cirsium hydrophilum* var. *hydrophilum* (Suisun thistle) and *Cordylanthus mollis* ssp. *mollis* (soft bird's-beak) from the San Francisco Bay area of California. 50 CFR Part 17, Federal Register 62(224):61916–61921.

Van Driesche, J.; Van Driesche, R. 2000. Nature out of place. Island Press, Washington, DC.

van Wilgen, B.; Richardson, D.; Higgins, S. 2000. Integrated control of invasive alien plants in terrestrial ecosystems. Pages 118–128 *in* G. Preston, G. Brown, and E. van Wyk, eds. Best management practices for preventing and controlling invasive alien species. Symposium proceedings. Working for Water Programme, Cape Town, SA.

Weiss, J. 1999. Contingency planning for new and emerging weeds in Victoria. Plant Prot. Quart. 14:112–114.

Werner, P.A. 1975. The biology of Canadian weeds. 12. *Dipsacus sylvestris* Huds. Can. J. Plant Sci. 55:783–794.

Williams, T. 1997. Killer weeds. Audubon 99(2):24–31.

Williamson, M. 1996. Biological invasions. Chapman and Hall, London.

Williamson, M. 2000. The ecology of invasions. Pages 56–65 *in* G. Preston, G. Brown, and E. van Wyk, eds. Best management practices for preventing and controlling invasive alien species. Symposium proceedings. Working for Water Programme, Cape Town, SA.

Williamson, M.; Brown, K.C. 1986. The analysis and modelling of British invasions. Philos. Trans. R. Soc. Lond. B Biol. Sci. 314:505–522.

Zarillo, K. 1999. A progress report of the Brevard County Brazilian Pepper Busters public education activities and training manual. Pages 155–162 *in* D.T. Jones and B.W. Gamble, eds. Florida's garden of good and evil. Florida Exotic Pest Plant Council, West Palm Beach, FL.

Photo with chapter title: Rosy wolfsnail. Photo by Ron Heu, State of Hawaii Department of Agriculture, Honolulu, HI.

Classical Biological Control of Invasive Alien Plants in Natural Areas

James E. Corrigan

Around 1868, the cottony cushion scale (*Icerya purchasi* Maskell) was first observed on citrus trees in California (Sawyer 1996). Populations of this insect spread throughout the citrus-growing areas of the west coast by the 1880s. There was no effective control for this species, and its destructive impact threatened the viability of the citrus industry. In 1887, it was discovered that the cottony cushion scale was native to Australia, where it did not cause problems. A predaceous ladybird beetle called the vedalia beetle (*Rodolia cardinalis* (Mulsant)), and a parasitic fly, *Cryptochetum iceryae* (Williston), were found attacking the scale in Australia. Small populations of these natural enemies were imported to California in1888 and released in citrus orchards. The vedalia beetles multiplied profusely on scale-infested trees. They were widely distributed by citrus growers and, within two years, the beetles were controlling populations of cottony cushion scale statewide. The fly species established and became the dominant control agent in coastal areas. Both the pest species and its natural enemies survive in California to this day. Except for occasional, localized outbreaks where pesticides have killed the biological control agents, the cottony cushion scale has not been a threat to the citrus industry for over 100 years (Sawyer 1996; Van Driesche and Bellows 1996).

The case of cottony cushion sale represents the first well-documented, successful application of classical biological control. It also illustrates the basic paradigm of classical biological control: coevolved natural enemies of invasive alien species can permanently reduce host or prey densities (Turner 1985). The successful control of cushiony cotton scale encouraged citrus growers' organizations in California to give virtually unconditional support to biological control research for a period of about 80 years (Sawyer 1996). This support sustained the emerging discipline of biological control and allowed for the development of an increasingly sophisticated understanding of the ecological basis for its practice.

Today, it is well established that classical biological control can be a uniquely effective approach to managing problems created by alien species. In the last 110 years since the program against cottony cushion scale, about 540 insect pests have been the targets of 1200 natural enemy introductions worldwide (Van Driesche and Bellows 1996), and at least 130 plant species the targets of about 500 species of invertebrate herbivores (Julien and Griffiths 1998). Although not every introduction has been successful, many serious pest situations have been controlled with biological control, and billions of dollars in food, fiber, human comfort, and habitat quality have been saved (Tisdell 1990). Projects have been carried out in most of the inhabited regions of the world and the international exchange of biological control agents and technology knows few political, geographical, or economic borders (IIBC 1994). Modern proponents of biological control believe that problems with chemical pest controls (for instance, pest resistance and nontarget effects), combined with increasing concerns about environmental quality, create an ideal opportunity for the future practice of biological control (Nechols and Kauffman 1992; Waage 1996).

The vast wilderness areas of Canada are one of the world's greatest natural resources. These areas contain habitats in a relatively undisturbed condition and sustain biological communities that are representative of the evolutionary history of temperate North America (White et al. 1993). When such unique habitats are threatened by invasive alien species, proponents of classical biological control see it as the best option for intervention because of its potential for permanent, wide-ranging control, limited nontarget effects, and few ongoing costs (Van Driesche and Bellows 1996; McFadyen 1998). DeLoach (1991) states: "Biological control of undesirable weeds can contribute to the conservation of natural areas because it is much less intrusive than the broad spectrum chemical and mechanical controls presently in use. It is also a positive alternative to doing nothing and allowing a few species of weeds to dominate."

Some scientists, however, have ecological and ethical concerns about using classical biological control as a pest management option (Howarth 1991; Simberloff 1992; Lockwood 1996; Simberloff and Stiling 1996; Louda et al. 1997; Strong 1997). Much of the criticism centers on what the imported natural enemies, brought in to target economically important pests (such as pastureland weeds), will do to nontarget hosts in adjacent natural ecosystems (Howarth 1991; Simberloff 1992; Louda et al. 1997).

Further, several of the important cost-benefit relationships of biological control of economically important pests do not apply to pests of natural areas (Simberloff 1992; IIBC 1994; Hokkanen and Lynch 1995). Successful classical biological control in any cropping system is, by far, the most economical control method available (Van Driesche and Bellows 1996). However, there is no easily measured economic windfall that results from controlling invasive alien plant species in natural habitats (Nechols and Kauffman 1992; Simberloff 1992; IIBC1994; Hokkanen and Lynch 1995; Simberloff and Stiling 1996). Therefore, cost-benefit analyses that focus on potential economic gains versus actual implementation costs do not favor the initiation of projects in natural areas. In a funding environment increasingly driven by profit motivation, the economic rationale for conducting programs against pests with limited economic impact is particularly weak. This is not to say that there is no value in habitat conservation or restoration, but simply to point out that there may not be a tangible economic gain from undertaking these programs.

In the past 15 years, government-supported biological control programs have been delayed or shut down in Australia and the United States as a result of challenges put forward by groups of concerned scientists and/or members of the public (Cullen and Delfosse 1985; Lockwood 1993). Proponents of classical biological control face increasingly difficult scientific, economic, and perhaps legal obstacles if they wish to initiate new programs in natural areas. Properly addressing concerns about environmental safety will increase the costs of initiating such projects. Such obstacles could result in the underutilization of a technology that is uniquely able to address problems of alien invasive species on the spatial and temporal scale on which they occur.

The literature on classical biological control is voluminous and extremely detailed. Comprehensive review is beyond the scope of this chapter but can be found in Huffaker and Messenger (1976) and Van Driesche and Bellows (1996). I will therefore focus on specific issues that are relevant to using biological control against alien plants in natural areas, using as an example the most prevalent taxon of weed biological control agents, the phytophagous (plant-eating) insects.

To evaluate the potential value of classical biological control as a tool in nature conservation, these important issues must be discussed: the rationale for controlling invasive alien plant species in natural areas; the process of finding, importing, releasing, and monitoring control agents; and the problems, limitations, and challenges of classical biological control programs.

Why Control Invasive Alien Plant Species?

Empirical examples and ecological reasoning demonstrate that natural communities can face unique, long-term threats to their integrity from alien invasive species (Simberloff, this publication, p. 29). Species that disrupt community stability at the level of the primary producers in the trophic web, that is, plants, can have profound effects on community structure (Haber, this publication, p. 43). Which species will become serious invaders cannot be predicted with any degree of certainty. It is not inconsistent with human value systems or practices to try to protect the identity of natural areas, even though the maintenance of the absolute evolutionary stasis of any natural community is a biological impossibility (discussed below). Finally, assessment of the need to control an alien pest species must necessarily allow for incomplete scientific evidence of its potential impact and must consider the needs and desires of society at large.

The rationale for biologically controlling invasive alien plant species in natural areas is based on two lines of arguments. The first stresses the need to protect the integrity of natural ecosystems; the second, the absence of viable alternatives.

Protection of Natural Ecosystems

Arguments have been put forward to suggest that there is no real reason to manage alien pest species in natural ecosystems (Thiery 1982; Westman 1990). Concepts such as the "balance of nature" and the existence of climax ecosystems fail to model long-term community change because permanent, spatially defined natural communities are not considered to exist on an evolutionary time scale (Thiery 1982; Johnson 1985; Pimm 1991; Constanza et al. 1992; Lockwood 1996). Exactly what we are trying to "conserve" in natural ecosystems (specific taxa? evolutionary history? community integrity and/or functions?) or for how long is unclear. Given the universal nature of the human influence on the modern world, it is unrealistic to find or to maintain any natural area of the earth in a pristine condition (Bonnicksen 1984; Johnson 1985; Cairns 1995; Lozon and MacIsaac 1997). Therefore, should any ecosystem be manipulated based substantially on perceived needs to protect a natural identity that is neither intact nor permanent?

The terms "pest species" and "control" are based on human perceptions of value and, unlike terms such as "population" or "species", have virtually no identity independent of human interests (Drake et al. 1989; Constanza et al. 1992; Lockwood 1996; Williamson 1996; Harris 1997). Thus, the question of controlling a particular alien species in a natural ecosystem becomes a human value judgment, which is difficult to defend on the basis of scientific or evolutionary principles— "An evaluation of the aesthetic qualities of the landscape is necessarily a subjective task" Westman (1990).

Some people argue that a hands-off approach to alien species management in natural ecosystems is the most practical and biologically ethical approach for the long term (for example, Constanza et al. 1992). Their arguments are based partially on the belief that evolutionary forces, acting independently of human activity, will moderate short-term community perturbations caused by alien invasive species. They declare that human knowledge of the ecology of complex communities is insufficient to allow us to manipulate ecosystems in a truly beneficial manner and they question whether we have the ethical right to try to do so. As well, to support their assertion that these conservation projects have no chance of success in the long term and are not worth undertaking, they state that all human activities for conservation are merely a "finger in the dike" in the face of the global ecosystem.

There are counter arguments to the views expressed above. It is not difficult to demonstrate that our society believes in, and practices, ecosystem management to conserve nature. It is well established that humans hold the ecological uniqueness of their natural areas in considerable societal value (Lockwood 1996; Schmitz and Simberloff 1997). Independent of human considerations, "species and ecosystems have morally relevant interests in surviving and maintaining themselves as integrated wholes with particular self-identities" (Lockwood 1996).

When we work against species that are believed to be environmental pests of natural ecosystems, we do so to protect the natural identity of those ecosystems (Lockwood 1996). Westman (1990) states: "Vegetation management policies in public parks in the United States call for the removal of alien species to the extent feasible. The underlying goal is to preserve samples of wilderness by restoring plant communities to the 'natural state' that existed prior to extensive human influence."

The sentiment that humans should act to preserve the integrity of natural areas exists in the face of the impossibility of keeping such areas unchanged over evolutionary time or totally free of human influence. Areas with relatively high degrees of endemism and community integrity have relatively more value as natural areas (Lockwood 1996), and some of these areas are thought to be sufficiently "natural" to justify human intervention to maintain their integrity. Monocultures of invasive plants do not provide the same level of species diversity or ecological richness values that can be seen in the more natural communities.

It is logically inconsistent to claim that humans have no ethical right to try to manipulate natural ecosystems. We grant ourselves that right in all other forms of ecosystem management (for example, agriculture, forestry, fishing, mining, and urban planning). Moreover, we already have modified every ecosystem on Earth to a greater or lesser extent (Johnson 1985). Therefore, management of the community composition of natural areas is a continuation, not an initiation, of human influence in these ecosystems. Finally, while it is true that evolutionary forces will operate in situations of alien introductions into natural ecosystems, the short-term ecological results might be more unpredictable, immediate, and devastating than would be considered acceptable by most of us (Crosby 1986; Schmitz and Simberloff 1997).

Absence of Viable Alternatives

The scope of influence of alien environmental pest species can be continental and permanent (Simberloff, this publication, p. 29). No control option that would require repeated "treatments" is feasible for widespread use against invasive alien plants in natural areas (Hokkanen and Lynch 1995; McFadyen 1998). Chemical controls, augmentative or inundative biological controls, and most cultural controls cannot be applied to a widely dispersed and abundant pest population in an economic or efficacious manner and will not be effective unless the pest species is restricted to a limited geographical range. The most realistic options that have long-term, ecological potential against alien environmental plant pests are that of natural control (no controls initiated) or the use of classical biological control (Hokkanen and Lynch 1995).

Characteristics of Successful Pest Suppression

The history of classical biological control offers enough examples of successful pest suppression to generalize on what constitutes a successful outcome:

- The creation of increased biotic resistance to an alien species that is not sufficiently suppressed by native natural enemies and competitors.

- The establishment of resident populations of coevolved natural enemies (biological control agents) of the alien pest species in sufficient abundance to provide effective control of the target host in their new ecosystem.

- The spread of effective populations of the biological control agents through some or all of the range of the alien pest species.

- Perpetual control with no ongoing implementation efforts or costs. Both pest and natural enemy populations continue to coexist at low densities.

Successful control of plant pests results in increased productivity in cropping systems, reduced pesticide use, greater numbers and diversity of desirable plant species after suppression of dense weed populations, and preservation of natural environments in time and space (Van Driesche and Bellows 1996).

Implementing a Classical Biological Control Program

For both economic (costs of program) and ecological reasons (proven safety and efficacy record), natural enemies that have been successfully employed against the target plant in other bioregions should be considered first for use in biological control programs (Drake et al. 1989; Harris 1991; Barbosa and Segarra-Carmona 1993; McFadyen 1998). If such information is not available, researchers must work in the area where the plant is native, doing survey collections to find the natural enemies of the plant species. Potential control agents must then be assessed for safety and for their ability to control the plant pest. Although biological control practitioners expect to improve their ability to select effective control agents, most acknowledge that rigorous prediction of the success of these agents will elude them (Harris 1997; McFadyen 1998). Predictions of effectiveness for unproven agents are usually no better than "possible" or "unlikely" in the early phases of a program.

The safety of a classical biological control agent lies in the degree of specificity it has to the intended target species (Nechols et al. 1992). The goal of host-specificity testing is to identify any plant species, other than the targeted host, on which the herbivore can complete a life cycle. The critical question is whether the herbivore can sustain itself on the nontarget plant for multiple generations (Harley and Forno 1992; McEvoy 1996). Detailed reviews of the rationale and methodology of testing are given in Harley and Forno 1992, McEvoy 1996, and Van Driesche and Bellows 1996.

Wan and Harris (1997) advocate a risk assessment approach to host-specificity testing. This involves measuring an agent's biological success on nontarget plants, relative to its host plant, to develop a numerically based indication of the probability of a trophic shift to that species. Such a risk assessment testing procedure allows for the possibility of approving agents that do feed, develop, or oviposit on a nontarget species to some extent. Although this recommendation was published in 1997, it has not been extensively adopted in the United States or Canada (Alfred F. Cofrancesco, US Army Engineer Research and Development, Vicksburg, MS, personal communication).

Import and Release of Biological Control Agents

Once a potential biological control agent is found outside Canada, representatives of the public interest (expert government regulators) must decide whether the potential benefits of introducing the herbivore, which may control the alien plant pest, outweigh the risks to nontarget species, cropping systems, or natural communities. Regulators usually require a virtual guarantee that the agent will be safe to North American ecosystems as it is essentially impossible to "recall" an agent once it is released. Unfortunately, it is impossible to make absolute guarantees when novel complex biological interactions are involved. Such guarantees provide false assurance that could be legally challenged should unforeseen circumstances occur. A numerical risk assessment requires that regulators acknowledge that any project of this type must balance potential benefits and risks in a manner that is acceptable to the public.

In the absence of such a risk assessment, the safety of introducing an agent that feeds on nontarget plants under certain experimental conditions remains a qualitative judgment. Agents have been approved for importation that could develop on nontarget species to some extent, but only if some or all of the following conditions were met:

- the alternative host species is not thought to be economically or ecologically important;

- the agent will not attack the nontarget plant in situations where the target host species is present;

- the threat to the nontarget species is greater from the alien plant pest itself than it would be from the biological control agent; and

- the value of controlling the plant pest would outweigh the cost of nontarget damage (both estimated values).

Once approval to import an agent is granted, the live agents and all associated host plant, soil, and packing materials are received in a government-approved quarantine facility. There, all extraneous materials are destroyed, leaving only the population of biological control agents, which are checked for parasites and diseases. If necessary, the population is reared in quarantine, sometimes for several generations, to ensure that none of the agent's own natural enemies, and no antagonists of any other species, are released into the ecosystem.

On completion of the above, the alien biological control agent is placed into the ecosystem. If the ecosystem spans several jurisdictions or even countries, all involved must agree to the release—nonhuman species do not respect political borders. Cooperation between jurisdictions and countries is critical to the initiation of this kind of biological control program.

Postrelease Assessment of Biological Control Agents

All control programs, including those using the classical biological control approach, must have clear goals (for example, increased crop yields, a more diverse native community) that are stated at the outset (Harris 1997). Attaining these goals separates effective programs from ineffective ones. The following characteristics are frequently used as indicators of the success of biological control introductions (Andow et al. 1997):

- average pest population is lower after the establishment of the biological control agent than it was before;

- as the agent expands its range, there is a reduction in the pest population in these areas; and

- if the pest is protected from the agent, then pest survival increases.

Traditional postrelease assessments usually occur in two sequential steps. First, researchers determine whether the agent has been successful in colonizing the new area. The alien agent is considered to be established if it is recovered at the site two seasons after release (Harris 1997). Second, researchers assess the impact that an established agent is having on the population of its target host. Population density data collected before (often immediately before) and after the release is the most common method of doing this. Such "time series" data are frequently convincing in clear-cut cases, but it has been suggested that results from properly designed control versus treatment experiments, complete with replication and statistical analyses, are required to establish the scientific validity of any program McClay (1995). Such "scientific" evaluations of the impact caused by biological control agents may not be easy to obtain. The complexity of the potential community interactions and the inherently stochastic nature of releases at any particular site often preclude the use of control versus treatment experiments. Simply establishing control and treatment sites, with little regard to whether they really account for extraneous variables in actual field situations, does not necessarily produce a scientific result and it should not be regarded as the only way to assess a program.

Harris (1997) published a set of guidelines for evaluating biological control programs for plant species. He emphasizes practical, cost-effective sampling protocols and recognition of the goals of the program from its outset. His monitoring guidelines are likely to produce meaningful results and should be sufficiently practical to be adopted by most biological control programs.

Problems, Limitations, and Challenges

Proponents of classical biological control are faced with problems, limitations, and challenges related to host specificity, inappropriate uses, high development costs, limited success rates, and funding opportunities.

Host Specificity

The most common concern expressed about the classical biological control of plants is that the biocontrol agents will feed on nontarget plant species in the area.

Insect species have successfully colonized virtually every nonmarine habitat on the planet and, with the exception of coal and petroleum products, there is hardly a source of organic carbon that is not used by an insect taxon (Mathews and Mathews 1978). Based on the number of species and ecological diversity of the Class Insecta, as well as the nature of evolutionary selection, insect species suitable for use in classical biological control programs can be expected to exist in the natural world.

Insects considered for use for biological control tend to be species described as trophic specialists. Such insects have lost the ability to survive on a wide range of hosts in order to gain evolutionary benefits from exploiting a narrower and more uniform set of host taxa (Strong et al. 1984; Smith and Remington 1996).

Trophic specialists recognize appropriate hosts by detecting chemicals produced exclusively by their host plant taxon. With this ability, specialists can find their hosts even if the plants are rare or patchy in their distribution (Chapman 1975; Bush 1975; Mathews and Mathews 1978; Van Driesche and Bellows 1996; Van Driesche and Hoddle 1997). Further, trophic specialists have evolved an ability to overcome any repellent or toxic effects of specific secondary plant compounds, thereby gaining the advantage of being able to utilize a resource that is not available to most herbivores (Strong et al. 1984). Due to their evolution from a common ancestor, food plants of a particular taxonomic group will usually contain similar chemicals (for example, the pungent and acrid members of the Cruciferae family— cabbage, broccoli, brussel sprouts, and cauliflower). Therefore, specialist herbivores would be expected to attack a set of taxonomically related plant species. Any plant species that does not have the correct chemical profile will not be detected or, if detected, will fail to stimulate the insect to begin its sequence of feeding or ovipositional behaviors.

Compared with vertebrates, individual insects possess extremely limited abilities to deviate from a fixed set of responses to the world around them (Mathews and Mathews 1978). Their relatively short life spans and limited neural capacities favor individuals that follow a well-established ecological pattern of evolution (Mathews and Mathews 1978). Trophic specialists have evolved to react to specific chemical cues that identify their host taxa as food. If such an insect cannot find a suitable host species, it will starve in the presence of plants that may be nutritionally tolerable but are not recognized as food.

More than 130 plant species have been the targets for over 500 species of invertebrate herbivores in about 1000 separate projects (Julien and Griffiths 1998). Less than 8% of the released agents have been observed to do any significant nontarget feeding. More importantly, such feeding has been short term and/or had little to no economic impact (Van Driesche and Bellows 1996; McFadyen 1998).

McFadyen (1998) lists eight cases where phytophagous biological control agents were recorded as attacking nontarget species. In five of these cases, this was anticipated at the time of the initial introduction and, in all cases, any economic losses were outweighed by the benefits of the control program.

On occasion, plant biological control agents have been observed to broaden their feeding ranges temporarily when their populations reach "outbreak" levels (Harris 1990; Van Driesche and Bellows 1996). When a biological control agent is being introduced against an alien plant species, the host plant itself already exists at outbreak abundance levels, relative to its native range. Some phytophagous agents will develop populations that quickly build up on the abundant populations of their host plant. At some point, the exponentially increasing numbers of natural enemies virtually use up their available host resources. This is the desired result of a biological control program, and it often results in the near total (90–99%) collapse of the targeted plant's population (Dennill et al. 1993; Van Driesche and Bellows 1996).

The temporary overabundance of the natural enemies may cause individuals to feed on nontarget plant species. If host-specificity tests have been conducted properly, the control agent will find these plant species fundamentally unsuitable for sustained development. The outbreak populations of the natural enemies will collapse within one or two generations of the crash of their principal host, with the abundance of host plant material being the main limiting factor on their population size. The agent and the targeted host plant will then develop a long-term, stable relationship in which both populations exist in greatly reduced abundance from their respective outbreak levels (Harris 1990; Van Driesche and Bellows 1996).

It is theoretically possible that a population of an agent may adapt sufficiently to a new host species to cause long-term problems. However, there is no evidence that any phytophagous organism tested prior to release and then used in a weed biological control program has ever caused any permanent harm to an agricultural crop (Waterhouse and Norris 1987 cited in Van Driesche and Bellows 1996; Hokkanen and Lynch 1995). Concerns about the nontarget effects of biological control programs have traditionally been restricted to economically important plant species. Restricting these statements to agricultural crops or economic losses may be failing to acknowledge damage to noncrop species. While this is possible, I suspect that substantial impact by a weed biological control agent on any nontarget plant would have been noted in the literature (for example, Louda et al. 1997).

Inappropriate Uses

Classical biological control is not the "magic bullet" that provides solutions to all pest problems. There are a number of situations relevant to environmental pest species in which these techniques are not appropriate.

Native pest species that have had a long period of association with their natural enemies, which are also native to the bioregion, are not good candidates for classical biological control as such; there is no trophic relationship to restore between the pest and the native enemy. Native enemies can be used as inundative control (see Harris and Shamoun, this publication, p. 291) in cases where the balance between the pest and the enemy is temporarily destroyed due to other environmental factors. In such situations, the enemy populations are augmented in order to bring the pest under control. Within a few years, populations will inevitably revert to levels consistent with the coevolutionary history of the two species. This necessitates using these agents as "biopesticides" that must be reapplied every time and everywhere that suppression of the pest population is desired. Such a strategy would not be economically feasible when attempting to control alien environmental pests.

An alien plant species that is considered to be a pest in certain ecological situations and a beneficial species in others is not a good candidate either. In classical biological control it is hoped that a biological control agent, when established, will persist perpetually in the ecosystem and spread throughout the range of its targeted host species (Turner 1985). There is no practical way of limiting this dispersal to certain areas and not to others (McFadyen 1998).

Some alien plant pests will be too closely related to beneficial native or introduced species for them to be acceptable targets for classical biological control. The role of host-specificity testing is to determine what species, other than the target, might be able to sustain populations of the biological control agent. It is not surprising that such tests reveal certain natural enemies to be capable of attacking nontarget plants that are

beneficial in North American ecosystems. Both the costs of conducting host-specificity testing and the likelihood that no suitable agent will be found increase with the number of close, beneficial relatives to the potential target species that are found in North America.

Development Costs

Although the safety record of classical biological control is commendable, its low record of success limits wider practice of this control methodology. The proportion of weed biological control programs that have resulted in successful control is reported to be between 25% (Van Driesche and Bellows 1996) and 40% of all conducted programs (Tisdell 1990). As all classical biological control agents are introduced alien species themselves, it is difficult to predict their success. In economic terms, the combination of costs (up to several million dollars), potential maximum return (perpetual pest control), and likelihood of a successful program (less than 40%) mean that classical biological control projects that use unproven agents are extremely speculative investments. This is one reason why these programs are usually run by government agencies.

Understanding of cost issues is critical to the use of biological control against environmental pests in natural ecosystems. A complete classical biological control project targeting an unresearched plant species can be expected to take about 20 scientist-years and may cost four to nine million dollars (Harris 1997, 1998a; McFadyen 1998). A substantial portion of the expenses occur in the early phases of the program during foreign exploration, preliminary screening of agents, and host-specificity testing. These expenses must be spent before a suitable agent has been identified or imported to the country with the pest problem. There is no guarantee that suitable agents will be found. If suitable species are found, there is a better than a 50% chance that when introduced, these agents will fail to solve the problems caused by an alien plant pest.

While the majority of the costs for classical biological control are incurred during the initial implementation of the program, the economic benefits of successful classical biological control continue to accrue forever. There are many reports of the enormous economic benefits of successful classical biological control programs relative to the costs of implementing them (Huffaker and Caltagirone 1986; Tisdell 1990; Van Driesche and Bellows 1996). The average benefit to cost ratio for Australian biological control projects (10.6:1) was considerably higher than that for nonbiological methods

(2.5:1) undertaken by the same agency (Tisdell 1990). Given these statistics, why can it be so difficult to obtain proper funding for classical biological control programs?

Funding

Funding support, not safety, often is the most important limiting factor to doing effective classical biological control (Van Driesche and Bellows 1993). Classical biological programs are conducted over 10–20 years (P. Harris, Agriculture and Agri-Food Canada, Lethbridge, AB, personal communication), which is considerably longer than the mandate of most funding agencies. Hence, agencies are unable or unwilling to commit funds for a complete program at its outset. Most sponsoring agencies want to be involved with the highest-profile part of a program—the actual release of agents. They are less interested in providing funding for preliminary assessments of the nature of the pest problem, research to streamline the selection of effective agents, and postrelease assessments of indirect impacts of the biological control agents. Critics of biological control have expressed valid concerns about the lack of rigorous pre- and postrelease monitoring of programs, but it has been difficult to get funding agencies to understand the need for such studies, and even more difficult to get them to pay for them (McFadyen 1998).

Despite these obstacles, the potential for wide-ranging, perpetual control can create a cost-benefit environment that favors the initiation of classical biological control programs against certain pest species. Who then should pay for the research needed to conduct classical biological control programs? Here are two viewpoints:

> Biological control doesn't provide products with repeated marketability, but rather solves problems permanently at the regional or national level.—Van Driesche and Bellows 1996

> Classical biological control should be treated as the provision of a public or collective good. It will be undersupplied if left to free market forces.—Tisdell 1990

Once established, effective control agents disperse throughout the host's range and become a permanent controlling force on their host species. Individual growers are not compelled to pay for this type of program as they will profit from its success whether they pay for it or not. There is no "product" to be sold on an annual basis. Since there is no ongoing "market", commercial pest control interests have no reason to invest in these research programs (Hokkanen and Lynch 1995). In fact, successful classical biological control of a pest represents devastatingly effective competition for businesses hoping to sell "control" to a large number of individual growers on an annual basis. Therefore, the nature of classical biological control effectively removes the largest player in pest control, the pesticide industry, from consideration as a funding source.

Practitioners of classical biological control against economic pests must find substantial funding support to initiate their programs, with no guarantee of any return on this investment. For these reasons, classical biological control must be supported on the basis of its general benefit to society (Reichelderfer 1985). The support of governments or nonprofit, nongovernmental agencies has always been essential to conducting classical biological control projects and will continue to be in the future (Waage 1991; Van Driesche and Bellows 1993).

Considering the difficulty in getting appropriate funding to conduct classical biological control programs against economically important pest species, what kind of financial support can be expected for programs against environmental pests of natural areas? Often, there is little tangible economic benefit in the conservation or restoration of a natural community, and no individual or group will realize substantial financial profits from this kind of program. Under these circumstances, it is even more critical that nonprofit agencies, working in the public interest, bear the costs of conducting classical biological control programs in natural areas.

Traditionally governments have assumed these financial responsibilities, but current federal government policies on biological control favor "out of government" cosponsorship of programs by specific interest groups (P. Harris, Agriculture and Agri-Food Canada, Lethbridge, AB, personal communication). One can see why a growers' collective (for example, a commodity-based marketing board) might be interested in cosponsoring a program against an economic pest of their commodity. It is less clear how the nonprofit, nongovernmental organizations that characteristically are involved in environmental issues would either have the funds available to cosponsor a program or be willing to commit large amounts to such fundamentally speculative investigations. It will be very difficult to find the funding needed to conduct classical biological control programs in natural areas. This is one of the most critical limiting factors.

The process can be somewhat streamlined by first considering agents that have been successfully used against the plant pest in other bioregions (Harley and Forno 1992; Hokkanen and Lynch 1995; Van Driesche and Bellows 1996). All costs of foreign exploration and prescreening, as well as much of the cost of host-specificity testing can be avoided (McFadyen 1998). A similar alternative is to piggyback a program with one being developed by another country (Harris 1998). Again, most of the prerelease costs will have been assumed in the other jurisdiction.

Harris (1998) compared the costs and efficacy for Canada conducting its own biological control programs versus adopting a program initiated in another jurisdiction. The other jurisdiction is most often the United States, as it will have already assessed the safety of potential agents for importation to temperate North America. Harris showed that 80% of the biocontrol agents developed in Canadian biological control programs successfully became established, while only 33% of those adopted from programs in other countries did so. However, the average screening and assessment efforts for a Canadian program took 6.6 scientist years and cost $2.3 million, while similar efforts for an adopted program took only 0.24 scientist years and cost under $100 000 (Harris 1998). Obviously, the lower success rate of adopted programs is more than compensated for by their extremely low implementation costs. If the plant species is of concern to Canadian interests and if the host-specificity characteristics of the agent are not in conflict with Canadian concerns, it is worth trying agents that other jurisdictions have paid for. However, only some Canadian pest problems can be addressed in this manner; others require original research.

Conclusions

There are only two realistic options available to address large-scale, long-term problems created by alien pest species in natural ecosystems: do nothing and let nature takes its course, or use classical biological control against certain alien species.

Society, as represented by government, must decide what the pest species are and what is to be done about them. The decision to employ a classical biological control program must be made for each pest situation on a risk assessment basis. Fundamental to the concept of risk assessment is the fact that exact, comprehensive scientific prediction is not a realistic possibility. Classical biological control may not be "science" in an academic sense (Anderson 1995; Hager and

McCoy 1998), but its benefits to society are demonstrated and undeniable. The safety record of classical biological control, which in recent times has been questioned by critics (Howarth 1991; Simberloff and Stiling 1996; Louda et al. 1997), arguably is better than most large-scale environmental manipulations (for example, agriculture, forestry, fisheries, power generation).

If society, as represented by government, considers classical biological control programs to be an acceptable management tool, it must be willing to pay to properly support such programs. One of the strongest criticisms presented in the past decade is that practitioners fail to monitor the consequences of their introductions. Only if the funding agencies accept program durations of at least 20 years can the responsible post-release monitoring advocated by critics and expected by society be done.

Because problems with alien species in natural areas are continental and perpetual, the potential of classical biological control in nature conservation is unique, demonstrated, and real. The challenge to proponents of classical biological control will be to persuade society that this tool can be used in a safe and ethical manner and that the ecological benefits of successful programs against alien plant pests of natural areas justify the expenditures needed to run such programs.

Acknowledgments

I would like to thank the Department of Environmental Biology, University of Guelph, and the North American Wetland Conservation Council for financial support during the preparation of this manuscript. Drs. Rose De Clerck-Floate, Gard Otis, and several other reviewers provided valuable comments on various incarnations of this effort. Thanks to Dr. Peter Harris, Gary Eden, Axel Larsen, Gerry Lee, and Donna MacKenzie for valuable guidance and support through the "Loose-strife Years." Very special thanks to Renata Claudi for a fantastic editing job! Finally, I want to thank my teacher, Dr. John Laing, and all of my students from the "bug courses"—you kept me on my toes!

References

Anderson, M.G. 1995. Interactions between *Lythrum salicaria* and native organisms: a critical review. Environ. Manage. 19:225–231.

Andow, D.A.; Ragsdale, D.W.; Nyvall, R.F. 1997. Biological control in cool temperate regions. Pages 1–28 *in* D.A. Andow,

D.W. Ragsdale, and R.F. Nyvall, eds. Ecological interactions and biological control. Westview Press, Boulder, CO.

Barbosa, P.; Segarra-Carmona, A. 1993. Criteria for the selection of pest arthropod species as candidates for biological control. Pages 5–24 in R.G. Van Driesche and T.S. Bellows, eds. Steps in classical arthropod biological control. Thomas Say Publications in Entomology—Proceedings. Entomological Society of America, Lanham, MD.

Bonnicksen, T. 1984. A call for accountability. Restor. Manage. Notes 1:12–13.

Bush, G.L. 1975. Sympatric speciation in phytophagous parasitic insects. Pages 187–206 in P.W. Price, ed. Evolutionary strategies of parasitic insects and mites. Plenum Press, New York, NY.

Cairns, J., Jr. 1995. The influence of the information age, world globalization, and ecosystem health upon ecological risk assessment. Ecosyst. Health 1:81–87.

Chapman, R.F. 1975. The insects: structure and function. English Universities Press, London, UK.

Constanza, R.; Norton, B.G.; Haskell, B.D., eds. 1992. Ecosystem health: new goals for ecosystem management. Island Press, Washington, DC.

Crosby, A.W. 1986. Ecological imperialism. Cambridge University Press, Cambridge, UK.

Cullen, J.M.; Delfosse, E.S. 1985. Echium plantageneum: catalyst for conflict and change in Australia. Pages 249–292 in E.S. Delfosse, ed. Proceedings of the VI International Symposium on Biological Control of Weeds. Agriculture Canada, Ottawa, ON.

DeLoach, C.J. 1991. Past successes and current prospects in biological control of weeds in the United States and Canada. Nat. Areas J. 11:129–142.

Dennill, G.B.; Donelly, D.; Chown, S.L. 1993. Expansion of host-plant range of a biocontrol agent Trichilogaster acaciaelongifoliae (Pteromalidae) released against the weed Acacia longifolia in South Africa. Agric. Ecosyst. Environ. 43:1–10.

Drake, J.A.; Mooney, H.A.; di Castri, F.; Groves, R.H.; Kruger, F.J.; Rejmanek, M.; Williamson, M., eds. 1989. Biological invasions: a global perspective, SCOPE 37. John Wiley and Sons, New York, NY.

Hager, H.A.; McCoy, K.D. 1998. The implications of accepting untested hypotheses: a review of the effects of purple loosestrife (Lythrum salicaria) in North America. Biodivers. Conserv. 7:1069–1079.

Harley, K.L.S.; Forno, I.W. 1992. Biological control of weeds, a handbook for practitioners and students. Inkata Press, Melbourne, Australia.

Harris, P. 1990. Environmental impact of introduced biological control agents. Pages 289–300 in M. Mackauer, L.E. Ehler, and J. Roland, eds. Critical issues in biological control. Intercept Press, Andover, UK.

Harris, P. 1991. Classical biocontrol of weeds: its definition, selection of effective agents, and administrative-political problems. Can. Entomol. 123:827–849.

Harris, P. 1997. Monitoring and impact of weed biological control agents. Pages 215–223 in D.A. Andow, D.W. Ragsdale, and R.F. Nyvall, eds. 1997. Ecological interactions and biological control. Westview Press, Boulder, CO.

Harris, P. 1998. Evolution of classical weed biocontrol: meeting survival challenges. Bull. Entomol. Soc. Can. 30:134–143.

Hokkanen, H.M.T.; Lynch, J.M., eds. 1995. Biological control: benefits and risks. Cambridge University Press, New York, NY.

Howarth, F.G. 1991. Environmental impact of classical biological control. Annu. Rev. Entomol. 36:485–509.

Huffaker, C.B.; Caltagirone, L.E. 1986. The impact of biological control on the development of the Pacific. Agric. Ecosyst. Environ. 15:95–107.

Huffaker, C.B.; Messenger, P.S., eds. 1976. Theory and practice of biological control. Academic Press, New York, NY.

[IIBC] International Institute of Biological Control. 1994. Using biodiversity to protect biodiversity. Biological control, conservation and the biodiversity convention. CABI Publishing, Wallingford, Oxon, UK.

Johnson, H.B. 1985. Consequences of species introductions and removals on ecosystem function. Pages 27–56 in E.S. Delfosse, ed. Proceedings of the VI International Symposium on Biological Control of Weeds. Agriculture Canada, Ottawa, ON.

Julien, M.H.; Griffiths, M.W. 1998. Biological control of weeds: a world catalogue of agents and their target weeds. 4th. ed. CABI Publishing, Wallingford, Oxon, UK. 240 p.

Lockwood, J.A. 1993. Environmental issues involved in biological control of rangeland grasshoppers (Orthoptera: Acrididae) with exotic agents. Environ. Entomol. 22:503–518

Lockwood, J.A. 1996. The ethics of biological control: understanding the moral implications of our most powerful ecological technology. Agric. Hum. Values 13:2–19.

Louda, S.M.; Kendall, D.; Connor, J.; Simberloff, D. 1997. Ecological effects of an insect introduced for the biological control of weeds. Science 277:1088–1090.

Lozon, J.D.; MacIsaac, H.J. 1997. Biological invasions: are they dependent on disturbance? Environ. Rev. 5:131–144.

Mathews, R.W.; Mathews, J.R. 1978. Insect behavior. John Wiley and Sons, New York, NY.

McClay, A.S. 1995. Beyond "before-and-after": experimental design and evaluation in classical weed biocontrol. Pages 213–219 in E.S. Delfosse and R.R. Scott, eds. Proceedings of the VIII International Symposium on Biological Control of Weeds. CSIRO Publishing, Melbourne, Australia.

McEvoy, P.B. 1996. Host specificity and biological control. Bioscience 46:401–405.

McFadyen, R.E.C. 1998. Biological control of weeds. Annu. Rev. Entomol. 43:369–393.

Nechols, J.R.; Kauffman, W.C. 1992. Introduction and overview. Pages 1–5 in W.C. Kauffman and J.E. Nechols, eds. Selection criteria and ecological consequences of importing natural enemies. Thomas Say Publications in Entomology—Proceedings. Entomological Society of America, Lanham, MD.

Nechols, J.R.; Kauffman, W.C.; Schaefer, P.W. 1992. Significance of host specificity in classical biological control. Pages 41–52 in W.C. Kauffman and J.E. Nechols, eds. Selection criteria and ecological consequences of importing natural enemies. Thomas Say Publications in Entomology—Proceedings. Entomological Society of America, Lanham, MD.

Pimm, S.L. 1991. The Balance of Nature? Ecological issues in the conservation of species and communities. University of Chicago Press, Chicago, IL.

Reichelderfer, K. 1985. Factors affecting the economic feasibility of the biological control of weeds. Pages 135–144 in E.S. Delfosse, ed. Proceedings of the VI International Symposium on Biological Control of Weeds. Agriculture Canada, Ottawa, ON.

Sawyer, R.C. 1996. To make a spotless orange—biological control in California. Iowa State University Press, Ames, IA.

Schmitz, D.C.; Simberloff, D. 1997. Biological invasions: a growing threat. Issues Environ. Sci. Technol. 8:33–40.

Simberloff, D. 1992. Conservation of pristine habitats and unintended effects of biological control. Pages 104–117 in W.C. Kauffman and J.E. Nechols, eds. Selection criteria and ecological consequences of importing natural enemies. Thomas Say Publications in Entomology—Proceedings. Entomological Society of America, Lanham, MD.

Simberloff, D.; Stiling, P. 1996. How risky is biological control? Ecology 77:1965–1974.

Smith, H.R.; Remington, C.L. 1996. Food specificity in interspecies competition. Bioscience 46:436–447.

Strong, D.R. 1997. Fear no weevil? Science 277:1058–1059.

Strong, D.R.; Lawton, J.H.; Southwood, Sir Richard. 1984. Insects on plants: community patterns and mechanisms. Harvard University Press, Cambridge, MA.

Thiery, R.G. 1982. Environmental instability and community diversity. Biol. Rev. (Cambridge) 57:671–710.

Tisdell, C. 1990. Economic impact of biological control of weeds and insects. Pages 301–316 in M. Mackauer, L.E. Ehler, and J. Roland, eds. Critical issues in biological control. Intercept Press, Andover, UK.

Turner, C.E. 1985. Conflicting interests and the biological control of weeds. Pages 203–226 in E.S. Delfosse, ed. Proceedings of the VI International Symposium on Biological Control of Weeds. Agriculture Canada, Ottawa, ON.

Van Driesche, R.G.; Bellows, T.S. 1993. Conclusions. Pages 87–88 in R.G. Van Driesche and T.S. Bellows, eds. Steps in classical arthropod biological control. Thomas Say Publications in Entomology—Proceedings. Entomological Society of America, Lanham, MD.

Van Driesche, R.G.; Bellows, T.S. 1996. Biological control. Chapman and Hall, New York, NY.

Van Driesche, R.G.; Hoddle, M. 1997. Should arthropod parasitoids and predators be subject to host range testing when used as biological control agents? Agric. Hum. Values 14:221–226.

Waage, J.K. 1991. Biological control: the old and the new. In A.S. McClay, ed. Proceedings of the Workshop on Biological Control of Pests in Canada, 11–12 October 1990, Calgary, AB. Alberta Environmental Centre, Vegreville, AB.

Waage, J. 1996. Yes, but does it work in the field? The challenge of technology transfer in biological control. Entomophaga 41:315–332.

Wan, F.-W.; Harris, P. 1997. Use of risk analyses for screening weed biocontrol agents: Altica carduorum Guer. (Coleoptera: Chrysomelidae) from China as a biocontrol agent of Cirsium arvense L. Scop. in North America. Biocontrol Sci. Technol. 7:299–308.

Waterhouse, D.F.; Norris, K.R. 1987. Biological control, Pacific prospects. Inkata Press, Melbourne, Australia.

Westman, W.E. 1990. Park management of exotic plant species: problems and issues. Conserv. Biol. 4:251–260.

White, D.J.; Haber, E.; Keddy, C. 1993. Invasive plants of natural habitats in Canada. Canadian Wildlife Service, Environment Canada/Canadian Museum of Nature, Ottawa, ON.

Williamson, M. 1996. Biological invasions. Chapman and Hall, New York, NY.

Photo with chapter title: The biocontrol beetle, *Galerucella calmariensis* (L.), feeding on purple loosestrife (*Lythrum salicaria* L.). Photo by Eric Coombs, Oregon Department of Agriculture, Salem, OR.

Biological Control of Weeds in Canada: Results, Opportunities, and Constraints

Peter Harris and Simon F. Shamoun

Biological control refers to the deliberate use of natural enemies (predators, parasites, pathogens, and competitors) to reduce a pest species to an acceptable density. There are three approaches: classical (inoculative), inundative (bioherbicide), and manipulative (conservation). The choice depends on whether the pest is native or alien, present on cultivated or uncultivated land, how persistent the species is, and whether the goal of control is economic or environmental. In this paper the target pests are weeds, but the approaches and principles are also applicable to insects and other organisms. With one exception, the Canadian weed biological control program targets weeds that cause economic losses in agriculture and forestry. This has required that biological control be integrated into crop management and be acceptable to the general public.

Classical biological control agents are self-perpetuating with varying dispersal abilities to provide continuing control. Typically the targets are introduced plants that form dense persistent populations on uncultivated grasslands. The agents are frequently insects, but diseases and nematodes can be used. Whatever the species that is used, it must not harm desirable plants. Classical biological control is unlikely to be effective against short-term transitional weeds unless the agent disperses extremely well, increases rapidly, and has a high impact. Given the right problem, classical biological control is the cheapest and most environmentally friendly solution.

Some oppose classical biological control because it involves establishing an alien species which, as such, does not belong in a natural Canadian environment. However, the habitat is no longer native if an alien weed dominates it. Biological control can usually transform a community dominated by an alien weed to a native community with a small weed component and population of its biological control agent. The US *Agricultural Risk Protection Act*, 2000, recognizes this benefit. More meaningful concerns reflect the need for biological control and the host range of the agents.

Establishing the need for classical biological control involves weighing the costs versus the benefits in economic and ecological terms, which includes the possible impact on nontarget organisms. Demonstrat-

ing that an agent will be safe costs about two scientist-years, or about $800 000. For an in-depth discussion, see Corrigan in this publication (p. 279) and Harris (2000a) The enabling legislation is Canada's *Plant Protection Act*.

The basic criterion of safety used in North America is that the insect does not develop on desirable plants when confined to them. Certainly plants unsuitable in the tests are not at risk. However, during testing, larvae commonly develop on other plants in the host genus even when they do not attack them in nature. Unfortunately most alien weeds are in genera with native species; therefore, the test normally indicates that native plants are vulnerable, although less than 5% of the agents will attack them in nature. The discrepancy between the test and the field results arises because, for most insects, host selection is the responsibility of the egg-laying female. Thus, to identify problems more accurately, biological control agents developing on native plant species in the test need to be further subjected as adults to field tests, acceptable to the regulators, in regions where the native plant species occur.

Classical biological control is used against alien forest weeds, but in Canada forest losses are largely from native plants. This dictates the use of inundative biological control, which uses native organisms, typically fungi, that are grown on a nutrient medium and then sprayed on the weed in a problem area. This creates a temporary local outbreak that declines in one to five years to the normal level in the environment. Damage to nontarget plants must be limited, which means that the controlling organism either has a narrow host range or is restricted by the application method. The primary use of this method has been against native plants that increase following logging or other disturbances to interfere with forest regeneration. Watson and Wall (1995) provide background information. In agriculture, inundative biological control is of interest for major crop weeds that are not controlled by other means. The enabling legislation is Canada's *Pest Control Products Act*. Present constraints to this method are the high cost of registration and the often small market for the product.

Manipulative biological control modifies a habitat to improve the competitive advantage of existing natural enemies or decrease that of competitors. There is no special enabling legislation.

Federal weed biocontrol programs, carried out by Agriculture and Agri-Food Canada and the Canadian Forest Service (CFS), Natural Resources Canada, have economic rather than ecological goals. For agricultural projects, government funds are used to match those from commodity groups or industry. In forestry the same end is achieved by joint CFS–industry–university projects. Ecological benefits, such as increases in native species, are not project goals and are usually not measured. Bell (1983) suggested that invasive alien weeds were displacing 50 rare native Australian plants. A similar situation may exist in Canada; however, there is little funding to work on such problems unless the weed also causes economic loss, and even then, ecological benefits are rarely documented.

Classical Biological Control

Some ecologists question the need for biological control of weeds in pastures. They argue that most weeds are pioneer species and the common succession model suggests that good pasture management results in stable dominants ("climax species") replacing the pioneers. However, some invading alien weeds (in the absence of grazing) form stable dominants that are only temporarily reduced by herbicides. This contradicts the conventional view of ecological succession. The state and transition model offers an alternative theory: that a variety of plant communities ("state" in the model) can form stable communities. If these are disrupted, there is a period with transitional plants, which are eventually replaced by a new stable community that may or may not be that previously present (Harris and Wilmhurst 2000). The replacement of stable native communities by a stable community dominated by an alien weed is compatible with the state and transition model. In principle, stable dominant weeds and long-lasting transitional species are the best targets for classical biological control. Most Canadian classical programs of weed biological control target alien weeds that reduce forage yields or that cover in burs or poison livestock.

In Canada 20 weed species have been targeted since 1950. Control agents were established on 18 of these weeds. From this group, 11 species have been reduced in at least some habitats. Biological control often results in a plant community that consists of the understory of the previously dominant weed (or that adjacent to it) with a small amount of the weed present.

If, however, the land is subject to overgrazing, the new state may be dominated by another undesirable plant. Four Canadian projects on uncultivated land are described below; weed biomass was reduced in all and the habitat largely restored in three, indicating that classical biological control has environmental benefits. Mention is also made of two weeds of cultivated land overseas, ragweed (*Ambrosia artemisiifolia* L.) in Russia and rush skeletonweed (*Chondrilla juncea* L.) in Australia: this habitat has not been targeted in Canada.

Canadian Projects on Uncultivated Land

St. John's-wort (*Hypericum perforatum* L.), a European plant, was the target of pioneering biological control work by the Australians in the 1920s. The same insect species were released in 1944 in the western United States, where the weed had rendered over 810 000 ha of rangeland unproductive. Of these, a defoliating beetle, *Chrysolina quadrigemina* (Suffr.) (Figure 1), was particularly effective and returned most of the region to native range in fair to good condition, with the weed at about 1% of its former density (Huffaker and Kennet 1959). Release in south-central British Columbia occurred in 1952, as a vigorous chemical control program had not stopped the spread of the weed. The impact of *C. quadrigemina* in summer-dry sites and *C. hyperici* (Forst.) in summer-moist sites was similar to that observed in California, although delayed up to 10 years (Harris et al. 1969) while the beetles adjusted to fall and spring rather than winter breeding (Peschken 1972). A photosensitizing chemical in the plant excludes summer breeding. The use of beetles ended the chemical spray program in British Columbia. Unfortunately, much of the economic benefit was lost as diffuse and spotted knapweed (*Centaurea diffusa* Lam.

Figure 1. Defoliating beetles *Chrysolina quadrigemina* (large) and *C. hyperici* (smaller).

and *C. maculosa* Lam.) replaced St. John's-wort. Release of the beetles in Ontario reduced the weed and resulted in removal of St. John's-wort from the provincial noxious weed list. In Nova Scotia many sites are too moist for *Chrysolina hyperici,* but the beetle merely has to survive at low densities because it is a vector of a native fungus that kills the weed and generally keeps it below a 1% cover (Jensen 2000a).

Leafy spurge (*Euphorbia esula* L.) came to Canada from Eastern Europe with prairie settlement. It forms dense persistent stands, commonly with a 100% cover. As cattle avoid grazing areas with greater than 10% spurge cover, all forage is effectively lost. Spurge costs and losses in North Dakota were estimated at US$105 million/year (Leistritz et al. 1992), which for Manitoba prorates to US$16.4 million/year. Despite herbicide programs, the weed is an expanding problem throughout western Canada.

On warm, dry sites with coarse soils, the root-feeding beetle *Aphthona nigriscutis* Foudr. (Figure 2), provides effective control. On sand dunes in Spruce Woods Park, Manitoba (Figure 3), the dry weight of spurge on the beetle release site declined by 96%, then increased slightly following several moist summers. The 10-year decline of spurge was 87%, while grasses and sedges increased 2.6-fold and forbs 1.9-fold. On a sandy loam site at Maxim, Saskatchewan, the 10-year spurge reduction due to *A. cyparissiae* (Koch) was 89%. Grass, mostly Kentucky bluegrass (*Poa pratensis* L.), increased threefold and forbs sevenfold. *Aphthona lacertosa* (Rosh.) is the effective control species on heavy Regina, Saskatchewan, clay and in prairie brush stands (Harris 2000b). The northern prairie skink (*Eumeces s. septentrionalis* Baird), a species of concern in Canada, is restricted to short vegetation with bare sandy patches in the Assiniboine Delta region of Manitoba. Leafy spurge was displacing it and threatening its habitat, but this has been reversed by biological control (E. Bredin, personal communication). Mico (1993) found that average spurge cover in the three years sampled was 14% compared with 50% recorded previously. There were 18 taxa of vascular plants recorded in areas where the root-feeding beetle was present compared with 6 taxa in areas without beetles. Concern for a native spurge, *Euphorbia robusta* (Engelm.) Small ex Britt. and Britt., a scattered plant on dry sites in the northwest United States, has declined. This species was initially attacked by *A. nigriscutis* on a Wyoming site. With the decline of leafy spurge, and accompanying decline in beetle density, *E. robusta* now receives little damage and has

Figure 2. Root-feeding beetle *Aphthona nigriscutis.*

Figure 3. Spurge under control after release of *Aphthona nigriscutis*, Spruce Woods Park, MB; spurge survives in the background shaded area and in a clump over an anthill because the beetles avoided both these areas.

increased from 36 to 230 plants (J.L. Baker, personal communication).

Diffuse and spotted knapweed (*Centaurea diffusa* Lam. and *C. maculosa* Lam.), by1972, dominated about 300 000 ha of dry grasslands in south-central British Columbia and threatened 8.4 to 10.7 million ha in western Canada for a direct annual loss of $58 million/year (Harris and Cranston 1979). Usually control is achieved by a single control agent species per habitat, but a combination of control agents has been needed for the knapweeds. Two seed-head flies, *Urophora affinis affinis* (Frauenfeld) (Figure 4) and *U. quadrifasciata* (Meig.), reduced knapweed seed production by about 80%. Control requires over 93% reduction (Roze 1981). Adding the root-gall beetle *Sphenoptera jugoslavica* (Oben.) (Figure 5) to diffuse knapweed in warm, dry sites, the root weevil *Cyphocleonus achates* Fåhr to spotted knapweed in light soils, and the root moth *Agapeta zoegana* L. (Figure 6) to both knapweeds in mesic sites achieved this. Spotted knapweed seed production fell at Chase, British Columbia, from over 40 000/m^2 in 1974 to 370/m^2 in 1987 with the insect complex. Seed production increased slightly (1660/m^2) in the wetter summer of 1988 (Harris 1991) for an average reduction of 97.5%. There is less knapweed, but grass is still depressed due to grazing pressure.

Diffuse knapweed seed production at White Lake, British Columbia, fell an average of 97.7% with the two seed-head flies and *S. jugoslavica* (Harris 1991). Bunchgrasses have returned, in part aided by restriction of the site to wildlife grazing. Very likely there are other benefits to knapweed control. Lacey et al. (1989) reported that runoff and sediment yield were higher for spotted knapweed plots than for bunchgrass controls.

Purple loosestrife (*Lythrum salicaria* L.) is the only weed targeted in Canada for environmental reasons. This European plant rapidly colonizes open moist soils exposed by falling water levels. It can also invade undisturbed marshes to displace up to 60% of the native vegetation. The US Fish and Wildlife Service funded biological control of loosestrife after it became clear that its dense stands supported little wildlife: two plant species and a turtle species were threatened in areas of heavy infestation and the black tern (*Chlidonias niger* (L.)) populations in those areas were declining (Thompson et al. 1987). Most Canadian infestations are still south of latitude 51°N, but loosestrife's European limit is 65°N. The northern leopard frog (*Rana pipiens* Schr.), a formerly abundant species that is now of special concern, breeds in temporary ponds with vegetation less than a metre tall. The invasion of Manitoba wetlands by purple loosestrife, which grows up to 2 m, is one

Figure 4. Longitudinal section of a gall formed by the fly *Urophora affinis affinis* in the seed head of diffuse knapweed; puparium (*left*) and larva (*right*).

Figure 5. The root-gall beetle *Sphenoptera jugoslavica* on diffuse knapweed.

Figure 6. The root moth *Agapeta zoegana* on spotted knapweed.

reason for the present depressed frog population (Canadian Wildlife Service 2000).

Several loosestrife control insects tested by the United States were provided to Canada and have become established. The University of Guelph project for the propagation and release of two defoliating beetles, *Galerucella calmariensis* (L.) and *G. pusilla* (Duft.), has been particularly successful. In three years, loosestrife biomass at several release sites declined by over 95% and the stands are now dominated by cattails, reed canary grass (*Phalaris arundinacea* L.), and sedges. Some beetle feeding occurred on two native species, swamp loosestrife *(Decodon verticillatus* (L.) Ell.) and winged loosestrife (*Lythrum alatum* Pursh). This appears to be a short-term spillover by starving beetles (Corrigan et al. 1998). *Galerucella calamariensis* has spread 10 km/year along waterways and is now established throughout southern Ontario (J. Corrigan, personal communication).

Despite its success, the biological control program was attacked from within the university because it had been started without Canadian data on the weed impact, without clearly stated goals, and without adequate follow-up (Dale 1998). Subsequently, Treberg and Husband (1999) reported that in spite of its prevalence, loosestrife had no impact on plant species richness. This probably applies to most invasive weeds and accounts for the rapid return of the original state following treatment with biological control agents. There is anecdotal evidence that wildlife has also returned to the treated sites, but no published data.

All biological control projects need a sound action plan, sound screening of the organism to be released, and monitoring of the impact until the weed, the control agents, and other organisms have reached equilibrium. Unless adequate funding is available to complete the entire program, attacks on nontarget species must be expected.

Overseas Projects on Cultivated Land

Classical biological control is rarely used against alien weeds of cultivated crops, partly because cropping practice disrupts the life cycle of most control agents. One example of its use on cultivated land is from Russia, on common ragweed (*Ambrosia artemisiifolia* L.), accidentally introduced there from North America. Ragweed increased to dominate crops in parts of Russia and prevented abandoned fields from returning to the native steppe. The defoliating beetle *Zygogramma suturalis* F., obtained from Canada, was established and

controlled the weed on over 1500 ha (mainly in alfalfa and sainfoin) in the release area. This resulted in two- to threefold yield increases (Kovalev and Vechernin 1986). Thus, biological control has been effective in stable infestations of the weed, but there has been no control in the transitional infestations of annually rotated crops (Reznik et al. 1991). The beetles are only capable of dispersing a few hundred metres and thus, in transitional infestations, most die without finding new hosts. If, however, the agent disperses well, then biological control can be used for weeds in annual crops. This was demonstrated in Australia by the success of the wind-spread rust *Puccinia chondrillinae* Bub. & Syd. as the control agent of rush skeletonweed (*Chondrilla juncea* L.) (Cullen 1985). Classical biological control of annual crop weeds should perhaps be tried in Canada with agents selected for dispersal ability.

Inundative Biological Control

The growing demand for forest production and sustainability has increased the intensity of forest management (Wall et al. 1992). This requires good control of the vegetation competing with young conifers (Shamoun 2000). Mechanical removal, manual brushing, or herbicides can control such vegetation, but are expensive and have nontarget effects that are of environmental concern. Inundative biological control of vegetation with native pathogens is an alternative that can increase the early conifer growth rate and shorten harvest time (Wall and Hasan 1996). It is particularly valuable in ecologically sensitive areas such as riparian zones and lowland forest sites (Shamoun 2000).

A few native plant species cause most of the problem of forest regeneration, with often a single species invading the cutover. This contrasts with agricultural crops, where the problem is usually caused by a multitude of weed species, most of which can be controlled by a single herbicide. In some cases, however, inundative control can be effective in agricultural settings. An agricultural alien that has been targeted for inundative control is round-leaved mallow (*Malva pusilla* Sm.). Cultural and herbicidal control has not stopped its propagation, particularly in Manitoba on soils rich in organic matter. It reduces yields of relatively competitive crops, such as wheat (by up to 20%), and prevents the growing of flax and canola. Application of a mallow-specific native fungus, *Colletotrichum gloeosporioides* f. sp. *malvae* (Penz.) Penz. & Sacc., rapidly eliminates this weed. It should be commercially available shortly. Unfortunately cost may restrict its use to high value vegetable crops (Jensen 2000b). Cost is the major restriction to developing further products of this type. This obstacle could be partly overcome by the increase in health and ecological concerns about herbicides. According to Sukopp and Trautmann (1981), herbicides are responsible for the decline of 89 of the 581 rare plants in Germany. As mentioned previously, Bell (1983) gives several examples of rare native plants endangered by invasive alien weeds in Australia.

The largest groups of forest competitors are vigorous perennials that colonize rapidly after disturbance such as fire and harvesting. Shrubs and fast-growing deciduous trees normally succeed them before being replaced by conifers (Marks and Bormann 1972). The initial colonizers are short lived but they still suppress natural and planted conifer seedlings. Partial weed defoliation with foliar pathogens allows the conifers to grow through them. For example, marsh reed grass (*Calamagrostis canadensis* (Michx.) Beauv.) forms dense, almost pure stands over 2 m tall in high snow areas that shade, compete for nutrients and space, and smother young conifers by snow press (Figure 7). Application of a native snow mold causes 15% mortality and a 64% reduction in the aboveground dry weight of the grass (Mallett et al. 2000). The mold returns to a normal environmental level in one to five years. Therefore, one or two applications allow conifers to escape. Red raspberry (*Rubus idaeus* ssp. *strigosus* (Michx.) Focke), salmonberry (*R. spectabilis* Pursh), and thimbleberry (*R. parviflorus* Nutt.) cause similar problems. *Fusarium avenaceum* (Fr.:Fr.) Sacc. is a promising control fungus when formulated on rice grains and the inoculum combined with an organosilicone adjuvant. One or two applications cause substantial *Rubus* spp. foliar

damage (Figure 8). This allows the conifers to reach the "free to grow stage" in one to three years (Oleskevich et al. 1998). Formulated products of both fungi and their use for biological control are patented, and the priority now is for registration (Mallett 1999; Shamoun and Oleskevich 1999).

Deciduous trees that sprout vigorously following cutting also compete with young conifers and cause problems on utility rights-of-way. The application of the native wood-rotting fungus *Chondrostereum purpureum* (Pers.: Fr.) Pouzar (Figure 9) to the stumps prevents sprouting (Wall 1994; Shamoun and Hintz 1998a,b). The fungus is a saprotroph that grows in the stumps and logs of many deciduous trees.

In British Columbia, Shamoun and Hintz (1998a) studied the use of two isolates of *C. purpureum* against red alder (*Alnus rubra* Bong.) in hydro rights-of-way. In 1994, they compared two formulated fungal products of *C. purpureum* isolates (PFC 2139 and PFC 2140), a control formulation treatment, two chemical herbicide treatments, and manual cutting (slash). Although resprouting of cut alder stumps occurred throughout the six treatments after 18 months (spring 1995), by midsummer resprout mortality of 65–100% occurred on many stumps. Alder stumps treated with the isolates of *C. purpureum* and with the chemical herbicides showed significantly less living sprouts than those treated with manual cutting and the control formulation, with a mean of less than one living resprout per stump. Both fungal isolates gave similar results. At two years posttreatment (1996), stumps treated with PFC 2139 and with one of the chemical herbicides had a 100% stump mortality. The Canadian Forest Service's Pacific Forestry Centre and its commercial partner, MycoLogic Inc. of the University of Victoria, are currently collaborating

Figure 7. Marsh reed grass invading a conifer regeneration site in northern British Columbia. Photo courtesy Donna Macey, CFS, PFC, Victoria, BC.

Figure 8. Red raspberry infected with *Fusarium avenaceum* (*left*) and untreated (*right*).

on obtaining registration and commercialization of *C. purpureum* (Shamoun and Hintz 1998b). A similar wood decay promoter is used for the control of American black cherry (*Prunus serotina* Ehrh.) in the Netherlands (Ravensberg 1998).

In Quebec, a test of two *C. purpureum* isolates (CQP1 and 1B) was started in 1992 and 1993 on pin cherry (*Prunus pensylvanica* L.), trembling aspen (*Populus tremuloides* Michx.), white birch (*Betula papyrifera* Marsh.), and sugar maple (*Acer saccharum* Marsh.) on two Hydro-Québec 700 or 350 kV power line corridors. The trees were mechanically cut and the stumps treated with one of the isolates in June or August. Sprouting was greatly reduced by both isolates after the first year and was even more successful in the ensuing years. Three years after treatment, in spite of a variation between the target hosts and the isolates, control varied from 76% to 100% (Gosselin 1996).

The semi-shade-tolerant plants that increase in abundance in cutovers on nutrient-poor soils often later form a persistent barrier to young coniferous regenerations. Their leaves tend to be thick and waxy, a character that impedes the entry of herbicides and most pathogens (Oleskevich et al. 1996). One example is salal (*Gaultheria shallon* Pursh), a shrub that is normally controlled by habitat manipulation, but that is also a candidate for inundative control using a unique fungus, *Valdensinia heterodoxa* Peyronel (Figure 10) (Shamoun et al. 2000).

Another group that causes difficulties for young conifers is dwarf mistletoes (*Arceuthobium* spp.) (Figure 11). These perennial parasitic plants infect conifers, causing large economic losses (Shamoun and DeWald 2001). The host-specific fungus, *Colletotrichum gloeosporioides* (Penz.) Penz. & Sacc. (Figure 12), rapidly destroys the shoots and berries of mistletoe (Ramsfield et al. 1999; Shamoun 1999). In addition, *Nectria neomacrospora* Booth & Samuels (Figure 13) substantially reduces mistletoe shoot and seed production. Prevention of mistletoe infestation of new stands can be achieved with a mix of the pathogens sprayed on the affected border and on trees within stands (Shamoun 1998).

Figure 10. Foliar lesion of salal caused by *Valdensinia heterodoxa*.

Figure 11. Western hemlock dwarf mistletoe (*Arceuthobium tsugense* (Rosen.) G.N. Jones) on a branch of western hemlock (*Tsuga heterophylla* (Raf.) Sarg.).

Figure 9. Basidiocarps of *Chondrostereum purpureum* on a red alder stump.

Figure 12. *Colletotrichum gloeosporioides* colonization of western hemlock dwarf mistletoe berries and aerial shoots.

Figure 13. *Nectria neomacrospora* infecting western hemlock dwarf mistletoe swelling.

These examples of the many fungi under investigation offer hope of making forestry and agriculture more environmentally friendly. Progress is slow, partly due to fear of pathogens. This fear probably stems from the major forest losses suffered by introduction of alien diseases such as chestnut blight, Dutch elm disease, and white pine blister rust (Manion 1981). Native pathogens that have been used in planned biological control programs do not propagate as aggressively as the alien pathogens did (Cook et al. 1996). However, registration requirements for the use of these pathogens are based on hypothetical dangers, which make the requirements difficult and extremely costly to implement. Native organisms, in contrast to alien control agents, can be field tested in Canada before registration. Field testing, together with recent advances in molecular and genetic technology (for example, polymerase chain reaction, or PCR–DNA) that permit the monitoring of the environmental fate, impact, and disease epidemiology in test releases, should facilitate the registration process. Field

tests, and risk analysis based on epidemiological modeling and molecular markers, indicate risks from using native pathogens as biological controls are extremely low (de Jong et al. 1996; Shamoun and Wall 1996; Hintz et al. 2001). However, trust of new technology by the public will be won slowly through familiarization with it. From a practical, social, economic, and ecological viewpoint, inundative biological control should be viewed as an essential component of integrated forest vegetation management. This is less true in agriculture, unless more herbicides are restricted and withdrawn, which would then foster the development of alternative methods for controlling agricultural pests. A remaining problem is that the narrow host range of the species used as inundative biological controls inevitably means a relatively small market. If the costs of production and registration could be reduced, this would be less of a problem.

Habitat Manipulation

Two applications of inorganic fertilizer to cedar–hemlock sites dominated by salal allow these conifers to attain canopy closure and suppress this weed. The semi-shade-tolerant salal, which is present in mature conifer stands, increases on logging. On nutrient-poor sites it forms a dense groundcover with a thick persistent root mat that excludes other plants by competing for nutrients, by interfering with the mycorrhizal fungi needed by conifers, and by releasing toxins that suppress their growth. The addition of nutrients breaks the salal dominance and restores the habitat. This simple manipulation is worth $35 million/year to the forest industry (Preston 2000). Habitat manipulation is often particularly suitable for controllable habitats. For example, maintaining relatively long, dense grass reduces the dandelion problem on lawns; therefore, part of the solution may be less mowing. Aquatic weed problems in reservoirs and irrigation canals usually result from nutrient run-off, which can sometimes be reduced by having a grass buffer zone to catch run-off from arable fields.

Western blue flag (*Iris missouriensis* Nutt.) is a threatened species that has disappeared from one site since 1964, and is now confined to six small, mostly decreasing stands in southern Alberta. The iris requires spring-wet and summer-dry meadows, and thus both draining and damming have been detrimental; as well, some sites have been affected by herbicide (2,4-D) drift, to which the iris is sensitive. On all sites, the previously dominant rough fescue (*Festuca scabrella* Torr.) and tufted hair grass (*Deschampsia caespitosa* (L.)) Beauv.) have been replaced by smooth brome (*Bromus inermis* Leyss.), the result of prolonged heavy grazing. Cattle avoid the iris and some grass grazing is beneficial for it, but competition from the shallow, dense brome root mat is detrimental (Gould 1999). Less or no grazing does not displace brome once it has become dominant. It is, however, intolerant of a seasonally high water table (Hansen et al. 1999), whereas the iris is favored by spring flooding. This suggests a solution involving manipulation of the water table, but funding for such environmental concerns is limited.

The small Garry oak (*Quercus garryana* Dougl.) habitat of southern Vancouver Island is under pressure. Most of the habitat is now occupied by the City of Victoria and Douglas-fir (*Pseudotsuga menziesii* (Mirb.) Franco var. *menziesii*), which as the result of fire control, predominates. Much of the remainder is park managed for recreation (Ussery 1997). Adding to the pressure on this habitat is the alien species Scotch broom (*Cytisus scoparius* (L.) Link), which forms thickets that block up to 65% of the light (Peterson and Prasad 1998). Eighteen of the native indicator plants for the site are shade intolerant and at their northern limit (Klinka et al. 1989). One endangered and one threatened plant species are also found here. Scotch broom stands degenerate in 20–25 years to be replaced by a native and introduced shrub complex and not the Garry oak association (Ussery 1997). Scotch broom is not controlled by mowing, burning, or pulling, although large stems are killed by cutting. New Zealand is leading a consortium investigating classical biocontrol of the weed, and the Canadian Forest Service has found several native diseases that could possibly be used to control it. Unfortunately, neither the agriculture nor forestry industry is interested in the biocontrol of Scotch broom because the Garry oak habitat is not commercially important to them. However, the protection of the Garry oak habitat, and to a lesser extent, the western blue flag, involves more than controlling an invasive weed. Saving them will need government legislation and control of habitat management.

Summary and Conclusions

Both invasive alien and native weeds affect natural habitat as well as cultivated crops and forest tree plantations throughout Canada. Biological control using natural enemies of the weed has been researched over the past 50 years and several successes are outlined in this review. Classical biological control is usually applied against invasive alien weeds of rangeland and uncultivated areas where the use of herbicides is not economical (although they are sometimes used with government subsidies). Classical biological control usually benefits native species, although this has rarely been documented. Inundative biological control can replace herbicides in a number of applications, or it can reduce the amount of herbicide required. Habitat manipulation is often incorporated as part of the management regime for weed control. However, the protection of endangered species may require government legislation or land purchase and management.

Federal funding and legislation control the pace and direction of both classical and inundative biological control. Public funds for agricultural and forest weeds are directed to projects supported by user groups or industry, which ensures that weeds causing economic problems are targeted. Weeds causing strictly environmental problems, where the public is the beneficiary of control, are not usually targeted for biocontrol. If control programs are to be instituted against them, government needs to provide all the funding.

The federal government also controls the enabling legislation that governs the release of classical biological control agents (*Plant Protection Act*) and the registration of inundative ones (*Pest Control Products Act*). The testing procedures required under these acts are time-consuming, costly, and frustrating as they have not kept pace with real needs or new developments in science. A long track record shows that for classical biological control, risk is restricted to native plants closely related to the target weed. The required larval no-choice development test fails to distinguish hosts from nonhosts in the host genus 70% of the time. As the adult is responsible for host selection, there is a need for adult field tests to be done in the native region. Inundative biological control has a shorter track record and the tests are based on presumed and unsubstantiated public fears. This is a necessary growth stage, but registration requirements need to be reviewed and changed when experience shows them to be irrelevant or inappropriate. Both the theory and the findings reviewed here indicate that using native pathogens in their own region for controlling a weed presents little risk.

There is an increasing public desire to understand the rationale for using a particular strategy for an environmental problem. For weed biological control the information could be provided on a Web site outlining the problem and discussing the options for dealing with it; this would inform the public and provide feedback to researchers about concerns. A justification report is already required for starting a classical weed biological control program and the World Wide Web would offer an excellent opportunity for distribution of this information. Information along these lines is already available for inundative control of forest weeds at a Pacific Forestry Centre Web site: http://www.pfc. forestry.ca/biotechnology.

A prerequisite for both classical and inundative weed biological control is a thorough investigation of the problems and options. One common deficiency in classical biological control projects is that studies are terminated before impact studies have been completed. Impact is part of the registration process for inundative biological control. The need in classical biological control is no less urgent, but it comes after visible results are apparent. One solution is for government to insist that funding provision is made for impact studies before a study is started.

References

Bell, A. 1983. Native plants facing extinction. Ecosystems 37:21–26.

Canadian Wildlife Service. 2000. Northern leopard frog. Prairie population. Environment Canada Web site. http://www.speciesatrisk.gc.ca/Species/English/SearchDetail.cfm?SpeciesID=551 (accessed 22 July 2000).

Cook, R.J.; Bruckart, W.; Coulson, J.; Goettel, M.; Humber, R.; Lumsden, R.; Maddox, R.; McManus, J.; Moose, M.; Meyer, L.; Quimby, P.; Stack, J.; Vaughn, J.L. 1996. Safety of microorganisms intended for pest and plant disease control: a framework for scientific evaluation. Biol. Control 7:333–351.

Corrigan, J.E.; Mackenzie, D.L.; Simser, L. 1998. Field observations of non-target feeding by Gallerucella calmariensis (Coleoptera:Chrysomelidae), an introduced biological control agent of purple loosestrife, Lythrum salicaria (Lythraceae). Proc. Entomol. Soc. Ont. 129:99–106.

Cullen, J.M. 1985. Bringing the cost benefit analysis of biological control of Chondrilla juncea up to date. Pages 145–152 in E.S. Delfosse, ed. Proceedings of the VI International Symposium on Biological Control of Weeds, 19–25 August 1984, University of British Columbia, Vancouver, BC. Agriculture Canada, Ottawa, ON.

Dale, C. 1998. Scientists ponder project purple. Alternatives J. 24:3.

de Jong, M.D.; Sela, S.T.; Shamoun, S.F.; Wall, R.E. 1996. Natural occurrence of Chondrostereum purpureum in relation to its use as a biological control agent in Canadian forests. Biol. Control 6:347–352.

Gosselin, L. 1996. Biological control of stump sprouting of broad-leaf species in rights-of-way with Chondrostereum purpureum. I. Virulence of tested strains and susceptibility of target hosts. Ph.D. thesis, Laval University, Sainte-Foy, QC.

Gould, J. 1999. Status of the western blue flag (Iris missouriensis) in Alberta. Alberta Environment/Conservation Association, Edmonton, AB. Alberta Wildlife Status Rep. 21. 22 p.

Hansen, P.; Thompson, W.; Godfrey, S. 1999. Classification and management of riparian and wetland sites of Alberta's grassland and natural region, and parts of adjacent sub-regions. Montana Forest and Conservation Experiment Station, University of Montana, Missoula, MT. 342 p.

Harris, P. 1991. Classical biocontrol of weeds: its definition, selection of effective agents, and administrative-political problems. Can. Entomol. 123:827–849.

Harris, P. 2000a. Classical biological control of weeds. Agriculture and Agri-Food Canada Web document. http://res2.agr.ca/lethbridge/weedbio/index.htm (accessed 13 July 2000).

Harris, P. 2000b. Leafy and cypress spurge, Euphorbia esula L. and E. cyparissias L. Agriculture and Agri-Food Canada Web document. http://res2.agr.ca/lethbridge/weedbio/hosts/blfysprg.htm (accessed 14 August 2000).

Harris, P.; Cranston, R. 1979. An economic evaluation of control methods for diffuse and spotted knapweed in western Canada. Can. J. Plant Sci. 59:375–382.

Harris, P.; Peschken, D.; Milroy, J. 1969. The status of biological control of the weed Hypericum perforatum in British Columbia. Can. Entomol. 101:1–15.

Harris, P.; Wilmhurst, J. 2000. Rationale of weed biological control. Agriculture and Agri-Food Canada Web document. http://res2.agr.ca/lethbridge/weedbio/rational.htm (accessed 20 July 2000).

Hintz, W.E.; Becker, E.M.; Shamoun, S.F. 2001. Development of genetic markers for risk assessment of biological control agents. Can. J. Plant Pathol. 23:13–18.

Huffaker, C.B.; Kennet, C.E. 1959. A ten year study of vegetational changes associated with biological control of Klamath weed. J. Range Manag. 12:69–82.

Jensen, K. 2000a. Colletotrichum gloeosporioides (Penz.) Penz. & Sacc. f. sp. hypericum. Fungal disease. Agriculture and Agri-Food Canada Web document. http://res2.

agr.ca/lethbridge/weedbio/agents/acolglo.htm (accessed
13 July 2000).

Jensen, K. 2000b. *Colletotrichum gloeosporioides* (Penz.) Penz.
& Sacc. f. sp. *malvae*. Fungal disease of mallow. Agriculture and Agri-Food Canada Web document. http://
res2.agr.ca/lethbridge/weedbio/agents/acolglom.htm
(accessed 21 July 2000).

Klinka, K.; Rajina, V.J; Ceska, A.; Seagel, A.A. 1989. Indicator
plants of coastal British Columbia. University of British
Columbia Press, Vancouver, BC. 288 p.

Kovalev, O.V.; Vechernin. V.V. 1986. Description of a new wave
process in populations with reference to the introduction
and spread of the leaf beetle *Zygogramma suturalis* F.
(Coleoptera:Chrysomelidae). Entomol. Rev. 65:93–112.

Lacey, J.R.; Marlow; C.B.; Lane, J.R. 1989. Influence of spotted knapweed (*Centaurea maculosa*) on surface runoff
and sediment yield. Weed Technol. 3:627–631.

Leistritz, F.L.; Thompson, F.; Leitch, J.A. 1992. Economic impact
of leafy spurge (*Euphorbia esula*) in North Dakota. Weed
Sci. 40:275–280.

Mallett, K.I. 1999. Process for biological control of *Calamagrostis canadensis* using a low basidiomycete. US Patent
No. 5,993,802. Assignee: Her Majesty the Queen in Right
of Canada, as represented by the Minister of Natural
Resources, Ottawa, Canada.

Mallett, K.I.; Schreiner, K.A.; Gaudet, D.A. 2000. Effect of
cottony snow mold on mortality and biomass of *Calamagrostis canadensis* under controlled environmental
conditions. Biol. Contrl. 18:193–198.

Manion, P.D. 1981. Tree disease concepts. Prentice-Hall, Inc.,
Englewood Cliffs, NJ. 389 p.

Marks, P.L.; Bormann, F.H. 1972. Re-vegetation following
forest cutting: mechanisms for return to steady-state
nutrient cycling. Science 176:914–915.

Mico, M.A. 1993. Biological control of leafy spurge (*Euphorbia
esula* L.) with the black dot beetle (*Aphthona nigriscutis*
Foudras) in central Manitoba. B.Sc. thesis, University
of Manitoba, Winnipeg, MB. 71 p.

Oleskevich, C.; Shamoun, S.F.; Punja, Z.K. 1996. The biology
of Canadian weeds. No. 105. *Rubus strigosus* Michx.,
R. parviflorus Nutt., *R. spectabilis* Pursh. Can. J. Plant
Sci. 76:187–201.

Oleskevich, C.; Shamoun, S.F.; Vesonder, R.F.; Punja, Z.K. 1998.
Evaluation of *Fusarium avenaceum* and other fungi for
potential as biological control agents of invasive *Rubus*
species in British Columbia. Can. J. Plant Pathol. 20:12–18.

Peschken, D.P. 1972. *Chrysolina quadrigemina* (Coleoptera:
Chrysomelidae) introduced from California to British
Columbia against the weed *Hypericum perforatum*: comparison of behaviour, physiology, and colour in association with post-colonization adaptation. Can. Entomol.
104:1689–1698.

Peterson, D.J.; Prasad, R. 1998. The biology of Canadian
weeds. 109. *Cytisus scoparius* (L.) Link. Can J. Plant
Sci. 78:497–504.

Preston, C. 2000. Weed them and reap. Natural Resources
Canada, Canadian Forest Service, Web document. http://
nrcan-rncan.gc.ca/cfs-scf/science/prodserv/story11_e.html

Ramsfield, T.D.; Shamoun, S.F.; Punja, Z.K.; Hintz, W.E. 1999.
Variation in the mitochondrial DNA of the potential bio-
logical control agent *Chondrostereum purpureum*. Can.
J. Bot. 77:1490–1498.

Ravensberg, W.J. 1998. BioChon® effective biological and
environmentally friendly product. Koppert Biological
Systems, The Netherlands. Pest Leaflet. 2 p.

Reznik, S.Ya.; Belokobyl'skiy, S.A.; Lobanov, A.L. 1991. Effect
of agroecosystem stability on ambrosia leaf beetle *Zygogramma suturalis* (Coleoptera: Chrysomelidae) population
density. Entomol. Rev. 69:109–114.

Roze, L.D. 1981. The biological control of *Centaurea diffusa*
Lam. and *C. maculosa* Lam. by *Urophora affinis* Frauen-
feld and *U. quadrifasciata* Meigen (Diptera:Tephritidae).
Ph.D. thesis, University of British Columbia. 208 p.

Shamoun, S.F. 1998. Development of a biological control strategy for management of dwarf mistletoes. Pages 36–42
in R. Sturrock, comp. Proceedings of the 45th Western
International Forest Disease Work Conference, 15–19 September 1997, Prince George, BC.

Shamoun, S.F. 2000. Application of biological control to vegetation management in forestry. Pages 87–96 *in* N. Spencer,
ed. Proceedings of the X International Symposium on
Biological Control of Weeds, 4–14 July 1999, Bozeman,
MT. Montana State University, Bozeman, MT.

Shamoun, S.F.; Countess, R.; Vogelgsang, S., Oleskevich, C.
2000. The mycobiota of salal (*Gaultheria shallon*) collected on Vancouver Island and the exploitation of fungal
pathogens for biological control [abstract]. Can. J. Plant
Pathol. 22:192.

Shamoun, S.F.; DeWald, L. 2001. Management of dwarf
mistletoes by biological, chemical and genetic methods.
In B. Geils et al., eds. Mistletoes of North American conifers. North American Forestry Commission, Washington,
DC. In Press.

Shamoun, S.F.; Hintz, W.E.1998a. Development of *Chondrostereum purpureum* as a biological control agent for red alder in utility rights-of-way. Pages 308–310 *in* R.G. Wagner and D.G. Thompson, comps. Third International Conference on Forest Vegetation Management. Popular summaries. Ontario Ministry of Natural Resources, Ontario Forestry Research Institute, Sault Ste. Marie, ON. For. Res. Info. Pap. 141.

Shamoun, S.F.; Hintz, W.E. 1998b. Development and registration of *Chondrostereum purpureum* as a mycoherbicide for hardwood weeds in conifer reforestation sites and utility rights-of-way. Page 14 *in* Programme and abstracts. IV International Bioherbicide Workshop, 6–7 August 1998, University of Strathclyde, Glasgow, UK.

Shamoun, S.F.; Oleskevich, C. 1999. *Fusarium avenaceum* and its use as a biological control agent for *Rubus* species. US Patent No.5,985,648. Assignee: Her Majesty the Queen in Right of Canada, as represented by the Minister of Natural Resources, Ottawa, Canada.

Shamoun, S.F.; Wall, R.E. 1996. Characterization of Canadian isolates of *Chondrostereum purpureum* by protein content, API ZYM and isozyme analyses. Eur. J. For. Pathol. 26:333–342.

Sukopp, H.; Trautmann, W. 1981. Causes of the decline of threatened plants in the Federal Republic of Germany. Pages 114–116 *in* H. Synge, ed. The biological aspects of rare plant conservation. J. Wiley and Sons, Chichester, UK. 558 p.

Thompson, D.Q.; Stuckey, R.L.; Thompson, E.B. 1987. Spread, impact and control of purple loosestrife (*Lythrum salicaria*) in North American wetlands. US Department of the Interior, Fish and Wildlife Service Research Vol. 2. 55 p.

Treberg, M.A.; Husband, B.C. 1999. Relationship between the abundance of *Lythrum salicaria* (purple loosestrife) and plant species richness along the Bar River, Canada. Wetlands 19:118–125.

Ussery, J. 1997. Managing invasive plant species in the Garry oak meadow vegetation communities. A case study of Scotch broom. M.Sc. thesis, Simon Fraser University, Burnaby, BC. 109 p.

Vinogradova, E.B. 1989. Characteristics of reproduction and adult diapause in *Zygogramma suturalis* (Coleoptera: Chrysomelidae) in Stavropol' Territory. Entomol. Rev. 68:1–11.

Wall, R.E. 1994. Biological control of red alder using stem treatments with the fungus *Chondrostereum purpureum*. Can. J. For. Res. 24:1527–1530.

Wall, R.E.; Hasan, S. 1996. Management of plant pathogens for vegetation management control in forestry. Pages 1–19 *in* S.P. Raychaudhuri and K. Maramorosch, eds. Forest trees and palms—diseases and control. Oxford and IBH Publishing Co., PVT, Ltd. New Delhi, India

Wall, R.E.; Prasad, R.; Shamoun, S.F. 1992. The development and potential role of mycoherbicides for forestry. For. Chron. 68:736–741.

Watson, A.K.; Wall, R.E. 1995. Mycoherbicides: their role in vegetation management in Canadian forests. Pages 74–82 *in* P.J. Charest and L.C. Duchesne, comps. Recent progress in forest biotechnology in Canada. Natural Resources Canada, Canadian Forest Service, Petawawa National Forestry Institute, Chalk River, ON. Inf. Rep. PI–X–120. 144 p.

Afterword: Predictive Ecology for a Proactive Approach to Alien Invaders

Patrick Nantel

My most memorable encounter with an alien species was in June 1991. With my field assistants, I was sampling a white oak (*Quercus alba* L.) stand in the Ottawa Valley for a survey of rare plants of the region. Gypsy moth (*Lymantria dispar* (L.)) larvae were booming at the expense of a forest type very rare in Quebec. Their population was so dense that we could hear a constant rain of caterpillar droppings on the leaf litter. Defoliation was so high that the oak trees produced a new flush of leaves in July. Cores from these trees showed a growth ring of much less than 0.1 mm wide for that year.[1]

I learned later that a European strain of gypsy moth had been accidentally introduced in eastern North America more than a century ago. I remained intrigued by such a sudden variation in abundance, and as many ecologists may have before, I asked myself why some species are so successful and others so rare.

Although invasion biology is a relatively new subdiscipline, it essentially addresses the same broad problem faced by its "mother" discipline, ecology, for the past 100 years—to explain the variation over time and space in abundance of living organisms. One of my favorite mentors, the late Robert H. Peters, taught me very convincingly that prediction is a better aim for science than explanation. His argument was simple: predictions can be tested, explanations cannot. Quantitative predictions are even better, because they are easier to communicate and to check against observations.

In this short essay, I will try to show that for solving an environmental problem such as the one created by alien species invading natural areas, predictive models are the tools of choice for a proactive approach. I do this by quickly reviewing a small sample of recent advances in the prediction of ecological invasion by alien species.

Evaluating the "Tens Rule"

One of the quantitative predictive methods presented in this publication is the "tens rule" (see Simberloff, p. 29 and 269). The rule stipulates that about 10% of all alien species released to the wild will establish self-maintaining populations and that about 10% of these species will become invasive (Williamson and Brown 1986). This has been referred to as a good rule of thumb (Williamson 1996). In his remarkably lucid *Arithmetic of Life and Death*, Shaffner explains: "In general, rules of thumb are guidelines people invent to explain phenomena that they can't prove. If these rules seem to work, then other people use them and they eventually become widespread, perhaps too much so" (Shaffner 1999). This has prompted me to test the tens rule.

Let's look first at alien plants. Haber (this publication, p. 43) tells us that Canada's flora consists of about 5800 species of vascular plants and that 20–27%, or 1160–1566, are alien species. Using the tens rule, we can calculate that (1) 11 600–15 660 alien vascular plants were therefore released in Canada's wild places and (2) 116–157 of them are or will be pests. The first figure seems improbable. For comparison, a very comprehensive gardening encyclopaedia I have at home describes 6000 species of ornamental and edible plants suitable for the climates of Canada. Many of these species have been intentionally introduced in gardens across the country, and yet they represent only half the number that should have been brought into the country from elsewhere, according to the tens rule. As for a check of the second figure, we can look at Table 4 in Hendrickson (this publication, p. 68): it identifies 27 species of plants that are invasive in Canada's forests, an ecosystem that covers more than half of the country—17–23% of the number the tens rule gives.

Let's now look at alien insects. Hendrickson (this publication, p. 59) tells us that 180 species of insects feeding on woody plants have become established in Canada. Again, the tens rule provides us with two figures: (1) about 1800 alien insects (feeding on woody plants) have been released in the wild and (2) about 18 alien insects are or will be pests. The second figure seems reasonable, but again the first seems too large.

My test of the tens rule is not to be taken too seriously. Nevertheless, for plants and insects, the available data are at odds with the figures generated through the rule: much more than 10% of alien species

---

[1] In a good growing season, most oaks achieve growth rings of 0.5–2.0 mm.

released (introduced) should have become established; otherwise we are forced to accept unrealistic numbers of introductions. Also, much less than 10% of the established species have become pests, at least within the plant realm. Data for the aquatic alien plant species in the Great Lakes basin show that, among the 160 species known to have been introduced in the basin, 9% have had significant ecological and economic effects (Mills et al. 1993, in MacDonald, this publication, p. 161). If the tens rule is applied, only 1% (10% of 10%) of the introduced species would have become invasive.

Before going further, we should ask why anyone would want to predict the number of likely pests among a number of candidate species. The main problem with the rule is inherent: it does not define a pest in quantitative terms; it does not indicate what variable and what threshold value of this variable can be used to classify a species as a pest. Moreover, the number alone cannot be used to assess potential damage because one pest species can cause, at a given site, as much damage as two or more could collectively elsewhere (that is, total impact is not necessarily proportional to the number of pests). Each species has a different probability of becoming invasive. Therefore, it would be more useful to determine the invasive probability for each species in a given set from an analysis of its biological attributes and then to predict where a given alien species may invade.

Predicting Invasion

Some have noted that invasion biology remains largely an anecdotal science, meaning that alien species invasions of natural ecosystems have been described piecemeal (case by case). However, the number of publications on predicting the identity, potential impact, or distribution of alien species has increased rapidly since 1986 (Kolar and Lodge 2001).

Biological Characteristics of Alien Plant Invaders

One promising study on predicting probable invaders comes from an analysis of the flora of New Brunswick. Goodwin et al. (1999) looked at 165 pairs of species, in which one of each pair was a European species that had successfully invaded New Brunswick (invasive) and the other of the pair was a congeneric European species that had not invaded North America (noninvasive). Both pair members preferred human-disturbed habitats. In an analysis of 110 pairs, they found that stem height and length of flowering period were significantly different between the two groups. The authors then incorporated these variables in a predictive model and tested the model on the remaining 55 pairs. The results were disappointing; the model proved no better at predicting invasiveness than random.

More interesting results were achieved when Goodwin et al. looked at the native range of each species in terms of number of "regions" it occupied in Europe. On average, the European range of the invasive species contained about 14 more regions than the range of the noninvasive member of the pair. When the authors used range in their model as a predictor of invasiveness and tested it on the 55 pairs, the model correctly predicted invasiveness in 70% of the test species. The researchers concluded that species "likely to be accidentally picked up and moved to a new location (continent) due to their wide distribution are the same species that are likely to succeed in a new environment due to their wide environmental tolerance."

The above results could guide proactive approaches to the problem of invasive alien species. For instance, a statistical model was used to predict which southern African plants would become weeds in Australia (Scott and Panetta 1993). Researchers in Canada could do a similar study on European species. Using the New Brunswick model, they could set the threshold number of regions a species occupies in Europe above which it is likely to invade eastern Canada. Then by screening *Flora Europaea* (Tutin et al. 1964) for species that occupy more regions than the threshold number, they could produce a list of potential invaders. Pictures and descriptions of those species not yet detected in eastern Canada (or only occurring in a small number of populations) could be distributed to volunteer organizations (and posted on the World Wide Web) with guidelines on what to do if such a species is positively identified. Horticultural associations and nurseries could also be alerted to the potential threat that these plants pose and their support enlisted in finding ways to discourage their importation and spread in North America.

Although the New Brunswick study did not succeed in identifying biological attributes that could predict the invasiveness of its test plants, a review of studies done in other regions concluded that "invasive plants tended to be unevenly distributed phylogenetically, have a history of invasion (either species, genus, or family), reproduce vegetatively, and have low variability in seed crops" (Kolar and Lodge 2001).

A recent study, however, has found that plant invaders may be hiding a key attribute responsible for their invasiveness in their internal functioning (Nagel and Griffin 2001). The authors compared the amount of energy spent on building leaves (what plant physiologists call the leaf construction cost) in wetland plants, including the famous purple loosestrife (*Lythrum salicaria* L.). They found that for building each square millimetre of leaf, abundant plants of a given disturbed wetland spend much less energy than less abundant plants. They concluded: "the construction of more leaf surface area with low energetic expense, such as that exhibited by both invasive *L. salicaria* and weedy *Parthenocissus quinquefolia*[2] in this study, may provide some species with a competitive advantage over others. More indirectly, low energy requirements for leaf construction could allow such species to invest more energy in other strategies, such as reproductive efforts or root growth." This sounds like advice from an economists: lower your production cost and you can cover the globe!

From a biological perspective, the above result is significant: "Since every growth strategy has an energy consequence, energy can be a basic unit of comparison between organisms" (Nagel and Griffin 2001). As exciting as this discovery is, leaf construction cost is not readily available for most species and measuring it for the hundreds of potential plant invaders could take considerable resources. It would nevertheless be interesting to examine the possible correlation between leaf construction cost and the extent of species' native range.

Geographical Range of Alien Invaders

Advances in and widespread availability of information and computing technology have led to a new approach in predicting species invasions. Researchers are using tools from biodiversity informatics and quantitative geography to map the probable distribution of an invasive alien species (Peterson and Vieglais 2001). The method involves large distributed databases of species occurrences and sophisticated algorithms (called Genetic Algorithm for Rule-set Prediction, or GARP[3]). It is built on the concept of the "niche", which refers

to a "set of tolerances and limits in multidimensional space that define where a species is potentially able to maintain populations" (Peterson and Vieglais 2001). These tolerances and limits determine conditions under which a species is able to invade a particular region. With GARP, the niche is modeled using variables associated with the geographic limitation of species, such as temperature, precipitation, elevation, and vegetation.

Predicting the probable geographical range of a species is then done through three steps: (1) modeling niches in ecological space, (2) evaluating these niche models based on native distributions, and (3) using the models to determine the area that could be invaded. It is theoretically possible to create such predictive ecological models and projections for all species not native to a particular region. For instance, the probable distribution of the Asian long-horned beetle (*Anoplophora glabripennis* (Mots.)) has been projected on a map of North America using a niche model developed from a data set describing the distribution of the species in Asia (Peterson and Vieglais 2001). The projection shows, among other things, that eastern North America is highly habitable for the species but not the Pacific coast. As an illustration of a proactive measure such prediction could lead to, the authors concluded: "if more detailed modeling efforts support the initial results, Asian shipping could be focused on the Pacific Coast, where danger of invasion by this species is low, and direct shipments to vulnerable areas such as the Atlantic seaboard could be avoided."

Selling Proactive Measures

A society aiming for sustainable development has only two basic options. The first is to produce wealth through economic activities and, once society is wealthy enough, repair the damage these activities have caused to the natural capital. For this option, society may have to use a relatively large part of its wealth for implementing technologically and financially intensive reactive measures. The second option is to develop wealth, maybe less rapidly, while proactively controlling to some extent economic activities to ensure that the natural capital remains intact. Both options have their advantages and risks. I believe that until the 1960s, no society had made a conscious choice on this matter. Today, the choice remains in large part an issue of values.

The cost of reactive measures against invasive alien species in Canada is far from well documented. This impedes decision-making on reactive versus proactive

---

[2] *P. quinquefolia* (L.) Planch., or Virginia creeper, is a weed, native to North America.

[3] An implementation of GARP is accessible over the Internet at the San Diego Supercomputer Center (http://biodiversity.sdsc.edu/cgi-bin/BSW/screen.cgi) and should soon be available as a desktop computer application. A beta version can be downloaded at http://tsadev.speciesanalyst.net/Z.X/.

measures. A paper on the environmental and economic cost of alien invaders in Canada presented at a recent symposium found economic data for 16 species of 50 species examined and the data was solid for only 9 of the 16 (RNT Consulting 2002). The costs of research and control measures for the nine species totaled $5.5 billion in cumulative costs and over $456 million in ongoing annual costs. This does not include losses in agriculture, forestry, fisheries, recreational opportunities, and tourism due to invasive alien species.

Proactive measures are often a hard sell, especially if they entail some direct costs. It is a situation similar to what exists in medicine: because health is determined by so many factors, staying healthy can never, with any certainty, be directly attributed to preventive treatment. The lesson learned is that proactive measures need to be grounded in sound predictive science.

In 1999, I returned to the white oak stand that had been so heavily defoliated eight years before. All the trees looked healthy, but the landowner had started to cut some down. I saw a few gypsy moth caterpillars, including one being attacked by a native bug. I still feel puzzled by the variation in abundance among living species. However, I must admit that for others, alien species are more a perplexing problem than an interesting puzzle.

Photo with chapter title: Gypsy moth larva. Photo by Klaus Bolte, CFS, Ottawa.

References

Goodwin, B.J.; McAllister, A.J.; Fahrig, L. 1999. Predicting invasiveness of plant species based on biological information. Conserv. Biol. 13(2):422–426.

Kolar, C.S.; D.M. Lodge. 2001. Progress in invasion biology: predicting invaders. Trends Ecol. Evol.16:199-204.

Nagel, J.M.; Griffin, K.L. 2001. Construction cost and invasive potential: comparing Lythrum salicaria (Lythraceae) with co-occurring native species along pond banks. Am. J. Bot. 88:2252–2258.

Peterson, A.T.; Vieglais, D.A. 2001. Predicting species invasions using ecological niche modeling: new approaches from bioinformatics attack a pressing problem. BioScience 51:363–371.

RNT Consulting Inc. 2002. Environmental and economic costs of alien invasive species in Canada. Proceedings of Applying Biodiversity Information, A National Symposium,11 Apr. 2002, Gatineau, QC.

Scott, J.K.; Panetta, F.D. 1993. Predicting the Australian weed status of southern African plants. J. Biogeogr. 20:87–93

Shaffner, G. 1999. The arithmetic of life and death. Ballantine Books, New York, NY.

Tutin, T.G.; Heyward, V.H.; Burges, N.A.; Valentine, D.H.; Walters, S.M.; Webb, D.A., eds. 1964. Flora Europaea. Volumes 1–5. Cambridge University Press, Cambridge, United Kingdom.

Williamson, M. 1996. Biological invasions. Chapman and Hall, London.

Williamson, M.; Brown, K.C. 1986. The analysis and modelling of British invasions. Philo. Tran. R. Soc. Lond. B. Biol. Sci. 314:505–522.

Glossary

algae: organisms responsible for 90% of the earth's photosynthesis; found in most habitats; formerly classified as a plant subkingdom; now often divided among several kingdoms (e.g., Protista, or Protoctista, Monera, Plantae); algae vary from single-celled to large and complex.

alien (= exotic, introduced, nonindigenous, nonnative) species: in the context of the present publication, species that have crossed natural barriers and entered ecosystems where they have not existed previously in recorded history, usually as a result of human action.

allelopathy: a plant's ability to suppress the growth of other plants through the production of toxic substances.

ammocoete: the freshwater larval stage of a lamprey (the adults can be either freshwater, brackish, or marine depending on the species).

amphipod: any of a large order (Amphipoda) of highly motile marine crustaceans with one set of feet for jumping or walking and another for swimming.

anadromous: referring to fish that live most of their adult lives in seawater, but return to their natal freshwater streams and rivers to spawn.

anoxia: a total lack of or a reduced supply of oxygen to tissues.

augmentative biological control: see *inundative biological control*.

autecology: the study of organisms at the level of individuals, populations, or species in relation to their physical environment (i.e., humidity, light, salinity, and nutrient levels); also known as physiological ecology.

ballast water: water used as a weight by modern ships to achieve a balanced condition; ballast tanks are filled when cargo is unloaded and discharged when cargo is taken on; a ship is said to be "in ballast" when it carries no cargo, only ballast.

benthic: referring to the bottom of an ocean, a lake, and other water bodies; a benthic species is a bottom-dwelling or anchored species; cf. *epibenthic, pelagic*.

benthos: the biogeographic region at the bottom of an ocean, a lake, and other water bodies; also collectively refers to all organisms living on, in, or near the bottom of water bodies, including running and standing waters, saltwater and freshwater.

biocide: any synthetic product used to kill (herbicide, pesticide, nematocide, fungicide, insecticide).

biofouling: the gradual accumulation of waterborne organisms, such as bacteria, barnacles, mussels, and algae, on artificial surfaces (ships' hulls, piers, buoys, air-conditioning systems, water pipes) in continuous contact with water, causing corrosion of the structures.

biological control (*also* **biocontrol**): a population-level process initiated by humans in which one species' population lowers that of another species by mechanisms such as predation, parasitism, or competition; cf. *classical biological control, inundative biological control*.

biological magnification: the systematic increase in concentrations of certain chemicals (e.g., DDT) from lower to higher trophic levels in the food chain; such chemicals do not break down rapidly in the environment, are taken up but not metabolized by primary producers, and can be stored in animal tissues.

biomass: a quantitative estimate of living organisms of one species (species biomass) or of all the species in a community (community biomass), measured in terms of mass, volume, or energy in calories, for a unit area or volume of the habitat.

bioregion: an area that constitutes a natural ecological community.

biota: the plant and animal life of a specific region or of a given time period.

bioturbation: the churning and stirring of sediment by organisms, which can result in mixing and increased compaction of the sediment.

bivoltine: reproducing twice a year; cf. *multivoltine, trivoltine, univoltine*.

brittle star: an echinoderm (phylum Echinodermata) with five arms radiating from a central disk; resembling a starfish but with longer, more discrete, fragile arms.

bryozoans: minute moss-like animals (phylum Bryozoa) that form colonies on the seabed or on other hard substrates; mostly filter-feeding.

chiton: a benthic, grazing mollusk with a shell divided into plates.

chronosequence: a sequential set of variables (e.g., changes in structure and composition of a forest stand) collectively describing the development of an ecological community.

cladocerans: small, transparent crustaceans of the order Cladocera; found mainly in freshwater; often called water fleas.

classical biological control: the establishment of natural enemies (e.g., parasite, predator, or disease) of an invasive alien pest to reduce or control its densities.

congeners: species belonging to the same genus.

conspecific: "of the same species"; refers to individuals or populations of the same species.

contracting party to the Convention on Biological Diversity (CBD): countries that have incorporated the CBD into their legal systems (by ratification, acceptance, approval, or accession) and have placed written instruments, which are formal evidence of consent to be legally bound, in a designated depository.

coralline: resembling coral.

crustose: forming or resembling a crust.

crustose (coralline) algae: bottom-living, heavily calcified, encrusting algae.

cryptic species: an organism that is so similar to another that the two are difficult to distinguish from each other; also an organism that can conceal itself by means of coloration or markings similar to its background.

cryptogenic: not demonstrably native or introduced; used to describe a species when reliable data are not available to determine whether the species is endemic to an area or whether it has come from elsewhere.

cyprinid fish: any of a large family (Cyprinidae) of freshwater fishes (e.g., carp).

diatom: any of a division (Bacillariophyta) of single-celled, mostly photosynthetic, aquatic microorganisms; major component of phytoplankton; marine and freshwater species; two shapes, round and thinly elliptical; cell walls contain silica.

dinoflagellate: any of a division (Pyrrophycophyta) of single-celled aquatic microorganisms; about half are photosynthetic; mostly marine, but also many freshwater species; characterized by two flagella (whip-like structures); in their bloom cycle, some species are toxic (red tide), others bioluminescent.

dioecious: having male and female reproductive organs on separate plants or in separate individuals; cf. *monoecious*, *hermaphroditic*.

diploid: having a double set of chromosomes in each cell nucleus.

disjunct site: a site separated from its usually contiguous parts.

ecosystem service: an ecological economics concept in which natural ecosystem processes (e.g., biodegradation of human wastes in soils and water, nutrient cycling in the soil) are a service to humans; these services can limit human values or activities according to their supply.

encrusting: covering with or forming a crust.

endemism: the character or quality of being endemic (belonging or native to).

ephemeral algae (seaweed): all algal species that live for less than a year, i.e., are not annuals or perennials.

epibenthic: living at the surface of or just above the bottom sediments of a water body; cf. *benthic*.

epifauna: animals living on river bottoms, sea beds, etc. or attached to submerged object, plants, or animals; cf. *infauna*.

epiphyte: a plant that lives on the surface of another plant, but does not obtain nourishment from it.

epizootic: a temporary and widespread outbreak of disease in animals; equivalent to *epidemic* in human medicine.

estuary: the wide lower part of a river that meets the ocean or sea, where seawater is diluted by freshwater and tidal effects are evident; also the drowned mouth of a river or an arm or inlet of the sea affected by freshwater; cf. *stratified estuary*.

eukaryotic: describing a cell (or an organism with such cells) with internal membranes that partition the cell into regions (e.g., a distinct nucleus) for different functions; applies to all protists, plants, animals, and fungi.

eurytherm: an organism able to tolerate a relatively wide range of temperatures .

eutrophic: describing a body of water or a confined ocean region (e.g., a bay) rich in plant nutrients and characterized by seasonal periods of oxygen deficiency resulting from the dense growth of algae or other plants; cf. *mesotrophic, oligotrophic*.

eutrophication: the enrichment of waters, marine and fresh, by nutrients (e.g., phosphates) that accelerate the growth of algae and other plant life.

feral: originally domesticated, but having returned to the wild.

foliose: leaf-like, filamentous.

food chain: a simplified linear representation of the feeding relationship of consumers and the consumed, beginning with primary producers (plants), which capture energy from the environment, and ending with the largest carnivores; cf. *trophic web*.

fouling: see *biofouling*.

fucoid: of or relating to seaweeds, especially those of the genus *Fucus*.

fynbos: a richly diverse vegetation type, low-growing, typically fire-adapted, and largely evergreen; found only in the coastal and mountainous regions of South Africa.

gastropods: mollusks of the class Gastropoda, usually having stalked eyes, an asymmetrically coiled shell, and a large foot for movement; found in terrestrial as well as aquatic habitats (e.g., snails).

genome: the genetic information in one complete set of chromosomes and all associated genes for a given organism.

halogen: a highly reactive group of electronegative nonmetallic elements (fluorine, chlorine, bromine, iodine, and astatine).

hermaphroditic: having both male and female reproductive organs on the same plant or in the same individual; cf. *dioecious, monoecious*.

infauna: animals living within the sediments of river bottoms, sea beds, etc.; cf. *epifauna*.

infraspecific: referring to taxonomic categories below the rank of species.

interaction web: an experimentally determined configuration of species interactions in an ecological community.

intertidal: see *littoral*.

introduced species: see *alien species*.

inundative biological control: the periodic release, after mass propagation, of imported or native enemies of an invasive alien species to augment existing populations of these enemies (inundative releases); these enemies are not expected to become permanent controls.

isopods: small flat-bodied crustaceans with seven pairs of legs belonging to the order Isopoda; includes terrestrial (e.g., pillbugs), marine, and freshwater species.

iteroparous: applied to animals that reproduce offspring several times during their life span; cf. *semelparous*.

kelp: large, brown seaweeds of cold, temperate waters, especially members of the orders Laminariales and Fucales.

limpet: any of several varieties of mostly gastropod mollusks with a single, low, cone-shaped shell and a thick, fleshy foot by means of which it clings to rocks or timbers.

littoral: referring to the part of the shore that is covered at high tide and uncovered at low tide and where organisms are adapted to alternating exposure to air and water (through tides, waves, or spray); cf. *sublittoral*.

littorinid: any of a family (Littorinidae) of marine gastropod mollusks with globular shells (e.g., common periwinkle).

macroalgae: multicellular algae (green, brown, and red algae) large enough to be visible, having filamentous, sheet, or mat-like forms (e.g., seaweeds).

macrophyte: a vascular plant, visible to the naked eye, especially one in an aquatic habitat (e.g. sea grasses).

megalopa (pl. megalopae): the last larval stage in the life cycle of crabs; similar in appearance to the adult form.

meroplanktonic species: any of various organisms that spend part of their life cycle, usually the larval or egg stages, as plankton.

mesic: pertaining to environments and habitats with a moderate degree of moisture in the soil.

mesotrophic: describing a body of water or a confined ocean region (e.g., a bay) having an intermediate amount of plant nutrients and therefore moderately productive; cf. *eutrophic, oligotrophic*.

monoecious: having female and male reproductive organs on a single plant or in the same individual; cf. *dioecious, hermaphroditic*.

monospecific: containing one species.

morphometry: the measurement of external form.

multivoltine: reproducing more than three times a year; cf *bivoltine, trivoltine, univoltine*.

mycorrhizal fungi: fungi that attach to the feeder roots of a plant and produce filaments that extend the root system; the plant benefits from improved nutrient and water uptake, while the fungi receive plant-produced carbon.

naturalized: describing an alien species that has become widespread and readily adapted to local conditions.

nematode: any of a phylum (Nematoda) of elongated, cylindrical, unsegmented worms, tapered at both ends; parasitic in plants or animals (e.g., golden nematode) or free-living in soil and water, where they play an important role in the destruction and recycling of organic matter.

neotropic(al): referring to the Neotropical Region, encompassing southern Mexico, Central and South America, and the West Indies; one of six regions with a distinct and characteristic assemblage of animal taxa.

nitrogen-fixing: conversion of molecular nitrogen to the reduced organic form.

nudibranchs: an order (Nudibranchia, "naked gills") of predatory marine gastropods (subclass Opisthobranchia), commonly called sea slugs; a residual shell is shed in adulthood exposing the gills; noted for their striking coloration; cf. *sacoglossan*.

oligochaetes: a class (Oligochaeta) of segmented worms (phylum Annelida) with bristles or hairs (often not visible) on each segment that help with movement; two main groups, aquatic (mostly freshwater) and terrestrial (namely earthworms); mostly detritus feeders; cf. *polychaete*.

oligotrophic: describing a body of water or a confined ocean region (e.g., a bay) that is low in plant nutrients and has a large amount of dissolved oxygen throughout; cf. *eutrophic, mesotrophic*.

ovigerous: bearing eggs.

oviparous: producing young by means of eggs that are expelled from and hatch outside the body; common among birds, amphibians, reptiles, and most bony fishes; cf. *ovoviviparous, viviparous*.

ovoviviparous: producing young by means of eggs that stay inside the body for incubation and development and hatch just before or after expulsion; common among many reptiles and some cartilaginous fishes.

paramoebiasis: diseases of marine fish, crustaceans, and echinoderms caused by amoebae of the genus *Paramoeba*.

parasitoid: an insect whose larvae feed upon the living tissue of a host in such a way that the host is not killed until larval development is finished.

parthenogenesis: reproduction of a new individual from an ovum without fertilization; occurs naturally in some lower order animals (e.g., bees).

pelagic: relating to aquatic organisms that live in the upper layers of the ocean without direct dependence on the shore or bottom or on deep-sea sediment; cf. *benthic*.

phenology: the study of the relations between climate and periodic biological phenomena, particularly seasonal changes (e.g., plant flowering).

phytophagous: feeding mainly or exclusively on plants.

phytoplankton: aquatic floating plants; cf. *plankton, zooplankton*.

plankton: plants and animals, ranging from microscopic to small (e.g., jellyfish), that drift unattached in the ocean or freshwater; cf. *phytoplankton, zooplankton*.

polychaetes: a class (Polychaeta) of segmented worms (phylum Annelida), varying widely in body forms and in feeding behaviors (detritus eaters to predators); abundant in marine sediments; some freshwater and terrestrial species; cf. *oligochaete*.

protist (also protoctist) : any of a kingdom (Protista, or Protoctista) of mostly single-celled, eukaryotic organisms (e.g., slime molds, amoebas) that are not distinctly plants, animals, or fungi; many have flagella (whip-like structures) for locomotion.

pseudoperennial: [of algae] regenerating from residual basal material after dying back.

rhizome: the underground section of a plant stem bearing both roots and shoots.

riparian: pertaining to or situated on the bank of a watercourse (e.g., river or stream).

sacoglossans: an order (Sacoglossa) of herbivorous marine gastropods (subclass Opisthobranchia), commonly called sea slugs or cell suckers; equipped with a tongue-like feeding organ for piercing algal walls; shells small or absent; usually cryptically colored; cf. *nudibranch*.

saprotroph: an organism that extracts food energy from dead organic matter.

semelparous: applied to animals that produce all offspring in a single reproductive event then die (e.g., salmon); cf. *iteroparous*.

siphonaceous: referring to organisms (e.g., green algae) composed of long tubes (siphons), each having a hard outer cell wall and few cross-walls so that several nuclei reside in a single cytoplasm.

spatfall: the process by which free-swimming larvae of shellfish settle on a suitable surface, where these now-sessile larvae (known as spat) mature.

sphaeriids: freshwater bivalves of the mollusk family Sphaeriidae; also known as fingernail clams because of their small size (3–20 mm); immatures attach themselves to birds, vegetation, etc., giving sphaeriids a relatively high dispersal capacity; as filter feeders, sphaeriids are important for keeping water clear; cf. *unionids*.

stenotherm: an organism able to survive in only a narrow range of temperatures.

stochastic: conjectural; involving randomness, chance, or probability.

stratified estuary: an estuary in which salinity increases with depth as well as along its length.

sublittoral: (marine) referring to the part of the shore below the low tide mark and extending to the edge of the continental shelf; most sublittoral organisms are constantly submerged; cf. *littoral*.

subtidal: see *sublittoral*.

taxon: a named taxonomic group of any rank (e.g., class, family, genus, species) to which an organism is assigned in a hierarchical classification system; a taxon may be a single species or a group of related species, distinct enough from others to be treated separately.

thallus (pl. thalli): the vegetative structure (i.e., the part that grows and develops) of certain organisms (seaweeds, certain fungi); composed of cells that do not differentiate into roots, stems, and leaves; forms range from simple to extensively branched.

trivoltine: reproducing three times a year; cf. *bivoltine, multivoltine*, and *univoltine*.

trophic level: any of a series of positions in a food chain or web, from producers to primary, secondary, and tertiary consumers; usually no more than five trophic levels; see *food chain*.

trophic shift: a change in what a consumer eats (e.g., principally herbivorous species temporarily becoming a carnivore).

trophic specialist: a species having very specialized feeding needs (e.g., monarch butterfly larvae feed exclusively on milkweed).

trophic (or food) web: a realistic representation of feeding relationships in a community with a flow of energy and materials proceeding from species to species, none having a unique, fixed trophic level; when depicted graphically, the lines drawn between the various predators and prey resemble a web; cf. *food chain*.

tunicates: marine animals (e.g., sea squirts) comprising the phylum (or subphylum) Urochordata; a notochord extends the length of the body but does not usually persist throughout life; so-named for a body covering called a "tunic", on which there are two siphons through which seawater is drawn to obtain nutrients (e.g., phytoplankton) and to exchange gases; solitary or colonial; sedentary (attaching to rocks, boats, etc.) or planktonic drifters.

unionids: freshwater bivalves of the mollusk family Unionidae; often called freshwater pearly mussels, but actually clam-like, burrowing in the mud rather than attaching to firm substrates; inner shell often pearly pink or purple; the larvae (glochidia) attach to fish and amphibians, aiding in unionid dispersal; as filter feeders, unionids are important for keeping water clear; cf. *sphaeriids*.

univoltine: reproducing once a year; cf. *bivoltine, multivoltine*, and *trivoltine*.

vagile species: one that is free to move about and to change location.

vascular plant: a plant containing conducting differentiated tissue, i.e., xylem elements to transport water and mineral salts up from the roots and phloem elements to transport sugar and other organic substance from the leaves.

veliger: the free-swimming larval stage of many mollusks (e.g., snails, clams); characterized by a swimming organ called a velum, which consists of two large semicircular lobes bearing long cilia.

velocity barrier: a physical structure or natural formation (e.g., waterfall, culvert, dam) that slows down or completely impedes the movement of species, such as salmon, on a river or stream.

viviparous: bearing live young after their development within the body; applicable to humans and most other mammals; cf. *oviparous, ovoviviparous*.

zoea (pl. zoeae or zoeas): the free-swimming (meroplanktonic) larval stage of crabs and other decapod crustaceans of the infraorders Anomura and Brachyura, characterized by one or more spines on the carapace and rudimentary limbs on the abdomen and thorax.

zoogeographic: relating to a branch of geography dealing with the relationships between geography and animal populations, in particular, the effect of geography on species distribution.

zooplankton: aquatic floating animals; cf. *phytoplankton, plankton*.

Sources

We created definitions based on these sources and in-house expertise.

Blackwell, W.H.; Powell, M.J. Where have all the algae gone, or, how many kingdoms are there? Am. Biol. Teacher 57(March): 160–167.

Expert Center for Taxonomic Identification. World Biodiversity Database v2.1 [online]. Accessed July 2002. http://www.eti.uva.nl/Database/WBD.html

Flagg, S.D.; Kosinski, B.; Dhannawat, M.; Hussain, J. 2001. Annelida [online tutorial]. Biology Instruction and Agricultural Education, Clemson University, Clemson, SC. Accessed July 2002. http://www.clemson.edu/pal/111/diversity/Annelida/

Guiry, M.D.; Dhonncha, E.N. 2002. AlgaeBase [online]. Accessed 29 Jan. 2002. http://www.algaebase.com

International Maritime Organization. 2002. Global Ballast Water Management Programme [online]. Accessed July 2002. http://globallast.imo.org/index.asp

Jackson, J.A., ed. 1997. Glossary of geology. 4th ed. American Geological Institute, Alexandria, Va.

Market House Books Ltd., compiler. 2000. A dictionary of biology. 4th ed. Oxford University Press, Oxford, UK. 648 p.

Monterey Bay Aquarium Research Institute (MBARI). 2001. Phytoplankton [online]. Accessed July 2002. http://www.mbari.org/~conn/botany/phytopl/Default.htm

Morris, C., ed. 1992. Academic Press dictionary of science and technology. Academic Press, San Diego, CA.

Pearsall, J.; Trumble, B., eds. 1996. The Oxford English reference dictionary. 2nd ed. Oxford University Press, Oxford, UK.

UN Office of Legal Affairs (OLA), Treaty Section. 2001. Treaty Reference Guide [online]. Accessed July 2002. http://untreaty.un.org/ola-internet/Assistance/Guide.htm

Index

freshwater mollusks. *See* mollusks, freshwater

Fucus distichus, 138

Fucus serratus, 134(f), 135

Fucus spiralis, 114, 126(t)

fungi: as biocontrol agents, 35, 295–8; as pathogens, 41, 59–61, 243(t), 244, 250(t)–251(t)

Furcellaria lumbricalis, 134(t), 135

Fusarium avenaceum, 296

Galerucella calmariensis, 264, 265(f), 295

Galerucella pusilla, 295

Gambusia affinis, 81(t), 210(t)

game farms, 12(t), 107

Gammarus fasciatus, 79(t), 81

garlic mustard, 45, 46–8, 67, 68(t)

Garrison Diversion project, 206

Garry oak, 52(f), 54, 67, 244, 299

gars, 208(t)

Gasterosteus aculeatus, 80(t), 81, 210(t)

Gaultheria shallon, 297

Gayralia oxysperma, 114, 126(t)

Gelidium vagum, 114, 127(t)

Gemma gemma, 130(t)

genetic impact, 11, 33, 105, 106, 194–5

genetically modified organisms, 226

giant African snail, 32, 35, 270–1, 273

Gillia altilis, 79(t)

Gilpinia frutetorum, 62(t)

Gilpinia hercyniae (European spruce sawfly), 59, 62(t), 66, 250(t)

Gilpinia viminalis, 62(t)

GISP (Global Invasive Species Programme), 13, 23–6, 143

gizzard shad (*Dorosoma cepedianum*), 80(t), 86, 208(t)

Glechoma hederacea, 68(t)

Global Ballast Water Management Programme (GloBallast program), 22

Global Environment Facility (GEF), 22

global warming, 12(t), 107–8

globalization, and alien species, 19, 27, 246–7

Globodera pallida, 249(t)

Globodera rostochiensis, 243, 246, 249(t)

glossy buckthorn, 46, 49(f), 50(f), 51, 68(t), 78(t), 225

Glugea hertwigi, 79(t)

Glyceria maxima, 77(t)

golden nematode, 243, 246, 249(t)

golden paintbrush, 54, 55(f)

golden shiner, 208(t)

golden trout, 209(t)

goldeye, 208(t)

goldfish (*Carassius auratus*), 80(t), 170–1, 201, 208(t)

Gossyparia spuria, 62(t)

goutweed, 46

Grandidierella japonica, 130(t)

grapevine corky bark virus, 246

Grapholita molesta, 62(t), 243, 249(t)

grass carp (*Ctenopharyngodon idella*): accidental introduction of, 80(t), 208(t), 226; as a biocontrol agent, 104, 107, 273

grasses: biological control, 293; crested wheatgrass, 32, 44, 46, 54; smooth brome, 46, 54, 105, 299

grassland (prairie), 16, 104–5

Grateloupia doryphora, 114, 127(t)

gray squirrel, 31

grazing, by sea urchins, 139

Great Lakes Fishery Commission, 222, 228, 235

Great Lakes–St. Lawrence River basin: aquatic organisms, 75(t)–80(t), 81–5, 220; control programs, 88–9, 221–7, 228–9; description, 73–4, 219–20; fish, alien, 80(t)–81(t), 81–2, 84–6, 204–5, 220; pathways of introduction, 75(t)–81(t), 81–2, 86–8, 223–7; rate of introduction, transfer, 12, 74, 83–5, 86–8; restoration (post-1960s), 212–13

greater redhorse, 175

green crab: in Atlantic Canada, 137(f), 139, 148(t), 179–81, 184–5, 234–5; on Pacific coast, 117, 181, 182(f), 183–5, 235; potential impact, 185, 234–5

green mussel (*Musculista senhousia*), 129(t), 136

green swordtail, 210(t)

Gremmeniella abietina, 250(t)

ground ivy, 68(t)

guppy 210(t)

Gymnocephalus cernuus (ruffe), 81(t), 97, 201, 210(t), 220, 223–4

Gymnosporangium fuscum, 249(t)

gypsy moth (*Lymantria dispar):* 62(t); characteristics, 64, 66, 151; control efforts, 35, 152, 154–8, 271; defoliation of trees, 34, 64, 152–4; impact, 29, 32, 63, 154–5, 246, 250(t); invasion history, 64, 151–2, 153(f)

Gyrodactylus salmonis, 120

habitat modification. *See specific species and invaded habitats*

habitats, disturbed, 29–31, 41, 44–5, 52–3, 229

hairy prairie-clover, 54

Halichondria bowerbanki, 128(t), 147(t)

Haliplanella lineata, 128(t)

head smut of corn, 249(t)

heart-podded hoary cress, 248(t)

Hedera helix, 52, 68(t)

Hedya nubiferana, 62(t)

Helix aspersa, 249(t)

Hemichroa crocea, 62(t)

Hemichromis letourneauxi, 211(t)

Hemithea aestivaria, 62(t)

herbicides, 222

herbivory, 29, 32

hermaphroditism, 187–8

Herpestes javanicus, 15, 273

Hesperis matronalis, 68(t)

Hessian fly, 248(t)

Heterarthrus nemoratus (late birch leaf edgeminer), 62(t), 250(t)

Heterodera glycines, 243, 246, 249(t)

Heteromastus filiformis, 129(t)

highbush-cranberry, 68(t)

Hiodon alosoides, 208(t)

Hobsonia florida, 129(t)

Homadaula anisocentra, 62(t)

Homarus americanus, 121

Hoplocampa brevis, 62(t)

Hoplocampa testudinea, 62(t)

Hordeum pusillum, 54

horticulture: cultivars, invasive, 263–4; introduction of fungal pathogens, 59–60; as pathway, 12(t), 107, 122, 225, 259

hound's-tongue, 44

house mouse, 69(t)

house sparrow, 67, 107

Huchen salmon, 209(t)

Hucho hucho, 209(t)

Hudson Bay drainage basin, 88, 93, 98, 205–6

Hudson River, 73(f), 74, 87

hull fouling, 12(t), 121

human activity, and spread of alien species, 43, 46, 52–3, 73, 106, 151

Hyadaphis tataricae, 61(t)

Hyalella azteca, 82

hybridization, 53

Hydrocharis morsus-ranae, 46, 48–51, 77(t), 161, 165, 225, 244, 255

Hylastinus obscurus, 248(t)

Hylobius transversovittatus, 264

Hymenomonas roseola, 76(t)

Hypericum perforatum, 221, 292–3

Hypophthalmichthys nobilis, 80(t), 226

ice plant, 31

Icerya purchasi, 279

Ichthyocotylurus pileatus, 79(t)

Ictalurus punctatus, 209(t)

Ictiobus cyprinellus, 104, 208(t)

Idiocerus stigmaticalis, 61(t)

Ilex aquifolium, 68(t)

Ilyanassa obsoleta, 29, 129(t)

Impatiens glandulifera, 76(t)

Indian mongoose, 15, 273

insects: as biocontrol agents, 44, 66, 107, 221, 264, 265(f), 272–3, 283–5, 292–5; competitive advantage, 63, 66; in forests, 61–5, 106, 243(t), 244, 250(t)–251(t); plant quarantine pests, 243–7, 248(t)–251(t); on prairies, 32. *See also specific insects, e.g.,* gypsy moth

inspections: for gypsy moths, 156–7; for zebra mussels, 99

integrated pest management (IPM), 271

International Joint Commission (IJC), 235

International Maritime Organization (IMO), 22, 143, 224, 237

International Plant Protection Convention (IPPC), 23, 70

intertidal zone: Atlantic Canada, 133–4, 138, 181; *Codium fragile,* 30, 134(t), 135–6, 140–2; common periwinkle, 29, 137–8, 137(f), 147(t); green crab, 117, 137(f), 139, 148(t), 181, 183–4; SG, 114–17

introduced pine sawfly (*Diprion similis*), 62(t), 63, 65, 250(t)

introduced species (intentional): aquarium releases, 161, 164, 165–6, 227; in Atlantic Canada, 137; economic losses, 201; effect on aquatic food webs, 211–12;

fish, 103–4, 202–8, 223; in Great Lakes–St. Lawrence River, 169–71, 223–4; in Newfoundland, 69(t); in Prairie provinces, 94–5, 103–5; risk assessments, 213–14, 233; in SG, 116, 118(t), 119–20; unforeseen results, 11, 30, 175, 201–2, 213. *See also* biological control; pathways of introduction; *specific species and invaded habitats*
inundative biological control, 106–7, 199–200, 273, 291, 295–8
invasional meltdown, 34–5
Invasive Plants of Canada Project (IPCAN), 43
invertebrates: soil, 65–6. *See also* aquatic invertebrates
Ips typographus, 106
Iris germanica, 127(t)
Iris missouriensis, 298–9
Iris pseudacorus, 77(t), 114–15, 127(t), 165
Irish moss, 134, 137(f)

Japananus hyalinus, 61(t)
Japanese beetle, 249(t)
Japanese cedar longhorned beetle, 246
Japanese chestnut, 59
Japanese eel, 175
Japanese mysterysnail (*Cipangopaludina japonica*), 80(t),191–2
Japanese oyster. *See* Pacific oyster
Japanese oyster drill (*Ceratostoma inornatum*), 117, 120, 129(t)
Japanese weathervane scallop, 118(t)
Japanese white-eye, 34
Johnson grass, 249(t)
Juglans cinerea, 60
Juncus compressus, 77(t)
Juncus gerardii, 77(t), 81, 127(t)
Juncus inflexus, 77(t)

karnal bunt of wheat, 246
Kasshabog Lake, 161–4
kelp ecosystem, 24, 134–6, 139–42
Kentucky bluegrass, 44
khapra beetle, 246
Koinstylochus ostreophagus, 128(t)
kokanee. *See* sockeye salmon
Kumamoto oyster, 118(t), 120–1

Lachnellula wilkommii, 250(t)
lag times, 35–6, 269
lake chub, 208(t)
lake herring. *See* cisco
lake trout, 34, 116, 210(t)
lake whitefish, 96, 202, 206, 209(t)
Laminaria longicruris, 139–42
Lampsilis radiata radiata, 190
larch casebearer (*Coleophora laricella*), 62(t), 66, 250(t)
larch sawfly (*Pristiphora erichsonii*), 62(t), 66, 250(t)
largemouth bass, 210(t), 212
Lasmigona subviridis, 79(t)
late birch leaf edgeminer (*Heterarthrus nemoratus*), 62(t), 250(t)
leaf construction cost, 305

leafy spurge, 44, 53–4, 105, 293
Lepisosteus platyrhincus, 208(t)
Lepomis gibbosus, 210(t)
Lepomis humilis, 80(t)
Lepomis macrochirus, 210(t)
Lepomis microlophus, 80(t)
Leptinotarsa decemlineata, 248(t)
Lepus americanus, 69(t)
lesser cattail (*Typha angustifolia*), 78(t), 115, 127(t)
Leucoma salicis, 62(t), 250(t)
Leucosolenia nautilia, 128(t)
Ligustrum sp., 68(t)
limber pine, 61
Limnoperna fortunei, 195–6
Limnoria tripunctata, 130(t)
Lina tremulae, 61(t)
Linaria genistifolia subsp. *dalmatica*, 44
Linaria vulgaris, 44
little barley, 54
little cherry virus, 246, 249(t)
Littorina littorea (common periwinkle), 29, 133, 137–8, 137(f), 147(t)
Littorina saxatilis, 29
Lomentaria hakodatensis, 114, 127(t)
long-armed hermit crab, 29
longjaw cisco, 31
longleaf pine, 274
longnose sucker, 208(t)
Lonicera tatarica, 68(t)
Lophopodella carteri, 79(t)
Lota lota, 210(t)
Lotus formosissimus (seaside bird's-foot lotus), 54, 55(f)
Lupinus lepidus (prairie lupine), 54, 55(f)
Lycopus asper, 77(t)
Lycopus europaeus, 77(t)
Lyctus brunneus, 61(t)
Lymantria dispar. *See* gypsy moth
Lymantria monarcha, 246
Lyrodus takanoshimensis, 130(t)
Lysimachia nummularia, 77(t)
Lysimachia vulgaris, 77(t)
Lythrum salicaria. *See* purple loosestrife

Machu Picchu Program, 20
Macrophya punctum-album, 62(t)
Macropsis fuscula, 61(t)
Macropsis graminea, 61(t)
Macropsis mendax, 61(t)
Macropsis notata, 61(t)
Macropsis ocellata, 61(t)
Macropsis vicina, 61(t)
Malva pusilla, 295
mammals, alien, 131(t)
Manila clam (*Venerupis philippinarum*), 115, 116, 117, 120, 130(t)
Manitoba: alien aquatic organisms, 93, 94–7; Delta Marsh, 93, 94–5, 96(f); drainage basins, 93; monitoring for zebra mussels, 94, 97–100; plants at risk, 53–4
Manitoba maple, 45, 51–2
Manitoba Purple Loosestrife Project, 56, 254, 259–66

marine alien species. *See entries beginning with* aquatic
marine ecosystems. *See* Atlantic Canada; Strait of Georgia
marsh reed grass, 296
marsh snail, 147(t)
Marsilea quadrifolia, 77(t)
Martes americana, 67
masked shrew, 69(t)
Mayetiola destructor, 248(t)
mechanical controls, 221–2, 271–2
Mediterranean flour moth, 248(t)
Melaleuca quinquenervia, 30, 272
Melanosiphon intestinalis, 114, 126(t)
Melita nitida, 130(t)
Membranipora membranacea, 135, 138–42, 148(t)
Mentha arvensis, 77(t)
Mentha gentilis, 77(t)
Mentha ×piperita, 77(t)
Mentha spicata, 77(t)
Mesembryanthemum crystallinum, 31
Messa nana, 62(t), 250(t)
Micropterus dolomieu, 210(t), 212
Micropterus salmoides, 210(t), 212
Micropterus spp., 223–4
mink, 69(t)
mirror carp, 170–1
Misgurnus anguillicaudatus, 80(t)
Mizuhopecten yessoensis, 118(t)
Molgula manhattensis, 131(t)
mollusks: clams (including unionids), 115–17, 129(t)–130(t), 187–8, 190–4; mussels (mostly mytilids), 129(t), 136, 137(f), 138, 195–6; oysters, 114, 117, 118(t), 120–1, 129(t),148(t); periwinkles, whelks, 29, 137–8, 137(f), 147(t); snails (*see* snails). *See also* aquatic invertebrates; quagga mussels; zebra mussels
mollusks, freshwater: 187–96, 198(t); characteristics, 188–90, 194–5; dispersal mechanisms, 190–2; introduction, 189(f), 198(t); reproductive potential, 187–8; traits, 187, 192–6, 198(t); traits, species at risk, 187, 194, 196–7; *vs.* zebra/quagga mussels, 195–6. *See also* aquatic invertebrates
monitoring alien species: efficient monitoring needed, 67–70, 88, 274–5; in GL-St.L., 88–9; green crab, 185; in Saskatchewan, 108; zebra mussels, 94, 97–100, 224–5
Monocorophium acherusicum, 130(t)
Monocorophium insidiosum, 130(t)
Montane Cordillera Ecozone, 41, 53, 54
moose, 67, 69(t)
Morone americana, 80(t), 81–2, 210(t)
Morone chrysops (white bass), 94, 96–7, 207, 210(t)
Morone saxatilis, 203, 226
Morus alba, 53, 68(t)
Morus rubra, 53
mountain ash sawfly (*Pristiphora geniculata*), 62(t), 250(t)
mouse: deer, 69(t); house, 69(t)
Moxostoma hubbsi, 175
Moxostoma carinata, 175